THE DOG
GUIDE TO
POSTGRADUATE
STUDY

1991

THE NEWPOINT PUBLISHING COMPANY LIMITED, LONDON

CREDITS

Published by
The Newpoint Publishing Company Limited
Newpoint House
St James' Lane
London N10 3DF
Tel: 081 444 7281
Telefax: 081 444 5825
©1990 The Newpoint Publishing Company Limited
A Reed International Company

British Library Cataloguing in Publication Data

The DOG guide to postgraduate study——1991
  1. Universities and colleges——Great Britain——Graduate work——Directories
  2. Research——Great Britain——Directories
  378'.1553'02541 L915
  ISBN 0 86263 314 1

Typeset by Systemset, Stotfold and AVS Typesetting Ltd, London
Printed and bound in Great Britain by BPCC Hazell Books
Aylesbury, Bucks, England
Member of BPCC Ltd.

Editorial Assistant
Helen Morris

Editorial Manager
Heather Perry

Listings Assistant
Sarah Steward

Listings Editor
Paula Hammond

Listings Manager
Phil Brecht

Production Controller
Jane Hitchins

Production Manager
Rachel Wynne

Divisional Sales Manager
Jeannie Stubbings

Advertisement Manager
Neil Roberts

Sales Executives
James Fairclough
Julian Newberry

Art Director
Phil Bushell

Editorial Director
Bill Leask

Publishing Director
Clive Marshall

Development Director
Tony Corder

Managing Director
Anthony Felix

How to use this book

ADVICE AND INFORMATION

Read this section for information on general aspects of further education. There is information on:
- choosing and applying for a course
- postgraduate funding
- postgraduate life
- long term prospects for employment
- considerations for overseas students

POSTGRADUATE OPPORTUNITIES

This section is designed to help you pinpoint the courses or research opportunities of interest to **you**.
- Find your general area of interest then read the pages on specific subject groups within it. Here you will find a brief introduction to study at this level, a discussion of its relevance to employment, and likely sources of funding.
- Next, proceed to the lists that follow. These comprise all full and part-time courses and research opportunities available, with more detailed information provided by those institutions with advertisements.

POSTGRADUATE INSTITUTIONS

This section provides background information about all the institutions whose courses are listed in Section 2. If you are interested in a particular institution's postgraduate opportunities, write or phone for further information. If you only know **where** you might like to study, use this section to see whether the general subject areas of interest to

Coventry Polytechnic
Full-time and sandwich courses

Faculty of Applied Science

MSc Post-graduate Diploma
- Information Technology for Management

BEng Honours Degree
- Materials Technology

BSc Honours Degrees
- Applied Chemistry
- Applied Physics
- Computer Science
- Geography
- Mathematics
- Statistics and Operational Research

BSc Honours Degrees in Combined Science
- majoring in
- Biochemistry
- Environmental Science
- Mathematics, Statistics and Computing
- Medical Instrumentation
- Polymer Science and Technology
- Recreation and the Countryside
- two subject combinations from
- Biology
- Chemistry
- Computer Science
- Economics
- French
- Geography
- German
- Mathematics
- Materials
- Physics
- Statistics

Higher National Diplomas
- Computer Studies
- Mathematics, Statistics and Computing
- Physical Science:
  - Biomolecular Sciences
  - Chemistry
  - Materials
  - Physics

Faculty of Engineering

MBA Degree
- Manufacturing Industrial Management

MEng Degree
- Civil Engineering

MSc/Post-graduate Diplomas
- Advanced Manufacturing Systems
- Computer Aided Engineering
- Control Engineering
- Engineering
- Robotics and Automation

BEng Honours Degrees
- Aerospace Systems Engineering
- Automotive Engineering Design
- Civil Engineering
- Civil Engineering and Construction
- Combined Engineering Studies
- Communications Systems Engineering
- Computer and Control Systems
- Electrical and Electronic Engineering
- Information Systems Engineering
- Manufacturing and Business Studies
- Manufacturing Systems Engineering
- Mechanical Engineering

BSc Honours Degrees
- Building Engineering
- Building Management
- European Engineering Studies
- Product Design

Higher National Diplomas
- Automotive Engineering
- Construction (Civil Engineering Studies or Building Studies)
- Electrical and Electronic Engineering
- Engineering (Computer Systems)
- Engineering (Mechanical)
- Manufacturing Management
- Mechanical Engineering
- Product Design
- Production Engineering (Manufacturing Systems)

Faculty of Art and Design

MA/Post-graduate Diploma
- Electronic Graphics

BA Honours Degrees
- Communications Studies
- Fine Art
- Graphic Design
- Industrial Design (Product)
- Industrial Design (Transport)
- Technical Communication

Polytechnic Diploma
- Craft Design and Technology

Foundation Art Course

Coventry Business School

BA Honours Degrees
- Business Administration
- Business Studies
- Economics
- Industrial Economics

LLB Honours Degree
- Business Law

Higher National Diplomas
- Business Studies
- Horse Studies (Management and Technology)

Diplomas
- Employment Relations
- Management

Polytechnic Diploma
- Accountancy

Faculty of Social, Biological and Health Sciences

MA Degree
- Regional Planning

BA Honours Degrees
- Applied Social Science
- Economic Development and Planning
- Modern Languages
- Modern Studies

BSc Honours Degrees
- Applied Biology
- Physiotherapy

Diplomas
- College of Occupational Therapists
- Social Work

Certificate
- District Nursing

For a prospectus or further information contact Paul Hughes in the Academic Registry on Coventry (0203) 838482 or write to him at the address below.

Coventry Polytechnic

Priory Street, Coventry CV1 5FB.
Tel: (0203) 631313.
Fax: (0203) 258597.
Telex: 9312102228(CP G).

you are covered by the institution and, if so, refer back to Section 2 for more information on the specific opportunities available.

INDEXES
These are particularly useful as they will refer you to where:
- *specific study categories appear throughout the book*
- *institutions offering extra information have placed their advertisements.*

To ensure that you understand how each section of this book works, on its own and in conjunction with the rest, consult the 'Guide'notes that begin each section. These provide clear instructions on their structure and use.

THE NEWPOINT APPROACH
Every effort has been made to make this the most complete guide to postgraduate study available; covering all full and part-time courses and research opportunities offered in the UK.

Since research prospects can change very quickly, we recommend that you use this book to find where your area of interest is currently shared, and then go on to consult the appropriate institutions' own prospectuses. This way, you will be sure of gaining the most precise and up-to-date information possible.

More information about opportunities for graduates can be found in GO 91, *which is available free from your careers service.* Coping with Postgraduate Funding *(£3.50, also by Newpoint) gives comprehensive advice on applying for awards and the practical alternatives and is available through specialist bookshops or direct from the publishers.*

Prifysgol Cymru · University of Wales
BANGOR

Students 3300   Postgraduate students 570
The University of Wales, Bangor is situated on a hill-top site overlooking the sea, the mountains of Snowdonia, and the cathedral city of Bangor. Across the beautiful Menai Strait lies the Island of Anglesey, with its miles of coastline and fine beaches. We offer the following postgraduate courses.

Master Courses by instruction and dissertation (12 months)

MSc
Animal Parasitology
Applied Mathematics
Cellular and Molecular
   Plant Science
Ecology
Environmental Forestry
Fisheries Biology and
   Management
Forest Industries Technology
Marine Archaeology

MA
Applied Linguistics
Arthurian Literature
Banking and Finance
Church and Secular Power
Editorial Musicology
Ethnomusicology
English
English as a Second or
   Foreign Language

Marine Environmental
   Protection
Marine Geotechnics
Mathematics
Modern Chemical Laboratory
   Practice
Physical Oceanography
Pure Mathematics
Rural Resource Management
Shellfish Biology, Fisheries &
   Culture
Timber Engineering
World Animal Production

Music
Performance (Music)
Religious Studies
Social Work (2 years)
Theoretical Linguistics
Tudor Government
Welsh
Welsh History

There are also advanced courses available in Education, Music and Theology, leading to degrees of MEd, MMus, and MTh respectively.

Diploma Courses by Instruction (9 months)
These courses are available in most of the above subjects.

MPhil (2 years) or PhD (3 years) by Research in the Faculty of Science
Agriculture, Animal Biology (including Zoology and Applied Zoology), Applied Mathematics and Computation, Biochemistry, Chemistry, Electrical and Electronic Engineering Science, Forestry, Ocean Sciences (Marine Biology and Oceanography), Plant Biology (including Botany and Agricultural Botany), Psychology, Pure Mathematics, Soil Science, Wood Science.

MPhil (2 years) or PhD (3 years) by Research in the Faculty of Arts
Archaeology, Economics, Education, English, History, Modern Languages, Linguistics, Music, Religious Studies, Sociology and Social Policy, Welsh, Welsh History.

Address for further information and applications:
The Academic Registrar, Dept DOG 91, University of Wales, Bangor, Gwynedd LL57 2DG, UK. Tel: 0248 351151

CONTENTS

1

ADVICE AND INFORMATION

This section introduces you to using the *DOG Guide to Postgraduate Study* as an essential aid to finding the right course at the right institution. It covers general aspects of postgraduate study such as:
• the pros and cons
• the choice
• varying methods of application
• grant sources
Finally, there is a study of the additional concerns of the overseas student, for whom these general considerations are only the beginning.

ASTON UNIVERSITY

Location: The University is situated in Birmingham and a ten minute stroll gives access to all the services and recreations of the United Kingdom's second city. Situated at the heart of Britain's road and rail networks, it has good access to all parts of the country.

Accommodation: There are University-owned residences both on the campus and at Handsworth University Village. Most of the accommodation consists of self-catering flats.

PhD/MPhil Research Programme

Programmes are by course work and dissertation for those holding honours degrees or equivalent.

Masters Programmes:

Business Administration
Business Administration by Distance-Learning
Information Technology
Personnel Management and
   Business Administration
Public Sector Management
Software Engineering with Applications
Teaching English
Teaching English by Distance-Learning
Telecommunications Technology

Diploma Programmes:

Business Administration
Personnel Management and
   Business Administration
Public Sector Management
Software Engineering with Applications
Teaching English
Teaching English by Distance-Learning
Telecommunications Technology

Further details:

Jean Elkington — Secretary
Overseas External Relations Group
Aston University
Aston Triangle
Birmingham B4 7ET, UK
Tel: 021-359-3611

Guide to postgraduate choices

This section provides an introduction to the theory and practice of further study. Even if you are determined to undertake further study as the next stage in your career, there are many additional considerations which should shape your decision on the subject, type of course and institution.

In addition to the general advice and information given in 'Introduction to postgraduate study' and 'Life as a postgraduate student', please pay special attention to the details of grant-giving bodies. You should consult the relevant organisations and other publications for more information on any aspect of choosing, applying for and following a postgraduate course.

If you have any problems or queries regarding the advice given here, or on other sources of information, please write to (or telephone) us at Newpoint. We'll do all we can to help.

Study at the Centre

When you undertake postgraduate study at the Polytechnic of Central London, you are right at the heart of Britain. You are close to major libraries, professional institutes, the seat of government and the media. Many of these facilities of London have direct relevance to your studies.

Not only are you at the centre of the capital, you are also at the centre of affairs at PCL. PCL is a cosmopolitan community which each year welcomes many students from all over the world. Our prime concern is for students and their education - a concern we have been carrying our for 150 years. We combine a long history of academic excellence with up to date teaching and research. This combination will fit you, on completion of your course, for a career in a variety of fields.

Our Faculties cover the areas of Business, Management and Social Studies; Engineering and Science; the Environment; Law, Languages and Communication; and at the Harrow College, Art and Design. All offer courses for postgraduate students. Amongst these are:

MSc/MA courses in Transport Planning and Management, Film and TV Studies, Applied Social Research, Manpower Studies, Biotechnology, Decision Sciences, Diplomatic Studies, Marketing, Twentieth Century Historical Studies, Digital Signal Processing Systems, Water Pollution Control, Biotechnology, Town Planning, Urban Design

Diplomas in Management Studies, Planning, Conference Interpretation Techniques, Architecture, Personnel Management, Diplomatic Studies, Technical and Specialised Translation, East-West Trade Studies, Linguistics

This is just a small selection of our courses. Research degrees can be taken in most areas. Full details are in our *Postgraduate Prospectus*(1991 Entry). For your copy, write today to:

**Central Admissions Unit,
PCL, 309 Regent Street,
London W1R 8AL.
Tel: 071-911 5000.**

THE POLYTECHNIC
OF CENTRAL LONDON

Introduction to postgraduate study

The range of postgraduate study, both taught and research, makes choosing a course and institution difficult. How do you approach the problem and what are the pitfalls to avoid?

Higher education need not necessarily end with finals, though the days are long gone when a first degree could be seen as an automatic right of passage to further study. Many students decide to continue their education in the same or different institutions, and are considered eligible to do so. In Britain approximately one in five go on to do postgraduate study. Latest destination fugures available from AGCAS show that in 1988 23.2 per cent of university graduates and 15.4 per cent of those graduating from polytechnics went on to do further study of some kind: either academic, for a higher degree, or full-time training courses needed to enter certain professions.

Will possession of a postgraduate qualification automatically enhance career prospects? In the case of some qualifications - almost certainly yes. There are some careers for which possession of a professional certificate or diploma is essential, others for which a 'conversion course' is definitely

useful. As far as vocational postgraduate courses are concerned then, nearly always yes. Students hoping to take higher level academic courses may be encouraged to learn that the market value of a postgraduate qualification is such that it increases starting salaries by an average of £1500. This has to be balanced very carefully of course against both the increasing cost of taking a postgraduate course and the lack of earnings during it. A further argument for taking an academic course is that many students actually find a job through contacts made during their research. Ultimately, like most decisions, it has to be a personal one, and you must weigh up the pros and cons of postgraduate study for yourself.

Higher degrees by instruction

A Master's degree normally lasts one year, sometimes two, and consists of course work (lectures, seminars and classes), with an emphasis on training in research methodology. A thesis, or dissertation, is an invariable element; the research project may take up the final term or, in some places, has to be pursued and written up during the long vacation. The study can be an end in itself, enabling graduates to follow up some specialised interest they may have developed while studying for a first degree, or be a way to gain some

UNIVERSITY COLLEGE LONDON

GRADUATE STUDIES IN CHEMICAL AND BIOCHEMICAL ENGINEERING

MPhil/PhD by research

The department has acknowledged outstanding research facilities and is an SERC Centre for Biochemical Engineering. Opportunities for research currently exist in a wide range of areas, including:

Crystallization	Biotransformation engineering
Fluidization	Microbial and animal cell culture
Mixing and non-Newtonian flow	Downstream processing
Reaction engineering	Recovery of recombinant proteins
Combustion	Bioprocess monitoring and control
Instrumentation	Bioprocess simulation

SERC CASE and quota award studentships are available and a number of research programmes are in collaboration with other leading groups at UCL.

MSc Course in Chemical Process Engineering

A one-year full-time course for graduate scientists and engineers who wish to enter the process industries or progress further to the research degrees of MPhil and PhD.

The course consists of two modules: six months of taught courses followed by six months of an individual research project.

Diploma in Chemical Engineering

A nine-month full-time conversion course for scientists and engineers who wish to acquire a training that will qualify them for a professional career in chemical engineering.

This course may also be used by those who do not have the required background to enter the MSc course directly.

MSc Course and Diploma in Biochemical Engineering

Two parallel courses are presented for graduates with an honours degree in:
(i)   Biochemistry, microbiology or appropriate biological science;
(ii) Chemical engineering.

These deal with the fundamentals of biochemical engineering which underlie the biological industries and include fermentation, enzyme, food and effluent processing. The courses emphasize plant design and pilot-plant operation.

Write for more details and postgraduate booklet to:

Miss V H Potter
Department of Chemical and Biochemical Engineering
University College London, Torrington Place,
LONDON WC1E 7JE.

special qualification which they consider will be vocationally useful. Linguistics students, for example, may concentrate on particular aspects of the discipline which are relevant to teachers of English as a foreign language.

On the other hand, study may be perceived as a bridge, a period in which to pick up the basic elements of research needed to go on to seek a doctorate. While students are normally expected to have graduated in the same, or a relevant, subject, some Master's courses are clearly designed for the purpose of conversion to a new and often complex discipline. One such course is intelligent and knowledge-based systems, in the growth area of artificial intelligence and fifth generation computers, which can be taken by those whose original degrees have been in mathematics, philosophy, linguistics, computing or psychology, for example.

Some conversion courses are open to graduates in any subject, for example Cranfield Institute of Technology's one year MSc in CAD/CAM, - a conversion course open to numerate graduates in any discipline to train in computer aided design and manufacture (second class honours degree required); Essex University's conversion course in computer studies, again leading to an MSc and open to graduates in any subject with some experience of programming; and Reading University's two-year course in surveying, with 25 places for students with at least an upper second, and leading to professional surveying qualifications.

Adults returning to education are welcomed (often with minimal academic qualifications) to study something which fits into their working background. Social workers may look into social service planning; telecommunications engineers take

MScs in modern technological aspects of their profession; teachers might look for MAs in educational psychology or sociology, or the history of art or literature.

Higher degrees by research

A minority of Master's degrees are awarded simply after a period of research and the submission of a thesis. PhD (or DPhil) courses take a minimum of three years and students are expected not only to carry out some original work which makes a definite contribution to knowledge but also to produce a thesis. The research bodies who provide the funds don't just want creative ideas but evidence of an ability to communicate them.

Nobody would suggest that doctoral research is easy, but it is important. The introduction to an Economic and Social Research Council (ESRC) booklet says: 'The relationship between senior and junior scholars is the central mechanism by which universities live'. It goes on to describe the four phases of preparing a research thesis, each of which has its own problems and difficulties.

- *The matching of student and supervisor.* Some supervisors like to let their students have a lot of independence, others provide them with plenty of help and advice. The more eminent the supervisor, the more likely he or she will be to receive invitations to lecture abroad. A potential student should look into the possibility of there being an alternative available if this should happen, especially at the beginning of the project.
- *The preparation of a research outline.* This is necessary if there is to be a planned programme of work leading to an effective result. The ESRC booklet says, 'Graduate schools abound with legends of students who

became bogged down in libraries, or who spent too long on their fieldwork, or who had no idea of the extent of crucial manuscript holdings until their arrival at an archive, or who didn't realise that there was a dissertation on unrestricted university shelves in a field closely related to their own.'

- *Research and development of the outline.* This can involve learning basic skills like typing and indexing, keeping a 'diary of development', and maintaining an interest in other people's work; obsessive over-concentration makes for a solitary student.
- *Writing the thesis.* It is suggested that chapters of the draft should be handed to supervisors as they are produced, so they can see that a sensible balance of content, form and argument is being kept up. Speed is important; few universities allow thesis production to drag on and on. Many academics will echo the proposition of Professor Tim Gray of Essex University, that a doctorate should take no more than four years overall, and the ESRC's claim that, 'It is possible to produce a thesis of excellent quality within three years, excluding the time taken to prepare for and sit a viva'. After all, routine experiments can be boring if over-prolonged and the writer may be facing the demands of a new job at the same time.

Certificates and diplomas

There is, of course, nothing new in students continuing their studies with the aim of improving their career prospects: these days they usually have a profession or job in mind. For some professions a specific qualification is demanded for entry; the Postgraduate Certificate of Education (PGCE) for prospective teachers is a case in point.

The professional entrance requirement for social workers is the Certificate of Qualification in Social Work (CQSW) which follows graduation in a relevant subject and at least one year's practical experience.

Law is another example of a profession requiring specific knowledge, which may be acquired by the non-law graduate through attendance on a one-year course. Funding for this has become very difficult to obtain from most local authorities but, following a shortfall in recruitment of trainee solicitors, sponsorship from the big law firms has become much more widely available, as has the provision of courses. It is now estimated that 20 per cent of graduates entering the legal profession have degrees in subjects other than law. Details are available from careers advisory services.

There are other occupations in which it is not absolutely necessary to hold certificates or diplomas, but where it can help. Journalism, personnel work, tourism, and business and/or administration are some of them.

The advantage of such courses, which provide an academic background as well as practical instruction in a vocational subject, is that their successful conclusion should provide complete or partial exemption from professional exams. They do not, however, guarantee employment; nor, indeed, do they necessarily give an applicant an advantage over others who went into employment earlier and are seeking further qualifications on a part-time or day release basis or by distance learning.

Banks, and other financial service institutions, particularly like to take on new recruits (whether they are graduates or not) early enough for them to become committed to the 'culture of the company'. The assiduous reading of careers literature, and

 **Roehampton Institute** Digby Stuart Froebel Southlands Whitelands **Postgraduate Courses**

The Institute offers a number of courses in a variety of disciplines, for example:

1 FACULTY OF ARTS AND HUMANITIES
Diplomas in Arts Administration, Modern Theatre Practice, Calligraphy, Music Therapy, Drama Therapy

2 FACULTY OF EDUCATION
Postgraduate Certificate of Education
MA in Educational Studies
MSc in the Practice of Science Education
Advanced Diploma/Certificate in Early Childhood Studies
Diplomas in Mathematical Education, Science Education,
and in the Teaching of Music

3 FACULTY OF SCIENCE
MSc in Behavioural Biology and Healthcare
MSc in Psychological Counselling
Diplomas in Systemic Therapy and Counselling

4 FACULTY OF SOCIAL SCIENCES
MA in the Sociology and Anthropology of Travel and Tourism

For more details write or telephone:
The Registrar, Roehampton Institute, Roehampton Lane, London SW15 5PU
Telephone: 081-878 8117

UNIVERSITY OF DUBLIN
TRINITY COLLEGE

Trinity College, established in 1592, is situated in the heart of Dublin. The University has a long history of promoting post-graduate education, the development of which continues apace particularly with the introduction of a number of taught masters and diploma courses relating to recently developed subjects.

Research Degrees may be undertaken in any Department in any subject for which supervision can be provided and resources are available. MSc. MLitt, PhD. University of Dublin International Postgraduate Studentships and Trinity College Postgraduate awards (restricted to EC nationals) are available. Some but not all professional degrees are also open to graduates of other Universities (MAI (engineering); MDentSci).

The following taught courses are offered:

Masters Programmes
MEd, MBA, MAI, MSc — Clinical Biochemistry, Community Health, Economic Science (European Studies)*, Economic Science (Policy Studies)*, Engineering Structures, Manufacturing, Microelectronics, Computer Systems Design, Engineering (by course module), Environmental Sciences, Management*, Management Practice, Organisational Behaviour*, Business Administration Programmes, Theoretical Physics, Molecular Genetics†, Physical Sciences in Medicine, Management Science, MPhil — Ecumenics*, Peace Studies*, Anglo-Irish Literature, Linguistics, Applied Linguistics, Reformation & Enlightenment Studies, Textual & Visual Studies, Womens' Studies.
* Jointly taught with Associated Institutions.

Postgraduate Diplomas
Dental Health, Ecumenics*, Computer Modelling and Simulation, Computers in Education, Computers for Engineers, Highway and Geotechnical Education, Management for Engineers & Scientists, Project Management, Gynaecology and Obstetrics, Industrial Relations, Peace Studies*, Counselling Psychology, Quality Control, Sports Medicine, Toxicology, Physiotherapy (Obstetrics & Gynaecology).

UNIVERSITY
OF DUBLIN
TRINITY COLLEGE

Enquiries: Graduate Admissions, West Theatre, Trinity College, Dublin, Dublin 2, Ireland. Telephone: 772941 ext 2182

discussion, not only with people in higher education but also with those in the field of intended employment, will help you assess which is the best decision for you.

Money matters

A second degree is not, by any means, open to all graduates. Entrance requirements are high, and rising. Even someone who has obtained a good degree and the offer of a place may not find it possible to take it up. The problem may centre on the perennial question - who pays?

Most postgraduates are supported by grants and bursaries awarded by local authorities, government departments, industry and research councils (it is not always appreciated that the only postgraduate course for which grants are mandatory is the PGCE). Postgraduate studentships are more valuable than undergraduate grants and parental income is irrelevant; awards to those on certificate and diploma courses, however, are made under the same conditions as applied at the first degree stage. It is rare for them to be mandatory; most are subject to stringent quotas, and applicants often have to compete on a national basis for places.

There are always some students who, determined to pursue some aspect of a discipline only touched upon in the first degree, find ways in which to fend for themselves financially, or they may be supported by parents, wives or husbands. The Pro Vice-Chancellor of Essex looked into the sources of postgraduate funding and found that 'a surprising number' of graduate students did not receive any public money. Most were arts students on one-year MA courses.

Will you find a place?

In general, it is the grant-making bodies, especially the research councils, who call the tune in setting up entry criteria, though individual universities and polytechnics may well stiffen these further for particularly popular courses.

The choice of subject is important. For the more popular courses a minimum entry standard of an upper second is the norm. But if the research bodies have a say in the entry requirement, they have even more so in deciding who receives funding. It is still true that it is easier to find a place on courses in many cases than it is to find the necessary finance, and this is particularly so in the case of arts and social science courses. It is government policy that far more studentships and grants are awarded to students on courses in science and technology. Of the three examples mentioned on page 00, two - the Essex and Cranfield courses - attract Science and Engineering Research Council (SERC) studentships, while students on the Reading one can apply for funding through an Economic and Social Research Council (ESRC) competition. Referring to this policy in a speech in 1988, higher education minister, Robert Jackson stated, 'My view is that we could do with less emphasis on knowledge for its own sake. I make no apologies for using economic language.' In short, the more obviously vocational the course, the higher the chances of obtaining both a place and funding.

A new qualification

Anyone aspiring to reach chartered status in the engineering profession should know about the MEng degree, which does not fit into the conventional pattern of undergraduate/postgraduate progression. This is both 'enhanced' -

Brunel

THE UNIVERSITY OF WEST LONDON

Brunel University comprises the Faculties of *Technology, Science, Social Sciences,* and *Education and Design.*

The main campus is located in Uxbridge, with a second campus on the Thames at Runnymede. The University is thus conveniently near London, the Thames Valley, the national motorway system and Heathrow Airport.

As a campus University, Brunel benefits from excellent facilities and amenities as well as purpose-built laboratories, library and academic and residential accommodation.

Research opportunities and postgraduate Masters' courses are offered by all departments. The following courses are currently available on a full-time (1 year) or part-time (2 or 3 years) basis.

Natural and Applied Science
Applied Immunology
Computer Science*
Computer Studies (Dipl)#
Environmental Pollution Science
Medical Anthropology
Medical Biochemistry
Medical Radiation Physics*
Numerical Analysis
Science of Advanced Materials

Social Sciences
Britain and the European Community
Business Finance
Communications and Technology
Criminal Justice
Educational Psychology#
Family Therapy*
Financial Management in the Public Sector
Health Promotion˙
Industrial Relations
Public and Social Administration
Science and Technology Studies
Socio-Legal Studies
Social Work*

Management
Business Administration+
Project Management+

Technology
Advanced Manufacturing Systems
Building Services Engineering#
Data Communications Systems
Digital Systems
Industrial Measurement Systems
Intelligent Systems
Microelectronic Systems Design
Non-destructive Testing of Materials#
Packaging Technology
Software Engineering
Surface Technology#
Welding and Adhesive Bonding of
    Engineering Materials

Education
Design and Technology (PGCE)#
Education
Education Technology
Physics with Technology (PGCE)#
Youth and Community Studies*

* part-time only, # full-time only, + Apply to: **Henley, the Management College, Greenlands,** Henley-on-Thames, Oxon. Tel: **0491 571455.** ˙ Apply to: West London Institute of Higher Education, 300 St. Margaret's Road, Twickenham, TW1 1PT. Tel: 01 891 0121.

Further information: Academic Secretary (DOG 90), Brunel University, Uxbridge, Middx, UB8 3PH. Tel: **0895 74000** *or* 24-hour answerphone: **0895 810496.**

in that it has built-in engineering applications, may be multi-disciplinary and have business administrative and financial skills in the curriculum, and always includes a major design project - and 'extended' - as it takes four or (if there is a sandwich option) five years to obtain.

Students may be invited to move into such courses after an assessment of their work for two years at first degree level. It is intended that no more than 20 per cent of those in universities and 10 per cent of polytechnic students will be allowed to do so.

Arts and social sciences

Employers, judging from their recruiting policies, don't seem entirely convinced that vocational qualifications are necessary. An increasing number of them (it may be as much as 50 per cent of those taking part in the annual Milk Round) say they are looking for good graduates and are not much concerned about the subject of their degrees. Certainly, some 45 per cent of vacancies currently notified to careers advisory services are for graduates of any discipline. As to postgraduates, it is being said that employers are only interested in taking on the best of them.

As mentioned earlier, however, in order to find employment some arts and social science graduates may have to consider transferring to 'useful' disciplines like accountancy, information technology or business studies, for which their first degrees are usually considered acceptable. Many language graduates find that they have to take a postgraduate course which teaches the skills of translating and interpreting or which concentrates on the application of their linguistic knowledge to business and commercial use.

Continuing in research

It certainly cannot be assumed that anyone with an academic bent, a good degree, and evidence of successful postgraduate training, is assured of a career doing research and teaching in an institution of higher education. Any available lectureships only go to the highly-qualified few. The AGCAS booklet *Postgraduate Research and Training* says, 'for university posts it is usually necessary to have undertaken post-doctoral work, published widely, and become a recognised leader in your field of study'.

Professional qualifications

There are a lot of places for those hoping to enter the social services. 40 institutions offer degrees for research into some of the many aspects of applied social studies and administration; 45 give degrees by instruction, as well as diplomas, in these fields. Social science students may elect to explore, say, race relations and community studies, women's studies, or industrial development, at several institutions.

Prospective librarians are well catered for: 16 universities and polytechnics offer higher degrees by research, in subjects ranging from bibliography to information systems management. In addition to this, 30 institutions give degrees by instruction in librarianship and related subjects.

Both kinds of higher degree are available in archive and museum studies. Departments usually specify desirable research areas: palaeography at King's College, London, and Manchester and Durham Universities; and arts policy and management at City University. Most degrees under this general heading have a variety of titles including cuneiform studies, archive

FLEXIBLE ROUTES TO ADVANCED AWARDS
Modular Master's Scheme

This scheme enables students to devise their own programmes of study, drawing upon a wide range of postgraduate level modules offered by the Polytechnic's Master's Degrees (listed below, and appropriate modules from the full range of undergraduate degrees. This flexibility allows students to tailor their study to suit their own specific requirements: programmes can be specialist or interdisciplinary, academic or vocational.

We also offer flexibility in the ways you can study. All of our courses have a credit accumulation framework. Credits can be accumulated to Certificate, Diploma or Master's level, through part-time or full time study, or a combination of the two.

Taught Master's Degrees

MA

Communications Planning*

Education Management

West Midlands Historical Studies

MSc

Applications of Psychology

Information Technology

Instrumental Chemical Analysis

Construction Management (with Loughborough University)

MBA

MEd

* To Be Confirmed

Master's degrees and postgraduate level modules are being developed in the following areas: **Women's Studies, Software Engineering, Biomedical Science, European Studies, Law** and **Environmental Science.**

For further details of the Modular Master's Scheme, and for general advice concerning taught postgraduate studies at Wolverhampton Polytechnic, contact John Berryman, Wolverhampton Polytechnic, Wulfruna Street, Wolverhampton WV1 1SB.

Research

Full time and part time supervised research forms a vital part of the academic programme of each of our Schools. Three categories of registration may be applied for: MPhil, MPhil with transfer possibility to PhD, and PhD direct. For further information, contact: Professor D R Crow, Dean Of Research, Wolverhampton Polytechnic, Wulfruna Street, Wolverhampton WV1 1SB.

General Information

To receive a Prospectus, please contact Public Relations, Wolverhampton Polytechnic, Wulfruna Street, Wolverhampton WV1 1SB. Fax (0902) 25015

WOLVERHAMPTON POLYTECHNIC

For advice on postgraduate courses contact Polytechnic Advice Centre, Graduate Careers Service, Wolverhampton Polytechnic, 183 Stafford Street, Wolverhampton, (0902) 322573, switchboard (0902) 321000.

administration, and fine arts; and these are available in 16 institutions.

Reasons for continued study

Even the best qualified graduates should indulge in some sensible introspection before embarking on further study. Motivation matters; it is not enough to drift into the next educational stage because you can't think of anything better to do. The value of 'creative procrastination' can be overstated, especially in these utilitarian times.

Most people have to look for a job sooner or later, and they may find hard-headed employers rather sceptical about an unexplained postponement of entry into their world. They may suspect (not entirely unfairly) that someone who simply preferred to shelter in the groves of Academe as long as possible doesn't possess the kind of qualities they think they are looking for. There will be a distinct advantage if you can explain why you chose to continue your studies, why you chose a particular course, and what you got out of it in terms of knowledge, skills and personal development.

Those for whom a switch in disciplines would seem the best option, may have a special problem. It is not always easy to change one's mode of thinking from an academic one to the pursuit of practical, vocational skills. Such jumps require a fair degree of intelligence and intellectual stamina and it is a fact that the highest flyers are not usually the ones required to make them.

Those who have the opportunity to take salaried posts as research assistants, while being registered for a higher degree, should weigh up the advantages and disadvantages of doing so. On the one hand, they will be better off than they would be on a grant or scholarship, but they will have to work for it and they may find that their research work will have to stick more closely to its prestated objectives. In any case, such openings only exist for those engaged in work of a scientific nature.

What of the future?

The whole of university life has to be affected by the availability of money, which is influenced by the decisions of the University Grants Committee. All the indications are that they will put much more emphasis in the future on research than on teaching. This, plus a steady erosion of the total sums available year by year, will inevitably mean the loss of staff and a reduction in the variety of courses on offer.

This may not affect first degree work so much; departments may drop one or more specialised options without materially devaluing the degree. Where it will matter most is in postgraduate work - the 'filling in the sandwich' - where courses by instruction or research will have to be dropped as teaching expertise is lost. More than one eminent academic holds the view that the number of one-year taught courses (especially the MA) is bound to drop, and many will disappear altogether.

Most of what is written above portrays a postgraduate degree as a kind of platform from which to spring either into further academic study or a chosen occupation. It is perfectly respectable, normal, even conventional, to continue one's education for such reasons. It would be wrong, however, to try to discourage those who have enjoyed their undergraduate work and wish to develop and deepen their understanding of a discipline, perhaps by exploring some specialised area which caught their interest *en passant* during their first degree.

Beryl Dixon

DUBLIN CITY UNIVERSITY

Ollscoil Chathair Bhaile Átha Cliath

Dublin City University
is located on a fifty acre campus in the northern suburbs of Dublin.
The location enjoys the benefits of a city centre, easy access to public transport, shops, theatre, music, the arts and other facilities.
The university has over 3,700 enrolled currently.

Postgraduate Research
opportunities leading to Masters (MSc, MA, MEng, MBS) and Doctorate (PhD) degree qualifications are available in the various disciplines listed below.

Post-graduates constitute 12% of the student population. '

Postgraduate Taught Programmes include:
Masters degrees in:
Communication/
Cultural Studies,
Computer Applications,
Business Administration,
Investment & Treasury,
Instrumental Analysis and
Postgraduate Diplomas in:
Accounting,
Journalism.

ACCOUNTING & FINANCE
APPLIED LANGUAGES
APPLIED PHYSICS
BIOLOGICAL SCIENCE
BUSINESS STUDIES

CHEMICAL SCIENCES
COMMUNICATION STUDIES
COMPUTER APPLICATIONS
CURRICULUM DEVELOPMENT
DISTANCE EDUCATION

ELECTRONIC ENGINEERING
MATHEMATICAL SCIENCES
MECHANICAL ENGINEERING
ORGANISATIONAL PSYCHOLOGY

For further information and an application form, apply to:
Office for Academic Affairs, Dublin City University, Dublin 9, Ireland.
Telephone: 370077 ; Telex: 30690; Fax: 360830.

UMIST
POSTGRADUATE STUDIES AND RESEARCH

Excellent facilities are available for research leading to the degrees of MSc and PhD in the following departments:

biochemistry and applied molecular biology, building engineering, chemical engineering, chemistry, civil and structural engineering, computation, control systems, corrosion and protection, electrical engineering and electronics, instrumentation and analytical science, language and linguistics, management, mathematics, mechanical engineering, materials science, optometry and vision sciences, paper science, pure and applied physics, textiles. Facilities are also available for students wishing to undertake total technology projects.

A wide variety of courses leading to the degree of MSc by examination and dissertion is also available.

For further information about postgraduate courses and research, please write to:
The Registrar, UMIST, PO Box 88, Manchester M60 1QD.

Life as a postgraduate student

Choosing a course and finding a place may seem to be the biggest hurdles, but what about day-to-day life? Is it any different to undergraduate life?

Life as a postgraduate involves the adjustment of some of the views of university life. Gone are the days of strolling in for one lecture a day, to be replaced by a steady timetable of longer hours every weekday, and probably significant amounts of 'homework'!

In your first year as a postgraduate, you will probably spend some time getting used to the new timetable, and as well as library and practical work, will have frequent chats with your supervisor as to what form your project should take. At this stage, your supervisor will be ready with help and advice, and should provide a clear programme for you to follow initially.

It is a good idea to read up on the supervisor's publications and other papers relevant to your project, to get some feel for the subject. As time progresses, you should be able to follow up your own ideas, and be able

to defend their content and relevance to the project.

Once you've settled in as a postgraduate, life can be just as much fun as it was during your time as an undergraduate - it just needs working harder at, that's all! Within your department you're bound to encounter like-minded people, who will be sociable in and out of work. Postgraduates usually have their own union club and common room, and are not excluded from joining other student societies. In fact, it's a good idea to join at least one club, just to be able to get away from it all for a little while every week.

The magical change from undergraduate to postgraduate can work wonders for your status with landlords, as you'll now be seen as a far more responsible person - maybe it's true! Finding accommodation should, therefore, be no more hassle than for an undergraduate. Many universities have particular rooms, flats, or houses set aside for one or more postgraduates, so this is worth investigating. In these cases, you may also be expected to act in some sort of official capacity, for example, as sub-

Heriot-Watt University
Faculties of Science and Engineering

POSTGRADUATE COURSES AND RESEARCH

Heriot-Watt University, Edinburgh, offers a wide range of postgraduate courses and opportunities for research. A **Guide to Postgraduate Study and Research** giving details of these is available from the Postgraduate Office (O), Heriot-Watt University, Riccarton, Edinburgh EH14 4AS.

SCIENCE

Actuarial Mathematics and Statistics
Diploma in Actuarial Science
Research: computer modelling in insurance; statistical network and spatial models; wave energy statistics; design of experiments; regression analysis.

Biological Sciences
MSc in Brewing and Distilling
MSc in Biotechnology
Research: aquaculture and aquatic resources; brewing and distilling; environmental biology and toxicology; food and biotechnology

Chemistry
Research: laser photochemistry and mass spectrometry; synthetic, organic and bio-organic chemistry; organometallics; polymer and solid state chemistry; fossil fuel and atmospheric chemistry.

Computer Science
MSc in Knowledge Based Systems
MSc in Human Computer Interaction
Research: deductive, large knowledge and object-oriented databases; evidential reasoning; expert systems; human-computer interaction — user interfaces, evaluation; computer vision — concurrent methods and image interpretation; systems, networks and programming methods.

Mathematics
MSc in the Mathematics of Nonlinear Models
Research: algebra; mathematical education — computer assisted learning; functional analysis; differential equations; computational mathematics; applied mathematics and modelling; continuum mechanics; topology; mathematical biology.

Physics
MSc in Optoelectronics and Laser Devices
Research: optical computing and non-linear optics; semiconductor physics and technology; fibre optic sensors; lasers; computational and theoretical physics; instrumentation — space research, meteorology, optical and acoustic sensors.

ENGINEERING

Building Engineering and Surveying
MSc in Construction Management✶
(Production Management/Corporate Strategy/Project Management/ Maintenance Management/Value Management)
MSc in Acoustics, Vibration and Noise Control✶
MSc in Building Services Engineering ✶/Management
Research: includes these topics and building technology

Chemical and Process Engineering
Research: offshore oil and gas processing; aquaculture engineering; powder production processes; enhanced oil recovery; biotechnology separation processes; plasma processing; dynamic wetting.

Civil Engineering
MSc in Highway Engineering/Hydraulic Engineering/Soil Mechanics/Structural Engineering/Structural Engineering Computational Technology
Research: includes these topics and offshore civil engineering; civil engineering systems; engineering education; geotechnical engineering.

Electrical and Electronic Engineering
MSc in Digital Techniques
MSc (Conversion Course) in Information Technology
MSc in Electrical Power Engineering
Research: advanced robotics; multi-sensor perception systems; intelligent control systems; image analysis; autonomous submersibles and sub-sea robotics; digital communications; microwave engineering; power electronics.

Mechanical Engineering
Research: dynamics of rotors; dynamics of nonlinear structures; finite element static and dynamic analysis; boiling and condensing heat transfer; energy studies; fluid mechanics; flexible manufacturing systems; computer-aided engineering including CAD/CAM; machine tool conditioning monitoring by acoustic emission; dynamics of marine risers.

Offshore Engineering
MSc in Subsea Engineering
Research: Moorings, dynamics of compliant structures; flow measurement using pulsed lasers; optical techniques in engineering measurement; applied holography; image processing using parallel computation; wind and wave interaction with offshore structures; ocean wave statistics; subsea storage systems; corrosion and materials engineering; underwater acoustics; active 3D sonar systems.

Petroleum Engineering
MEng in Petroleum Engineering
Research: Reservoir rock characterisation; reservoir and well damage studies; enhanced oil-recovery; multiphase flow of hydrocarbon systems; techno-economic study of offshore production systems; design of completion systems for deviated wells; directional drilling; expert systems for well completion design; oilfield scale; hydrate formation; gas condensate; phase behaviour and flow properties; sand production; well testing; rock mechanics.

Institute of Offshore Engineering
MSc in Marine Resource Development and Protection/ Marine Resource Management
Research: environmental impact assessment; marine pollution monitoring; policy and legislation; oil spill fingerprinting and modelling; water treatment technology; offshore safety and survival studies; diving science; bioresource and aquaculture development; island technologies.

MSc in Aquaculture Engineering
A course combining scientific and engineering inputs for graduate scientists and engineers concerned with the design, construction, maintenance and operation of aquaculture facilities on both land and sea.

Medical Laser Unit
MSc in Medical Physics (Lasers and Optics)

Modular MSc/Diploma
Offers the opportunity to combine elements from a 'menu' of available courses.

In most cases a postgraduate Diploma course is offered parallel to the Masters course for those whose initial qualifications do not meet the required standard for entry to the Masters course. The full-time duration of most Masters degree courses is one year (October to October) by full-time study; many courses also offer arrangements for part-time study; ✶ 'distance learning' mode also available.

warden of a hall, and to take on the resulting responsibilities.

All year round study

While the undergraduate is usually resident at university only during term time, the postgraduate attends at least 44 weeks of the year, and you may find that fairly hard to adjust to, especially for the first summer. Grants are usually paid at quarterly intervals, working out at not much more per week than an undergraduate grant, but can be supplemented by fees for demonstrations and your tutorial earnings.

From my own point of view as a science graduate, considerably more time is devoted to practical work than was spent in the laboratory as an undergraduate. But although spending most of the day in such an environment is quite a contrast to the undergraduate timetable, things are rarely monotonous; you'll find yourself taking part in informal discussions with other members of the laboratory, as well as attending more formal, regular departmental meetings, and you'll always be kept busy with various aspects of your research work.

Conducting tutorials

Science postgraduates are almost always expected to supervise undergraduate laboratory courses for a few hours each week, and frequently to conduct tutorial classes. This gives practice for budding academics, as well as widening your social circle!

Working longer hours means putting in some time at evenings and weekends in order to keep experiments going at crucial stages, and, in the final year, to get those last few results. You'll find it necessary to put in extra effort generally, and should never expect to keep 'office hours'.

For postgraduates in arts subjects, longer hours mean more time devoted to research in a more literary sense. Producing a thesis involves a great deal of in-depth study of relevant texts and discussion with your personal supervisor, so you must be prepared to put in considerable time on library work and in writing essays for debate. In all fields, however, the arguments put forward in support of whatever conclusions are reached need to be based on a sound knowledge of the subject matter, so spending a lot of time in the library is inevitable.

Attending conferences

Most departments organise lectures by home and visiting academics; in addition, postgraduates are usually expected to give some sort of presentation during their course and to attend those given by others. There are also opportunities to go along to outside conferences, courses and symposia, which are often quite fun as well as being instructive.

Most postgraduates also go to discussion groups with their supervisor and colleagues, to keep up with other topics under research. This also applies to arts students, perhaps even more so, as a thesis in this area is heavily dependent on carefully thought out themes, which are aided by debate with other interested parties.

Your ultimate aim is obviously to acquire the major qualification of a doctorate in your chosen area of research: the last hurdle is an oral examination of your thesis, at which one or more examiners ask detailed and searching questions in order to assess your grasp of the thesis subject itself and also allied topics. If, at this stage, parts of the thesis are unsatisfactory, you may be required to rewrite them in order obtain your doctorate. However, glaring

University of Stirling

The University of Stirling founded by Royal Charter in 1967 is a completely new university. Set in a magnificent campus located in Central Scotland adjacent to Edinburgh and Glasgow it is within easy reach of the ski slopes and scenic beauty of the Scottish Highlands. The University campus has a comprehensive range of shops, a well-equipped Theatre and Arts Centre, Library, Sports Centre and social facilities. As a campus University, computing, library, technical and ava facilities are located within a small distance from student residences.

Masters Programmes
The University offers a wide range of taught postgraduate courses leading to Masters Degrees (MBA, MSc, MLitt, MPhil, MEd) — 12 months except where otherwise stated, including Diplomas of about 8 months' duration, as modules within the Masters programme, where asterisked:

Accounting and Finance*, Applied Social Research*, Aquaculture*, Aquatic Pathobiology*, Aquatic Veterinary Studies*, Banking*, Business Administration*, Education*, Entrepreneurial Studies*, Environmental Resources Management*, Finance*, Housing*, Human Management*, Image and Identity in Modern Scotland, Industrial Relations*, Information Systems Management, Information Technology*, Investment Analysis, Management Information Systems*, Marketing*, Modern Poetry in English, Philosophy, Psychology, Public Relations*, Publishing Studies*, Religious Studies, Retail Management*, Social Justice, Social Work*, Software Engineering, Software Technology*, Technology Management,TEFL/TESL.

Diploma Courses
In addition to the diploma modules of Masters programmes, the University offers diploma courses in: Housing Administration (2 years), Social Work (2 years), Diploma in Accountancy, Diploma in Professional Accountancy, and certificate courses in Religious Studies and Business Administration.

Research facilities
Doctoral and Masters Degrees, PhD, MSc, MPhil, MLitt, MEd, by research are offered in all the areas above and in other Arts, Sciences and Social Science subjects.

Centre for English Language Teaching
The University offers courses to bring entrants to an adequate standard of linguistic competence prior to registration. First degrees (BA) in EFL are also available.

Further Details and Application Forms from
Postgraduate Admissions (GPS),
University of Stirling,
Stirling FK9 4LA, Scotland, UK.

City College NORWICH

POST-GRADUATE ADMINISTRATIVE/PERSONAL ASSISTANT COURSE

A full-time, fully integrated course, incorporating Personnel, Legal and Financial aspects of Business Administration, Oral and Written Communication, Shorthand, Typewriting and Information Processing, leading to The Royal Society of Arts

HIGHER DIPLOMA IN ADMINISTRATIVE PROCEDURES

Award of the Diploma is based on continuous assessment.
Work experience is an integral part of the course.

This course is designed for Graduates.

For further details contact:
Mrs Jean Ray, The Business School,
Norwich City College of Further & Higher Education,
Ipswich Road, Norwich, Norfolk NR2 2LJ.
Tel 0603-660011.

inconsistencies or errors ought to have been ironed out at the initial writing and editing stage; you may be relying heavily on friends for their proof-reading abilities!

The main thing to make sure of here is that you will be able to carry through your research project to a satisfactory conclusion within the time allowed by your grant.

Embarking on a postgraduate course is not an easy way to stay a student for a few years more, but neither is it too impossible a task. If you hope to be successful, you should be prepared to put in plenty of hard work, some original thought and sufficient time. Postgraduates can get the best of both worlds, with the student life still open to them, in many respects, whilst at the same time pursuing a worthwhile target. Although the hours are long, and the pay not too good, the satisfaction and final rewards should be compensation enough!

Jeanette Eldridge

Applications and grants

Applying for a postgraduate course is a hard, practical business. Grants are at a premium - how will you manage?

Each year about 130,000 graduates emerge from higher education establishments proudly clutching their brand new degree certificates. And then about a third rush straight back into full-time study and training courses. Why do they do it?

For some people it is the only sensible option - perhaps to get vocational qualifications for a particular job, or a higher degree with the hope of a research appointment. Or you may feel that you just have to spend more time studying the intricacies of the life cycle of the greater spotted grass snake!

Other people decide on postgraduate study as something to do in a difficult employment situation or as a way of delaying a decision. These may be perfectly valid reasons, but be careful: the competition for most postgraduate places is fierce, and a postgraduate grant now could preclude one later when you have something definite in mind.

Sources of information

Of course, your reasons for further study may dictate a certain course in a certain institution, but if not, then you need to find out where you can do the particular course or research degree. Reference books, such as this one, are an obvious starting point but they do not include all the relevant information. You also need to know:

- how many places there are
- what grants are available and how many there are (not necessarily as many as the number of places)
- the particular bias of the course or the department - what specialist options it offers
- what students think of the course and the institution itself, its facilities, research opportunities, teaching and supervisory staff and so on
- the research interests of the department and teaching staff (particularly important for research degrees)
- employment/further study undertaken by students after the course or research degree.

The first source of information is the postgraduate prospectus of the institution concerned. These are generally more informative than the undergraduate versions but you still need more detailed information. Your course tutor, careers advisers, teaching staff and research students in your present university or polytechnic will be able to help, and to give you an idea

of the reputation of the department concerned.

A visit to the institution you're considering will provide more of an insight. Obviously this can be expensive so it might be possible to combine it with an interview trip. Don't rely on the guided tour and the information given, though - get round on your own and do some ferreting! Find out what papers have been published recently, especially those relating to your particular areas of interest - this will be useful for the interview as well.

Making an application

Some courses, such as those for law and some areas of teacher training, fill up very quickly and it is important to apply early (in your first or second undergraduate year for law courses). Certainly you should be making definite moves towards applying for any courses or research degrees by the first term of your final year.

Some places are offered conditionally. This means that you may need a particular class of degree or have to complete a certain final year project to get a particular place.

A grant will normally be dependent on a certain class of degree - usually a second class honours degree for advanced course studentships and one-year taught courses for higher degrees. For research studentships a minimum of a 2i honours degree is usual. Further information is available in the careers information booklet *Postgraduate Research and Training*, published by the Association of Graduate Careers Advisory Services (AGCAS), and from the different award-making bodies (see below).

Except in a few specific instances, you should always apply directly to the institution concerned. When you have been offered a place, then an application for a grant should be made, usually through the individual department rather than to the award-making body. In some cases, such as studentships awarded by the British Academy, you can apply through your undergraduate department. Scottish students should apply direct to the Scottish Education Department. Residents of the Channel Islands and the Isle of Man should apply direct to their education departments.

If you are applying for social work or teacher training there are clearing house schemes which administer all applications, and there are a few other vocational courses which have joint application forms. Your careers adviser will have all the details.

Awards for postgraduate study

Unlike the awards for first degrees, awards for postgraduate study are not mandatory, apart from postgraduate teacher training courses in England and Wales. In fact, it is likely that whether or not you do a course or higher degree will depend on whether or not you get a grant, unless of course you can finance yourself.

Many course and research places carry an award with them under a quota scheme, so if you're offered that particular place, you're likely to get an award, provided that you meet all the requirements. There are, however, always far more applicants than places, so competition is fierce. Increasing competition may also be expected from nationals of European Community countries, who may qualify for full or 'fees only'awards.

The situation is further complicated by the fact that there are numerous award-making bodies, each with its own particular areas of responsibility and, of course, its own requirements in terms of class of degree, length of course and so on.

34

If you don't get an award from one of the main award-making bodies, you'll probably need to finance yourself. Talk to the department where you want to study. They may know of bursaries or prizes that could provide some money, or charities that could help. You could also consult *The Charities Digest, The Directory of Grant Making Trusts and The Grants Register*. Postgraduate students may in future be able to apply for student loans, although at the time of writing the situation for postgraduates is unclear, and individuals would be advised to contact their local authority grants and awards departments for advice.

The Department of Employment has information on Career Development Loans for vocational courses of up to one year. This is available from Career Development Loans, Department of Employment, Caxton House, Tothill Street, London SW1H 9NF.

Information about the type of award offered by the various bodies can be obtained direct from the organisation concerned, and your careers service may also have copies of their booklets. Applications should usually be made through the institution which offers you a place - *not direct to the award-making body.*

The situation for all postgraduate awards is tight. Although budgets are being maintained, there are always more research projects wanting funding than money available, and more potential students than awards.

There are two main systems of deciding who will be the lucky recipients of an award. Firstly, the course tutors may restrict the number of places offered to the number of awards allocated to the course, with perhaps a few places for self-financing students. To select only the right number of students, they may inflate the class of degree required.

Secondly, the award-making bodies may further inflate the class of degree required. In theory this could be 'a first or 2i', in practice a very good 2i or a first. It is therefore unwise to assume that you will get a research place just because you have a 2i honours degree. A lot will depend on the place you're applying for, the level of the other applicants and the all-important reference from your present department and course tutor or supervisor.

Award-making bodies
Agricultural and Food Research Council (AFRC)
Agriculture, food and related topics
Enquiries about studentships to:
AFRC
University Support Branch
Wiltshire Court
Farnsby Street
Swindon
Wiltshire SN1 5AT.

Awards:
- *Standard research studentships* to study for higher degrees in departments of UK universities or other places of higher education. Separate studentships are available to research institutes of the Agricultural and Food Research Service.
- *Veterinary training grants* for veterinary or science graduates taking one-year courses leading to an MSc.
- *Co-operative Award Studentships (CSAs)* - the main class of studentship award - for up to three years of research of relevance to food.
- *Advanced course studentships* in food-related science -one-year awards for courses leading to an MSc.

Residents of Northern Ireland, Isle of Man and the Channel Islands should

A HIGHER DEGREE FROM KENT

The University of Kent at Canterbury offers the following advanced courses, leading to MA, MSc or LLM degrees or Postgraduate Diplomas.

■ IN THE FACULTY OF SOCIAL SCIENCES

Applied Psychology of Mental Handicap Services
Applied Psychology of Mental Health Services
Business Administration (MBA)
Development Economics
Economics
Economics & Econometrics
European Business Administration (MEBA)
History, Philosophy & Social Relations of Science
International Commerical Law
International Conflict Analysis
International Relations

Management Science
Political Sociology
Political Thought
Social Anthropology
Social Anthropology & Computing
Social Work
Social Work Studies
Sociology & Social Research
South East Asian Studies
Women's Studies

■ IN THE FACULTY OF HUMANITIES

Applied Linguistics
Medieval & Tudor Studies
Modern Literature (since 1850)
Philosophy
Psychoanalytic Studies in the Humanities
Vocational Techniques for Career Linguists

■ IN THE FACULTY OF INFORMATION TECHNOLOGY

Computer Science (conversion)
Statistics

■ IN THE FACULTY OF NATURAL SCIENCES

Chemistry
Conservation of Soil Fertility
Fungal Technology
Optoelectronic Technology

Details of these courses, and of attractive opportunities for research leading to MA, MSc, MPhil and PhD degrees, are contained in the Graduate Prospectus available from:

The Graduate Office, The Registry, The University, Canterbury, Kent CT2 7NZ

UNIVERSITY OF KENT
AT CANTERBURY ■ ■ ■ ■

apply to their respective education departments - for addresses see Department of Education and Science.

British Academy (BA)
Studentships in the humanities
Honeypot Lane
Stanmore
Middlesex HA7 1AZ

Awards:
- *One-year studentships* for non-vocational courses normally leading to a qualification at the end of one year.
- *Major state studentships* for up to three years for a research degree.
- *'One plus three' studentships,* for those who undertake a one-year taught Master's course with a British Academy award and who subsequently go on to do research for a doctor's degree or for a further two years.

All candidates are in competition with each other.

British Academy awards are usually only available for people who are normally resident in England and Wales at the date of application. People resident in other countries should apply to their education department - for addresses see Department of Education and Science. Some provision is also made for nationals of European Community countries, provided they are resident in Great Britain at the time of application, and in the EC for the three years prior to the course.

Department of Agriculture and Fisheries for Scotland (DAFS)
Agriculture and related topics
Room 434
Pentland House
47 Robbs Loan
Edinburgh EH14 1TW

Awards: as for Ministry of Agriculture, Fisheries and Food (MAFF). Students apply direct to the DAFS for funding for a course or research project anywhere in the UK. The DAFS makes eight awards annually, normally to those who have been ordinarily resident in Scotland for the previous three years.

Residents of Northern Ireland should apply to:
Department of Agricultural for Northern Ireland (DANI)
Education and Information Division,
Room 657
Dundonald House
Belfast BT4 3SB
Residents of the Isle of Man or the Channel Islands should apply to their education department - for addresses see Department of Education and Science.

Department of Education and Science (DES)
Arts and humanities courses leading mainly to a certificate or diploma; studentships in information science and technology
Awards Branch
Honeypot Lane
Stanmore
Middlesex HA7 1AZ

Awards:
- *State bursaries* for designated professional and vocational courses, including librarianship and information science.
- *Research studentships* in librarianship, information science and technology (IT).
- *Advanced course studentships* in IT for suitable postgraduate courses.
- *Instant awards* in IT for a quick decision about awards for those who have at least one year's acceptable experience in industry.

MSc Courses
in the Faculties of Science and Technology

MOLECULAR SCIENCE OF MATERIALS
ELECTRONIC MATERIALS AND DEVICES
CHEMICAL ANALYSIS
SYNTHETIC METHODS
BULK SOLIDS HANDLING TECHNOLOGY
ENVIROMENTAL HEALTH
SCIENTIFIC AND ENGINEERING
SOFTWARE TECHNOLOGY

Most courses are offered on a full-time and part- time basis and some SERC grants are available.

Postgraduate diploma courses are also available in some of the above.

For further information contact: The Registry, Thames Polytechnic, Wellington Street, Woolwich, London SE18 6PF.
TEL: 081-316 8111

THAMES Polytechnic
L·O·N·D·O·N

LONDON CENTRE OF INTERNATIONAL RELATIONS

A new venture by the University of Kent at Canterbury. Students can now take an MA in International Relations in either London or Canterbury. The London Centre offers:

- *Full time and part time (evening) study.*
- *Admission in September 1990 (September or January for part time students).*
- *Opportunities also available for research leading to MPhil or PhD degree.*
- *Courses on a Semester basis.*

Contact: Hannah Eno, Programme Co-ordinator, London Centre of International Relations, 43 Harrington Gardens, London SW7 4JU.
Tel: 071 373 9949.

UNIVERSITY OF KENT AT CANTERBURY ■ ■ ■ ■

WEBSTER UNIVERSITY HAS BEEN TEACHING AMERICANS THEIR BUSINESS FOR 75 YEARS

Americans invented modern business methods. Webster University was there at the birth and is recognised as one of the leaders in the field.

Since 1986 Webster University has been in London teaching American know-how to students from all over the world.

We offer BA, MA and MBA Degrees in Computer Studies, International Studies and Business Administration. The University runs day and evening courses, five terms a year, in an informal, American style.

For full details just call:
071 630 7771
or write to us at
5 Grosvenor Gardens,
London SW1W OBD. England.

Webster
UNIVERSITY

SAINT LOUIS, MISSOURI
GENEVA · LEIDEN · LONDON · VIENNA

Accredited by the North Central Association of Colleges and Schools   WUD

DES awards are usually only available for students who are normally resident in England and Wales. Students resident elsewhere should apply to their own education department. Scotland - see Scottish Education Department; Northern Ireland - Department of Education (DENI), Rathgael House, Balloo Road, Bangor, County Down; Isle of Man - Isle of Man Educational Authority, Strand Street, Douglas; Channel Islands - Jersey Education Committee, St Helier, Jersey, or Guernsey Education Committee, St Peter Port, Guernsey.

Department of Health for Paramedical courses
Alexander Fleming House
Elephant and Castle
London SE1 6BY

Applications via the institution concerned.

Central Council for Education and Training in Social Work
Student Grants Office
261 Gray's Inn Road
London WC1X 8QT
For information about grants for courses in social work. Application via institution concerned.

Economic and Social Research Council (ESRC)
Social sciences
Postgraduate Training Division
Cherry Orchard East
Kembrey Park
Swindon SN2 6UQ

Awards:
- *Coursework studentship awards* for taught courses for a Master's level degree, normally for one year but occasionally for up to two years.
- *Research studentship awards,* generally for two years, with an extension for a third year for a higher degree by research. Includes Collaborative Awards in the Social Sciences (CASS).
- *Bursary awards* for full-time postgraduate study for up to two years on specific vocational certificate or diploma courses in business and management studies.
- In addition 'joint awards'are made by the ESRC and MRC/SERC in Cognitive Science (research or course work); and by ESRC and NERC for one year Master's courses in Geographic Information Systems.

Some places carry an award under the committee awards scheme (studentships) or the pool scheme (bursaries). Other awards are offered on a competitive basis.

For studentships, the applicant must be ordinarily resident in England, Wales or Scotland. For bursaries, the applicant must be resident in England and Wales. Other applicants should apply to their education authority. Students from the Channel Islands should apply to the ESRC but the Channel Islands authority will pay the award.

Local Education Authorities (LEA)

Awards for all postgraduate courses, except teaching, are discretionary and LEAs do not necessarily give awards. Some LEAs will consider grants for the following courses:

- accountancy - full-time conversion courses only
- careers advisory work (or try the Local Government Training Board, 4th Floor, Arndale House, Luton, Beds LU1 2TS)
- educational psychology - mandatory for PGCE, discretionary for diplomas or higher degree

THE UNIVERSITY OF BIRMINGHAM

The University offers a wide range of facilities for study towards postgraduate degrees, diplomas and certificates including research opportunities and taught courses. Its leafy campus, conveniently near the city centre, at the heart of England, comprises all the academic, cultural and sporting facilities to be expected of one of Britain's largest universities.

Research facilities are available in most disciplines for supervised research leading to the degrees of PhD and MLitt (2 years full-time), MDentSc, MMedSc, MSc, MPhil (Eng), MPhil (Arts), LLM, MJur and MPhil (Ed) (1 year full-time) and MPhil (Commerce and Social Science) (2 years full-time). These are normal minimum periods of registration which may vary in individual cases. Part-time registration may be available in some cases.

Taught courses are provided for the following qualifications:

MA
African and Carribean Literature in English
African Studies (with IEP Bordeaux)
Applied English Linguistics
Archaeological Practice
Byzantine Studies
Chaucer Studies
Cultural Studies
Cuneiform Studies
English as a Second/Foreign Language
European Culture and Society
Islamic Studies
Medieval Archaeology
Music
Music-Theatre
Philosophy
Playwriting Studies
Religion and Culture
Russian History, Language or Literature
Special Applications of Linguistics
Synoptic and Statistical Climatology
Shakespeare Studies
West African Studies

MSocSc
Accounting and Development Finance
Development Administration*
Development Finance*
Economic and Social History
Economic Development and Policy
Economic Planning
Economics
Health Management in Developing
    Countries*
Health Care Policy and Management*
Heritage Management*
Housing and Housing Policy
Industrial Archaeology*
Leisure Services and Tourism*
Local Economic Development
Money, Banking and Finance
Political Science
Public Service Management
Quality Assurance in Health Care*
Race and Education*
Russian and East European Studies
Social Policy
Social Services Management*
Social Work*
Social Policy and Politics in Western
    Industrialised Societies
Socio-Legal Studies*

Urban and Regional Studies*
West African Studies
*and Diploma

MBA
Business Administration*
Public Service
*and Diploma

MIS
Defence Studies*
Diplomacy*
European Community Studies*
International Studies

BPhil(Ed)
Education (Flexible modular structure over
    a range of options)

Med
Education (Flexible modular structure over
    a range of options)
Educational Psychology

MSc(Eng)
Biochemical Engineering
Construction Management
Engineering Project Management
    (Engineering Production)
Foundation Engineering
Highway Engineering for Developing
    Countries
Information Technology
Integrated Manufacturing Systems
Integrated Quality Systems
Integrated Management Systems
Operational Research
Traffic Engineering for Developing Countries
Water Resources Technology
Work Design and Ergonomics

MMedSc
Endocrinology
General Practice
Occupational Health
Psychiatry
Rheumatology

MCDH
Community Dental Health

MDentSc
Clinical Community Dentistry
Oral Pathology

Oral Surgery and Oral Medicine
Orthodontics

MPhil
Cognitive Science
Plant Breeding & Crop Improvement

MSc
Applied Genetics
Applied Geophysics
Applied Radiation Physics
Clinical Psychology (two-year course)
Cognitive Science
Computer Science
Conservation and Utilisation of Plant
    Genetic Resources
Hydrogeology
Immunology
Landscape Development and
    Architecture
Applied Climatology and Meteorology
Pest Management
The Physics and Technology of
    Nuclear Reactors
Toxicology

Diplomas
African Studies
Applied English Linguistics
Development Education
Judaism and Jewish/Christian
    Relations
Landscape Development
    and Architecture
New Religious Movements
Mission Studies
Operational Research
Practical Archaeology
Pastoral Studies
Pest Management Systems
Philosophy
Social Science
Social Learning Theory and Practice
Software Engineering
Special Education — Difficulties in
    Learning; Emotional and Behaviour
    Difficulties; Visually Handicapped;
    Hearing impaired
Study of Islam
Theology
Toxicological Studies
Water Resources Engineering for
    Developing Countries

Detailed information is available on all these facilities and on how to apply. Write, saying what subject of study you are interested in, to: The Academic Secretary and Secretary (PG), The University of Birmingham, Edgbaston, PO Box 363, Birmingham B15 2TT, United Kingdom. Telex: 333762 UOBHAM G

- law - some LEAs give awards for the Finals course
- music and drama courses - for performers
- ordination courses
- secretarial work - may have to be done locally
- teaching - mandatory
- youth and community work

Medical Research Council (MRC)
Areas relevant to medicine
20 Park Crescent
London W1N 4AL

Awards:
- *Research studentships* at universities and MRC research establishments for up to three years.
- *Advanced course studentships* leading to an MSc in the biomedical field and lasting one calendar year.

Students must be normally resident in England, Wales, Scotland or Northern Ireland. Students resident in the Channel Islands or the Isle of Man should apply to their education authorities.

Ministry of Agriculture, Fisheries and Food (MAFF)
Topics relevant to agriculture, horticulture and food
Room 105
Nobel House
17 Smith Square
London SW1P 3JR

Awards:
- *Research studentships* for training in research techniques leading to a higher degree, initially for two years, which may be extended to three years. Include Co-operative awards in Science and Engineering (CASE).
- *Advanced course studentships* for taught postgraduate courses, usually for one-year courses.

Around 78 MAFF studentships are awarded each year.

Candidates must be normally resident in England and Wales. Students from Scotland should apply to DAFS. Those from Northern Ireland should apply to:
the Department of Agriculture for Northern Ireland
Dundonald House
Upper Newtonards Road
Belfast BT4 3SB
If you are from the Isle of Man or the Channel Islands, you are not eligible for MAFF awards and should apply to your education department.

Natural Environment Research Council (NERC)
Topics related to the earth, seas and waters and their living resources, and to the atmosphere
Polaris House
North Star Avenue
Swindon
Wiltshire SN2 1EU

Awards:
- *Research studentships* for research training on designated topics for up to three years.
- *Advanced course studentships* for recognised courses lasting for up to one year.
- *Co-operative Awards in Sciences of the Environment (CASE)* -jointly in academic institutions and industry, public authorities or research institutes.
- *Industrial studentships* to allow scientists in industry to obtain further training on suitable courses of instruction.

NERC awards are for students normally resident in the European Community. Candidates resident in Northern Ireland, the Channel Islands and the

CITY University

Students can obtain an MSc, MBA or MA degree or a diploma by following full-time or part-time courses in a wide range of subjects. Research for MPhil and PhD degrees may be undertaken on a full-time or part-time basis.

Schools: Engineering; City University Business School; Mathematics, Actuarial Science and Statistics.

Academic departments: civil engineering, mechanical engineering and aeronautics, electrical, electronic and information engineering, systems science, mathematics, actuarial science and statistics, computer science, chemistry, optometry and visual science, social sciences, information science, arts policy and management, music, clinical communication studies, journalism, business studies, business systems analysis, banking and finance.

Centres: studies in property valuation and management, continuing education, social statistics research unit.

MSc courses
Civil engineering (structures)
Civil engineering (highways and transport)
Water resources engineering
Transport management
Structures for hazards
Information engineering
Information systems and technology
Statistics and operational research techniques
Computer science
Industrial and administrative sciences
Information science
Business systems analysis and design
Human communication
Clinical communication studies
Health psychology
Music information technology
Shipping, trade and finance
Internal auditing and management
Property investment

MBA courses
Engineering management
Finance
Human resource management
Marketing
Export management and international business
Information technology management

MA courses
Arts administration
Arts management in education

Librarianship and arts administration
Museums and gallery administration
Arts criticism
Music
Law
Communications policy studies
Journalism

Diploma courses
Information engineering
Arts administration
Business systems analysis and
    design
Journalism
Information science
Law
Actuarial science
Industrial and administrative
    sciences
Clinical communication studies
Shipping, trade and finance
Music information technology
Internal auditing and management

Application forms and further
information from:

**The Academic Registrar
City University
Northampton Square
London EC1V 0HB**

Isle of Man should apply to their education authority.

Recognised places carry awards under the quota system but there is also an appeals system.

Scottish Education Department (SED)
Arts and humanities subjects and professional and vocational training courses in a wide range of subjects
Awards Branch
Gyleview House
3 Redheughs Rigg
South Gyle
Edinburgh EH12 9HH

Awards:
- *Major Scottish studentships* for up to three years leading to a doctorate or higher degree in arts subjects.
- *Scottish studentships* for not more than one year for certain full-time certificate or diploma courses, excluding those which are mainly professional or vocational.
- *Postgraduate Students' Allowances Scheme* usually for one-year courses of professional or vocational training, such as information technology, teacher training, social work training, youth and community work training, librarianship, business administration and management. Also Master's courses in art and design.

All awards are on a competitive basis, except for some vocational courses, eg teacher training.

The SED usually only makes awards for students who are normally resident in Scotland at the time of application.

Science and Engineering Research Council (SERC)
Science and technology not covered by the other research councils, including experimental psychology and areas integrating science and technology with social sciences. Also some areas of business and industrial administration and management
Secretary's Department (PTSS) Polaris House
North Star Avenue
Swindon SN2 1ET

Awards:
- *Research studentships* in particular topics for up to three years at approved institutions.
- *Advanced course studentships* for accepted postgraduate courses, usually up to 12 months in length.
- *Mathematics pools awards* for research projects in maths at institutions not covered above.
- *Co-operative Awards in Science and Engineering (CASE)* for research studentships jointly sponsored by a university or polytechnic and a body in the public or private sector.
- *Instant awards scheme* for people already in employment who want to do postgraduate training or research.
- *Overseas studentships* for people who want to study abroad.
- *Engineering mathematics awards* for maths graduates doing postgraduate training in engineering departments.
- *Joint SERC/ESRC studentships* for courses and research programmes integrating science or technology with the social sciences.
- *Industrial studentships* to top up a postgraduate award for those with experience in employment to enable them to obtain postgraduate training wihtout undue financial hardship.
- *Total Technology* - a new approach to engineering PhDs or sometimes advanced courses, to give a broader training, including a research project on an industrial problem in a firm, a design project and business and related subjects.

- *Information Technology Conversion Courses* - awards designed to encourage graduates in management and the arts as well as in science and engineering, to take a one-year conversion course to train in information technology.

SERC is the largest award-making body, with numerous different schemes for different courses and students. Priority areas for research and advanced courses include biotechnology, energy, industrial robotics, information technology, manufacturing technology and polymer engineering. If you live in Northern Ireland, the Isle of Man or the Channel Islands you should apply to your education authority - for addresses see Department of Education and Science.

Elizabeth Ingleton. Additional Information: Chris Swanson

LANCASTER
U N I V E R S I T Y

GRADUATE COURSES AND RESEARCH
Taught courses (Master's and Diplomas)

The Management School
Accounting and Finance, MBA, Economics, Management Learning, Organisational Analysis, Information Management, Operational Research

Science and Technology
Chemistry, Environmental & Ecological Sciences, Engineering, Mathematics, Physics

Humanities
Creative Writing, Cultural Studies, English, History, Linguistics, Modern Languages, Philosophy, Religious Studies, Theatre Studies, Values in the Environment

Social Sciences
Education, Law, Politics and International Relations, Social Work, Sociology, Women's Studies

Research
You can register as a research student (M.Phil or Ph.D) in any of our departments. We welcome enquiries from well qualified applicants from both the U.K. and overseas. Studentships may be available for suitably qualified candidates.

Located close to the Lakeland Hills and Yorkshire Dales, Lancaster University has a lively modern campus with excellent cultural and recreational facilities. Lancaster has over 5,500 students of whom 1800 are postgraduate, many from a wide range of overseas countries.

Further information from:
Graduate Admissions Officer
Graduate Studies Office
University House
Lancaster
LA1 4YW
Tel: (0524) 65201 ext 2032

Further study for overseas students

The procedures for gaining access to postgraduate courses in Britain are diverse, as the preceding chapters have illustrated, but for overseas students the process is even more complicated. Despite the welcome extended by so many UK institutions, students must still tackle the problem of entering and staying in the country and arranging funding for both the course and their own living expenses.

The decision to study for a postgraduate qualification is, as previously indicated, not one to be taken lightly. All students are strongly advised to consider whether their future career prospects will be enhanced by further study, and balance the loss of at least one year's earnings, in addition to the cost of the course, against the potential value of the extra qualification. For overseas students these questions are even more crucial. It will obviously cost more to live and study in Britain than at home. You also need to know how valuable a British postgraduate qualification will be.

The value of a further qualification

As far as this is concerned, you really need to find out in your own country. Without boasting too much, we pride ourselves in the knowledge that our range of postgraduate courses is one of the widest available and that our standards of education are among the best in the world. But we cannot claim to know whether our specific courses are highly regarded by every employer in every country! Certainly, as a general rule, British postgraduate academic qualifications (MA, PhD etc) should stand you in good stead for a research or teaching post in most universities and other higher education establishments. Our vocational courses in, for example, social work or librarianship, are usually well regarded, and people have been coming here to study for them for some time. Qualifications in business and in hotel management should be marketable worldwide, while many overseas governments themselves pay for students to gain British qualifications in economics, agriculture, science and technology. However, you should really ask the advice of employers, educational establishments and careers advisers in your own country before making the final decision.

With regard to the first point - help may be available with funding, and certainly is with finding accommodation. If you decide to come to study in Britain, you will be made to feel welcome. Most institutions have a tradition of welcoming and catering for overseas students. We are aware that you will need much more detailed information on choosing a course, a place to live, and so have written a companion volume, *The Guide to Postgraduate Study in Britain*, which covers all these matters in greater detail.

Money matters

British institutions charge fees at two different rates. Overseas students have to pay the full cost which in 1990-91 varied from £3870 to £10,500 depending on whether the course was in a university, polytechnic or college and whether it was an arts or science course or one with a considerable clinical content. Students from an EC country however, qualify for the lower rate fee of £1890. In addition it has been calculated by the British Council that you would need a further £5000-6000 at least (based on 1990 figures) for a year's living expenses. Costs outside the capital, of course, could be lower.

Where does the money come from? You may be eligible for financial help from your own government, international bodies, or sometimes the UK government. Awards are given by various agencies including the British Council, the Commonwealth Scholarship Plan, Foreign and Commonwealth Office Scholarship and Award Scheme, Overseas Development Administration Technical Co-operation Training Programme and, for US citizens, there is the possibility of a Fulbright scholarship. For more information you should contact first of all your own Ministry of Education, then a British Council office, British Embassy or High Commission, or, if you are already in this country, your own embassy.

Arrival and immigration

First, check your government's regulations on currency transfer to the UK, particularly if you are relying on private funding, and the arrangements for the payment of fees and grant if you hope to get a scholarship. You will need to provide evidence to the British immigration authorities that you have sufficient funding for your stay.

You will also need proof that you are a genuine student on a *bona fide* course. The latter is any course which requires you to attend for a minimum of 15 hours a week daytime study. In addition, you must be able to show that you have the necessary qualifications and command of English to follow the course and that you intend to leave the UK on its completion.

Students from Commonwealth countries must be able to produce such evidence at the port of arrival. Those from certain countries, including some Commonwealth ones, also need visas. If you arrive with all the necessary documents you will probably be given permission to stay for 12 months. (If your course takes longer you may apply for an extension). It is much easier however if, before leaving home, you apply in advance for entry clearance. If you arrive at Immigration in possession of a valid visa, Entry Certificate or Home Office Letter of Consent, obtained from an official British representative in your country, formalities will be much simpler.

EC students are exempted from the above requirements initially. You may enter Britain for six months without having to furnish evidence of student status. But if your course lasts for longer, as most do, the above regulations will concern you too.

Work restrictions

Unfortunately we have to warn you that in Britain it is not normally possible to earn enough money to pay your way through college while studying full time and, in addition, many overseas students are not permitted to look for even part-time employment. Some are, and may therefore supplement their incomes, but you should not rely on being able to do so.

The stamp in your passport will tell you whether you may look for any kind of work. If you are prohibited from working and are found doing so, the result could be refusal for you to stay in Britain or prosecution. EC students, except from Spain and Portugal, may work without restriction, and you are normally given permission for any employment which forms an essential part of your course.

The British Council and its local offices in your own country also produce very helpful fact sheets.
If you are already studying on an undergraduate course in Britain, the UK Council for Overseas Student Affairs also produces fact sheets, but may be contacted only through a member of your institution's welfare service or students' union.

Useful publications

Association of Recognised English Language Schools (ARELS) Handbook (ARELS)
Awards for Commonwealth University Staff (Association of Commonwealth Universities, address as below)
British Association of State Colleges in English Language Teaching (BASCELT) Handbook (BASCELT)
British Qualifications (Kogan Page)
British Universities Guide to Graduate Study (Association of Commonwealth Universities, address as below)

Directory of Grant Making Trusts (Charities Aid Foundation, 48 Penbury Road, Tonbridge)
Directory of Postgraduate and Post Experience Courses (Council for National Academic Awards, 344-354 Gray's Inn Road, London WC1X 8BP)
The Guide to Postgraduate Study in Britain(Newpoint Publishing Company Ltd)
Education Year Book (Longman Group Ltd, Longman House, Burnt Mill, Harlow, Essex, CM20 2JE)
Graduate Studies (Hobsons Press, Bateman Street, Cambridge CB2 1LZ)
The Grants Register (Macmillan, Houndmills, Basingstoke, Hampshire RG21 2XS)
Higher Education in the United Kingdom (Longman Group Ltd for the Association of Commonwealth Universities, address as below)
How to Live in Britain (Macmillan Educational Publishers for the British Council)
Learn English in Britain with ARELS-FELCO (ARELS-FELCO, address as below)
Local Authority Courses in English for Overseas Students (British Council, address as below)
Schedule of Postgraduate Courses in United Kingdom Universities (Association of Commonwealth Universities, address as below)
Scholarship Guide for Commonwealth Postgraduate Students (Association of Commonwealth Universities, address as below)
Short Courses in TEFL, EFL and ESP (British Council, address as below)
Study Abroad (UNESCO, 7 Place de Fontenou, 75700 Paris, France and from Her Majesty's Stationery Office, PO Box 569, London SE1)
Summer Courses in TEFL, EFL and ESP (British Council, address as below)

Useful organisations

ARELS-FELCO (Association of Recognised English Language Schools), 2 Pontypool Place, Valentine Place, London SE1 8QF. Tel: *071 401 2551*
Association of Commonwealth Universities John Foster House, 36 Gordon Square, London WC1H 0PF. Tel: *071 387 8572*
British Council, 10 Spring Gardens, London SW1A 2BN. Tel: *071 930 8466*
Central Bureau for Educational Visits and Exchanges, Seymour Mews House, Seymour Mews, London W1H 9PE. Tel: *071 486 5101*
Department of Employment, Caxton House, Tothill Street, London SW1H 9HT. Tel: *071 213 3332*
Joint Council for the Welfare of Immigrants, 115 Old Street, London EC1V 9JR. Tel: *071 251 8706*
NARIC, (National Academic Recognition Information Centre), British Council, see above

National Advice Centre for Postgraduate Medical & Dental Education & Training 7 Marylebone Road, London NW1 5HH. Tel: *071 637 5766*
National Union of Students (NUS), Nelson Mandela House, 461 Holloway Road, London N7 6LJ. Tel: *071 272 8900*
Immigration and Nationality Department, Public Enquiry Office, Home Office, Lunar House, Wellesley Road, Croydon CR9 2BY. Tel: *081 686 0688*
UK Immigrants Advisory Service, 7th Floor, Brettenham House, Savoy Street, London W2 5SW. Tel: *071 251 8706*
World University Service (WUS) 20-21 Compton Terrace, London N1 2UN. Tel: *071 226 6747*

Beryl Dixon

2

POSTGRADUATE OPPORTUNITIES

This section lists all postgraduate taught courses and research opportunities in the UK. They are divided into 12 subject areas, which in turn are grouped into four general sections (see below).
Before the course list for each subject area or chapter, there is a brief introduction to postgraduate studies in that area, a discussion of future prospects and some likely sources of funding.

Guide to subjects and courses

*There are two types of postgraduate study: **taught courses** that include tuition, coursework, exams and, in most cases, a research project or dissertation; **research opportunities**, listed by department, that involve individual research culminating in the presentation of a thesis. The course listing incorporates both types of postgraduate study, but is restricted to full time and part time courses or research whose duration will exceed two terms or six months.*

*The course listing is divided into four general sections containing 12 major subject areas, each of which is broken down into relevant subject headings. Within each subject heading the **taught courses** are listed under the specific names by which they are known under the heading 'Higher degrees by instruction' and the **research opportunities**, which lack the formal structures and therefore the specific names of taught courses, are listed using department, school or division names under the heading 'Higher degrees by research'.*

So, a hypothetical Department of Operational Research at the University of Bogus, offering research opportunities leading to the degrees of PhD and MSc, would have an entry as follows:

Operational research
Bogus U PhD/MSc

The distinction between higher degrees by instruction and research is omitted for the following subject headings as they all clearly contain taught courses only:

Diploma of Management Studies (DMS)
Master of Business Administration (MBA)
Secretarial linguist
Secretarial studies: RSA dip/LCCI cert/dip
Other secretarial qualifications
All PGCE courses
Theology: ordination
Social work: CQSW

Each subject group is followed by advertisements for courses that appear within the listing and that are relevant to that particular subject group. All courses within the listing that are advertised have one of two types of code appended to them: a □ indicates that the course advertisement appears at the end of the listing, an italic abbreviation (eg, 'Lang') indicates that the advertisement appears at the end of another subject group (in this example, 'Languages and literature'). The abbreviation for each subject group is shown in the pages which follow.

This facility should be used in conjunction with the 'Advertisers index' on page 526. The index provides quick and easy access to courses advertised by particular institutions.

For further details on the institutions, please refer to the list of institutions on page 461.

ARTS/LANGUAGES

General arts *Arts*
67 General
68 Archaeology
69 Archives, paleography, museum studies
70 Area studies: European
72 Area studies: non European
74 Art history, fine art
76 Graphics, fashion, textiles
78 History: ancient
78 History: general
81 History: Medieval, modern
82 History: social, economic
83 Journalism, printing
85 Law

89 Music
91 Performing arts
92 Philosophy
93 Theatre, film, TV
95 Theology
97 Theology: ordination
97 Three dimensional art/design

Languages and literature *Lang*
106 General
106 Classics
107 English language & studies
109 English literature: pre Victorian
112 English literature: Victorian to present day
114 French
116 German

117 Interpreting, translating
118 Italian
119 Linguistics, philology, phonetics
120 Russian & East European
121 Spanish
123 Languages & literature: other European
124 Languages & literature: other non European
126 Languages & literature: Semitic

BUSINESS/EDUCATION/SOCIAL SCIENCES

Business, administration and management *Bus*
139 General
141 Accountancy, finance
143 Administration
147 Business studies
151 Diploma of Management Studies (DMS)
151 Ergonomics, work study
152 Hotel & catering management
152 Industrial management
155 Marketing
156 Master of Business Administration (MBA)
156 Operational research
157 Personnel, industrial relations, manpower studies
158 Safety & hygiene
158 Secretarial linguist
159 Secretarial studies: RSA dip
161 Secretarial studies: LCCI cert/dip
161 Other secretarial qualifications

Education *Educ*
181 General (excluding post experience courses)
186 Curriculum studies
188 PGCE: first, infants
189 PGCE: primary, middle
189 PGCE: secondary
190 PGCE: art
190 PGCE: languages
190 PGCE: music
190 PGCE: physical education
190 PGCE: science
191 PGCE: other categories

Social sciences *Soc*
202 General
203 Anthropology
205 Careers work
205 Economics
211 Government, politics
214 Librarianship, information science
215 Psychology
217 Public & social administration
220 Social work: CQSW
220 Social work, youth & community work
223 Sociology, social studies

ENGINEERING/TECHNOLOGY/ ENVIRONMENT

Computer studies *Comp*
243 General
246 Computer engineering
247 Computer science
250 Information technology
254 Systems analysis

Engineering and technology *Eng*
269 General
273 Aeronautical, marine technology
274 Agricultural engineering & related studies
275 Bioengineering
277 Chemical engineering
278 Civil, structural engineering
281 Communications, control, systems engineering
285 Construction, building services engineering
289 Electrical engineering
291 Electronic engineering
297 Fuel science, energy studies, nuclear engineering
299 Industrial, engineering design
303 Mechanical engineering
309 Metallurgy, materials science
311 Production engineering, technology
314 Technology, industrial studies
317 Transport studies, port management

Environmental studies *Env*
351 General
353 Agriculture
357 Animal science, husbandry
358 Architecture, design
360 Ecology, soil science, conservation
362 Environmental control
365 Geography
367 Geology, geophysics, surveying
369 Horticulture, forestry, crop production
371 Meteorology, oceanography
372 Tourism, recreation management
372 Town planning, urban & regional planning

MATHEMATICS/SCIENCES

Biological sciences *Biol*
385 General
386 Anatomy, physiology, neurology
389 Biochemistry, endocrinology, toxicology
391 Biology, botanical sciences
395 Biotechnology
396 Genetics, virology, immunology
397 Nursing
398 Studies allied to dentistry
400 Studies allied to health & medicine
409 Surgery

GUIDE TO SUBJECTS AND COURSES 2

410 Veterinary studies
411 Zoology

Chemical sciences *Chem*
419 General
419 Chemistry
422 Food science, dietetics
423 Pharmacy, pharmacology
424 Polymer science & technology

Mathematics *Math*
435 General

436 Mathematics
438 Numerical theory & method
439 Statistics

Physics and allied subjects *Phy*
447 General
448 Astronomy, space physics
448 Atomic, nuclear physics
449 Medical, radiation physics
450 Physical science
451 Physics

Abbreviations

The following abbreviations are used throughout the book. The list includes, amongst others, professional body abbreviations used within the main course listings. Where a particular course, within the main course listings, refers to a professional body, the reader may assume that the course leads to examinations (often in the form of levels or stages) that are *either* set or approved by the professional body or recognised as being an acceptable qualification for membership of the professional body. The specific details of whether examinations are set or approved, or recognised, are not included within the main listing; neither is the particular level or stage to which a course is designated. Prospective applicants interested in such a course should contact the relevant institutions on page 461.

ACA	Associate of the Institute of Chartered Accountants in England and Wales
ACCA	Associate of the Association of Certified Accountants
ACIB	Association of chartered institute of bankers
AFOM	Associate of the Faculty of Occupational Medicine (Royal College of Physicians)
AgC	Agricultural College
ALS	Association of Legal Secretaries
ALSPT	Associate of the London School of Polymer Technology
AMSPAR	Association of Medical Secretaries, Practice Administrators & Receptionists
ATPL	Airline Transport Pilot's Licence
BCS	British Computer Society
BCL	Bachelor of Civil Law
BD	Bachelor of Divinity
BLing	Bachelor of Linguistics
BLD	Bachelor of Landscape Design
BMus	Bachelor of Music
BS	Business School
BTP	Bachelor of Town Planning
CDip AF	Certified diploma in accounting and finance

CRCH	Central Register and Clearing House
C	College(s)
CA	College of Art
CAA Lic Cat	Civil Aviation Authority
A,C & X	Licences: Categories A, C & X
CAD	College of Art & Design
CAg	College of Agriculture
CAM dip	Diploma awarded by the Communication, Advertising & Marketing Education Foundation
CAT	College of Art(s) & Technology
CC	College of Commerce
CCT	College of Commerce & Technology
CE	College of Education
CEng	Chartered Engineering Council examination
cert	Certificate
CFE	College of Further Education
CFHE	College of Further & Higher Education
CHE	College of Higher Education
CHFE	College of Higher & Further Education
CIPFA	Chartered Institute of Public Finance & Accountancy
CPE	College of Physical Education
CPL	Commercial Pilot's Licence
CPL (H)	Commercial Pilot's Licence (Helicopter)
CQSW	Certificate of Qualification in Social Work

CT	College of Technology
CTA	College of Technology & Art(s)
Dent	Dental
dip	Diploma
DipIng	Diplome Ingenieur
DipLib	Diploma in Librarianship
DMS	Diploma of Management Studies
DipMTh	Diploma of Music Therapy
DPhil	Doctor of Philosophy
ESRC	Economic and Social Research Council
HCIMA	Hotel, Catering & Institutional Management Association
Hosp	Hospital
ICAEW	Institute of Chartered Accountants of England and Wales
IMLS	Institute of Medical Laboratory Sciences
ISVA	The Incorporated Society of Valuers and Auctioneers
ICMA	Institute of Cost & Management Accountants
ICSA	Institute of Chartered Secretaries & Administrators
IHE	Institute of Higher Education
IL	Institute of Linguists
ILEx	Institute of Legal Executives
IM	Institute of Marketing
IMS	Institute of Management Services
Inst	Institute
IPM	Institute of Personnel Management
IPS	Institute of Purchasing & Supply
IR	Instrument Rating
IT	Institute of Technology
KQC	King's College. Queen Elizabeth College, Chelsea College
Lang	Languages
LCCI	London Chamber of Commerce & Industry
LRS	Licence in Religious Studies
LHCIMA	Licentiate of the Hotel, Catering & Institutional Management Association
LLM	Master of Laws
LSE	London School of Economics & Political Science
LSPT	London School of Polymer Technology
LTh	Licence of Theology

MA	Master of Arts
MAcc	Master of Accountancy
MA(Econ)	Master of Arts (Economics)
MA(Ed)	Master of Arts (Education)
MA(LD)	Master of Arts (Landscape Design)
MA(Theol)	Master of Arts (Theology)
MA(UrbDes)	Master of Arts (Urban Design)
MAgr	Master of Agriculture
MAgric	Master of Agriculture
MAgrSc	Master of Agricultural Science
MAgrSci	Master of Agricultural Science
MAppSci	Master of Applied Science
MArch	Master of Architecture
MBM	Master of Business Management
MBA	Master of Business Administration
MBSc	Master of Business Science
MCD	Master of Civic Design
MCom	Master of Commerce
MCommH	Master of Community Health
MDes	Master of Design
MDS	Master of Dental Surgery
Med	Medical/ine
MEd	Master of Education
MEng	Master of Engineering
MFA	Master of Fine Art
MIOA	Membershipof Institute of Acoustics
MJur	Master of Jurisprudence
MLD	Master of Landscape Design
MLib	Master of Librarianship
MLing	Master of Linguistics
MLitt	Master of Letters
MLS	Master of Library Studies
MMedSc	Master of Medical Science
MMedSci	Master of Medical Science
MMet	Master of Metallurgy
MMus	Master of Music
MPA	Master of Public Administration
MPH	Master of Public Health
MPharm	Master of Pharmacy
MPhil	Master of Philosophy
MPsychol	Master of Psychology
MSc	Master of Science
MSc(Econ)	Master of Science (Economics)
MSc(Ed)	Master of Science (Education)
MSc(MedSci)	Master of Science (Medical Science)
MSc(SciEduc)	Master of Science (Science Education)
MSc(Tech)	Master of Science (Technology)
MSocSc	Master of Social Science
MSSc	Master of Social Science
MSt	Master of Studies
MSW	Master of Social Work
MTD	Master of Transport Design

MTech	Master of Technology	**RSC**	Royal Society of Chemistry
MTP	Master of Town Planning	**RSCN**	Registered Sick Childrens'
MTPI	Master of Town Planning		Nurse
MTh	Master of Theology	**RTPI**	Royal Town Planning Institute ·
MTheol	Master of Theology		
Mus	Music	**S**	School(s)
MVM	Master of Veterinary Medicine	**SA**	School of Art
MVSc	Master of Veterinary Science	**SAD**	School of Art & Design
MQB	Mining Qualifications Board	**SAg**	School of Agriculture
		Sec	Secretarial
P	Polytechnic	**SERC**	Science and Engineering
PhD	Doctor of Philosophy		Research Council
PGCE	Postgraduate Certificate in	**SOAS**	School of Oriental & African
	Education		Studies
PRI	Plastics & Rubber Institute	**SSEES**	School of Slavonic & East
			European Studies
RGN	Registered General Nurse		
RIBA	Royal Institute of British	**TC**	Technical College
	Architects		
RICS	Royal Institution of Chartered	**U**	University
	Surveyors	**UC**	University College
RMN	Registered Mental Nurse	**UMIST**	University of Manchester
RNMH	Registered Nurse for the		Institute of Science &
	Mentally Handicapped		Technology
RSA	Royal Society of Arts	**US**	United States

2

Arts/languages

General arts

Before embarking on postgraduate studies in the arts, it is worth examining your true motives and reasons for doing so. It is also important to consider whether a further qualification will be a help or a hindrance to your career prospects.

General arts covers a wide spectrum of subjects, many of them unrelated. There could be several reasons for wanting to pursue further studies in the arts, some of them good, some not so good and others downright bad.

Among the best possible reasons is a desire to obtain knowledge or skills which will make you more attractive in the job market. However, not all courses have a practical content; some may be academic studies of the subject and not intended to be particularly vocational in their slant. So check to see if there are useful attachments or work experience, and find out what happened to last year's crop of postgraduates. Did they find the sort of jobs they were looking for or did they have to ma'e do with something entirely unconnected with their studies?

Art for art's sake?

You may, of course, desire further study out of sheer love for the subject, and because of the intellectual challenge. That is no bad reason but it may make it more difficult to get a job. You will have to put up convincing arguments when a prospective employer asks why you delayed your jobhunt.

Examine your motives before applying for a postgraduate course. Are you really so enamoured of the subject that you are willing to scrimp and save for a further year or two instead of earning a reasonable salary? Or do you just want to put off making a decision about your future career?

A postgraduate qualification is essential for certain careers and can sometimes facilitate entry to others. But be wary. In some fields, graduates with a higher degree can be thought to be over qualified and unwilling to settle for the same level of salary as other newcomers.

Postgraduate advantage

A doctorate is more or less a prerequisite for an academic post in higher education, though its possession will not guarantee a job. For teaching in schools, you need the Postgraduate Certificate in Education (PGCE). Details will be found in the section on education.

Training in the conservation of paintings and textiles is nearly all postgraduate. In the field of fashion, a higher degree from a prestigious institution such as the Royal College of Art or St Martin's can boost one's career prospects, while fashion shows provide a shop window for one's work.

A postgraduate diploma is required for the relatively new careers of art, dance, drama and music therapy. Such therapists work with the mentally ill, the mentally or physically handicapped, or the socially disadvantaged. For music one must be, first of all, professionally qualified, and for the other therapies primary degrees must have some relevance, for example, physical education or dance education for dance.

The required standard

Arts administration is another career in which a postgraduate qualification, like the City University diploma, is becoming increasingly the norm. Students acquire a general knowledge of financial, legal and personnel matters, and undertake a period of secondment with a professional organisation. They should have some previous relevant experience.

Growing numbers of staff both in national and local authority museums and art galleries have completed a postgraduate course in museum and gallery administration or museum studies. Manchester's diploma concentrates on the fine and decorative arts, while the Leicester course is intended for those interested in archaeology, the natural sciences, the local history, folk life and history of science.

While the government does offer some training in archive work to graduates with appropriate first degrees, for most other appointments, particularly in local government, a relevant postgraduate qualification is more or less essential.

Media training courses

All forms of journalism involve some sort of training scheme. The completion of a suitable postgraduate course can give you an advantage in your jobhunting, whether with newspapers, periodicals, radio or television. Postgraduate courses in different areas of journalism are run by the City University, University of Wales, the London College of Printing and Lancashire Polytechnic. The South Glamorgan Institute of Higher Education mounts a 20-week intensive pre-entry journalism course for graduates, who sit the same National Council for the Training of Journalists (NCTJ) examinations as those on full one-year non-graduate courses.

Publishing is another difficult field to enter, and one that attracts many graduates. All the institutions offering postgraduate courses in printing and publishing studies or publishing and book production proudly quote the success stories of their graduates.

Before setting your heart on these or any of the other courses listed in this section, make early enquiries about finance. Public funding in the arts and humanities is particularly difficult. Some grants will continue to be available through the British Academy, on a competitive basis, so much will depend on your performance at undergraduate level. Competition is likely to hot up, too, because the increasing number of Master's courses means more pressure on the funds available. Students on vocational courses may apply for Local Education Authority discretionary awards, but policies vary with the authority and most are cutting back. Check in the section on applications and grants to see what the sources of finance are likely to be in your case.

Joan Llewelyn-Owens

This listing contains **taught courses** (under the heading 'Higher degrees by instruction') and **research opportunities** (under the heading 'Higher degrees by research'). All study exceeds two terms or six months and is offered on both a full-time and part-time basis unless otherwise indicated. Post-experience and in-service courses are only included when advertised.

☐   This symbol indicates that the **taught course(s)** or **research opportunities** are advertised at the end of this listing.

Biol   An italic abbreviation indicates that an advertisement has been placed at the end of another chapter.

☆   This symbol indicates full-time study only.

△   This symbol indicates part-time study only.

For quick reference to advertisements, please use the 'Advertiser's course entry index'. For further information regarding the listing, please refer to page 53.

General

Higher degrees by instruction

Applied research methods
Ealing C London dip☆

Arts administration
Roehampton I dip☆

Arts management in education
City U MA

Business information technology systems
Strathclyde U MSc☆/dip☆

Church & secular power
Bangor, U of Wales MA☆

Cultural studies
Cheltenham & Gloucester CHE MA△
Leeds U MA

Economic & social history
York U MSc☆

Editorial musicology (Renaissance/Baroque periods)
Bangor, U of Wales MA☆

Emblem studies
Glasgow U dip☆

History & philosophy of science
Cambridge U MPhil☆

Independent study
East London P MA/MSc/dip

International studies
Newcastle U MA☆
Sheffield U MA☆/dip☆
Southampton U MSc(SocSci)/ cert☆/dip   *Soc*

Local studies
St Andrews U dip☆

Medieval studies
Belfast Queen's U MA☆
London U Queen Mary & Westfield C MA   ☐

Photography
Edinburgh CA dip☆

Proficiency in a special arts subject
Glasgow U dip☆

Publishing & book production
South West P dip   ☐

Religious studies
Bangor, U of Wales MA☆

Sociology of contemporary culture
York U MA☆   *Soc*

Women's studies & education
Lancaster U MA

Women's studies & languages
Lancaster U MA

Women's studies & sociology
Lancaster U MA

Higher degrees by research

Advanced studies
Manchester P PhD/MPhil

Arts & humanities
Manchester P PhD/MPhil

Arts & languages
Kingston P PhD/MPhil
Wales P PhD/MPhil

Cartoons & caricature
Kent U PhD/MPhil

Communication & cultural studies
Bristol P PhD/MPhil/dip

Communication & media
Dorset Inst PhD/MPhil

Cultural studies
Cheltenham & Gloucester CHE PhD/MPhil

Leeds U PhD/MPhil

Humanities
Hatfield P PhD/MPhil
Humberside CHE PhD/MPhil
Liverpool P PhD/MPhil
Middlesex P PhD/MPhil/dip△
Oxford P PhD/MPhil
West London IHE MPhil☆

Humanities, social & cultural studies
Wolverhampton P PhD/MPhil

Independent study
East London P PhD/MPhil
Lancaster U PhD/MPhil

Interdisciplinary studies in social sciences
Kent U PhD/MPhil

Logic
Middlesex P PhD/MPhil/dip△

Modern studies
Staffordshire P PhD/MPhil

Peace studies
Middlesex P PhD/MPhil/dip△

Women's studies
Lancaster U PhD/MPhil
Middlesex P PhD/MPhil/dip△
Ulster U DPhil/MPhil

Archaeology

Higher degrees by instruction

Anthropological archaeology
Oxford U MSt☆

Archaeological conservation
Durham U dip☆
London U UC MSc☆

Archaeological method
Southampton U MA☆

Archaeological practice
Birmingham U MA

Archaeological science
Southampton U MSc☆

Archaeological studies
Bradford U dip☆

Archaeological textile studies
Manchester U MA☆

Archaeology
Belfast Queen's U MA☆
Cambridge U MPhil☆
Edinburgh U MLitt☆

Exeter U MA
London U SOAS MA
London U UC MA/MSc
Manchester U MA☆
Nottingham U MA
Oxford U MSt☆
Reading U MA

Archaeology & pre history
Sheffield U MA☆/dip☆

Archaeology (British Isles in the Anglo Saxon & Medieval periods)
London U UC MA☆

Archaeology (post excavation studies)
Leicester U MA/dip

Archaeology of the Roman empire
Newcastle U MPhil☆

Archaeometallurgy
London U UC MSc☆

Bioarchaeology
London U UC MSc☆

Celtic archaeology
Glasgow U MPhil☆

Ceramic & lithic analysis in archaeological research
London U UC MA☆

Classical archaeology
Cambridge U dip☆
Edinburgh U MLitt☆/MSc☆/dip☆
Liverpool U MA☆
Oxford U MPhil☆/MSt☆

Classical archaeology (Greece)
London U UC dip☆

Classical studies
St David's UC MA☆   *Lang*

Cuneiform studies
Birmingham U MA

Early British studies
Aberystwyth, UC of Wales MA☆

Early man & the environment
Durham U MA☆

Early Medieval archaeology
Durham U MA☆

Egyptology
Swansea UC MA☆

Environmental archaeology & paleaoeconomy
Sheffield U MSc

European archaeology
Oxford U MPhil☆/MSt☆

Field & analytical techniques in archaeology
London U UC MA☆

Funerary archaeology & human skeletal studies
Sheffield U MSc

Greek & Roman archaeology
Newcastle U MA☆

History of the English landscape
Reading U MA

Industrial archaeology
Birmingham U MSocSc/dip

Islamic archaeology
Newcastle U MA☆

Marine archaeology
Bangor, U of Wales MSc☆/dip☆

Maritime studies
St Andrews U MLitt/MPhil☆/dip☆

Medieval archaeology
Birmingham U MA☆

Medieval British archaeology
York U MA☆

Medieval studies
York U MA/dip☆

Museum studies (archaeological)
London U UC MA☆

Oriental studies (cuneiform studies)
Oxford U MPhil☆/MSt☆

Oriental studies (Egyptology)
Oxford U MPhil☆/MSt☆

Osteology, palaeopathology & funerary archaeology
Bradford U MSc☆

Practical archaeology
Birmingham U dip☆

Prehistoric archaeology
Liverpool U BPhil☆
Newcastle U MPhil☆
Oxford U MPhil☆/MSt☆

Quaternary research
Cambridge U MPhil☆

Quaternary studies
City of London P MSc△

Roman archaeology
Durham U MA☆

Roman social & cultural history
Reading U MA

Scientific methods in archaeology
Bradford U MA☆/dip☆

Social anthropology
Durham U MA☆/dip☆

Higher degrees by research

Ancient history & archaeology
Birmingham U PhD/MLitt

Archaeological conservation & materials science
London U UC PhD☆/MPhil☆

Archaeological sciences
Bradford U PhD/MPhil

Archaeological studies
Leeds U PhD/MPhil

Archaeology
Bangor, U of Wales PhD/MPhil
Belfast Queen's U PhD/MSc
Cambridge U PhD☆/MLitt☆
Cardiff U of Wales C PhD☆/ MPhil☆
Dorset Inst PhD/MPhil/dip
Durham U PhD/MA/MPhil
Edinburgh U PhD/MLitt
Exeter U PhD/MPhil
Glasgow U PhD/MLitt
Leicester U PhD/MA/MPhil
London U UC PhD☆/MPhil☆
Manchester U PhD/MA
Newcastle U PhD/MLitt
Oxford U DPhil☆/MLitt☆
Reading U PhD/MPhil
St David's UC PhD☆/MA☆
Southampton U PhD/MPhil
York U DPhil/MPhil

Archaeology & prehistory
Sheffield U PhD/MPhil

Archaeology of the Roman provinces
London U UC PhD☆/MPhil☆

Art & archaeology
London U SOAS PhD/MPhil

Classical & archaeological studies
Nottingham U PhD/MPhil

Classical archaeology
Edinburgh U PhD/MLitt
Liverpool U PhD/MPhil
London U UC PhD☆/MPhil☆

Classics
Reading U PhD/MPhil

Classics & archaeology
Bristol U PhD/MLitt
Lancaster U PhD/MPhil

Egyptology
Liverpool U PhD/MPhil
London U UC PhD☆/MPhil☆

Evolution of human environments
Durham U PhD/MA/MPhil/MSc

Geological sciences
London U UC PhD☆/MPhil☆

History
Exeter U PhD/MPhil

Human environment studies
London U UC PhD☆/MPhil☆

Micropalaeontology
London U UC PhD☆/MPhil☆

Palaeoecology centre
Belfast Queen's U PhD/MSc

Prehistoric archaeology
Liverpool U PhD/MPhil
London U UC PhD☆/MPhil☆

Western Asiatic archaeology
London U UC PhD☆/MPhil☆

Archives, paleography, museum studies

Higher degrees by instruction

Archive administration
Aberystwyth, UC of Wales dip☆
Bangor, U of Wales dip☆
Liverpool U MArAd☆

Archive studies
London U UC MA/dip

Archives
Loughborough U MA

Art gallery & museum studies
Manchester U dip☆   □

Art history & theory
Essex U MA

Cuneiform studies
Birmingham U MA

Editorial musicology (Renaissance/Baroque periods)
Bangor, U of Wales MA☆

English (Medieval studies)
Belfast Queen's U MA

Ethnology & museum ethnography
Oxford U MPhil☆/MSt☆

Gallery studies
Essex U MA☆

Heritage
Newcastle U MA☆

Museum studies
Leicester U MA/MSc/dip

Museum studies (archaeological)
London U UC MA☆

Museums & gallery administration
City U MA

Oriental studies (cuneiform studies)
Oxford U MPhil☆/MSt☆

Overseas records management & archive administration
London U UC MA

Palaeography
Aberystwyth, UC of Wales cert☆

Higher degrees by research

Art gallery & museum studies
Manchester U MPhil☆

Arts policy & management
City U PhD/MPhil

Library, archive & information studies
London U UC PhD☆/MPhil☆

Museum studies
Leicester U PhD/MPhil

Palaeography
London U King's C PhD☆/MPhil☆
Manchester U PhD/MPhil

Palaeography & diplomatic studies
Durham U PhD/MA/MLitt

Area studies: European

Higher degrees by instruction

18th century European art & aesthetics
Essex U MA☆

20th German literature & society
St Andrews U MLitt/MPhil☆/dip☆

Anglo American studies
Sussex U MA

Anglo Saxon studies
London U UC MA
Manchester U MA△

Area studies
London U LSE MA

Area studies (Eastern Europe & Russia)
London U SSEES MA

Britain & the European community
Brunel U MA△

Business administration
Hull U MBA☆

Celtic studies
Edinburgh U MLitt☆
Oxford U dip☆

Community studies in Western Europe
Belfast Queen's U MA

Comparative European studies
Sussex U MA

Contemporary East European studies
Sussex U MA☆

Contemporary French studies
Portsmouth P MA△/dip△

Contemporary German studies
Ealing C London MA△/dip△

Contemporary West European studies
Sussex U MA

Cultural studies
Ealing C London MA△
Leeds U MA

Culture & society in contemporary Europe
Southampton U MA/dip

Dutch studies
Liverpool U MA☆

Early British studies
Aberystwyth, UC of Wales MA☆

Early Celtic studies
Cardiff U of Wales C MA☆

Economics of the European community
Exeter U MA☆

English & Hispanic studies
Glasgow U MPhil

English (Anglo Irish studies)
Belfast Queen's U MA

European area studies
Surrey U MA☆/dip☆

European culture & society
Birmingham U MA

European history
East Anglia U MA☆

European politics
Manchester U MA(Econ)☆

European social policy
London U LSE MSc

European studies
Keele U MA/dip
London U LSE MSc
Reading U MA

Franco-Italian Renaissance studies
Exeter U MA

French studies
Liverpool U MA   *Lang*
Reading U MA
St Andrews U MLitt/MPhil☆/dip☆
Sussex U MA
Warwick U MA/MPhil

German literature since the second world war
Newcastle U MA☆

German studies
Liverpool U MA☆
Sussex U MA
Warwick U MA

Hispanic studies
London U UC MA☆

History & culture of the Dutch Golden Age
London U UC MA☆

Humanities
North London P MA△

Icelandic studies
Leeds U dip☆

International conflict analysis
Kent U MA

International relations
Nottingham U MA☆/dip☆

International studies
Birmingham U MSocSc/dip
Reading U MA

Irish studies
Belfast Queen's U MA/MSScΔ

Italian studies
Reading U MA

Local studies
St Andrews U Dip☆

Modern British studies
Warwick U MA/dip☆

Modern French & English literature
Swansea UC MA☆

Modern French studies
Loughborough U MA△

Modern German studies: literature of a divided Germany
Aberdeen U MLitt

National Trust for Scotland studies
St Andrews U MLitt

Northern Renaissance studies
Sussex U MA

Political economy & political culture: Britain & France
Nottingham U MA

Political science
Birmingham U MSocSc

Political sociology of development
Leeds U MA

Politics & government of Western Europe
London U LSE MSc

Religion, culture & development
London U King's C MA☆

Renaissance studies
London U Birkbeck C MA△

Russian & East European studies
Birmingham U MA☆
Oxford U MPhil☆
Swansea UC MA☆/MSc(Econ)☆

Russian or Slavonic studies
Edinburgh U MLitt☆

Russian studies
Manchester U MA☆
Sheffield U MA   *Lang*
Sussex U MA

Scandinavian studies (Medieval & West Norse studies)
London U UC MA

Scandinavian studies (modern)
London U UC MA

Scottish literature
Glasgow U MPhil

Scottish studies
Edinburgh U MLitt☆
St Andrews U MLitt/dip☆

Slavonic studies
Oxford U dip☆
Sheffield U MA

Soviet & East European studies
Glasgow U MPhil/dip

Spanish literature & film since 1939
Newcastle U MA☆

Strategic studies
Aberdeen U MLitt☆

Trade & development
Lancaster U MSc☆

Viking studies
Nottingham U MA☆

Welsh history
Bangor, U of Wales MA☆
Swansea UC MA☆

Western European social studies
Exeter U MA

Western European studies
Hull U dip☆

Higher degrees by research

American & Commonwealth arts & studies
Exeter U PhD/MPhil

Applied linguistics & area studies
Manchester UMIST PhD/MSc

Area studies & languages
North London P PhD/MPhil

Byzantine & modern Greek studies
London U King's C PhD☆/MPhil☆

Celtic studies
Edinburgh U PhD/MLitt
Manchester U PhD/MA/MPhil

Classical civilisation
North London P PhD/MPhil

Classical tradition in European thought, art & institutions
London U Warburg Inst PhD☆/MPhil☆

Commonwealth studies
London U Inst of Commonwealth Studies PhD☆/MPhil☆

Contemporary European studies
Sussex U DPhil/MPhil

Contemporary French & German studies
Aston U PhD/MPhil

European & international studies
Reading U PhD/MPhil

European & modern Dutch studies
Hull U PhD/MPhil

European governmental studies
Edinburgh U PhD/MPhil

European institutions
Middlesex P PhD/MPhil/dip△

European policies research
Strathclyde U PhD☆/MPhil☆/MSc☆

European studies
Bradford U PhD/MPhil
Central London P PhD☆/MPhil☆
Kent U PhD/MA/MPhil
Loughborough U PhD☆/MPhil☆
Manchester UMIST PhD/MSc

European studies & modern languages
Ulster U DPhil/MPhil

French studies
Lancaster U PhD/MPhil
Manchester U PhD/MPhil
Newcastle U PhD/MLitt
Reading U PhD/MPhil
Sussex U DPhil/MPhil
Warwick U PhD/MA/MPhil

Geography
Strathclyde U PhD☆/MPhil☆/MSc☆

German & Scandinavian studies
Newcastle U PhD/MLitt

German studies
Birmingham U PhD/MLitt/MPhil
Lancaster U PhD/MPhil
Sussex U DPhil/MPhil
Warwick U PhD/MA/MPhil

German, Austrian & Swiss affairs
Nottingham U PhD/MPhil

Greek civilisation
Glasgow U PhD/MLitt

Hispanic studies
Belfast Queen's U PhD/MA
Edinburgh U PhD/MLitt
Hull U PhD/MPhil
Nottingham U PhD/MPhil

Historical & critical studies
Portsmouth P PhD☆/MPhil☆

History
London U SSEES PhD/MPhil

Humanities
Teesside P PhD☆/MPhil☆

Iberian studies
Keele U PhD/MA

International studies
Birmingham U PhD/MPhil
Cambridge U PhD/MLitt

Irish studies
Belfast Queen's U PhD/MA

Italian studies
Lancaster U PhD/MPhil
Manchester U PhD/MPhil
Reading U PhD/MPhil

Languages & area studies
Portsmouth P PhD☆/MPhil☆
Sunderland P PhD/MPhil

Languages & European studies
Wolverhampton P PhD/MPhil

Modern Dutch studies
Hull U PhD/MPhil

Modern languages
Sheffield City P PhD/MPhil

Northern Renaissance studies
Sussex U DPhil/MPhil

Russian & East European studies
Birmingham U PhD/MLitt/MPhil
Swansea UC PhD/MPhil

Russian & Slavonic studies
Sheffield U PhD/MPhil

Russian studies
Keele U PhD/MA
Leeds U PhD/MA/MPhil
Manchester U PhD/MA/MPhil
Sussex U DPhil/MPhil

Scandinavian studies
Hull U PhD/MPhil
London U UC PhD☆/MPhil☆

Scottish studies
Aberdeen U PhD☆/MLitt☆/MPhil☆
Edinburgh U PhD/MLitt

Slavonic & East European studies
Oxford U DPhil☆/MLitt☆

Slavonic studies
Belfast Queen's U PhD/MA
Edinburgh U MLitt
Nottingham U PhD/MPhil

Soviet & East European studies
Glasgow U PhD/MLitt   Soc

Spanish & Latin American studies
London U UC PhD☆/MPhil☆
Newcastle U PhD/MLitt

Spanish & Portuguese studies
Manchester U PhD/MPhil

Spanish & Spanish American studies
London U King's C PhD☆/MPhil☆

Spanish politics & literature since 1936
Bristol P PhD△/MPhil△/dip△

Tocqueville studies
Buckingham U DPhil/MPhil

Welsh history
Swansea UC PhD/MPhil

Welsh studies
Cardiff U of Wales C PhD☆/
 MPhil☆

Western European studies
Exeter U PhD/MPhil

Yugoslav studies
Bradford U PhD☆/MPhil☆

Area studies: non European

Higher degrees by instruction

Advanced Jewish studies
Leo Baeck C MA☆

African studies
Birmingham U MA☆
Edinburgh U MSc☆/dip☆

American literature since 1945
Aberystwyth, UC of Wales MA☆

American literature, film or culture
Exeter U MA☆

American studies
East Anglia U MA☆
Exeter U MA☆
Liverpool U MA☆
Manchester U MA
Nottingham U MA

Amerindian studies
St Andrews U MLitt☆/MPhil☆/
 Dip☆

Ancient Near Eastern & Mediterranean studies
Edinburgh U MLitt☆

Ancient Near Eastern civilisation
London U SOAS MSc

Anglo American studies
Sussex U MA

Arabic studies
Leeds U MA
St Andrews U MLitt

Area studies
London U LSE MA

Area studies (Africa)
London U SOAS MA

Area studies (Afro American & Afro Caribbean)
London U SOAS MA

Area studies (Far East)
London U SOAS MA

Area studies (Latin American & the USA)
London U King's C MA

Area studies (Near & Middle East)
London U SOAS MA

Area studies (South Asia)
London U SOAS MA

Area studies (South East Asia)
London U SOAS MA

Area studies (United States)
London U Inst of Historical
 Research/US Studies MA □

Chinese studies
Oxford U MSt☆

Cultural studies
Ealing C London MA△
Leeds U MA

Development economics
East Anglia U MA☆

Development studies
East Anglia U MA☆/cert☆
Leeds U MA

Economics of Latin America
London U Queen Mary &
 Westfield C MSc

Geography of Africa & the Middle East
London U SOAS MSc

Greek civilisation
Leeds U MA☆

Hebrew & Jewish studies
London U UC MA☆

History & related studies
London U Inst of Historical
 Research/US Studies MA☆

Icelandic studies
Leeds U MA☆

Indian, Tibetan or Buddhist studies
Bristol U MA

Indonesian & Malay studies
London U SOAS MA

International conflict analysis
Kent U MA

International relations
Nottingham U MA☆/dip☆

International studies
Birmingham U MSocSc/dip
Reading U MA

Islamic studies
Kent U MA/dip

Japanese studies
Sheffield U MA

Judaism & Jewish-Christian relations
Birmingham U dip☆

Latin American government & politics
Essex U MA☆

Latin American studies
Cambridge U MPhil☆
Glasgow U MPhil/dip☆
Liverpool U MA/dip
Newcastle U MA☆/MPhil☆
Oxford U MPhil☆

Middle East politics
Exeter U MA

Middle Eastern studies
Manchester U MA

Modern Jewish studies
Oxford U MSt☆

Modern Middle Eastern history
Durham U MA☆

Modern Middle Eastern studies
Durham U MA☆

Native American studies
Essex U MA☆

North American geographical studies
London U Birkbeck C MA△

North American studies
Edinburgh U MLitt☆/MPhil☆

Oriental studies
Cambridge U MPhil☆

Oriental studies (Indian studies)
Oxford U MPhil☆/MSt☆

Oriental studies (Islamic art & architecture)
Oxford U MPhil☆/MSt☆

Oriental studies (modern Jewish studies)
Oxford U MPhil☆/MSt☆

Oriental studies (modern Middle Eastern studies)
Oxford U MPhil☆/MSt☆

Oriental studies (Ottoman studies)
Oxford U MPhil☆/MSt☆

Persian studies
Edinburgh U MLitt☆

Political science
Birmingham U MSocSc

Political sociology of development
Leeds U MA

Pre Columbian & colonial art in Middle & South America
Essex U MA☆

Public policy in Latin America
Oxford U MSc☆

Quechua studies
St Andrews U dip☆

Religion, culture & development
London U King's C MA☆

Sociology & social anthropology
Hull U MA☆/MSc☆ *Soc*

South East Asian studies
Kent U MA/dip

Southern African studies
York U MA☆

Turkish studies
Edinburgh U MLitt☆

United States history & politics
Keele U MA

West African studies
Birmingham U MSocSc/dip

Higher degrees by research

Africa
London U SOAS PhD/MPhil

African & Caribbean studies
Kent U PhD/MA/MPhil

African studies
Aberdeen U PhD☆/MLitt☆/MPhil☆
Birmingham U PhD☆/MPhil☆
Cambridge U PhD/MLitt
Glasgow U PhD/MLitt
Liverpool U PhD/MPhil
Oxford U DPhil☆/MLitt☆
Sussex U DPhil/MPhil

American & Commonwealth arts & studies
Exeter U PhD/MPhil

American studies
Aberystwyth, UC of Wales PhD☆/MPhil☆
East Anglia U PhD/MPhil
Exeter U PhD/MPhil
Hull U PhD/MPhil
Keele U PhD/MA
Kent U PhD/MA/MPhil
Manchester U PhD/MPhil
Middlesex P PhD/MPhil/dip△
Nottingham U PhD/MPhil
Sussex U DPhil/MPhil

Arabic & Islamic studies
Exeter U PhD/MPhil

Arabic studies
St Andrews U PhD/MPhil

Area studies & languages
North London P PhD/MPhil

Canadian studies
Edinburgh U PhD/MPhil

Caribbean studies
Warwick U PhD/MA/MPhil

Chinese studies
Central London P PhD☆/MPhil☆
South Bank P PhD/MPhil

Chinese, Japanese & North East Asian studies
Leeds U PhD/MA/MPhil

Commonwealth studies
London U Inst of Commonwealth Studies PhD☆/MPhil☆
Stirling U PhD/MPhil

Development studies
Leeds U PhD/MPhil

East Asian studies
Newcastle U MA

European & international studies
Reading U PhD/MPhil

Far East
London U SOAS PhD/MPhil

Geography
London U SOAS PhD/MPhil
Strathclyde U PhD☆/MPhil☆/MSc☆

Hispanic studies
Belfast Queen's U PhD/MA

International studies
Birmingham U PhD/MPhil
Cambridge U PhD/MLitt

Islamic studies
Birmingham U PhD☆/MPhil☆
Kent U PhD/MPhil

Japanese studies
Sheffield U PhD/MPhil

Jewish studies
Birmingham U PhD☆/MPhil☆

Languages & area studies
Portsmouth P PhD☆/MPhil☆

Latin American studies
Cambridge U PhD☆ □
Glasgow U PhD/MLitt
Liverpool U PhD/MPhil
London U Inst of Latin American Studies PhD/MPhil
Oxford U DPhil☆/MLitt☆

Middle Eastern & Islamic studies
Durham U PhD/MPhil

Middle Eastern studies
Central London P PhD☆/MPhil☆
Manchester U PhD/MPhil

Modern Arabic studies
Leeds U MA

Modern languages
Sheffield City P PhD/MPhil

Near & Middle East
London U SOAS PhD/MPhil

Near Eastern studies
Manchester U PhD/MA/MPhil

Oriental studies
Cambridge U PhD☆/MLitt☆
Durham U PhD/MA/MLitt
Liverpool U PhD/MPhil
Oxford U DPhil☆/MLitt☆

Sociology & social anthropology
Hull U PhD/MPhil *Soc*

South Asian studies
Sussex U DPhil/MPhil

South East Asia & the Islands
London U SOAS PhD/MPhil

South East Asian studies
Hull U PhD/MPhil
Kent U PhD/MPhil

Southern African studies
York U DPhil/MPhil

Spanish & Latin American studies
London U UC PhD☆/MPhil☆
Newcastle U PhD/MLitt

Third World studies
Liverpool U PhD/MPhil

West African studies
Birmingham U PhD☆/MPhil☆/MSocSc☆

Art history, fine art

Higher degrees by instruction

18th century European art & aesthetics
Essex U MA☆

Advanced training in art therapy
Hertfordshire CAD dip△

Aesthetics & theory of art
Essex U MA☆

Architectural history
Keele U MA△

Art & architecture
Kent IAD MA

Art & design
Middlesex P cert
Robert Gordon's IT dip✰

Art & design (extension studies)
Bristol P dip

Art direction
Watford C dip✰

Art historical studies
Edinburgh U MLitt✰

Art history
Aberystwyth, UC of Wales MA
East Anglia U MA
Glasgow U MPhil
Leeds P MA△
St Andrews U MLitt/dip✰

Art history & theory
Essex U MA

Art therapy
Hertfordshire CAD MA△/dip
Sheffield U dip

Arts administration
Roehampton I dip✰

Chartered surveying (general practice - chattels option)
Southampton IHE RICS

Conservation of fine art
Gateshead C dip✰
Newcastle P MA✰

Conservation of paintings
London U Courtauld Inst of Art
   dip✰

Conservation of wall paintings
London U Courtauld Inst of Art
   dip✰

Critical theory
Essex U dip✰

Decorative arts
Glasgow U dip✰

Drawing & painting
Glasgow SA dip✰

Environmental art
Glasgow SA dip✰

Fine & applied arts
Ulster U dip

Fine art
Birmingham P MA
Byam Shaw SA cert
Cardiff IHE MA△   □
Glasgow SA MA✰
Heriot-Watt U dip✰
Goldsmiths' C London U MA△
London U UC dip✰
Manchester P MA
Newcastle U MFA✰
Nottingham P MA△
Reading U MFA✰
Robert Gordon's IT dip✰

Ulster U MA✰/dip✰

Fine art (drawing, painting & sculpture)
Edinburgh CA MFA✰

Fine art (painting, printmaking & alternative media)
Chelsea CAD MA✰

Fine arts
Birmingham U MA✰

Gallery studies
Essex U MA✰
St Andrews U MLitt

History & theory of 19th & 20th century art
Essex U MA✰

History & theory of art & design
Ulster U dip△

History & theory of modern art
Chelsea CAD MA△

History & theory of Renaissance & Baroque art, 1400-1700
Essex U MA✰

History of art
Edinburgh U MSc✰/dip✰
London U Birkbeck C MA△
London U Courtauld Inst of Art
   MA✰/dip✰
Manchester U dip✰
Oxford U dip✰
Sussex U MA
Warwick U dip✰

History of art & design
Birmingham P MA/dip
Winchester SA dip△

History of design
Middlesex P MA✰
Royal CA MA✰

Industrial design in England from 1688-1914
Essex U MA✰

Literature & the visual arts 1840-1940
Reading U MA

Medieval English language, literature & art
Keele U MA

Northern Renaissance studies
Sussex U MA

Oriental studies (Islamic art & architecture)
Oxford U MPhil✰/MSt✰

Painting
Central St Martins CAD cert✰
Heriot-Watt U MFA✰/dip✰
Royal CA MA✰

Pre Columbian & colonial art in Middle & South America
Essex U MA✰

Printmaking
Brighton P MA△/dip△
Glasgow SA dip✰

Public art & design
Duncan of Jordanstone CA
   MPhil✰

Sculpture
Central St Martins CAD cert✰
Edinburgh CA dip✰
Glasgow SA dip✰
Heriot-Watt U MBA✰/dip✰
Royal CA MA✰

Sculpture studies
Leeds U MA✰

Social history of art
Leeds U MA✰

Studio studies with art history
Aberystwyth, UC of Wales MA/
   dip✰

Valuation & auctioneering (fine arts & chattels)
Southampton IHE ISVA✰

Visual Islamic & traditional arts
Royal CA MA✰

The word & visual imagination
St David's UC MA   *Lang*

Higher degrees by research

Architecture
Manchester U PhD/MPhil
Newcastle U PhD/MLitt/MSc

Art
Coventry P PhD/MPhil
Open U PhD/MPhil/BPhil
Robert Gordon's IT PhD/MPhil
South West P PhD/MPhil

Art & archaeology
London U SOAS PhD/MPhil

Art & design
Birmingham P PhD/MPhil
Brighton P PhD/MPhil
Canterbury Christ Church C
   PhD/MPhil
East London P PhD/MPhil
Lancashire P PhD/MPhil
Goldsmiths' C London U PhD/
   MPhil
Middlesex P PhD/MPhil
Sunderland P PhD/MPhil
West Glamorgan IHE PhD/MPhil

Wolverhampton P PhD/MPhil

Art & design history
Brighton P PhD/MPhil

Art education
Bristol P dip

Art gallery & museum studies
Manchester U MPhil☆

Art history
Aberystwyth, UC of Wales
 MPhil☆
East Anglia U PhD☆/MPhil☆
Leicester P PhD/MPhil
Newcastle P PhD☆/MPhil☆
Nottingham U PhD/MPhil
St Andrews U PhD/MPhil

Art history & communications
Coventry P PhD/MPhil

Art history & related studies
Middlesex P PhD/MPhil

Art history & theory
Essex U PhD/MPhil
Lancashire P PhD/MPhil

Arts & design
Kingston P PhD/MPhil

Arts policy & management
City U PhD/MPhil

**Classical tradition in European
thought, art & institutions**
London U Warburg Inst PhD☆/
 MPhil☆

Combined studies
South West P PhD/MPhil

Communication arts
Sheffield City P PhD/MPhil

Core & theoretical studies
Ulster U DPhil/MPhil

Cultural history
Royal CA PhD☆/MA☆

Design
Leeds P PhD/MPhil/dip
Napier P PhD/MPhil
Portsmouth P PhD☆/MPhil☆

Fine & applied art
City of London P PhD☆/MPhil☆
Ulster U DPhil/MPhil

Fine art
Birmingham P PhD/MPhil
Brighton P PhD/MPhil
Bristol P dip
Coventry P PhD/MPhil
Edinburgh U PhD/MLitt
Kingston P PhD/MPhil
Lancashire P PhD/MPhil
Leeds U PhD/MPhil
Leicester P PhD/MPhil
Liverpool P PhD/MPhil

Goldsmiths' C London U PhD/
 MPhil
London U UC PhD☆/MPhil☆
Manchester P PhD/MPhil
Middlesex P PhD/MPhil
Newcastle U PhD/MLitt
Nottingham P PhD☆/MPhil☆
Nottingham U PhD/MPhil
Sheffield City P PhD/MPhil

Fine arts
Birmingham U PhD/MLitt/MPhil

Fine arts & music
East Anglia U PhD☆/MPhil☆

History & theory of art
Kent U PhD/MA/MPhil

History of art
Aberdeen U PhD☆/MLitt☆/
 MPhil☆
Bristol U PhD/MLitt
Cambridge U PhD☆/MLitt☆
Glasgow U PhD/MLitt
Leicester U PhD/MPhil
London U Birkbeck C PhD/MPhil
London U Courtauld Inst of Art
 PhD/MPhil
Goldsmiths' C London U PhD/
 MPhil
London U Queen Mary &
 Westfield C PhD☆/MPhil☆
London U UC PhD☆/MPhil☆
Manchester U PhD/MPhil
Oxford U DPhil☆/MLitt☆
Reading U PhD/MPhil
Sussex U DPhil/MPhil
Warwick U PhD☆/MA☆/MPhil☆

History of art & design
Kingston P PhD/MPhil
Manchester P PhD/MPhil
Staffordshire P PhD/MPhil

**History of art and
complimentary studies**
Birmingham P PhD/MPhil

History of design
Royal CA PhD

Humanities
Oxford P PhD/MPhil

Northern Renaissance studies
Sussex U DPhil/MPhil

Painting
Duncan of Jordanstone CA
 PhD☆/MPhil☆
Royal CA PhD☆/MA☆

Painting & printmaking
Sheffield City P PhD/MPhil

Printmaking
Royal CA PhD☆

Sculpture
Royal CA PhD☆

Visual & performing arts
Newcastle P PhD☆/MPhil☆

Visual arts
Aberystwyth, UC of Wales
 PhD☆/MPhil☆
Lancaster U PhD/MPhil
Leeds P PhD/MPhil/dip

Visual Islamic & traditional arts
Royal CA PhD☆/MA☆

Visual studies
Manchester P PhD/MPhil

Graphics, fashion, textiles

Higher degrees by instruction

Animation
Royal CA MA☆

Archaeological textile studies
Manchester U MA☆

Art & design
Humberside CHE MA△
Robert Gordon's IT dip☆

Art therapy
Goldsmiths' C London U MA△/
 dip

Audio visual studies
Edinburgh CA MDes☆/dip☆
Heriot-Watt U dip☆

Calligraphy
Roehampton I dip☆

Calligraphy & bookbinding
Roehampton I cert☆

Carpet technology & design
Kidderminster C dip☆

Ceramics
Edinburgh CA dip☆
Heriot-Watt U dip☆
Goldsmiths' C London U dip

Clothing studies
Scottish C of Textiles dip☆

Clothing technology
Leeds U dip☆
Manchester P dip☆

Communications
Goldsmiths' C London U dip☆

Computer graphics
Middlesex P MSc△

2 POSTGRADUATE OPPORTUNITIES

Computing in design
Middlesex P MA☆

Conservation of textiles
London U Courtauld Inst of Art
   dip☆

Creative embroidery
Brighton P dip△

Design
Glasgow SA MA☆
Liverpool U MDes☆

Design & media technology
London C of Printing MA☆/dip☆

Design (ceramics)
Staffordshire P MA☆

Design for film
Royal CA MA☆

Digital image processing
Cranfield IT MSc☆/dip☆   *Comp*

Drawing & painting
Glasgow SA dip☆

Dyeing & finishing
Leeds U MSc☆

Electronic graphics
Coventry P MSc/dip

Embroidered & woven textiles
Glasgow SA dip☆

Embroidery
Royal CA MA☆

Fashion & textiles
Birmingham P MA△/dip△
Leicester P MA☆
Winchester SA dip☆

Fashion & theatre costume
Edinburgh CA dip☆
Heriot-Watt U dip☆

Fashion design
Central St Martins CAD MA☆
Royal CA MA☆

Figure drawing
Manchester P cert△

Fine & applied arts
Ulster U dip

Furniture design
Edinburgh CA dip☆
Heriot-Watt U dip☆

Glass & stained glass design
Edinburgh CA dip☆
Heriot-Watt U dip☆

Graphic design
Birmingham P MA
Central St Martins CAD MA
Edinburgh CA dip☆
Glasgow SA dip☆
Heriot-Watt U dip☆
Leicester P MA☆
Royal CA MA☆

Graphic design & computers
Central St Martins CAD dip△

Graphic design studies
Ulster U MA△/dip△

History of dress
London U Courtauld Inst of Art
   MA☆

Holography
Royal CA MA☆

Illustration
Central St Martins CAD dip△
Edinburgh CA dip☆
Heriot-Watt U dip☆
Royal CA MA☆

Interior design
Edinburgh CA dip☆
Heriot-Watt U dip☆
Leicester P MA☆
Manchester P MA☆
Royal CA MA☆

Jewellery & silversmithing
Edinburgh CA dip☆

Knitted textiles
Royal CA MA☆

Knitwear
Royal CA MDes☆

Knitwear & knitted fabric design
Nottingham P MA☆

Metalwork & jewellery
Royal CA MA☆

**Narrative illustration & editorial
design**
Brighton P MA☆/dip△

Natural history illustration
Royal CA MA☆

Painting
Heriot-Watt U MFA☆/dip☆

Photography
Glasgow SA dip☆
Royal CA MA☆

Practice of art
Reading U MFA☆

Printed textile design
Glasgow SA dip☆

Printed textiles
Edinburgh CA dip☆
Heriot-Watt U dip☆
Royal CA MA☆

Printmaking
Central St Martins CAD dip
Edinburgh CA dip☆
Glasgow SA dip☆
Heriot-Watt U MFA☆/dip☆

Sculpture
Edinburgh CA dip☆
Heriot-Watt U MBA☆/dip☆

Studio studies with art history
Aberystwyth, UC of Wales MA/
   dip☆

Tapestry
Edinburgh CA dip☆
Heriot-Watt U MFA☆/dip☆
Royal CA MA☆

Technical & scientific illustration
Royal CA MA☆

Textile art
Goldsmiths' C London U dip

Textile design
Central St Martins CAD dip
Leeds U dip☆
Scottish C of Textiles dip☆

Textile industries
Leeds U dip☆

Textile science & engineering
Leeds U MSc☆

Textile technology
Manchester UMIST MSc/dip

Textiles
Birmingham P MA☆/dip☆
Manchester P MA

Theatre costume
Heriot-Watt U dip☆

**Typography & graphic
communication**
Reading U dip☆

**Woven textiles (including
furnishing textiles)**
Royal CA MA☆

Higher degrees by research

Animation
Royal CA PhD☆

Applied & decorative art
Ulster U DPhil/MPhil

Architecture, art & design
Humberside CHE PhD/MPhil

Art
Robert Gordon's IT PhD/MPhil

Art & design
Birmingham P PhD/MPhil
Cardiff IHE PhD/MPhil/dip△
Cheltenham & Gloucester CHE
   PhD/MPhil
East London P PhD/MPhil
Goldsmiths' C London U PhD/
   MPhil
Middlesex P PhD/MPhil
Sunderland P PhD/MPhil

West Glamorgan IHE PhD/MPhil
Wolverhampton P PhD/MPhil

Art & design education
Birmingham P PhD/MPhil

Art therapy
Goldsmiths' C London U PhD/
MPhil

Business management
Scottish C of Textiles PhD/MPhil

Ceramic technology
Staffordshire P PhD/MPhil

Clothing design & technology
Manchester P PhD/MPhil

Clothing technology
Leeds U PhD/MPhil/MSc

Communication arts
Sheffield City P PhD/MPhil

Communication arts & design
Manchester P PhD/MPhil

Communication design
Middlesex P PhD/MPhil

Communication studies
Goldsmiths' C London U PhD/
MPhil

Design
Bristol P dip
Leeds P PhD/MPhil/dip
London C of Printing PhD/MPhil
Napier P PhD/MPhil
Open U PhD/MPhil/BPhil
Sheffield City P PhD/MPhil
Teesside P PhD☆/MPhil☆
Ulster U DPhil/MPhil

Design & crafts
Heriot-Watt U MDes☆/MPhil△/dip

Drawing & painting
Heriot-Watt U MDes☆/MPhil△/dip

Fashion
Kingston P PhD/MPhil
Newcastle P PhD☆/MPhil☆

Fashion & textile design
Lancashire P PhD/MPhil
Leicester P PhD/MPhil

Fashion & textiles
Birmingham P PhD/MPhil
Liverpool P PhD/MPhil
Nottingham P PhD/MPhil

Fashion design
Royal CA PhD☆

Graphic design
Bristol P dip
Central St Martins CAD PhD△/
MPhil△
Coventry P PhD/MPhil
Kingston P PhD/MPhil
Lancashire P PhD/MPhil
Leicester P PhD/MPhil

Liverpool P PhD/MPhil
Royal CA PhD☆

Graphics technology
Manchester P PhD/MPhil

Illustration
Royal CA PhD☆

Interior design
Middlesex P PhD/MPhil
North London P PhD/MPhil
Royal CA PhD

Media & graphic design
Newcastle P PhD☆/MPhil☆

Metalwork & jewellery
Royal CA MA☆

Painting & printmaking
Sheffield City P PhD/MPhil

Photography
Napier P PhD/MPhil
Royal CA PhD☆

**Print media, publishing &
communication**
Napier P PhD/MPhil

Product design
Middlesex P PhD/MPhil

Silversmithing & jewellery
Birmingham P PhD/MPhil

Tapestry
Royal CA PhD☆

Textile & knitwear technology
Leicester P PhD/MPhil

Textile design
Royal CA PhD☆/MA☆
Scottish C of Textiles PhD/MPhil

Textile industries
Huddersfield P PhD/MPhil
Leeds U PhD/MPhil/MSc(Eng)

Textile science
Scottish C of Textiles PhD/MPhil

Textile studies
Bolton IHE PhD/MPhil

Textile technology
Scottish C of Textiles PhD/MPhil

Textiles
Manchester UMIST PhD/MSc
Winchester SA MPhil/dip

Textiles/fashion
Manchester P PhD/MPhil
Middlesex P PhD/MPhil

**Typography & graphic
communication**
Reading U PhD/MPhil

Visual & performing arts
Newcastle P PhD☆/MPhil☆

Visual arts
Aberystwyth, UC of Wales
PhD☆/MPhil☆

Lancaster U PhD/MPhil
Leeds P PhD/MPhil/dip

Visual communication
Nottingham P PhD☆/MPhil☆

**Visual communications &
fashion textiles**
Birmingham P PhD/MPhil

Visual studies
Manchester P PhD/MPhil

History: ancient

Higher degrees by instruction

Aegean & Anatolian prehistory
Bristol U MA☆

**Ancient & medieval
philosophies**
Nottingham U MA

Ancient history
London U UC MA
Newcastle U MA☆
Oxford U MPhil☆
St Andrews U MLitt/MPhil☆/dip☆

Anglo Saxon studies
London U UC MA
Manchester U MA△

Archaeology & pre history
Sheffield U MA☆/dip☆

**Archaeology (British Isles in the
Anglo Saxon & Medieval
periods)**
London U UC MA☆

Byzantine studies
Birmingham U MA☆

**Byzantine studies in Western
Europe**
Belfast Queen's U MA

Classical Armenian studies
Oxford U MSt☆

Classical civilisation
Leeds U MA☆

Classical studies
St David's UC MA☆   *Lang*

Classics
Leeds U dip☆

Classics & ancient history
St Andrews U MLitt/MPhil☆/dip☆
Swansea UC MA☆

Economic & social history
York U MSc☆

Egyptology
Swansea UC MA☆

Greek &/or Roman history
Oxford U MSt☆

Greek civilisation
Leeds U MA☆

History
Durham U MA☆

Jewish studies in the Graeco Roman period
Oxford U MSt☆

Late Antique & Byzantine studies
London U King's C MA
London U Royal Holloway & Bedford New C MA

Late antiquity & early medieval studies
Exeter U MA☆

Late Roman & Byzantine studies
St Andrews U MLitt/MPhil☆/dip☆

Late Roman studies
Bristol U MA☆
Nottingham U MA

Maritime studies
St Andrews U MLitt/MPhil☆/dip☆

Oral tradition & ethnology
Edinburgh U MLitt☆

Oriental studies (Jewish studies in the Graeco Roman period)
Oxford U MPhil☆/MSc☆

Religion & mythology in the ancient world
Bristol U MA☆

Roman civilisation
Leeds U MA☆

Roman frontier studies
Newcastle U MA☆

Roman social & cultural history
Reading U MA

Viking studies
Nottingham U MA☆

Higher degrees by research

Ancient history
Belfast Queen's U PhD/MA
Cardiff U of Wales C PhD☆/ MPhil☆
Edinburgh U PhD/MLitt
London U UC PhD☆/MPhil☆
Oxford U DPhil☆/MLitt☆

St Andrews U PhD/MPhil

Ancient history & archaeology
Birmingham U PhD/MLitt

Archaeology
Reading U PhD/MPhil

Archaeology & prehistory
Sheffield U PhD/MPhil

Biblical studies
Bangor, U of Wales PhD☆/ MPhil☆

Classical civilisation
North London P PhD/MPhil

Classics
Bangor, U of Wales PhD☆/ MPhil☆
Reading U PhD/MPhil

Classics & ancient history
Durham U PhD/MA/MLitt
London U Birkbeck C PhD/MPhil
Swansea UC PhD/MPhil

Ethnology & prehistory
Oxford U DPhil☆/MLitt☆

Hellenic, Roman & Byzantine studies
Birmingham U PhD/MLitt/MPhil

Prehistoric archaeology
London U UC PhD☆/MPhil☆

Roman Britain
Open U PhD/MPhil/BPhil

Roman law
Aberdeen U PhD☆/MPhil☆

History: general

Higher degrees by instruction

20th century French studies
Nottingham U MA

Amerindian studies
St Andrews U MLitt☆/MPhil☆/ Dip☆

Architectural history
Keele U MA△

British history
Leeds U MA

Church & secular power
Bangor, U of Wales MA☆

Church history (patristic & modern)
London U Heythrop C MTh

Commonwealth history
London U Birkbeck C MA

Comparative history
Essex U MA/dip

Computer applications for history
London U Inst of Historical Research/US Studies MA

Cultural history
Aberdeen U MLitt

Cultural studies
Leeds U MA

Early British studies
Aberystwyth, UC of Wales MA☆

Early Celtic studies
Cardiff U of Wales C MA☆

Early music
Royal C of Mus cert☆

East Asian studies
Newcastle U MA☆

Ecclesiastical history
Edinburgh U MTh
Glasgow U MTh/dip
St Andrews U MPhil☆

Economic history
Swansea UC MSc (Econ)☆/dip☆

Education & local history
Leeds U MA

English & American history
East Anglia U MA

English & European history (12th & 13th centuries)
London U UC MA

English history
East Anglia U MA

English local & regional history
Goldsmiths' C London U MA△

English local history
Leicester U MA☆
Portsmouth P dip△

English studies (Shakespeare & the drama to 1640)
Oxford U MPhil☆

European & English history
Oxford U MPhil☆

European area studies
Surrey U MA☆/dip☆

European history
East Anglia U MA☆

European literary & historical studies
London U King's C MA

French drama & theatre history
Bristol U MA☆

Heritage management
Birmingham U dip

Historical musicology
London U King's C MMus
London U Royal Holloway &
Bedford New C MMus

Historical research
Lancaster U MA

Historical studies
Cambridge U dip☆
Lancaster U dip☆
Leicester U MA△
Sunderland P MA△

History
Belfast Queen's U MA☆
Durham U MA☆
Edinburgh U MLitt☆/MSc☆
Exeter U MA☆
Glasgow U MPhil
Huddersfield P MA△/dip△
Hull U MA☆
London U King's C MA☆
London U UC MA
Sheffield U MA/dip
Southampton U MA☆
Sussex U MA
Swansea UC MA☆

History & anthropology
London U UC MA

History & computing
Glasgow U MPhil

History & history of Wales
Cardiff U of Wales C MA/dip

History & philosophy of religion
London U King's C MA☆

History & philosophy of science
Cambridge U MPhil☆
Leeds U dip
London U Imperial C MSc

History & philosophy of science & mathematics
London U King's C MSc

History & philosophy of social & political science
Essex U MA☆

History & politics of the United States
Manchester U MA☆

History & related studies
London U Inst of Historical
Research/US Studies MA☆

History & theory of architecture
Architectural Association S of
Architecture dip☆

History (Central & Eastern Europe)
London U SSEES MA

History of design
Royal CA MA☆

History of dress
London U Courtauld Inst of Art
MA☆

History of education
London U Inst of Education MA

History of medicine
Cambridge U MPhil☆

History of modern architecture
London U UC MSc

History of science
Lancaster U MA
London U Imperial C MSc

History of science & technology
London U Imperial C MSc

History of science, medicine & technology
London U Imperial C MSc

History of scientific thought
Leeds U MA

History of technology
London U Imperial C MSc

History of the British Commonwealth & Empire or of the United States of America
Oxford U MPhil☆

History of the English landscape
Reading U MA

History, philosophy & social relations of science
Kent U MA

International business history
Reading U MA☆

International history
London U LSE MA/MSc

International studies
Salford U MA☆/cert☆

Late antiquity & early medieval studies
Exeter U MA☆

Latin American studies
Cambridge U MPhil☆
London U Inst of Latin American
Studies MA   *Soc*

Law, society & the economy in England, 1450-1660
Birmingham U MA☆

Legal & political theory
London U UC MA☆

Local & regional history
Leeds U MA
Nottingham U MA△

Local history
Cardiff U of Wales C MA△
Liverpool U MA☆

Local history, literature & cultural tradition
Sheffield U MA☆

London studies
London U Birkbeck C MA△

Maritime studies
St Andrews U MLitt/MPhil☆/dip☆

Medieval & Tudor studies
Kent U MA

Modern historical & political studies
Coventry P MA△/dip△

Modern Middle Eastern history
Durham U MA☆

National Trust for Scotland studies
St Andrews U MLitt

Oriental & African history
London U SOAS MA

Oriental studies (Ottoman studies)
Oxford U MPhil☆/MSt☆

Regional history
Brighton P MA△/dip△

Scottish history
Edinburgh U MLitt☆
St Andrews U MPhil☆

Scottish studies
St Andrews U MLitt/dip☆

Social policy history
Liverpool U MA△

Soviet & East European studies
Glasgow U MPhil/dip

Strategic studies
Aberdeen U MLitt☆
Salford U MA

Theology
Nottingham U MTh/dip   ☐

Tudor government
Bangor, U of Wales MA☆

United States history & politics
Keele U MA

Urban history
Leicester U MA

Victorian studies
Leicester U MA
London U Birkbeck C MA△

War studies
London U King's C MA/dip

Welsh history
Bangor, U of Wales MA☆
Swansea UC MA☆

West Midlands historical studies
Wolverhampton P MA△

Higher degrees by research

19th century British history
Buckingham U DPhil/MA/MPhil

Agricultural history
Reading U PhD/MPhil

American history
Birmingham U PhD/MLitt/MPhil

Amerindian studies
St Andrews U PhD☆/MPhil☆

Applied historical studies
Open U PhD☆/MPhil☆/BPhil☆

Byzantine & modern Greek studies
London U King's C PhD☆/MPhil☆

Church history
St David's UC PhD☆/MA☆

Civil law (Roman law)
Glasgow U PhD/LLM

Cultural history
Royal CA PhD☆/MA☆

Cultural studies
East London P PhD/MPhil

East Anglian studies
East Anglia U PhD/MPhil

Ecclesiastical history
Edinburgh U PhD/MPhil
Glasgow U PhD/MTh
St Andrews U PhD/MPhil

English & American history
East Anglia U PhD/MPhil

English & history
Manchester P PhD/MPhil

English local history
Leicester U PhD/MPhil

European history
East Anglia U PhD☆/MA☆/MPhil☆

European studies
Central London P PhD☆/MPhil☆

Historical & critical studies
Newcastle P PhD☆/MPhil☆
Portsmouth P PhD☆/MPhil☆
Sheffield City P PhD/MPhil

Historical studies
Bristol P PhD/MPhil
Robert Gordon's IT MLitt

History
Aberdeen U PhD☆/MLitt☆/MPhil☆
Aberystwyth, UC of Wales PhD☆/MPhil☆

Bangor, U of Wales PhD☆/MPhil☆
Bristol P PhD/MPhil
Bristol U PhD/MLitt
Cambridge U PhD☆/MLitt☆
Canterbury Christ Church C PhD/MPhil
Cardiff U of Wales C PhD☆/MPhil☆
Central London P PhD☆/MPhil☆
Cheltenham & Gloucester CHE PhD/MPhil
Durham U PhD/MA/MPhil
Edinburgh U PhD/MLitt
Essex U PhD/MPhil
Exeter U PhD/MPhil
Glasgow U PhD/MPhil
Hatfield P PhD/MPhil
Hull U PhD/MPhil
Keele U PhD/MA
Kent U PhD/MA/MPhil
Lancashire P PhD/MPhil
Lancaster U PhD/MPhil/dip☆
Leeds U PhD/MA/MPhil
Leicester U PhD/MPhil
Liverpool U PhD/MPhil
London U Birkbeck C PhD/MPhil
Goldsmiths' C London U PhD/MPhil
London U Inst of Historical Research/US Studies PhD/MPhil
London U King's C PhD☆/MPhil☆
London U Queen Mary & Westfield C PhD☆/MPhil☆
London U Royal Holloway & Bedford New C PhD/MPhil
London U SOAS PhD/MPhil
London U SSEES PhD/MPhil
London U UC PhD☆/MPhil☆
Manchester U PhD/MPhil
Middlesex P PhD/MPhil
Newcastle U PhD/MLitt
North London P PhD/MPhil
Nottingham U PhD/MPhil
Open U PhD/MPhil/BPhil
Reading U PhD/MPhil
St David's UC PhD☆/MA☆
Sheffield U PhD/MPhil
Southampton U PhD/MPhil
Staffordshire P PhD/MPhil
Stirling U PhD/MLitt
Strathclyde U PhD☆/MPhil☆
Sunderland P PhD/MPhil
Sussex U DPhil/MPhil
Swansea UC PhD/MPhil
Ulster U DPhil/MPhil
Warwick U PhD/MA/MPhil
Worcester CHE PhD/MPhil
York U DPhil/MA/MPhil

History & geography
Nottingham P PhD☆/MPhil☆

History & philosophy of mathematics
Open U PhD/MPhil/BPhil

History & philosophy of science
Belfast Queen's U PhD/MSc
Cambridge U PhD☆/MLitt☆
Leeds U PhD/MPhil
London U King's C PhD☆/MPhil☆

History & theory of architecture
Architectural Association S of Architecture PhD☆/MPhil☆

History & Welsh history
Cardiff U of Wales C PhD☆/MPhil☆

History of art
Bristol U PhD/MLitt

History of design
Royal CA PhD

History of ideas
Hatfield P PhD/MPhil

History of science
Edinburgh U PhD/MPhil
Glasgow U PhD/MPhil
Leicester U PhD/MPhil

History of science & technology
Keele U PhD/MA/MSc☆
London U Imperial C PhD/MPhil
Manchester UMIST PhD/MSc
Open U PhD/MPhil/BPhil

History of technology
Bath U PhD☆/MPhil☆

History, philosophy & social relations of science
Kent U PhD/MPhil

Humanities
Brighton P PhD/MPhil
Bristol P PhD/MPhil/dip
Huddersfield P PhD/MPhil
Leicester P PhD/MPhil
Oxford P PhD/MPhil
Teesside P PhD☆/MPhil☆
Thames P PhD/MPhil

Humanities, social & cultural studies
Wolverhampton P PhD/MPhil

Intellectual history
Sussex U DPhil/MPhil

International history
London U LSE PhD/MPhil

Latin American studies
Cambridge U PhD☆   ☐
London U Inst of Latin American Studies PhD/MPhil

Literary & cultural studies
Keele U PhD/MA

Local & community history
Keele U PhD/MA

Military studies
Manchester U PhD/MPhil

Politics & history
Coventry P PhD/MPhil

Scottish history
Edinburgh U PhD/MLitt
Glasgow U PhD/MLitt
St Andrews U PhD/MPhil

Scottish studies
Aberdeen U PhD☆/MLitt☆/
 MPhil☆

Soviet & East European studies
Glasgow U PhD/MLitt   *Soc*

Victorian studies
Leicester U PhD/MPhil
St David's UC PhD☆/MA☆

War studies
London U King's C PhD/MPhil

Welsh history
Aberystwyth, UC of Wales PhD/
 MPhil
Bangor, U of Wales PhD☆/
 MPhil☆
Swansea UC PhD/MPhil

Women's studies
York U DPhil/MPhil

History: Medieval, modern

Higher degrees by instruction

17th century studies
Durham U MA☆

19th century British history
Buckingham U MA
Swansea UC MA☆

20th century historical studies
Central London P MA△

Ancient & medieval philosophies
Nottingham U MA

Archaeology (British Isles in the Anglo Saxon & Medieval periods)
London U UC MA☆

Britain & America in the 18th century
Aberystwyth, UC of Wales MA☆

British history
Leeds U MA

Church, religion & society (1790-1940)
Cheltenham & Gloucester CHE
 MA

Combined historical studies: the Renaissance
London U Warburg Inst MPhil☆

Early modern English history
London U Birkbeck C MA△

Early modern history
Ulster U MA△/dip△

Early modern Wales
Aberystwyth, UC of Wales MA

English (Medieval studies)
Belfast Queen's U MA

English Renaissance: politics, patronage & literature
Reading U MA

English studies (English Medieval studies from 1100 to 1500)
Oxford U MPhil☆

English studies (English Medieval studies until 1100)
Oxford U MPhil☆

French studies
Hull U MA☆   *Lang*

History
Durham U MA☆
Hull U MA☆

History & philosophy of science
London U UC MSc

History of science
Lancaster U MA

Irish political studies
Belfast Queen's U MSSc

Late antiquity & early medieval studies
Exeter U MA☆

Later British modern history
London U LSE MA

Later Medieval studies, circa 1200-1450
London U Royal Holloway &
 Bedford New C MA

Medieval & Renaissance studies
St Andrews U MLitt/MPhil☆/dip☆

Medieval British archaeology
York U MA☆

Medieval British studies
Cardiff U of Wales C MA☆

Medieval Celtic studies
London U UC MA

Medieval English literature
Bristol U MA☆

Medieval history
St Andrews U MLitt/MPhil☆/dip☆

Medieval studies
Belfast Queen's U MA☆
Bristol U MA☆
Glasgow U MPhil/dip☆
Leeds U MA
Liverpool U MA☆
London U Birkbeck C MA△
London U Queen Mary &
 Westfield C MA   ☐
London U UC MA☆
Manchester U dip☆
Reading U MA/MPhil
York U MA/dip☆

Medieval Wales
Aberystwyth, UC of Wales MA

Modern history
Belfast Queen's U MA☆
Oxford U MSt☆

Modern history - history & culture
York U MA☆

Modern international studies
Leeds U MA☆

Modern Middle Eastern history
Durham U MA☆

19th & 20th century Wales
Aberystwyth, UC of Wales MA☆/
 dip☆

Oriental studies (classical & medieval Islamic history)
Oxford U MPhil☆/MSt☆

Oriental studies (Medieval Arabic thought)
Oxford U MPhil☆/MSt☆

Ottoman studies
Birmingham U MA☆

Politics & contemporary history
Salford U MA☆

Reformation studies
St Andrews U MPhil☆

Renaissance European literature
Glasgow U MPhil

Renaissance studies
London U Birkbeck C MA△
Warwick U MA

Social change in modern Europe
London U Inst of Historical Research/US Studies MA

The rise of the modern state
St Andrews U MPhil☆

Tudor government
Bangor, U of Wales MA☆

Victorian studies
Keele U MLitt

War & society in the 20th century
St Andrews U MPhil☆

Welsh history
Bangor, U of Wales MA☆
Swansea UC MA☆

Women's studies
Exeter U MA☆

Higher degrees by research

19th century British history
Buckingham U DPhil/MA/MPhil

American history
East Anglia U PhD/MPhil

Arts, culture & society in Britain from 1850 to the present day
Open U PhD/MPhil/BPhil

Classical tradition in European thought, art & institutions
London U Warburg Inst PhD☆/MPhil☆

History
Lancaster U PhD/MPhil/dip☆

History & philosophy of science
London U UC PhD☆/MPhil☆

History of medicine
London U UC PhD☆/MPhil☆

Humanities
Huddersfield P PhD/MPhil

Medieval history
Birmingham U PhD/MLitt/MPhil
Glasgow U PhD/MLitt
St Andrews U PhD/MPhil

Medieval studies
Lancaster U MA
Leeds U PhD/MPhil
Liverpool U PhD/MPhil
Reading U PhD/MPhil
York U DPhil/MPhil

Modern history
Belfast Queen's U PhD/MA
Birmingham U PhD/MLitt/MPhil

Dundee U PhD/MPhil
Glasgow U PhD/MLitt
Liverpool U PhD/MPhil
Oxford U DPhil☆/MLitt☆
St Andrews U PhD/MPhil
Swansea UC PhD/MPhil

Politics & contemporary history
Salford U PhD/MPhil/MSc

Renaissance studies
Warwick U PhD☆/MPhil☆

Romance languages & literatures
London U Queen Mary & Westfield C PhD☆/MPhil☆

Victorian studies
Keele U PhD/MLitt

Welsh history
Swansea UC PhD/MPhil

History: social, economic

Higher degrees by instruction

Area studies (the Commonwealth)
London U Inst of Commonwealth Studies MA☆   *Soc*

British history
Leeds U MA

Comparative British & European social history
Warwick U MA

Comparative labour history
Warwick U MA

Contemporary European culture
Exeter U MA☆

Economic & social change in Britain 1870 to the present day
London U Birkbeck C MA△/MSc△

Economic & social history
Birmingham U MSocSc☆
York U MSc☆

Economic history
Hull U dip☆
London U LSE MSc

Heritage
Newcastle U MA☆

History
Durham U MA☆

History & philosophy of science
London U UC MSc

History & related studies
London U Inst of Historical Research/US Studies MA☆

History in the Manchester region
Manchester P MA△

History of science
Lancaster U MA

Industrial & social history
Middlesex P MA△/dip△

International studies
Birmingham U MSocSc/dip
Warwick U MA/dip   *Soc*

Modern social history
Lancaster U MA

Negotiated studies
Loughborough U MA/MSc

Police studies
Exeter U MA

Political economy & political culture: Britain & France
Nottingham U MA

Politics, literature & culture in the German Democratic Republic
Reading U MA

Regional history
Brighton P MA△/dip△

Social & labour history
Swansea UC MA☆

Social anthropology
London U UC MSc

Social history
Essex U MA

Social history of art
Leeds U MA☆

Welsh history
Bangor, U of Wales MA☆
Swansea UC MA☆

Women's studies
Exeter U MA☆

Higher degrees by research

British policy studies
Sheffield U PhD

Development studies
Salford U PhD/MSc

Economic & social history
Belfast Queen's U PhD/
MSc(Econ)/MSocSc
Belfast Queen's U MSSc☆
Birmingham U PhD/MPhil/
MSocSc
Bristol U PhD/MLitt/MPhil
East Anglia U PhD/MPhil
Edinburgh U PhD/MPhil
Hull U PhD/MPhil
Kent U PhD/MPhil
Leeds U PhD/MA/MPhil
Leicester U PhD/MPhil
St Andrews U PhD/MPhil
Sheffield U PhD/MPhil
Swansea UC PhD/MPhil
York U DPhil/MPhil/MSc

Economic history
Aberdeen U PhD☆/MLitt☆/
MPhil☆
Exeter U PhD/MPhil
Glasgow U PhD/MLitt
Liverpool U PhD☆/MPhil☆
London U LSE PhD/MPhil
Newcastle U MA
Salford U PhD/MSc

Economics & economic history
Manchester P PhD/MPhil
Portsmouth P PhD/MPhil

Historical studies
Bristol P PhD/MPhil

History
Lancaster U PhD/MPhil/dip☆

History & philosophy of science
London U UC PhD☆/MPhil☆

History of medicine
London U UC PhD☆/MPhil☆

Humanities
Huddersfield P PhD/MPhil

Industrial & social history
Middlesex P PhD/MPhil/dip△

International studies
Birmingham U PhD/MPhil

Modern social & economic history
Bath U PhD☆/MPhil☆
Swansea UC PhD/MPhil

Police studies
Exeter U PhD/MPhil

Rural sociology/social history
Open U PhD/MPhil/BPhil

Scottish studies
Edinburgh U PhD/MLitt

Social history
Warwick U PhD/MA/MPhil

Social implications of technical change
Sussex U DPhil/MPhil

Sociology/social anthropology
Liverpool U PhD/MPhil   *Soc*

Welsh history
Swansea UC PhD/MPhil

Journalism, printing

Higher degrees by instruction

Bibliography, publishing & textual studies
Leeds U MA☆

Broadcast journalism
Bristol P dip☆

Communications
Goldsmiths' C London U dip☆

Copy writing
Watford C dip☆

Design & media technology
London C of Printing MA☆/dip☆

Documentary photography
Gwent CHE dip☆

Education & the mass media
Manchester U MEd☆

Journalism
City U MA☆/dip☆

Journalism studies
Cardiff U of Wales C dip☆

Media culture
Glasgow U MPhil
Strathclyde U MLitt☆/cert☆/dip☆

Media law
London U Queen Mary & Westfield C dip

Media production
Dorset Inst dip☆

Newspaper journalism
Lancashire P dip☆

Printing & publishing studies
London C of Printing dip☆   □

Printmaking
Central St Martins CAD dip

Royal CA MA☆

Publishing
Loughborough U MA
Watford C dip☆

Publishing & book production
South West P dip   □

Publishing studies
Stirling U MPhil☆/dip☆

Radio & television journalism
Lancashire P dip☆   □
London C of Printing dip☆

Radio journalism
Falmouth SAD dip☆   □

Typography & graphic communication
Reading U dip☆

Higher degrees by research

Communication studies
Goldsmiths' C London U PhD/
MPhil

Information media & technology
Hatfield P PhD/MPhil

Journalism
Cardiff U of Wales C PhD☆/
MPhil☆
City U PhD/MPhil

Literary & media studies
North London P PhD/MPhil

Media studies
Coventry P PhD/MPhil
Paisley CT PhD/MPhil
Ulster U DPhil/MPhil

Photography
Napier P PhD/MPhil
Royal CA PhD☆

Print media, publishing & communication
Napier P PhD/MPhil

Printing
South West P PhD/MPhil

Printing technology
Hatfield P PhD/MPhil

Typography & graphic communication
Reading U PhD/MPhil

Law

Higher degrees by instruction

Administration & information processing
North East Surrey CT RSA
  dip☆   *Bus*

Administrative & legal studies
Ulster U MA☆/dip☆

Advanced legal studies
Edinburgh U dip☆

Air & space law
London U UC dip☆

Bar Final Examination
Ealing C London ICSL☆

Bar vocational stage examinations
Central London P dip△

Business law
City of London P MA

Civil law
Oxford U BCL☆

Civil liberties & human rights
Leicester U MA/Dip/LLM

Commercial & corporate law
London U Queen Mary &
  Westfield C LLM

Commercial law
Aberdeen U LLM☆
Bristol U LLM☆

Common law
Aberystwyth, UC of Wales dip☆

Common Professional Examination
Birmingham P CPE☆
Brighton P cert△
Bristol P CPE☆
Central London P dip△
Law C CPE☆
Leeds P CPE☆
Manchester P CPE☆
Newcastle P CPE☆
Nottingham P CPE☆
Wales P CPE☆
Wolverhampton P CPE☆

Computers & law
Belfast Queen's U LLM

Construction law & arbitration
London U King's C MSc△/dip△

Criminal justice
Brunel U MA   ☐

Reading U MA

Criminal justice policy
London U LSE MSc

Criminology
Cambridge U MPhil☆
Cardiff U of Wales C
  MSc(Econ)☆/dip☆
Hull U MA☆/dip☆
Keele U MA

English legal studies
Bristol U dip☆

Environmental law
Aberdeen U LLM☆

European & international trade law
Leicester U Dip/LLM

European law & government
Aberystwyth, UC of Wales dip☆

European legal studies
Exeter U LLM☆

General legal studies
Bristol U LLM☆   ☐
Reading U LLM☆

Health care ethics
Manchester U MA☆

Human rights
Essex U LLM☆   *Soc*
Glasgow U LLM

Human rights, emergency law & discrimination
Belfast Queen's U LLM

Industrial relations with labour law
Manchester P dip△

Intellectual commercial arbitration law
London U Queen Mary &
  Westfield C dip

Intellectual property law
London U Queen Mary &
  Westfield C dip

International business law
Hull U dip☆/LLM☆
Manchester U LLM☆

International business legal studies
Exeter U LLM☆

International commercial law
Buckingham U LLM☆
Kent U LLM

International human rights law
Essex U LLM

International law
Cambridge U dip☆
Hull U dip☆/LLM☆
Liverpool U dip☆

London U LSE dip
London U UC dip☆
Manchester U dip☆
Nottingham U dip/LLM

International law & development
Glasgow U LLM

International law & relations
Aberystwyth, UC of Wales dip☆

Law
Bristol U dip☆/LLM☆
Cambridge U LLM☆
Cardiff U of Wales C LLM☆
City U MA☆/dip☆
Edinburgh U LLM
Glasgow U dip☆/LLM
Hull U MA☆/LLM☆
London U King's C LLM
London U LSE dip/LLM
London U SOAS dip/LLM
Manchester U LLM☆
Newcastle U LLM☆
Reading U LLM☆
Southampton U LLM

Law & employment relations
Leicester U cert△/dip△/LLM△

Law & science: intellectual property
London U Queen Mary &
  Westfield C MSc

Law in development
Warwick U LLM

Law in society
Warwick U LLM☆

Law Society Final Examination
Birmingham P LSFE☆
Bristol P LSFE☆
City of London P LSFE☆
Law C LSFE☆
Leeds P LSFE☆
Manchester P LSFE☆
Newcastle P LSFE☆
Nottingham P LSFE☆
Wolverhampton P r☆

Law, society & the economy in England, 1450-1660
Birmingham U MA☆

Laws
Belfast Queen's U dip
London U Queen Mary &
  Westfield C LLM
London U UC dip☆/LLM

Legal & political theory
London U UC MA☆

Legal practice
Aberdeen U dip☆
Dundee U dip☆
Edinburgh U dip☆
Glasgow U dip☆

Strathclyde U dip☆

Legal studies
Cambridge U dip☆
Durham U Dipl☆
Edinburgh U MSc/dip/LLM
Manchester U dip☆
Newcastle U MA☆

Marine law & policy
Cardiff U of Wales C MSc☆

Media law
London U Queen Mary &
  Westfield C dip

Medical ethics & law
London U King's C MA

Mineral law
Dundee U dip☆

Petroleum law
Dundee U dip☆

Police studies
Exeter U MA

Professional legal studies
Belfast Queen's U cert☆

Property law
Reading U LLM☆

Public law
Bristol U LLM☆
Reading U LLM☆

Resources law
Dundee U LLM☆

Rights, property & juustice
Aberdeen U LLM☆

Rights, property & justice
Aberdeen U LLM☆

Roman law
Glasgow U dip

Roman law & Roman-Dutch law
Aberdeen U LLM☆

Sea use law, economics & policy
London U LSE MSc

Shipping law
London U UC dip☆

Socio legal studies
Birmingham U MSocSc/dip
Brunel U MA/dip   *Soc*
Ealing C London MA△/dip△
Sheffield U MA☆   *Soc*

Transnational commercial law
Glasgow U MPhil

Welfare law
Leicester U dip/LLM
Liverpool P dip△

Higher degrees by research

Accountancy & business law
Stirling U PhD/MSc

Civil law
Edinburgh U PhD/LLM

Civil law (Roman law)
Glasgow U PhD/LLM

Commercial law studies
London U Queen Mary &
  Westfield C PhD☆/MPhil☆

Comparative law
Aberdeen U PhD☆/MPhil☆

Constitutional & administrative law
Edinburgh U PhD/LLM

Construction law & project management
London U King's C PhD☆/MPhil☆

Conveyancing & professional practice of law
Aberdeen U PhD☆/MPhil☆/LLM☆

Criminal justice studies
Leeds U PhD/MA/LLM

Criminological & socio legal studies
Sheffield U PhD/MPhil

Criminology
Cambridge U PhD☆/MLitt☆/
  MSc☆
Keele U PhD/MA

Criminology & social & philosophical study of law
Edinburgh U PhD/MPhil

Finance & law
Dorset Inst PhD/MPhil/dip

Government & law
Manchester U PhD/MPhil

Jurisprudence
Aberdeen U PhD☆/MPhil☆/LLM☆

Law
Aberystwyth, UC of Wales PhD/
  LLM
Anglia HEC PhD☆/MPhil☆
Belfast Queen's U PhD/LLM
Birmingham P PhD/MPhil
Birmingham U PhD/MJur/LLD/
  LLM
Bristol U PhD☆/LLM☆
Brunel U PhD/MPhil/LLM
Buckingham U DPhil/MPhil/LLM
Cambridge U PhD☆/MLitt☆
Cardiff U of Wales C PhD☆/
  MPhil☆/LLM☆

Central London P PhD☆/MPhil☆
City of London P PhD☆/MPhil☆
Dundee U PhD/LLM
Durham U PhD/BCL
East Anglia U PhD/MPhil/LLM
East London P PhD/MPhil
Essex U PhD/MPhil
Exeter U PhD/MPhil
Glasgow U PhD/LLM
Hull U PhD/MPhil/LLM
Keele U PhD/MA/LLM
Kent U PhD/MPhil
Kingston P PhD/MPhil☆/MPil△
Lancashire P PhD/MPhil
Lancaster U PhD/LLM
Leeds P PhD/MPhil/dip
Leeds U PhD/MA/LLM
Leicester P PhD/MPhil
Leicester U PhD/MPhil
Liverpool P PhD/MPhil
Liverpool U PhD/LLM
London U LSE PhD/MPhil
London U SOAS PhD/MPhil
Manchester P PhD/MPhil
Manchester U PhD/MPhil
Middlesex P PhD/MPhil
Napier U PhD/MPhil
Newcastle P PhD☆/MPhil☆
Newcastle U PhD/LLM
North London P PhD/MPhil
Nottingham U PhD/MPhil
Oxford U DPhil☆/MLitt☆/dip☆
Reading U PhD/MPhil/LLM
Sheffield U PhD/MPhil/LLM
Southampton U PhD/MPhil
Staffordshire P PhD/MPhil☆/
  MPil△
Strathclyde U PhD☆/LLM☆
Warwick U PhD☆/MPhil☆/LLM☆

Law & ethics in medicine
Glasgow U PhD/MSc(MedSci)

Law & government
South Bank P PhD/MPhil

Law studies
Sussex U DPhil/MPhil

Laws
London U King's C PhD/MPhil
London U Queen Mary &
  Westfield C PhD☆/MPhil☆
London U UC PhD☆/MPhil☆

Legal studies
Coventry P PhD/MPhil
Nottingham P PhD/MPhil☆
Ulster U DPhil/MPhil
Wolverhampton P PhD/MPhil

Management & legal studies
Wales P PhD/MPhil

Marine law & policy
Cardiff U of Wales C PhD☆/
MPhil☆/LLM☆

Petroleum & mineral law studies
Dundee U PhD/LLM

Police studies
Exeter U PhD/MPhil

Private law
Aberdeen U PhD☆/MPhil☆/LLM☆

Public international law
Edinburgh U PhD/LLM

Public law
Aberdeen U PhD☆/MPhil☆/LLM☆

Public sector administration & law
Sheffield City P PhD/MPhil

Roman law
Aberdeen U PhD☆/MPhil☆

Scots law
Edinburgh U PhD/MPhil

Socio legal studies
Exeter U PhD/MPhil
Oxford U DPhil☆/MLitt☆

Sociology
Exeter U PhD/MPhil

Music

Higher degrees by instruction

20th centuary music & composition
Durham U MA☆

20th century music
Belfast Queen's U MA

Accompaniment
Trinity C of Mus ☆

Advanced music course
Welsh C of Mus & Drama cert☆

Advanced musical studies
London U King's C cert☆

Advanced performers course
Royal Academy of Mus dip☆

Advanced postgraduate course
Trinity C of Mus ☆

Advanced solo studies
Guildhall S of Mus & Drama
cert☆

Advanced studies in musical composition
Manchester U dip☆

Royal Northern C of Mus dip☆

Advanced studies in musical performance
Manchester U dip☆
Royal Northern C of Mus dip☆

Advanced study (instrumental/ vocal/composition)
Royal C of Mus cert☆

Analytical musicology
Surrey U MMus☆

Arts administration
City U MA/dip

Composition
Birmingham U MA☆
Guildhall S of Mus & Drama
cert☆
Leeds U MMus
Goldsmiths' C London U MMus△
Reading U MMus☆
Royal C of Mus MMus☆/cert☆
Royal Northern C of Mus
MMus☆/dip☆
Surrey U MMus☆

Computer studies in musicology
Nottingham U MA

Computer-based electronic music techniques
Bangor, U of Wales dip☆

Conducting
Guildhall S of Mus & Drama
cert☆
Surrey U dip☆

Digital music technology
Keele U MA/MSc

Early music
Guildhall S of Mus & Drama
cert☆
Royal C of Mus cert☆

Editing & performance practice of early music
Bristol U MA

Editorial musicology (Renaissance/Baroque periods)
Bangor, U of Wales MA☆

Electronic music (introductory)
Royal C of Mus cert☆

Ethnomusicology
Bangor, U of Wales MA☆
Belfast Queen's U MA☆
Durham U MA☆
Goldsmiths' C London U MMus△

Historical musicology
Goldsmiths' C London U MMus△
London U King's C MMus
London U Royal Holloway &
Bedford New C MMus

Interpretation
Surrey U MMus☆

Jazz & studio music
Guildhall S of Mus & Drama
cert☆

Music
Bangor, U of Wales MMus☆
Birmingham U MA
Bristol U MA☆
City U MA
East Anglia U MMus
Edinburgh U MMus/dip
Exeter U MA/MMus
Glasgow U MMus☆
Leeds U MMus☆/dip☆
Liverpool U MMus
Manchester U MMus☆
Newcastle U MA☆
Oxford U MPhil☆/BMus☆
Royal Academy of Mus MMus☆
Sheffield U MMus/dip
Surrey U MMus
Sussex U MA
York U MA☆

Music & poetry of the Elizabethan Renaissance
Hull U dip☆

Music (1550-1650)
Durham U MA☆/MMus☆

Music (composition, performance, analysis)
Hull U MA☆/MMus

Music education
London U Inst of Education MA

Music information technology
City U dip

Music of the 18th century
Cardiff U of Wales C MA☆

Music (performance studies)
Birmingham P Dip△

Music performance studies
City U MA

Music technology
York U MA☆/MSc☆/dip☆

Music theory & analysis
Reading U MMus

Music therapy
Guildhall S of Mus & Drama
DipMTh☆/dip☆
Roehampton I dip☆

Musical composition
Cambridge U MPhil☆
Cardiff U of Wales C MMus☆
London U King's C MMus
London U Royal Holloway &
Bedford New C MMus
Newcastle U MMus☆
Southampton U MMus☆

2 POSTGRADUATE OPPORTUNITIES

Musical composition & analysis
Aberdeen U MMus☆

Musical performance
Aberdeen U MLitt☆
Cardiff U of Wales C MA☆
Newcastle U MMus☆
York U MA☆

Musical performance & related studies
London U Royal Holloway & Bedford New C MMus

Musical theory & analysis
Goldsmiths' C London U MMus△
London U King's C MMus
London U Royal Holloway & Bedford New C MMus

Musicological skills
Surrey U dip☆

Musicology
Cambridge U MPhil☆
Leeds U MMus
Reading U MMus☆

Opera conducting
Royal C of Mus cert☆

Opera studies
Guildhall S of Mus & Drama cert☆
Leeds U MMus

Opera training
Royal C of Mus cert☆

Orchestral conducting
Royal C of Mus cert☆

Orchestral training
Guildhall S of Mus & Drama cert☆

Performance & communication skills (The Guildhall Ensemble)
Guildhall S of Mus & Drama cert☆

Performance & related studies
Goldsmiths' C London U MMus△
Trinity C of Mus MMus☆

Performance (music)
Bangor, U of Wales MA☆

Performance arts
Middlesex P MA△

Performance studies
Reading U MMus☆
Royal C of Mus MMus☆
Royal Northern C of Mus MMus☆

Performing arts
Cardiff U of Wales C MA☆

Piano accompaniment
Guildhall S of Mus & Drama cert☆

Postgraduate extension study
Royal Northern C of Mus MA☆

Preliminary opera course
Royal C of Mus cert☆

Professional musicians' advanced - instrumental
Royal Scottish Academy Music & Drama cert☆

Professional musicians' advanced - opera
Royal Scottish Academy Music & Drama cert☆

Professional musicians' advanced - repetiteur
Royal Scottish Academy Music & Drama cert☆

Professional musicians' advanced - vocal
Royal Scottish Academy Music & Drama cert☆

Renaissance music
Belfast Queen's U MA

Repetiteur training
Guildhall S of Mus & Drama cert☆

Repetiteurs
Royal C of Mus cert☆

Sound recording
Surrey U MMus☆

Tonmeister studies
Surrey U dip☆

Vocal training
Guildhall S of Mus & Drama cert☆

Higher degrees by research

Composition
Aberystwyth, UC of Wales PhD☆/MPhil☆
Birmingham U PhD

Creative & performing arts
West London IHE MPhil☆

Ethnomusicolgy
Belfast Queen's U PhD/MA△/MSc☆

Fine arts & music
East Anglia U PhD☆/MPhil☆

Media & music
Lancashire P PhD/MPhil

Music
Aberdeen U PhD☆/MLitt☆/MMus☆/MPhil☆

Aberystwyth, UC of Wales PhD☆/MPhil☆
Bangor, U of Wales PhD☆/MPhil☆
Belfast Queen's U PhD/MA
Birmingham P PhD/MPhil
Birmingham U PhD/MA☆/MLitt/MPhil/DMus
Bristol U PhD/MA△/MLitt
Cambridge U PhD☆/MLitt☆
Canterbury Christ Church C PhD/MPhil
Cardiff U of Wales C PhD☆/MPhil☆
City U PhD/MPhil
Durham U PhD/MA/MMus
East Anglia U PhD/MPhil
Edinburgh U PhD/MPhil
Exeter U PhD/MPhil
Glasgow U PhD/MMus
Hatfield P PhD/MPhil
Hull U PhD/MPhil
Keele U PhD/MA
Kingston P PhD/MPhil
Lancaster U PhD/MPhil
Leeds U PhD/MA/MPhil☆
Leicester U PhD/MPhil
Liverpool U PhD/MPhil
Goldsmiths' C London U PhD/MPhil
London U King's C PhD☆/MPhil☆
London U Royal Holloway & Bedford New C PhD/MPhil
London U SOAS PhD/MPhil
Manchester U PhD/MMus/MPhil
Middlesex P PhD/MPhil
Napier P PhD/MPhil
Newcastle U PhD/MLitt
Nottingham U PhD/MPhil
Open U PhD/MPhil/BPhil
Oxford U DPhil☆/MLitt☆
Reading U PhD/MPhil
St Andrews U PhD/MPhil
Sheffield U PhD/MPhil
Southampton U PhD/MPhil
Surrey U PhD/MPhil
Sussex U DPhil/MPhil
Ulster U DPhil/MPhil
Worcester CHE PhD/MPhil
York U DPhil/MPhil

Music in performance
Manchester U MMusPerf

Musical composition
Leeds U PhD☆/MPhil☆
Nottingham U AMusD/AMusM

Scottish studies
Edinburgh U PhD/MLitt

Performing arts

Higher degrees by instruction

20th century German drama
Bristol U MA

Advanced design/stage management
Welsh C of Mus & Drama cert☆

Advanced drama course (English option)
Welsh C of Mus & Drama cert☆

Advanced studies in musical performance
Manchester U dip☆
Royal Northern C of Mus dip☆

Advanced training in dramatherapy
Hertfordshire CAD dip△

Arts administration
City U MA/dip

Composition
Reading U MMus☆

Contemporary dance & choreography
London Contemporary Dance S cert☆

Dance movement therapy
Hertfordshire CAD dip△
Roehampton I dip△

Dance studies
Laban Centre for Movement & Dance MA
Surrey U MA

Dance/movement therapy
Laban Centre for Movement & Dance MA

Drama
Drama Studio dip☆
East Anglia U MA△
Essex U MA☆
Hull U MA☆
London U King's C MA☆
Manchester U MA☆/dip☆

Drama & theatre studies
London U Royal Holloway & Bedford New C MA

Drama studies
Bristol U MA

Drama: the process of production
Goldsmiths' C London U MA△

Dramatherapy
Hertfordshire CAD MA△/dip

Dramatic art
Webber Douglas Academy cert☆/dip☆

Editing & performance practice of early music
Bristol U MA

Elizabethan & Shakespearean drama
Newcastle U MA/MPhil☆

English & European Renaissance drama
Warwick U MA

French drama & theatre history
Bristol U MA☆

French studies
Reading U MA

Humanities
North London P MA△

Music
Bangor, U of Wales MMus☆

Music performance studies
City U MA

Musical performance
Aberdeen U MLitt☆
Cardiff U of Wales C MA☆
Newcastle U MMus☆
York U MA☆

Musical performance & related studies
London U Royal Holloway & Bedford New C MMus

Musicology
Reading U MMus☆

Opera studies
Leeds U MMus

Performance & communication skills (The Guildhall Ensemble)
Guildhall S of Mus & Drama cert☆

Performance & related studies
Goldsmiths' C London U MMus△
Trinity C of Mus MMus☆

Performance (music)
Bangor, U of Wales MA☆

Performance arts
Middlesex P MA△

Performance studies
Reading U MMus☆
Royal C of Mus MMus☆
Royal Northern C of Mus MMus☆

Performing arts
Cardiff U of Wales C MA☆

Preliminary opera course
Royal C of Mus cert☆

Radio, film & TV
Bristol U cert☆

Theatre
Manchester P dip△

Theatre costume
Heriot-Watt U dip☆

Theatre design
Nottingham P MA☆/dip☆

Theatre studies
Lancaster U MA☆
Leeds U MA☆

Higher degrees by research

Arts policy & management
City U PhD/MPhil

Communication arts & design
Manchester P PhD/MPhil

Creative & performing arts
West London IHE MPhil☆

Dance
Middlesex P PhD/MPhil

Dance studies
Laban Centre for Movement & Dance PhD/MPhil
Surrey U PhD/MPhil

Drama
Bristol U PhD/MLitt
East Anglia U PhD/MPhil
Hatfield P PhD/MPhil
Hull U PhD/MPhil
Kent U PhD/MA/MPhil
Goldsmiths' C London U PhD/MPhil
London U Queen Mary & Westfield C PhD☆/MPhil☆
Manchester U PhD/MPhil
Middlesex P PhD/MPhil/dip△

Drama & theatre arts
Birmingham U PhD/MLitt/MPhil

Drama & theatre studies
London U Royal Holloway & Bedford New C PhD/MPhil

English & drama
Loughborough U PhD☆/MPhil☆

Humanities, performance & media
South West P PhD/MPhil

Movement studies
Canterbury Christ Church C PhD/MPhil

Music
Reading U PhD/MPhil

Performing arts
Brighton P PhD/MPhil
Leicester P PhD/MPhil

Study of cartoons & caricature
Kent U PhD/MPhil

Theatre studies
Lancaster U PhD/MPhil
Leeds U PhD/MA/MPhil
Ulster U DPhil/MPhil
Warwick U PhD☆/MA☆/MPhil☆

Visual & performing arts
Newcastle P PhD☆/MPhil☆

Visual communication
Nottingham P PhD☆/MPhil☆

Philosophy

Higher degrees by instruction

Ancient & medieval philosophies
Nottingham U MA

Ancient philosophy
Bristol U MA☆
Edinburgh U MSc☆

Applied ethics
Aberdeen U MLitt☆

Child development & philosophy of education
London U Inst of Education MA/MSc

Cognitive science & natural language
Edinburgh U MSc☆/dip☆

Computer studies (cognitive science)
Essex U MSc☆

Continental philosophy
Essex U MA☆
Warwick U MA

Cultural studies
Birmingham U MA

Cultural studies: discourse, power & political economy
Lancaster U MA

Death & immortality in Western thought
St David's UC MA☆

Ethics & philosophy of religion
Ulster U MA△/dip△

Health care ethics
Manchester U MA☆

History & philosophy of religion
London U King's C MA☆

History & philosophy of science
Leeds U dip
London U Imperial C MSc
London U UC MSc

History & philosophy of science & mathematics
London U King's C MSc

History & philosophy of social & political science
Essex U MA☆

History of scientific thought
Leeds U MA

History, philosophy & social relations of science
Kent U MA

Language & philosophy of criticism
Sheffield U MA

Logic & metaphysics
St Andrews U MLitt☆/MPhil☆/dip☆

Logic & scientific method
London U LSE MSc/dip

Medical ethics & law
London U King's C MA

Medieval philosophy
Belfast Queen's U MA☆

Moral philosophy
St Andrews U MLitt/MPhil☆/dip☆

Moral philosophy & aesthetics
Birmingham U MA

Philosophical studies
Essex U cert☆

Philosophical theology
Oxford U MPhil☆/MSt☆

Philosophy
Belfast Queen's U MA
Bristol U MA☆/dip☆
Cambridge U MPhil☆
Cardiff U of Wales C MA☆
Dundee U MA☆
Durham U MA/MSc
Edinburgh U MLitt☆/MSc☆
Exeter U MA☆/dip☆
Glasgow U MPhil
Hull U MA☆/MSc☆
Lancaster U MA
London U Birkbeck C MA△
London U Heythrop C MA
London U King's C MA
Nottingham U MA
Oxford U BPhil☆
Reading U MA

Sheffield U MA
Southampton U MA☆
Stirling U MPhil
Sussex U MA
Swansea UC MA☆
Warwick U MA/dip
York U MA/dip☆

Philosophy & literature
Warwick U MA

Philosophy & psychology
St Andrews U MLitt/dip☆

Philosophy & psychology of language
London U Birkbeck C MA△

Philosophy & the humanities
Essex U MA☆

Philosophy (epistemology & philosophy of science)
Kent U MA

Philosophy (philosophy & contemporary issues)
Kent U MA

Philosophy (socialist studies)
Kent U MA

Philosophy of education
London U Inst of Education MA
Manchester U MEd☆

Philosophy of language & logic
Birmingham U MA

Philosophy of language, logic & mind
Nottingham U MA

Philosophy of literature
Swansea UC MA☆

Philosophy of mind
Leeds U MA

Philosophy of religion
London U Heythrop C MTh

Philosophy of the natural & social sciences
Birmingham U MA

Political philosophy
York U MA☆

Political philosophy: the idea of toleration
York U MA☆

Practical reasoning
Essex U MA☆

Psychology of education & philosophy of education
London U Inst of Education MA

Scholastic philosophy
Belfast Queen's U dip

Social philosophy
London U LSE dip

Theology
Nottingham U MTh/dip ☐

Higher degrees by research

Classical tradition in European thought, art & institutions
London U Warburg Inst PhD☆/
MPhil☆

Cognitive studies
Sussex U DPhil/MPhil

Epistemics
Edinburgh U PhD/MLitt/MPhil

History & philosophy of science
Belfast Queen's U PhD/MSc
Leeds U PhD/MPhil
London U King's C PhD☆/MPhil☆
London U UC PhD☆/MPhil☆

History of ideas
Middlesex P PhD/MPhil/dip△

History of science & technology
Keele U PhD/MA/MSc☆

History, philosophy & social relations of science
Kent U PhD/MPhil

Humanities
Brighton P PhD/MPhil
Huddersfield P PhD/MPhil
Teesside P PhD☆/MPhil☆
Thames P PhD/MPhil

Intellectual history
Sussex U DPhil/MPhil

Interdisciplinary human studies
Bradford U PhD/MPhil

Literary & cultural studies
Keele U PhD/MA

Logic & metaphysics
St Andrews U PhD/MPhil

Logic & scientific method
Sussex U DPhil/MPhil

Moral philosophy
St Andrews U PhD/MPhil

Philosophy
Aberdeen U PhD☆/MLitt☆/
MPhil☆
Bangor, U of Wales PhD☆/
MPhil☆
Belfast Queen's U PhD/MA
Birmingham U PhD/MLitt/MPhil
Bradford U PhD/MPhil
Bristol U PhD/MLitt
Cambridge U PhD☆/MLitt☆
Cardiff U of Wales C PhD☆/
MPhil☆

City U PhD/MPhil
Dundee U PhD/MPhil
Durham U PhD/MA/MLitt/MSc
East Anglia U PhD/MPhil
Edinburgh U PhD/MLitt
Essex U PhD/MPhil
Exeter U PhD/MPhil
Glasgow U PhD/MLitt
Hatfield P PhD/MPhil
Hull U PhD/MPhil/MSc
Keele U PhD/MA
Kent U PhD/MA/MPhil
Lancaster U PhD/MPhil
Leeds U PhD/MA/MPhil
Liverpool U PhD/MPhil
London U Birkbeck C PhD/MPhil
London U King's C PhD☆/MPhil☆
London U UC PhD☆/MPhil☆
Manchester U PhD/MPhil
Newcastle U PhD/MLitt
North London P PhD/MPhil
Nottingham U PhD/MPhil
Open U PhD/MPhil/BPhil
Oxford U DPhil☆/MLitt☆
Reading U PhD/MPhil
St David's UC PhD☆/MA☆
Sheffield U PhD/MPhil
Southampton U PhD/MPhil
Stirling U PhD/MLitt
Sussex U DPhil/MPhil
Swansea UC PhD/MPhil
Warwick U PhD☆/MA☆/MPhil☆
York U DPhil/MPhil

Philosophy & politics
Ulster U DPhil/MPhil

Philosophy & religious studies
Middlesex P PhD/MPhil/dip△

Philosophy, logic & scientific method
London U LSE PhD/MPhil

Religion & ethics in Western thought
St David's UC PhD☆/MA☆

Religion & philosophy
London U SOAS PhD/MPhil

Scholastic philosophy
Belfast Queen's U PhD/MA

Theatre, film, TV

Higher degrees by instruction

American literature, film or culture
Exeter U MA☆

Animation
Royal CA MA☆

Art & technique of film making
London International Film S dip☆

Broadcast journalism
Bristol P dip☆

Classical French theatre
Glasgow U MPhil☆

Communication design
Manchester P MA

Communication studies (conversion)
Sunderland P MA△/dip△

Communications policy studies
City U MA

Computer visualisation & animation
Dorset Inst dip☆

Contemporary French theatre studies
Glasgow U MPhil☆

Dance studies
Surrey U MA

Design for film
Royal CA MA☆

Drama
Drama Studio dip☆
East Anglia U MA△
Essex U MA☆
Manchester U MA☆/dip☆

Drama & theatre studies
London U Royal Holloway &
Bedford New C MA

Drama studies
Bristol U MA

Drama: the process of production
Goldsmiths' C London U MA△

Dramatic art
Webber Douglas Academy cert☆/
dip☆

2 POSTGRADUATE OPPORTUNITIES

Education & the mass media
Manchester U MEd☆

Electronic imaging
Duncan of Jordanstone CA dip☆

Elizabethan & Shakespearean drama
Newcastle U MA/MPhil☆

English & European Renaissance drama
Warwick U MA

English studies (Shakespeare & the drama to 1640)
Oxford U MPhil☆

European theatre studies
Hull U dip☆

Film & television design
Kingston P dip☆

Film & television studies
Central London P MA△/dip△
Sunderland P MA△/dip△

Film & TV studies for education
London U Inst of Education MA

Film & video
Central St Martins CAD dip△

Film direction (including advertising & music promos)
Royal CA MA☆

Film production
Royal CA MA☆

Film studies
East Anglia U MA

French drama & theatre history
Bristol U MA☆

French theatre studies
Lancaster U MA

Humanities
North London P MA△

Independent film & video
Central St Martins CAD MA△

Journalism
City U MA☆

Mass communication
Glasgow U MPhil
Leicester U MA☆

Media culture
Glasgow U MPhil
Strathclyde U MLitt☆/cert☆/dip☆

Media law
London U Queen Mary & Westfield C dip

Modern theatre practice
Roehampton I dip☆

Opera studies
Leeds U MMus

Photography
Glasgow SA dip☆

Playwriting studies
Birmingham U MA

Radio & television journalism
Lancashire P dip☆ □

Radio, film & TV
Bristol U cert☆

Society & culture
Salford U MA△/MSc△

Spanish theatre & cinema studies
Aberystwyth, UC of Wales MA☆

Theatre
Manchester P dip△

Theatre costume
Heriot-Watt U dip☆

Theatre design
Glasgow SA dip☆
Nottingham P MA☆/dip☆

Theatre studies
Lancaster U MA☆
Leeds U MA☆

Video
Middlesex P MA☆

Viennese popular theatre
St Andrews U MLitt/MPhil☆/dip☆

Higher degrees by research

Animation
Royal CA PhD☆

Arts policy & management
City U PhD/MPhil

Communication arts & design
Manchester P PhD/MPhil

Communication design
Middlesex P PhD/MPhil

Communication studies
Liverpool U PhD/MPhil
Sheffield City P PhD/MPhil

Communications & image studies
Kent U PhD/MA/MPhil

Communications policy
City U PhD/MPhil

Communications studies
Leeds U PhD/MPhil

Contemporary French theatre studies
Glasgow U PhD/MLitt

Creative & performing arts
West London IHE MPhil☆

Cultural studies
Bradford U PhD/MPhil

Dance studies
Surrey U PhD/MPhil

Design & communications
Royal CA PhD☆/MA☆

Drama
Aberystwyth, UC of Wales MPhil☆
Bangor, U of Wales PhD☆/MPhil☆
Bristol U PhD/MLitt
East Anglia U PhD/MPhil
Glasgow U PhD/MPhil
Hatfield P PhD/MPhil
Hull U PhD/MPhil
Kent U PhD/MA/MPhil
Goldsmiths' C London U PhD/MPhil
London U Queen Mary & Westfield C PhD☆/MPhil☆
Manchester U PhD/MPhil
Middlesex P PhD/MPhil/dip△

Drama & theatre arts
Birmingham U PhD/MLitt/MPhil

Drama & theatre studies
London U Royal Holloway & Bedford New C PhD/MPhil

English & drama
Loughborough U PhD☆/MPhil☆

Film & media studies
Stirling U PhD/MLitt

Film & television studies
Central London P PhD☆/MPhil☆
Glasgow U PhD/MLitt

Film studies
East Anglia U PhD/MPhil
Kent U PhD/MA/MPhil
Warwick U PhD☆/MA☆/MPhil☆

Film, video & photography
Sheffield City P PhD/MPhil

German cinema
Bristol P PhD△/MPhil△/dip△

German theatre & drama since 1889
Bristol P PhD△/MPhil△/dip△

Historical & critical studies
Sheffield City P PhD/MPhil

Humanities, performance & media
South West P PhD/MPhil

Information & communication policy
Central London P PhD☆/MPhil☆

Literary & media studies
North London P PhD/MPhil

Mass communication
Leicester U PhD/MPhil

Mass media
Central London P PhD☆/MPhil☆

Media & graphic design
Newcastle P PhD☆/MPhil☆

Media & music
Lancashire P PhD/MPhil

Media studies
Coventry P PhD/MPhil
Paisley CT PhD/MPhil
Ulster U DPhil/MPhil

Photography
Napier P PhD/MPhil
Royal CA PhD☆

Photography & film
Central London P PhD☆/MPhil☆

Radio, film & television studies
Canterbury Christ Church C
PhD/MPhil

Television & film
Royal CA PhD☆
Strathclyde U PhD☆/MPhil☆

Television research
Leeds U PhD/MPhil

Theatre studies
Glasgow U PhD/MPhil
Lancaster U PhD/MPhil
Leeds U PhD/MA/MPhil
Ulster U DPhil/MPhil
Warwick U PhD☆/MA☆/MPhil☆

Visual communication
Nottingham P PhD☆/MPhil☆

Theology

Higher degrees by instruction

Advanced Jewish studies
Jews' C dip△
Leo Baeck C MA☆

Applied ethics
Aberdeen U MLitt☆

Aspects of Biblical interpretation
London Bible C MA

Bible & literature
Sheffield U MA

Biblical languages
Aberdeen U MTh☆

Biblical studies
Glasgow U MTh☆/dip☆
London U Heythrop C MTh
Manchester U MA(Theol)☆/dip☆
Sheffield U dip☆

Christian doctrine
London U Heythrop C MTh

Christian ethics
London U Heythrop C MTh

Christian ethics & practical theology
Edinburgh U MTh

Christianity in the non-Western world
Edinburgh U MTh

Church & secular power
Bangor, U of Wales MA☆

Church history
Aberdeen U MTh☆

Church history (patristic & modern)
London U Heythrop C MTh

Church, religion & society (1790-1940)
Cheltenham & Gloucester CHE
MA

Comparative development & international policy studies
Bristol U MSc

Divinity
Birmingham U BD☆
St Andrews U MPhil☆

Eastern Christian studies
Oxford U MPhil☆

Ecclesiastical history
Edinburgh U MTh
Glasgow U MTh/dip
St Andrews U MPhil☆

Ethics & philosophy of religion
Ulster U MA△/dip△

Evangelism
London Bible C Dip☆

Hebrew & Jewish studies
Jews' C MA

Hebrew & Old Testament studies
Edinburgh U MSc☆/MTh☆
Sheffield U MA

History & philosophy of religion
London U King's C MA☆

History of the Church
St David's UC MTh☆

Indian, Tibetan or Buddhist studies
Bristol U MA

Interfaith studies
St David's UC MA☆

Islamic societies & cultures
London U SOAS MA

Islamic studies
Kent U MA/dip

Jewish studies
Jews' C dip☆

Judaism & Christianity in the Graeco Roman world
Oxford U MPhil☆

Judaism & Jewish-Christian relations
Birmingham U dip☆

Literature & theology
Durham U MA☆

Liturgy & architecture
Birmingham U dip

Ministry
Edinburgh U dip
Glasgow U dip☆

Mission studies
Birmingham U dip☆

New religious movements
Birmingham U dip☆

New Testament language, literature & theology
Edinburgh U MTh

New Testament studies
Durham U MA☆
St Andrews U MPhil☆

Old Testament studies
St Andrews U MPhil☆

Oriental & African religious studies
London U SOAS MA

Overseas studies
London Bible C Dip☆

Pastoral studies
Birmingham U dip
Cardiff U of Wales C dip
London Bible C Dip☆
St John's C dip☆

Pastoral studies & applied theology
Aberdeen U cert/dip

Pastoral theology
London U Heythrop C MTh/dip☆
St Andrews U dip

Philosophical theology
Oxford U MPhil☆/MSt☆

Philosophy of religion
London U Heythrop C MTh

Political theology
Bristol U MA☆

Practical theology
Glasgow U MTh☆/dip☆

Practical theology & Christian ethics
St Andrews U MPhil☆

Problems of New Testament interpretation in modern study
Bristol U MA

Reformation studies
Aberdeen U MTh☆

Religion & mythology in the ancient world
Bristol U MA☆

Religion, culture & development
London U King's C MA☆

Religious education
Cheltenham & Gloucester CHE MA
London U Inst of Education MA
London U King's C MA
S Martin's C MA☆

Religious studies
Bangor, U of Wales MA☆
Bristol U MA☆
Lancaster U MA/dip
Leeds U MA/dip
Newcastle U dip☆
St David's UC LRS☆
Stirling U cert
Strathclyde U cert△

Social & pastoral theology
Manchester U MA(Theol)/dip

Sociology & religion
Lancaster U MA☆

Studies in religion & culture
Birmingham U MA

Systematic theology (including studies in Patristic Christianity)
Edinburgh U MTh

Theological studies
St John's C Dip☆

Theology
Aberdeen U MTh☆
Bangor, U of Wales MTh☆
Belfast Queen's U MTh
Birmingham U dip☆
Bristol U dip☆
Cambridge U MPhil☆/dip☆
Cardiff U of Wales C MTh☆
Durham U MA☆/MTheol☆
Edinburgh U MTh
Exeter U MA☆/dip
Glasgow U MTh/dip☆
Hull U MA/dip
Leeds U MA/dip
London U Heythrop C dip

London U King's C dip☆
Nottingham U MTh/dip ☐
Oxford U MPhil☆/MSt☆/Cert☆/Dip☆
Regent's Park C MSt☆/dip☆
St David's UC LTh
St John's C BTh☆/cert☆/dip☆
Southampton U MA
Welsh Independence C MTh

Theology & religious studies
London U King's C MTh

Higher degrees by research

Bible criticism & exegesis
Manchester U PhD/MA

Biblical criticism
Glasgow U PhD/MPhil

Biblical studies
Bangor, U of Wales PhD☆/MPhil☆
London Bible C PhD/MPhil
Sheffield U PhD/MPhil

Christian ethics & practical theology
Edinburgh U PhD/MPhil

Christianity in the non-western world
Edinburgh U PhD/MPhil

Church history
Aberdeen U PhD☆/MLitt☆/MPhil☆
St David's UC PhD☆/MA☆

Comparative religion
Manchester U PhD/MA

Divinity
Cambridge U PhD☆/MLitt☆
St Andrews U PhD/MPhil

Ecclesiastical history
Edinburgh U PhD/MPhil
St Andrews U PhD/MPhil

Hebrew & Jewish studies
London U UC PhD☆/MPhil☆

Hebrew & Old Testament studies
Edinburgh U PhD/MPhil

History of religions
Aberdeen U PhD☆/MLitt☆/MPhil☆/MTh☆

Humanities
Brighton P PhD/MPhil

Islamic studies
Birmingham U PhD☆/MPhil☆

Jewish studies
Jews' C PhD☆/MPhil☆

Ministerial studies
Spurgeon's C PhD☆/MPhil☆

New religious movements
Birmingham U PhD☆/MPhil☆

New Testament exegesis
Aberdeen U PhD☆/MLitt☆/MPhil☆

New Testament studies
Edinburgh U PhD/MPhil
St Andrews U PhD/MPhil

Old Testament studies
St Andrews U PhD/MPhil

Philosophy & religious studies
Middlesex P PhD/MPhil/dip△

Practical theology
Aberdeen U PhD☆/MPhil☆/MTh☆

Practical theology & Christian ethics
St Andrews U PhD/MPhil

Religion & ethics in Western thought
St David's UC PhD☆/MA☆

Religion & philosophy
London U SOAS PhD/MPhil

Religious studies
Canterbury Christ Church C PhD/MPhil
Cheltenham & Gloucester CHE PhD/MPhil
Edinburgh U PhD/MLitt
Edinburgh U PhD/MLitt
Lancaster U PhD/MPhil
Leicester U PhD/MA/MPhil
Goldsmiths' C London U PhD/MPhil
Newcastle U PhD/MLitt
Open U PhD/MPhil/BPhil
Stirling U PhD/MLitt
Sussex U DPhil/MPhil

Social & environmental education
Thames P PhD/MPhil

Systematic theology
Aberdeen U PhD☆/MPhil☆/MTh☆
Edinburgh U PhD/MPhil

Theology
Bangor, U of Wales PhD☆/MPhil☆/MTh☆
Belfast Queen's U PhD/MTh
Birmingham U PhD/MLitt/MPhil/BD
Cardiff U of Wales C PhD☆/MPhil☆
Cheltenham & Gloucester CHE PhD/MPhil
Durham U MA/MLitt/MTheol/BD

Exeter U PhD/MPhil
Hull U PhD/MPhil
London U Heythrop C PhD/MPhil
Manchester U PhD/MPhil
Nottingham U PhD/MPhil
Oxford U DPhil✩/MLitt✩
Regent's Park C MPhil✩/MSt✩
St David's UC PhD✩/MA✩
Salford CFE PhD✩/MPhil✩
Trinity C Bristol PhD/MPhil
Welsh Independence C PhD/
  MPhil

Theology & religious studies
Bristol U PhD/MLitt
Kent U PhD/MA/MPhil
Leeds U PhD/MA/MPhil
London U King's C PhD✩/MPhil✩
Southampton U PhD/MPhil

Theology (practical/systematic)
Glasgow U PhD/MTh

Theology: ordination

Ordination - Baptist
Bristol Baptist C ✩
Irish Baptist C ✩
North Wales Baptist C ✩
Northern Baptist C ✩
Scottish Baptist C ✩
South Wales Baptist C ✩
Spurgeon's C ✩

Ordination - Church of England
Chichester Theol C ✩
Cranmer Hall/St John's C ✩
Edinburgh Theol C ✩
Lincoln Theol C ✩
Oak Hill C ✩
Queen's C Birmingham ✩
Resurrection C ✩
Ridley Hall ✩
Ripon C ✩
St John's C ✩
St Michael's C ✩
St Stephen's House ✩
Salisbury & Wells Theol C ✩
Trinity C Bristol ✩
Westcott House ✩

Ordination - Church of Scotland
Aberdeen U ✩
St Andrews U ✩

Ordination - Congregational
Northern C ✩
Scottish Congregational C ✩

**Ordination - Congregationalist
(Welsh Independent)**
Welsh Independence C

Ordination - Methodist
Edgehill Theol C ✩
Queen's C Birmingham ✩
Wesley C ✩
Wesley House ✩

**Ordination - Presbyterian
Church of Wales**
United Theol C, Aberystwyth ✩

Ordination - Rabbinic
Jews' C ✩
Leo Baeck C ✩

Ordination - Roman Catholic
Allen Hall ✩

**Ordination - Scottish
Episcopalian**
Edinburgh Theol C ✩

Ordination - Unitarian
Welsh Independence C

Ordination - United Reformed
Mansfield C ✩
Northern C ✩
Queen's C Birmingham ✩
Welsh Independence C ✩
Westminster C Cambridge ✩

Three dimensional art/ design

Higher degrees by instruction

Advanced design research
London C of Furniture dip△

Art & design
Humberside CHE MA△
Middlesex P cert
Robert Gordon's IT dip✩

Bronze casting
Royal CA dip✩

Calligraphy & bookbinding
Roehampton I cert✩

Ceramic design
Glasgow SA dip✩

Ceramics
Cardiff IHE MA✩
Edinburgh CA dip✩
Heriot-Watt U dip✩

Ceramics & glass
Royal CA MA✩/MDes✩

Communication design
Manchester P MA

Computing in design
Middlesex P MA✩

Design
Edinburgh CA MDes✩/dip✩
Heriot-Watt U MDes✩/dip✩
Liverpool U MDes✩

Design & craft
Robert Gordon's IT dip✩

Design & development
Robert Gordon's IT MSc

Design management
Royal CA MDes✩

**Design of equipment for
disability**
London C of Furniture dip✩

Design research for disability
London C of Furniture MA

Film & television design
Kingston P dip✩

Fine & applied arts
Ulster U dip

Foundry practice
Royal CA cert✩

Furniture design
Edinburgh CA dip✩

Furniture design & technology
Buckinghamshire CHE MA✩

Furniture making
Royal CA MA✩

Glass & stained glass design
Edinburgh CA dip✩
Heriot-Watt U dip✩

History & theory of art & design
Ulster U dip△

Industrial design
Glasgow SA dip✩
Manchester P MA✩

Industrial design engineering
London U Imperial C MDes✩/
  dip✩

Industrial design for engineers
Teesside P MA✩

**Industrial design in England
from 1688-1914**
Essex U MA✩

Interior design
Glasgow SA dip✩
Manchester P MA✩
Middlesex P MA△
Royal CA MA✩

Jewellery & silversmithing
Edinburgh CA dip✩
Heriot-Watt U dip✩

Public art & design
Duncan of Jordanstone CA
MPhil☆

Sculpture
Central St Martins CAD cert☆
Glasgow SA dip☆
Royal CA MA☆

Sculpture studies
Leeds U MA☆

**Silversmithing & jewellery
design**
Glasgow SA dip☆

Studio studies with art history
Aberystwyth, UC of Wales MA/
dip☆

Theatre design
Glasgow SA dip☆
Nottingham P MA☆/dip☆

**Three dimensional computer
aided graphical technology
applications**
Teesside P MSc☆

Timber studies
Buckinghamshire CHE dip☆

Higher degrees by research

Architecture, art & design
Humberside CHE PhD/MPhil

Art
Robert Gordon's IT PhD/MPhil

Art & design
Canterbury Christ Church C
PhD/MPhil
Cardiff IHE PhD/MPhil/dip△
Cheltenham & Gloucester CHE
PhD/MPhil
East London P PhD/MPhil

Goldsmiths' C London U PhD/
MPhil
Middlesex P PhD/MPhil
Sunderland P PhD/MPhil
Wolverhampton P PhD/MPhil

Arts & design
Kingston P PhD/MPhil

Arts & technology in education
Thames P PhD/MPhil

Ceramics
Leeds U PhD/MPhil/MSc

Ceramics & glass
Royal CA PhD☆

Ceramics, glasses & polymers
Sheffield U PhD/MPhil

Communication arts
Sheffield City P PhD/MPhil

Communication arts & design
Manchester P PhD/MPhil

Communication design
Middlesex P PhD/MPhil

Design
Lancashire P PhD/MPhil
Leeds P PhD/MPhil/dip
London C of Printing PhD/MPhil
Napier P PhD/MPhil
Open U PhD/MPhil/BPhil
Portsmouth P PhD☆/MPhil☆
Sheffield City P PhD/MPhil
South West P PhD/MPhil
Teesside P PhD☆/MPhil☆

Design & communications
Royal CA PhD☆/MA☆

Design & crafts
Heriot-Watt U MDes☆/MPhil△/dip

Design & technology
Loughborough U PhD/MPhil

Design education
Royal CA PhD☆/MA☆

Fine art
Leicester P PhD/MPhil

Furniture making
Royal CA MA☆/MDes☆

Graphic design
Lancashire P PhD/MPhil

Holography
Royal CA PhD

Industrial design
Leicester P PhD/MPhil

Metalwork & jewellery
Royal CA MA☆

Product design
Middlesex P PhD/MPhil

Sculpture
Heriot-Watt U MDes☆/MPhil△/dip
Sheffield City P PhD/MPhil

Silversmithing & jewellery
Birmingham P PhD/MPhil
City of London P PhD☆/MPhil☆

Textile design
Scottish C of Textiles PhD/MPhil

Three dimensional design
Birmingham P PhD/MPhil
Brighton P PhD/MPhil
Kingston P PhD/MPhil
Manchester P PhD/MPhil
Middlesex P PhD/MPhil
Nottingham P PhD☆/MPhil☆

Visual & performing arts
Newcastle P PhD☆/MPhil☆

Visual arts
Aberystwyth, UC of Wales
PhD☆/MPhil☆
Lancaster U PhD/MPhil

Visual studies
Manchester P PhD/MPhil

Art gallery & museum studies

dip
1 year full time
18 - 20 places
MPhil
minimum 1 year full time
minimum 2 years part time
The Secretary, Art Gallery and Museum Studies Course, History of Art Department, University of Manchester, Manchester M13 9PL
Tel: 061 275 3312

The diploma course offers a core programme dealing with the administration and interpretation of arts collections. Practical projects are done in a variety of art galleries and museums and a public exhibition is mounted annually in the University's Whitworth Art Gallery. There is a four week period of museum attachment. An MPhil by thesis is available to holders of the diploma and to those with equivalent qualifications/experience.
Entrance requirements Degree or satisfactory equivalent qualification.
Grants DES.
Head of course Mr I G Wolfenden.

Commercial law, public law, general legal studies, law and philosophy

LLM
1 year full time
(or two years extended study)
Postgraduate Admissions Tutor, Faculty of Law, University of Bristol, Wills Memorial Building, Queens Road, Bristol BS8 1RJ
Tel: 0272 303030

We offer LLM courses lasting one year full-time or up to four years by extended study. You may obtain a Master's degree by specialising in commercial law or in public law or select from a variety of subjects and obtain your degree in general legal studies, or study for the LLM in law and philosophy. You study four subjects, and also submit a dissertation of about 10,000 words. There are about 35 subjects to choose from including applied contract law, banking law, competition law, international contracts, civil liberties and human rights, local government law, accident compensation, restitution. The teaching is usually by small group seminars.
Entrance requirements A good honours degree, normally in law, or other recognised legal qualification.

Criminal justice

MA
1 year full time
(2 full days pw)
2 years part time
(1 full day pw)
25 places
Convenor, MA Criminal Justice, Department of Law, Brunel University, Uxbridge, Middlesex UB8 3PH
Tel: 0895 56461

This is a taught MA course, focusing on crime, policing and the criminal justice system. It looks at law and criminal justice policy in a social and political context. It also serves as an introduction to socio-legal theory and empirical research in the social sciences. The degree comprises four examined courses, including a written dissertation which gives students the opportunity to put research methods to the test in pursuing a particular area of interest, raised by the taught courses. The course is aimed at criminal justice practitioners or anyone with an interest in crime and policing policy.
Entrance requirements Normally a degree in law or social science subjects.
Course convenor Dr Betsy Stanko.

Fine art

MA
2 years part time
10 places
HoD Fine Art, Faculty of Art and Design, Cardiff Institute of Higher Education, Howard Gardens, Cardiff CF2 1SP
Tel: 0222 551111 ext 5568

This exciting and innovative course provides an opportunity for artists to develop their work in association with study of the social & professional factors affecting it.
 Applications open to practising artists from the following disciplines : painting, sculpture, print making, photography and time based media.
 Each student must provide a work space outside the faculty situated within a reasonable travelling distance of Cardiff.
MA course tutor John Gingell.

History and related studies

MA
1 year full time
2 years part time
Secretary & Librarian,
Institute of Historical
Research/Institute of US
Studies, University of
London, Senate House,
London WC1E 7HU

The Institute is the main postgraduate facility for history in the University of London, and attracts historians from all over the world. Used by students from many other institutions, it also offers 3 MA courses of its own.
1. *Area Studies (United States):* provides options in geography, history, literature, politics, sociology, international relations and other aspects of US culture and society.
2. *Social change in Modern Europe:* a new course consisting of a core course on European Society in the 19th and 20th centuries plus options on particular countries and on anarchism and social democracy and communism.
3. *Computer applications for history:* a new course aiming to provide both a conceptual and a practical understanding of modern computer systems and their application to history.
Entrance requirements Normally include a good honours degree plus fluent written and spoken English.

Journalism, printing & publishing studies

MA/PgD/Diploma
full time
and part time
Senior Admissions Tutor,
Department of Printing &
publishing, London College
of Printing, Elephant &
Castle, London SE1 6SB
Tel: 071 735 8484

The aim of these courses is to provide an education and training for new entrants and practising persons in the subjects of scriptwriting and research and film and video production, photography and advertising and photojournalism. There are also opportunities in radio and print journalism, printing and publishing and design for media. On some courses work experience is arranged for students. Applications and information from the Schools of Media and Management, Printing technology, Design.
Entrance requirements A degree in a relevant subject or exceptional admission for applicants with suitable experience.

Latin American studies

MPhil
1 year full time
Centre of Latin American
Studies, University of
Cambridge, History Faculty
Building, West Road,
Cambridge CB3 9EF
Tel: 0223 335390

Specialisation in one of the following areas of study in the Latin American context: economics, rural sociology, history, social anthropology, modern literature, urban sociology, ethnohistory, archaeology. Three written papers and short dissertation required or in special cases longer dissertation only. Updated brochure available.
Entrance requirements Normally upper second class honours degree or equivalent.
Grants ESRC/British Academy.
Director Dr D A Brading.

Medieval studies

MA
1 year full time
The Registry, Queen Mary &
Westfield College,
Hampstead Campus,
Kidderpore Avenue, London
NW3 7ST
Tel: 071 435 7141

Queen Mary and Westfield College offers an interdisciplinary taught course leading to the University of London MA in Medieval Studies. The curriculum divides into three sections: A. A Medieval Language: B. Methods and techniques in Medieval Studies; C. Two special options currently drawn from : 1. Church and Society in Western Europe , 2. Heroic Epic and its Transformations, 3. The Medieval Lyric, 4. Arthurian Legend and Literature, 5. Literary Patronage in England in the latter Middle Ages, 6. Medieval English Drama, 7. Death in the Middle Ages, 8. Education in the Middle Ages, 9. The Archaeology of Medieval Italy. Assessment is by written project/examination, two essays, a dissertation and a viva voce examination.
Entrance requirements Normally a good degree in an arts subject.
Course director Dr Pamela M King.

Publishing & book production

Polytechnic diploma
28 weeks full time
Department of Printing,
Plymouth: Polytechnic South
West, Earl Richard's Road,
North Exeter, EX2 6AS
Tel: 0395 475009

This 28 week full-time course is designed to prepare students for a career in publishing. Arrangements can be made for students wishing to retrain or acquire specific skills, particularly those related to new technology. Overseas students have attended and been sponsored by their governments.

The course was established in 1979 and since then, 80% of its students have gained employment in publishing. The emphasis is on providing students with practical experience of all stages of publishing and production. The course enjoys an excellent relationship with publishers who provide sponsorship, advice, placement opportunity, and eventually employment to its students.

Course leader Professor Honeywell.

Radio & TV journalism

dip (Radio & TV journalism)
1 year full time
25 places
School of Journalism,
Lancashire Polytechnic,
Preston PR1 2TQ
Tel: 0772 201201

This is a postgraduate vocational course for students wishing to take up a career in broadcasting. It provides practical training by experienced professional broadcasters in a "newsroom" environment. The centre includes well-equipped radio and television studios. Students attend BBC and Independent Television and radio stations on attachments. The course also includes tuition in public administration, media law and shorthand.

Entrance requirements British or overseas degree in any discipline, or sponsorship by a broadcasting employer. Mature students with relevant career backgrounds in lieu of a degree will also be considered.

Grants LEA discretionary.

Radio journalism

CNAA PgD
1 year full time
24 places
Department of Radio
journalism, Falmouth School
of Art & Design, Woodlane,
Falmouth, Cornwall TR11
4RA
Tel: 0326 211082

This is an intensive vocational course for those who want to enter the radio industry on the current affairs side. The course also covers media law, central and local government, media analysis, shorthand and typing, and an element of television and computer skills. It is validated by CNAA and the industry validation body, JACTRJ. It is specifically geared to the wants and needs of the radio industry by concentrating on " hard " news to minimise any culture shock on going from the Falmouth newsroom to any other radio station newsroom, either Independent Radio or BBC.

Entrance requirements Degree or equivalent (or relevant career background in exceptional cases) and a demonstrated commitment to news.

Grants LEA discretionary.

Head of journalism Mr Colin Caley.

Theology

MTh
1 year full time
2 years part time
MPhil/PhD
Rev.Prof Heywood Thomas,
Department of Theology,
University of Nottingham,
University Park, Nottingham
NG7 2RD
Tel: 0602 484848 ext 2467

Nottingham University Department of Theology offers unique opportunities of postgraduate study in Mormonism, Early Christian Art and Archaeology and in the complete range of theological disciplines. Postgraduate work can be undertaken either as research or as examination-directed study. The strong tradition of postgraduate work is evidenced in the flourishing Postgraduate Colloquium to which all postgraduate students contribute.

Entrance requirements An upper second in Theology.

Head of department Rev.Prof Heywood Thomas.

Languages and literature

As in most areas of postgraduate study, with languages and literature there is a choice between academic and applied options. The universities, in the main, offer academic courses and opportunities for research; the polytechnics, colleges of higher education, and a few universities (usually the more 'technological' ones, such as Bath or Salford) offer applied courses which are more directly geared to training graduates for specific careers.

Academic study

The majority of postgraduates studying for higher degrees in languages and literature are pursuing purely academic interests. One of the roles of a university (one could argue that the role of a polytechnic is rather different) is to encourage the pursuit of knowledge for its own sake, irrespective of the demands of politicians, industry or commerce. It is for this reason that universities run Master's degree programmes in subjects such as 18th-century English literature, medieval languages, or Hebrew and Old Testament studies, even though these subjects are in no sense 'vocational'.

However, from the individual's point of view, even if you spend the next few years on purely academic pursuits, a time will inevitably come when the problem of finding a job looms large. In the past the natural progression was to teaching and research in the universities, but this route is now closed to all but the ablest (and luckiest) minority. There is, of course, the option of teaching elsewhere, and the possession of a higher degree will certainly be no disadvantage in most educational spheres; but in other kinds of employment an 'academic' higher degree will confer little, if any, benefit.

This should not necessarily deter a language or literature student with a real interest in academic study for its own sake. But there are other options. Apart from training in a completely different field, or going straight into employment, there are various 'applied' postgraduate courses, suitable for language and literature graduates, that are more relevant, in career terms, than an 'academic' higher degree.

Teaching

One of the most obvious options is to teach one's first degree subject, usually in secondary education. You will find further details of PGCE courses in the education section of this book.

Another popular, related choice is teaching English as a foreign language (TEFL). This is open to any graduate, though a first degree in English or modern languages is an advantage. As far as TEFL qualifications go, those who are seeking a long-term career would do well to take a PGCE course. However, PGCE courses with TEFL as a main subject often require applicants to have previous teaching experience. To gain this experience, it is possible to find a teaching post in a private language school - either in the UK or abroad - after taking a short course (usually lasting about four weeks) leading to the Royal Society of Arts/ University of Cambridge Local Examination Syndicate Certificate (RSA/ UCLES).

Taking a postgraduate course in applied linguistics can be helpful for career development in language teaching (it is necessary, for instance, for many of the more responsible posts advertised by the British Council). Normally, however, one would be expected to gain some teaching experience and teaching qualifications first.

Translating and interpreting

A way of using a modern languages degree in a very direct sense is to become a translator or interpreter. It cannot be repeated too often, however, that these professions are heavily over-subscribed, and demand really first-class language skills.

For those who are determined to find employment in interpreting or translating, a postgraduate qualification is not strictly necessary, but is advisable, simply because of the competition for jobs. Courses are listed on the following pages. Note that literary translation is a very specialised field, and one in which it is particularly difficult to make a living. It is far better, in career terms, to choose a course with more emphasis on commercial and technical work - even if the subject matter lacks appeal.

Clearly, choice of institution will depend on the languages offered. There is no problem finding French or

German, which are widely available, but for Spanish, Russian or Italian you may need to shop around - consult the prospectuses, as possible language combinations may change from year to year. With more unusual languages - often studied *ab initio* as subsidiary subjects - there is even more variation. The widest choice is offered by the Polytechnic of Central London, which offers separate (and highly regarded) courses in interpreting and translating: the diploma in conference interpretation techniques and the diploma in technical and specialised translation.

Secretarial and business studies

There are other 'applied' postgraduate courses which are of particular interest to modern language graduates. Secretarial linguist courses (some of which are now being renamed along the lines of 'information technology with languages', or similar titles) provide a good basis for a career using languages, either in Britain or abroad. Polytechnics and colleges and institutes of higher education offering such courses are listed in the section on business administration and management.

There are also several postgraduate marketing courses specifically aimed at modern language graduates, amongst them Salford's part-time MSc in marketing and a foreign language, Napier Polytechnic of Edinburgh's diploma in European marketing and languages, North Staffordshire Polytechnic's diploma in international marketing, and the diploma in European marketing management at Buckinghamshire College of Higher Education.

If you are interested in pursuing a business career in which you can make use of your languages, you can instead take any of a wide range of other courses, without language input. A Master of Business Administration (MBA), for instance, could be very useful, though it might be better to get some work experience before embarking on a course of this type.

Financial Support

The general points about postgraduate awards in the humanities, made in the section on applications and grants, apply. Prospective teachers will normally receive a mandatory grant for a PGCE from the local education authority. It may also be possible to get a discretionary LEA grant for a secretarial course, although it is likely that you will have to study locally.

Otherwise, options to investigate include Career Development loans, straight bank loans (the Association of MBAs, 15 Duncan Terrace, London N1 8BZ *Tel:* 071 837 3375, may be able to help arrange a loan for a postgraduate business course), or part-time study combined with employment.

In conclusion, the 'irrelevance' of academic postgraduate study should not be a deterrent if you are motivated by an overriding interest in a subject; but there are other options worthy of consideration, which may prove equally satisfying in the long run, when seen in the context of your whole career.

Helen Steadman

This listing contains **taught courses** (under the heading 'Higher degrees by instruction') and **research opportunities** (under the heading 'Higher degrees by research'). All study exceeds two terms or six months and is offered on both a full-time and part-time basis unless otherwise indicated. Post-experience and in-service courses are only included when advertised.

☐   This symbol indicates that the **taught course(s)** or **research opportunities** are advertised at the end of this listing.

Biol   An italic abbreviation indicates that an advertisement has been placed at the end of another chapter.

☆   This symbol indicates full-time study only.

△   This symbol indicates part-time study only.

For quick reference to advertisements, please use the 'Advertiser's course entry index'. For further information regarding the listing, please refer to page 53.

General

Higher degrees by instruction

Administration & information processing
North East Surrey CT RSA
dip☆ *Bus*

Anglo German literary relations
Leeds U MA

Applied European studies
South Bank P MA△/dip△

Arthurian literature
Bangor, U of Wales MA☆

Bibliography, publishing & textual studies
Leeds U MA☆

Bilingual business administration: French/German/Spanish/Russian/Italian
Stradbroke C RSA dip☆ *Bus*

Commonwealth literature
Leeds U MA☆

Contemporary European culture
Exeter U MA☆

Criticism & theory
Exeter U MA△

Cultural studies
Ealing C London MA△
Leeds U MA

East Asian studies
Newcastle U MA☆

English
Bangor, U of Wales MA☆/dip☆

English (dialectology)
Belfast Queen's U MA

European language & literature
London U Queen Mary & Westfield C MA ☐

French studies
Liverpool U MA ☐

Humour & society
Reading U MA☆

Independent study
East London P MA/MSc/dip

Language & literature in education
London U Inst of Education MA

Language in the multicultural community
Ealing C London MA△/dip△

Literature & the visual arts 1840-1940
Reading U MA

Management of new technology with modern languages
Newcastle P MSc☆/dip☆

Medieval studies
London U Queen Mary & Westfield C MA *Arts*

Philosophy & literature
Warwick U MA

Scottish literature
Glasgow U MPhil

Spanish & Italian
Durham U MA

The word & visual imagination
St David's UC MA ☐

Higher degrees by research

Advanced studies in the humanities
Edinburgh U PhD/MLitt

Arts & languages
Kingston P PhD/MPhil
Wales P PhD/MPhil

Critical & cultural theory
Cardiff U of Wales C PhD/MPhil

Cultural studies
Bradford U PhD/MPhil

Humanities
Humberside CHE PhD/MPhil

Humanities, performance & media
South West P PhD/MPhil

Humanities, social & cultural studies
Wolverhampton P PhD/MPhil

Independent study
East London P PhD/MPhil

Interdisciplinary human studies
Bradford U PhD/MPhil

Interdisciplinary studies in social sciences
Kent U PhD/MPhil

Japanese
Cardiff U of Wales C PhD☆/MPhil☆

Language & communications
Open U PhD/MPhil/BPhil

Language studies
Canterbury Christ Church C PhD/MPhil

Languages
Dorset Inst PhD/MPhil/dip

Literary theory
Middlesex P PhD/MPhil/dip△

Literature
Bradford U PhD/MPhil

Scottish literature
Glasgow U PhD/MPhil

Classics

Higher degrees by instruction

Ancient Near Eastern civilisation
London U SOAS MSc

Arabic
Durham U dip☆

Biblical languages
Aberdeen U MTh☆

Byzantine & modern Greek studies
London U King's C MA

Byzantine studies
Birmingham U MA☆

Classical archaeology
Edinburgh U MLitt☆/MSc☆/dip☆

Classical archaeology (Greece)
London U UC dip☆

Classical Armenian studies
Oxford U MSt☆

Classical civilisation
Leeds U MA☆
London U Birkbeck C MA△

Classical studies
Nottingham U MA
St David's UC MA☆ ☐

Classics
Aberystwyth, UC of Wales MA☆
Edinburgh U MLitt☆
Glasgow U MPhil
Leeds U dip☆
Liverpool U MA
London U Birkbeck C MA☆
London U King's C MA☆
London U Queen Mary & Westfield C MA
London U Royal Holloway & Bedford New C MA
London U UC MA☆

Classics & ancient history
St Andrews U MLitt/MPhil☆/dip☆
Swansea UC MA☆

Egyptology
Swansea UC MA✩

Greek
Durham U MA✩
Leeds U MA✩
Liverpool U MA✩
Newcastle U MA✩
St Andrews U MLitt/MPhil✩/dip✩

Greek & Latin
St Andrews U MLitt/MPhil✩/dip✩

Greek &/or Latin languages & literature
Oxford U MPhil✩/MSt✩

Greek civilisation
Leeds U MA✩

Hellenistic studies
Liverpool U MA

Humanities
North London P MA△

Jewish studies in the Graeco Roman period
Oxford U MSt✩

Judaism & Christianity in the Graeco Roman world
Oxford U MPhil✩

Late Antique & Byzantine studies
London U King's C MA

Late Roman & Byzantine studies
St Andrews U MLitt/MPhil✩/dip✩

Late Roman studies
Bristol U MA✩

Latin
Leeds U MA✩
Newcastle U MA✩
St Andrews U MLitt/MPhil✩/dip✩
Warwick U MA

Oriental studies (classical & medieval Islamic history)
Oxford U MPhil✩/MSt✩

Oriental studies (Jewish studies in the Graeco Roman period)
Oxford U MPhil✩/MSc✩

Roman civilisation
Leeds U MA✩

Roman social & cultural history
Reading U MA

Higher degrees by research

Archaeology
Reading U PhD/MPhil

Byzantine & modern Greek studies
London U King's C PhD✩/MPhil✩

Classical & archaeological studies
Nottingham U PhD/MPhil

Classical archaeology
Edinburgh U PhD/MLitt

Classical studies
Kent U PhD/MA/MPhil
Open U PhD/MPhil/BPhil

Classics
Aberystwyth, UC of Wales PhD✩/MPhil✩
Bangor, U of Wales PhD✩/MPhil✩
Birmingham U PhD/MLitt/MPhil
Cambridge U PhD✩/MLitt✩
Edinburgh U PhD/MLitt
Exeter U PhD/MPhil
Glasgow U PhD/MLitt
Keele U PhD/MA
Leeds U PhD/MA/MPhil
Leicester U PhD/MA/MPhil
Liverpool U PhD/MPhil
London U King's C PhD✩/MPhil✩
London U Queen Mary & Westfield C PhD✩/MPhil✩
London U Royal Holloway & Bedford New C PhD/MPhil
Newcastle U PhD/MLitt
Reading U PhD/MPhil
St Andrews U PhD/MPhil
St David's UC PhD✩/MA✩
Southampton U PhD/MPhil
Warwick U PhD✩/MA✩/MPhil✩

Classics & ancient history
Durham U PhD/MA/MLitt
London U Birkbeck C PhD/MPhil
Swansea UC PhD/MPhil

Classics & archaeology
Bristol U PhD/MLitt
Lancaster U PhD/MPhil

Comparative literary studies
Kent U PhD/MA/MPhil

Greek
Edinburgh U PhD/MLitt
Glasgow U PhD/MLitt
Liverpool U PhD/MPhil
London U UC PhD✩/MPhil✩
Manchester U PhD/MPhil
St Andrews U PhD/MPhil

Greek & Latin
Belfast Queen's U PhD/MA

Greek & Latin languages & literature
Oxford U DPhil✩/MLitt✩

Hebrew & ancient Semitic languages
Liverpool U PhD/MPhil

Hellenic, Roman & Byzantine studies
Birmingham U PhD/MLitt/MPhil

Hellenistic studies
Liverpool U PhD/MPhil

Latin
Belfast Queen's U PhD/MA
Edinburgh U PhD/MLitt
Glasgow U PhD/MLitt
Liverpool U PhD/MPhil
London U UC PhD✩/MPhil✩
Manchester U PhD/MPhil
St Andrews U PhD/MPhil

Medieval Latin
Cambridge U PhD✩/MLitt✩

English language and studies

Higher degrees by instruction

Advanced Arabic & English studies
Salford U dip✩

Applied linguistics
Birmingham U MA/BLitt/dip

Bibliography, publishing & textual studies
Leeds U MA✩

Communication studies (conversion)
Sunderland P MA△/dip△

Comparative literature
Edinburgh U MSc✩

Creative writing
Lancaster U MA

Critical theory
Nottingham U MA

English
Bangor, U of Wales MA✩/dip✩
Exeter U MA✩
Manchester U MA✩

English & Hispanic studies
Glasgow U MPhil

English (Anglo Irish studies)
Belfast Queen's U MA

English (English literature & language before 1525)
London U UC MA

English (Romanticism & Modernism)
Southampton U MA

English as a second or foreign language
Bangor, U of Wales MA☆/dip☆

English (dialectology)
Belfast Queen's U MA

English language
Glasgow U MPhil☆/dip☆

English language & development studies
East Anglia U dip☆

English language & linguistics
Sheffield U MA/dip

English language & literary studies
Nottingham U MA

English language & literature
Exeter U dip☆
Keele U dip☆

English language & Medieval literature
Durham U MA☆

English language & stylistics
London U Royal Holloway & Bedford New C MA

English language as a literary medium
Aberdeen U MLitt☆

English language studies
Newcastle U MA/MPhil/dip

English language teaching
Reading U dip☆
Warwick U MA

English language teaching & administration
Warwick U dip☆

English studies
Edinburgh U MLitt☆
Leeds U dip☆
London U King's C dip☆
Strathclyde U dip

Language & philosophy of criticism
Sheffield U MA

Language & style in later middle English
Sheffield U MA☆

Language as a literary medium
Aberdeen U MLitt☆

Language in education
Aberystwyth, UC of Wales dip☆

Language in the multicultural community
Ealing C London MA△/dip△

Language studies
Lancaster U MA

Linguistics & modern English language
Nottingham U MA/cert/dip

Linguistics for English language teaching
Lancaster U MA

Linguistics, special applications
Birmingham U MA

Medieval English language, literature & art
Keele U MA

Medieval languages
Edinburgh U MSc☆

Modern English
Leeds U MA☆

Modern English language
Glasgow U MPhil☆/dip☆
London U UC MA☆

Modern English language & cultural tradition
Sheffield U MA

Modern English language & linguistics
Sheffield U MA

Modern French & English literature
Swansea UC MA☆

Modern literature: theory & practice
Leicester U MA

Modern poetry in English
Stirling U MPhil☆

Philosophy & psychology of language
London U Birkbeck C MA△

Phonetics of English
Leeds U dip☆

Playwriting studies
Birmingham U MA

Shakespeare: language & power
Lancaster U MA☆

Women's studies & English
Lancaster U MA

Writing off-centre
Aberdeen U MLitt☆

Higher degrees by research

Anglo Saxon, Norse & Celtic
Cambridge U PhD☆/MLitt☆

Applied English language studies
Cardiff U of Wales C PhD/MPhil

Critical theory
Nottingham U PhD/MPhil

Discourse in context
Aston U PhD/MPhil

English
Aberdeen U PhD☆/MLitt☆/ MPhil☆
Aberystwyth, UC of Wales PhD/ MPhil
Belfast Queen's U PhD/MA
Bristol U PhD/MLitt
Cambridge U PhD☆/MLitt☆
Canterbury Christ Church C PhD/MPhil
Exeter U PhD/MPhil
Lancaster U PhD/MPhil
Leeds U PhD/MA/MPhil
Leicester U PhD/MPhil
London U Birkbeck C PhD/MPhil
London U King's C PhD☆/MPhil☆
London U Queen Mary & Westfield C PhD☆/MPhil☆
London U Royal Holloway & Bedford New C PhD/MPhil
Reading U PhD/MPhil
St David's UC PhD☆/MA☆
Sheffield City P PhD/MPhil
Southampton U PhD/MPhil
Ulster U DPhil/MPhil
Warwick U PhD☆/MA☆/MPhil☆

English & communication studies
Sunderland P PhD/MPhil

English & drama
Loughborough U PhD☆/MPhil☆

English & history
Manchester P PhD/MPhil

English language
Edinburgh U PhD/MLitt
Glasgow U PhD/MLitt
Liverpool U PhD/MPhil
Newcastle U PhD/MLitt
Sheffield U PhD/MPhil

English language & literature
Bangor, U of Wales PhD☆/ MPhil☆
Birmingham U PhD/MLitt/MPhil
Hull U PhD/MPhil

Keele U PhD/MA
London U UC PhD☆/MPhil☆
Manchester U PhD/MPhil
Middlesex P PhD/MPhil
Oxford U DPhil☆/MLitt☆
St Andrews U PhD/MPhil
Swansea UC PhD/MPhil

English language & Medieval literature
Durham U PhD/MA/MLitt

English literature
Cardiff U of Wales C PhD☆/MPhil☆

English literature & language
Cheltenham & Gloucester CHE PhD/MPhil

English studies
Bristol P PhD/MPhil
Durham U PhD/MA/MLitt
East Anglia U PhD/MPhil
Nottingham U PhD/MPhil
Stirling U PhD/MLitt
Strathclyde U PhD/MLitt

Historical & critical studies
Newcastle P PhD☆/MPhil☆

Humanities
Brighton P PhD/MPhil
Bristol P PhD/MPhil/dip
Huddersfield P PhD/MPhil
Liverpool P PhD/MPhil

Language & communications
Open U PhD/MPhil/BPhil

Language & linguistic science
York U DPhil/MPhil

Language & linguistics
Central London P PhD☆/MPhil☆
Essex U PhD/MPhil

Language studies
Brighton P PhD/MPhil
Canterbury Christ Church C PhD/MPhil
London U LSE PhD/MPhil

Languages
Heriot-Watt U PhD☆/MPhil☆

Linguistics & modern English language
Lancaster U PhD/MPhil

Literature & languages
Nottingham P PhD☆/MPhil☆

Modern languages
Aston U PhD/MPhil
Salford U PhD/MPhil

English literature: pre Victorian

Higher degrees by instruction

18th century prose fiction, literary criticism & literary periodicals
Aberystwyth, UC of Wales MA

19th century literary criticism & literary periodicals
Aberystwyth, UC of Wales MA

Anglo American literary relations
London U UC MA

Anglo Irish literature
Ulster U MA△/dip△

Arthurian literature
Bangor, U of Wales MA☆

Chaucer studies
Birmingham U MA△

Children's literature
Reading U MA△

Comparative literary studies
St Andrews U MLitt/MPhil☆/dip☆

Comparative literary theory
Warwick U MA☆

Comparative literature
East Anglia U MA☆
Edinburgh U MSc☆

Comparative literature in the medieval, Renaissance & modern periods
Aberystwyth, UC of Wales MA

Critical theory
Nottingham U MA
Sussex U MA☆

Elizabethan & Shakespearean drama
Newcastle U MA/MPhil☆

English
Bangor, U of Wales MA☆/dip☆
Exeter U MA☆
Hull U MA☆
Manchester U MA☆

English & American literature
East Anglia U MA

English & European Renaissance drama
Warwick U MA

English & European Romanticism
Durham U MA☆

English (English literature & language before 1525)
London U UC MA

English (Medieval studies)
Belfast Queen's U MA

English language & literary studies
Nottingham U MA

English language & literature
Exeter U dip☆
Keele U dip☆

English language & Medieval literature
Durham U MA☆

English literary research
Lancaster U MA

English literary studies: Milton & his Age
London U Royal Holloway & Bedford New C MA

English literary studies: Renaissance to Restoration
Leeds U MA☆

English literature
Dundee U dip☆
East Anglia U MA
Edinburgh U MSc☆
Glasgow U MPhil
Leeds U MA☆
Sheffield U MA/dip☆
Warwick U MA/dip

English literature & language after 1525
London U King's C MA

English literature & language after 1525: the 17th century
Goldsmiths' C London U MA

English literature & language before 1525
London U King's C MA

English literature after 1525: 1660-1790
London U Queen Mary & Westfield C MA☆

English literature of the Romantic period
Manchester U MA△

English literature: the 17th century
Goldsmiths' C London U MA

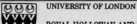

English Renaissance literature
Liverpool U MA☆
Sussex U MA

English Renaissance literature: Shakespeare or poetry
York U MA☆

English Renaissance: politics, patronage & literature
Reading U MA

English Romantic literature
York U MA☆

English studies
London U King's C dip☆
Strathclyde U dip

English studies (English literature, 1500-1660)
Oxford U MPhil☆

English studies (English Medieval studies from 1100 to 1500)
Oxford U MPhil☆

English studies (English Medieval studies until 1100)
Oxford U MPhil☆

English studies (English Romantic studies)
Oxford U MPhil☆

English studies (Shakespeare & the drama to 1640)
Oxford U MPhil☆

English studies (English literature, 1660-1800)
Oxford U MPhil☆

European literature (Medieval, Renaissance or modern literary studies)
Oxford U MPhil☆/MSt☆

European literature of the Middle Ages
Manchester U MA

Four Romantic writers
Cardiff U of Wales C MA☆

Language as a literary medium
Aberdeen U MLitt☆

Literature
Essex U dip☆
Open U MA△

Literature & oral culture
Sheffield U MA

Literature & the visual arts 1840-1940
Reading U MA

Literature of region and nation
Aberdeen U MLitt

Local history, literature & cultural tradition
Sheffield U MA☆

Medieval & Renaissance studies
St Andrews U MLitt/MPhil☆/dip☆

Medieval & Tudor studies
Kent U MA

Medieval British studies
Cardiff U of Wales C MA☆

Medieval English language & literature
Liverpool U MA☆

Medieval English language, literature & art
Keele U MA

Medieval English literature
Bristol U MA☆
Leeds U MA☆
Newcastle U MA/MPhil

Medieval studies
Leeds U MA
Reading U MA/MPhil
York U MA/dip☆

Middle English literature
Aberystwyth, UC of Wales MA

Modern literature (since 1850)
Kent U MA

Music & poetry of the Elizabethan Renaissance
Hull U dip☆

Northern Renaissance studies
Sussex U MA

Philosophy & literature
Warwick U MA

Philosophy of literature
Swansea UC MA☆

Renaissance drama (including Shakespeare)
Exeter U MA☆

Renaissance English literature
Sussex U MA

Renaissance European literature
Glasgow U MPhil

Renaissance literature & drama
Aberystwyth, UC of Wales MA

Scottish literature
Aberdeen U MLitt
St Andrews U MLitt/MPhil☆/dip☆

Shakespeare & the Shakespearian presence in English literature
Bristol U MA☆

Shakespeare studies
Birmingham U MA☆

St Andrews U MLitt☆/MPhil☆/dip☆

Shakespeare: language & power
Lancaster U MA☆

Sociology of literature
Essex U MA☆

Women in literature; feminist literary criticism
Aberystwyth, UC of Wales MA

Women writing
Essex U MA☆

Women's studies
Exeter U MA☆

The word & visual imagination
St David's UC MA   ☐

Writing off-centre
Aberdeen U MLitt☆

Higher degrees by research

19th & 20th century English literature
Bristol P PhD△/MPhil△

Anglo Saxon, Norse & Celtic
Cambridge U PhD☆/MLitt☆

Comparative European literature
Buckingham U DPhil/MA/MPhil

Comparative literary studies
Kent U PhD/MA/MPhil

Comparative literary theory & literary translation
Warwick U PhD☆/MPhil☆

Comparative literature
East Anglia U PhD☆/MPhil☆

Critical theory
Nottingham U PhD/MPhil

English
Aberdeen U PhD☆/MLitt☆/MPhil☆
Aberystwyth, UC of Wales PhD/MPhil
Belfast Queen's U PhD/MA
Bristol U PhD/MLitt
Cambridge U PhD☆/MLitt☆
Canterbury Christ Church C PhD/MPhil
Central London P PhD☆/MPhil☆
Dundee U PhD/MPhil
Exeter U PhD/MPhil
Lancaster U PhD/MPhil
Leeds U PhD/MA/MPhil
Leicester U PhD/MPhil
London U Birkbeck C PhD/MPhil

Goldsmiths' C London U PhD/MPhil

London U King's C PhD☆/MPhil☆

London U Queen Mary & Westfield C PhD☆/MPhil☆

London U Royal Holloway & Bedford New C PhD/MPhil

Reading U PhD/MPhil

St David's UC PhD☆/MA☆

Sheffield City P PhD/MPhil

Southampton U PhD/MPhil

Ulster U DPhil/MPhil

Warwick U PhD☆/MA☆/MPhil☆

English & American literature
East Anglia U PhD/MPhil
Kent U PhD/MA/MPhil

English & communication studies
Birmingham P PhD/MPhil
Sunderland P PhD/MPhil

English & history
Manchester P PhD/MPhil

English & related literature
York U DPhil/MPhil

English language & literature
Bangor, U of Wales PhD☆/MPhil☆
Birmingham U PhD/MLitt/MPhil
Hull U PhD/MPhil
Keele U PhD/MA
London U UC PhD☆/MPhil☆
Manchester U PhD/MPhil
Middlesex P PhD/MPhil
Oxford U DPhil☆/MLitt☆
St Andrews U PhD/MPhil
Swansea UC PhD/MPhil

English language & Medieval literature
Durham U PhD/MA/MLitt

English literary research
Lancaster U MA

English literature
Cardiff U of Wales C PhD☆/MPhil☆
Edinburgh U PhD/MLitt
Glasgow U PhD/MLitt
Hatfield P PhD/MPhil
Lancaster U PhD/MPhil
Liverpool U PhD/MPhil
Newcastle U PhD/MLitt
Sheffield U PhD/MPhil
Sussex U DPhil/MPhil

English literature & language
Cheltenham & Gloucester CHE PhD/MPhil

English studies
Durham U PhD/MA/MLitt
Nottingham U PhD/MPhil
Stirling U PhD/MLitt

Humanities
Huddersfield P PhD/MPhil
Leicester P PhD/MPhil
Liverpool P PhD/MPhil
Oxford P PhD/MPhil
Teesside P PhD☆/MPhil☆
Thames P PhD/MPhil

Literary & cultural studies
Keele U PhD/MA

Literature
Central London P PhD☆/MPhil☆
Essex U PhD/MPhil
Open U PhD/MPhil/BPhil

Literature & languages
Nottingham P PhD☆/MPhil☆

Medieval studies
Reading U PhD/MPhil

Modern & contemporary literature
Portsmouth P PhD☆/MPhil☆

Modern languages
Salford U PhD/MPhil

Northern Renaissance studies
Sussex U DPhil/MPhil

Shakespeare studies
Birmingham U PhD/MLitt/MPhil

English literature: Victorian to present day

Higher degrees by instruction

19th & 20th century English & United States literature
Essex U MA☆

19th century literary criticism & literary periodicals
Aberystwyth, UC of Wales MA

20th century English literature
Sussex U MA

20th century novel & 20th century poetry
Aberystwyth, UC of Wales MA

Anglo American literary relations
London U UC MA

Anglo German literary relations
Leeds U MA

Anglo Irish literature
Ulster U MA△/dip△

Children's literature
Reading U MA△

Comparative literary studies
St Andrews U MLitt/MPhil☆/dip☆

Comparative literary theory
Warwick U MA☆

Comparative literature
East Anglia U MA☆

Comparative literature in the medieval, Renaissance & modern periods
Aberystwyth, UC of Wales MA

Contemporary literary studies
Lancaster U MA☆

Critical theory
Nottingham U MA
Sussex U MA☆

English
Bangor, U of Wales MA☆/dip☆
Exeter U MA☆
Hull U MA☆
Manchester U MA☆

English & American literature of the 19th & 20th centuries
Hull U dip☆

English & American literature of the 20th century
Newcastle U MA/MPhil☆

English (Romanticism & Modernism)
Southampton U MA

English language & literary studies
Nottingham U MA

English language & literature
Exeter U dip☆
Keele U dip☆

English literary research
Lancaster U MA

English literary studies: classic modern writing in English
London U Royal Holloway & Bedford New C MA

English literature
Dundee U dip☆
East Anglia U MA
Edinburgh U MSc☆
Glasgow U MPhil
Leeds U MA☆
Sheffield U MA/dip☆
Warwick U MA/dip

English literature & language after 1525
London U King's C MA

English literature (20th century British fiction)
Keele U MA☆

English literature after 1525: 1880 to present day
London U Queen Mary & Westfield C MA☆

English literature in crisis 1890-1930
Hatfield P MA△/dip△

English studies
London U King's C dip☆
Strathclyde U dip

English studies (English literature, 1830-1900)
Oxford U MPhil☆

English studies (English literature, 1880-1980)
Oxford U MPhil☆

English studies (English Romantic studies)
Oxford U MPhil☆

English studies (English literature, 1880-1980)
Oxford U MPhil☆

European literature (Medieval, Renaissance or modern literary studies)
Oxford U MPhil☆/MSt☆

Ezra Pound & modern poetry
York U MA☆

Language as a literary medium
Aberdeen U MLitt☆

Literature
Essex U dip☆
Open U MA△

Literature & oral culture
Sheffield U MA

Literature & the visual arts 1840-1940
Reading U MA

Literature of region and nation
Aberdeen U MLitt

Literature of the Victorian period
Liverpool U MA

Local history, literature & cultural tradition
Sheffield U MA☆

Modern critical theory
Cardiff U of Wales C MA☆

Modern drama from the late 19th century
Exeter U MA☆

Modern English literature
London U Birkbeck C MA△
Nottingham U MA

Modern French & English literature
Swansea UC MA☆

Modern literary studies
Sunderland P MA△

Modern literature (since 1850)
Kent U MA

Modern literature: theory & practice
Leicester U MA

Philosophy & literature
Warwick U MA

Philosophy of literature
Swansea UC MA☆

Poetry in our time
Sheffield U MA

Scottish literature
Aberdeen U MLitt
St Andrews U MLitt/MPhil☆/dip☆

Sociology of literature
Essex U MA☆

Theatre studies
Leeds U MA☆

Theory & practice of modern fiction
Exeter U MA☆

Turn of the century: American & English fiction
York U MA☆

Victorian literature
Buckingham U MA
Leeds U MA☆
Nottingham U MA

Victorian novel
Aberystwyth, UC of Wales MA

Victorian studies
Keele U MLitt
Leicester U MA

Women & modern fiction
St Andrews U MLitt☆/MPhil☆/Dip☆

Women in literature; feminist literary criticism
Aberystwyth, UC of Wales MA

Women writing
Essex U MA☆

Women's studies
Exeter U MA☆

The word & visual imagination
St David's UC MA ☐

Writing off-centre
Aberdeen U MLitt☆

Higher degrees by research

19th & 20th century English literature
Bristol P PhD△/MPhil△

Comparative European literature
Buckingham U DPhil/MA/MPhil

Comparative literary studies
Kent U PhD/MA/MPhil
Manchester U PhD/MA

Comparative literary theory & literary translation
Warwick U PhD☆/MPhil☆

Comparative literature
East Anglia U PhD☆/MPhil☆

Critical theory
Nottingham U PhD/MPhil

English
Aberdeen U PhD☆/MLitt☆/MPhil☆
Aberystwyth, UC of Wales PhD/MPhil
Belfast Queen's U PhD/MA
Bristol U PhD/MLitt
Cambridge U PhD☆/MLitt☆
Canterbury Christ Church C PhD/MPhil
Central London P PhD☆/MPhil☆
Dundee U PhD/MPhil
Exeter U PhD/MPhil
Lancaster U PhD/MPhil
Leeds U PhD/MA/MPhil
Leicester U PhD/MPhil
London U Birkbeck C PhD/MPhil
Goldsmiths' C London U PhD/MPhil
London U King's C PhD☆/MPhil☆
London U Queen Mary & Westfield C PhD☆/MPhil☆
London U Royal Holloway & Bedford New C PhD/MPhil
Reading U PhD/MPhil
St David's UC PhD☆/MA☆
Sheffield City P PhD/MPhil
Southampton U PhD/MPhil
Ulster U DPhil/MPhil
Warwick U PhD☆/MA☆/MPhil☆

English & American literature
East Anglia U PhD/MPhil
Kent U PhD/MA/MPhil

English & communication studies
Birmingham P PhD/MPhil
Sunderland P PhD/MPhil

English & history
Manchester P PhD☆/MPhil

English & related literature
York U DPhil/MPhil

English language & literature
Bangor, U of Wales PhD☆/ MPhil☆
Birmingham U PhD/MLitt/MPhil
Hull U PhD/MPhil
Keele U PhD/MA
London U UC PhD☆/MPhil☆
Manchester U PhD/MPhil
Middlesex P PhD/MPhil
Oxford U DPhil☆/MLitt☆
St Andrews U PhD/MPhil
Swansea UC PhD/MPhil

English literary research
Lancaster U MA

English literature
Cardiff U of Wales C PhD☆/ MPhil☆
Edinburgh U PhD/MLitt
Glasgow U PhD/MLitt
Hatfield P PhD/MPhil
Lancaster U PhD/MPhil
Liverpool U PhD/MPhil
Newcastle U PhD/MLitt
Sheffield U PhD/MPhil
Sussex U DPhil/MPhil

English literature & language
Cheltenham & Gloucester CHE PhD/MPhil

English studies
Durham U PhD/MA/MLitt
Nottingham U PhD/MPhil
Stirling U PhD/MLitt

Historical & critical studies
Newcastle P PhD☆/MPhil☆

Humanities
Huddersfield P PhD/MPhil
Leicester P PhD/MPhil
Liverpool P PhD/MPhil
Oxford P PhD/MPhil
Teesside P PhD☆/MPhil☆
Thames P PhD/MPhil

Literary & cultural studies
Keele U PhD/MA

Literature
Central London P PhD☆/MPhil☆
Essex U PhD/MPhil
Open U PhD/MPhil/BPhil

Literature & languages
Nottingham P PhD☆/MPhil☆

Modern & contemporary literature
Portsmouth P PhD☆/MPhil☆

Modern languages
Salford U PhD/MPhil

Victorian literature
Buckingham U DPhil/MA/MPhil

Victorian studies
Keele U PhD/MLitt
Leicester U PhD/MPhil
St David's UC PhD☆/MA☆

French

Higher degrees by instruction

20th century French studies
Nottingham U MA

Advanced language studies
Salford U MA☆

Applied European studies
South Bank P MA△/dip△

Classical French theatre
Glasgow U MPhil☆

Comparative European literature
Buckingham U MA

Comparative literary studies
St Andrews U MLitt/MPhil☆/dip☆

Comparative literature
Sussex U MA

Contemporary European culture
Exeter U MA☆

Contemporary French fiction & drama
Swansea UC MA☆

Contemporary French language
Bristol U MA△

Contemporary French studies
Portsmouth P MA△/dip△

Contemporary French theatre studies
Glasgow U MPhil☆

Critical theory
Nottingham U MA

English (dialectology)
Belfast Queen's U MA

European languages & linguistics
East Anglia U MA☆

European literary & historical studies
London U King's C MA

European literature
East Anglia U MA☆

European literature (Medieval, Renaissance or modern literary studies)
Oxford U MPhil☆/MSt☆

European literature of the Middle Ages
Manchester U MA

European marketing & languages
Napier P dip☆

Franco-Italian Renaissance studies
Exeter U MA

French
Belfast Queen's U MA
Birmingham P IL△
Durham U MA
Hull U MA☆
London U Royal Holloway & Bedford New C MA
St Andrews U MLitt/MPhil☆/dip☆

French & Romance linguists
Aberystwyth, UC of Wales MA☆

French (Romance languages & literature)
Goldsmiths' C London U MA

French 19th & 20th century literature
Sheffield U MA

French autobiography
Liverpool U MA

French drama & theatre history
Bristol U MA☆

French fin de siecle world (literature, art & aesthetics)
Glasgow U MPhil

French language & French linguistics
Sheffield U MA

French language studies
Newcastle U MA△

French literature & thought, 1800 to the present day
Aberystwyth, UC of Wales MA☆

French studies
Hull U MA☆   □
Hull U dip☆
Liverpool U MA   □
Reading U MA
St Andrews U MLitt/MPhil☆/dip☆
Sussex U MA
Warwick U MA/MPhil

French theatre studies
Lancaster U MA

French/English translation through contrastive linguistics
Keele U MA

General & technical translation
London S of Translation Studies cert☆/dip☆ □

Interpreting & translating (French, German, Russian)
Bradford U MA☆/dip☆

Literature of 17th century France
Aberystwyth, UC of Wales MA☆

Literature of ideas from the Renaissance to the Revolution
St David's UC MA

Marketing & a foreign language
Salford U MSc△

Medieval & Renaissance studies
St Andrews U MLitt/MPhil☆/dip☆

Medieval French language & literature
Edinburgh U MSc☆

Medieval languages
Edinburgh U MSc☆

Modern French & English literature
Swansea UC MA☆

Modern French literature
Liverpool U MA
Stirling U MPhil△

Modern French studies
Leeds U MA
Loughborough U MA△

Modern languages
Bristol U MA
St Andrews U MLitt/MPhil☆/dip☆

Poetry & drama in 20th century France
Aberystwyth, UC of Wales MA☆

Politics & modern languages
Aberystwyth, UC of Wales dip☆

Renaissance European literature
Glasgow U MPhil

Romance languages & literature (French)
London U Queen Mary & Westfield C MA

Romance languages & literatures
London U Birkbeck C MA△
London U King's C MA☆
London U UC MA☆

Romance studies
Swansea UC MA

Sociology of literature
Essex U MA☆

Higher degrees by research

Applied linguistics & area studies
Manchester UMIST PhD/MSc

Comparative European literature
Buckingham U DPhil/MA/MPhil

Comparative literary studies
Kent U PhD/MA/MPhil
Manchester U PhD/MA

Comparative literature
East Anglia U PhD☆/MPhil☆
Sussex U DPhil/MPhil

Contemporary French & German studies
Aston U PhD/MPhil

Contemporary French theatre studies
Glasgow U PhD/MLitt

Critical theory
Nottingham U PhD/MPhil

European languages
Aberystwyth, UC of Wales PhD☆/MPhil☆
Swansea UC PhD☆/MA☆

European languages & linguistics
East Anglia U PhD☆/MPhil☆

European literature
East Anglia U PhD☆/MPhil☆

European studies
Loughborough U PhD☆/MPhil☆

European studies & modern languages
Ulster U DPhil/MPhil

French
Aberdeen U PhD☆/MLitt☆/MPhil☆
Belfast Queen's U PhD/MA
Bristol U PhD/MLitt
Cambridge U PhD☆/MLitt☆
Cardiff U of Wales C PhD☆/MPhil☆
Central London P PhD☆/MPhil☆
Durham U PhD/MA/MLitt
Edinburgh U PhD/MLitt
Exeter U PhD/MPhil
Hatfield P PhD/MPhil
Hull U PhD/MPhil

Keele U PhD/MA
Kent U PhD/MA/MPhil
Leicester U PhD/MPhil
Liverpool U PhD/MPhil
London U Birkbeck C PhD/MPhil
Goldsmiths' C London U PhD/MPhil
London U King's C PhD☆/MPhil☆
London U Queen Mary & Westfield C PhD☆/MPhil☆
London U Royal Holloway & Bedford New C PhD/MPhil
Nottingham U PhD☆/MPhil☆
St Andrews U PhD/MPhil
St David's UC PhD☆/MA☆
Sheffield U PhD/MPhil
Southampton U PhD/MPhil
Stirling U PhD/MLitt

French & Romance studies
Bangor, U of Wales PhD☆/MPhil☆

French language & literature
Birmingham U PhD/MLitt/MPhil
Glasgow U PhD/MLitt
Leeds U PhD/MA/MPhil
London U UC PhD☆/MPhil☆

French novels since 1940
Bristol P PhD△/MPhil△/dip△

French studies
Lancaster U PhD/MPhil
Manchester U PhD/MPhil
Newcastle U PhD/MLitt
Reading U PhD/MPhil
Sussex U DPhil/MPhil
Warwick U PhD/MA/MPhil

Humanities
Huddersfield P PhD/MPhil
Leicester P PhD/MPhil
Teesside P PhD☆/MPhil☆

Language
Napier P PhD/MPhil

Language studies
Canterbury Christ Church C PhD/MPhil
City of London P PhD☆/MPhil☆
Coventry P PhD/MPhil
London U LSE PhD/MPhil

Languages
Heriot-Watt U PhD☆/MPhil☆
Liverpool P PhD/MPhil
Manchester P PhD/MPhil

Languages & area studies
Portsmouth P PhD☆/MPhil☆
Sunderland P PhD/MPhil

Languages & European studies
Wolverhampton P PhD/MPhil

Literature & languages
Nottingham P PhD☆/MPhil☆

2 POSTGRADUATE OPPORTUNITIES

Medieval & modern languages
Cambridge U PhD☆/MLitt☆
Oxford U DPhil☆/MLitt☆

Modern languages
Aston U PhD/MPhil
Bath U PhD☆/MPhil☆
Bristol U PhD/MPhil
Dundee U PhD/MPhil
East Anglia U PhD☆/MPhil☆
Exeter U PhD/MPhil
Middlesex P PhD/MPhil
Newcastle P PhD☆/MPhil☆
Salford U PhD/MPhil
Sheffield City P PhD/MPhil
South Bank P PhD/MPhil
Southampton U PhD/MPhil
Strathclyde U PhD☆/MLitt☆

Office communication & languages
Lancashire P PhD/MPhil

Romance studies
Swansea UC PhD/MPhil

German

Higher degrees by instruction

20th century German drama
Bristol U MA

20th German literature & society
St Andrews U MLitt/MPhil☆/dip☆

Advanced language studies
Salford U MA☆

Anglo German literary relations
Leeds U MA

Applied European studies
South Bank P MA△/dip△

Comparative European literature
Buckingham U MA

Comparative literary studies
St Andrews U MLitt/MPhil☆/dip☆

Comparative literature
Sussex U MA

Contemporary European culture
Exeter U MA☆

Contemporary German studies
Ealing C London MA△/dip△
Strathclyde U MLitt△/dip△

Critical theory
Nottingham U MA

European languages & linguistics
East Anglia U MA☆

European literary & historical studies
London U King's C MA

European literature
East Anglia U MA☆

European literature (Medieval, Renaissance or modern literary studies)
Oxford U MPhil☆/MSt☆

European literature of the Middle Ages
Manchester U MA

European marketing & languages
Napier P dip☆

German
Birmingham P IL△
Cardiff U of Wales C MA☆
Durham U MA
Exeter U MA☆
London U Birkbeck C MA
Goldsmiths' C London U MA△
London U King's C MA
London U Queen Mary & Westfield C MA
London U Royal Holloway & Bedford New C MA
London U UC MA

German descriptive linguistics
St Andrews U MLitt/MPhil☆/dip☆

German language
St Andrews U MLitt/MPhil☆/dip☆

German language & linguistics
Newcastle U MA☆

German literature since the second world war
Newcastle U MA☆

German studies
Liverpool U MA☆
St Andrews U MLitt/MPhil☆/dip☆
Sussex U MA
Warwick U MA

Interpreting & translating (French, German, Russian)
Bradford U MA☆/dip☆

Marketing & a foreign language
Salford U MSc△

Medieval & Renaissance studies
St Andrews U MLitt/MPhil☆/dip☆

Medieval languages
Edinburgh U MSc☆

Modern German studies: literature of a divided Germany
Aberdeen U MLitt

Modern languages
Bristol U MA
St Andrews U MLitt/MPhil☆/dip☆

Politics & modern languages
Aberystwyth, UC of Wales dip☆

Politics, literature & culture in the German Democratic Republic
Reading U MA

Post war German studies
Loughborough U MA△

Proficiency in modern foreign languages
Newcastle U cert☆

Recent trends in German literature
Nottingham U MA

Renaissance European literature
Glasgow U MPhil

Sociology of literature
Essex U MA☆

Higher degrees by research

Comparative European literature
Buckingham U DPhil/MA/MPhil

Comparative literary studies
Kent U PhD/MA/MPhil

Comparative literature
East Anglia U PhD☆/MPhil☆
Sussex U DPhil/MPhil

Contemporary French & German studies
Aston U PhD/MPhil

Contemporary prose in East & West Germany
Bristol P PhD△/MPhil△/dip△

European languages
Aberystwyth, UC of Wales PhD☆/MPhil☆
Swansea UC PhD☆/MA☆

European languages & linguistics
East Anglia U PhD☆/MPhil☆

European literature
East Anglia U PhD☆/MPhil☆

European studies
Loughborough U PhD☆/MPhil☆

116

European studies & modern languages
Ulster U DPhil/MPhil

German
Aberdeen U PhD☆/MLitt☆/ MPhil☆
Bangor, U of Wales PhD☆/ MPhil☆
Belfast Queen's U PhD/MA
Bristol U PhD☆/MLitt☆
Cambridge U PhD☆/MLitt☆
Cardiff U of Wales C PhD☆/ MPhil☆
Central London P PhD☆/MPhil☆
Durham U PhD/MA/MLitt
Edinburgh U PhD/MLitt
Exeter U PhD/MPhil
Hatfield P PhD/MPhil
Hull U PhD/MPhil
Keele U PhD/MA
Kent U PhD/MA/MPhil
Leicester U PhD/MA/MPhil
Liverpool U PhD/MPhil
London U Birkbeck C PhD/MPhil
Goldsmiths' C London U PhD/ MPhil
London U King's C PhD☆/MPhil☆
London U Queen Mary & Westfield C PhD☆/MPhil☆
London U Royal Holloway & Bedford New C PhD/MPhil
London U UC PhD☆/MPhil☆
Nottingham U PhD/MPhil
Reading U PhD/MPhil
St Andrews U PhD/MPhil
St David's UC PhD☆/MA☆
Southampton U PhD/MPhil
Stirling U PhD/MLitt
Swansea UC PhD/MPhil

German & Scandinavian studies
Newcastle U PhD/MLitt

German cinema
Bristol P PhD△/MPhil△/dip△

German language & literature
Glasgow U PhD/MLitt
Leeds U PhD/MPhil
Manchester U PhD/MPhil

German studies
Birmingham U PhD/MLitt/MPhil
Lancaster U PhD/MPhil
Sussex U DPhil/MPhil
Warwick U PhD/MA/MPhil

German theatre & drama since 1889
Bristol P PhD△/MPhil△/dip△

Germanic studies
Sheffield U PhD/MPhil

Humanities
Huddersfield P PhD/MPhil

Leicester P PhD/MPhil

Language
Napier P PhD/MPhil

Language & humanities
Lancashire P PhD/MPhil

Language studies
Canterbury Christ Church C PhD/MPhil
City of London P PhD☆/MPhil☆
Coventry P PhD/MPhil
London U LSE PhD/MPhil

Languages
Heriot-Watt U PhD☆/MPhil☆
Liverpool P PhD/MPhil
Manchester P PhD/MPhil
Newcastle U PhD/MLitt

Languages & area studies
Portsmouth P PhD☆/MPhil☆
Sunderland P PhD/MPhil

Languages & European studies
Wolverhampton P PhD/MPhil

Literature & languages
Nottingham P PhD☆/MPhil☆

Medieval & modern languages
Cambridge U PhD☆/MLitt☆
Oxford U DPhil☆/MLitt☆

Modern languages
Aston U PhD/MPhil
Bath U PhD☆/MPhil☆
Bristol U PhD/MPhil
Dundee U PhD/MPhil
East Anglia U PhD☆/MPhil☆
Exeter U PhD/MPhil
Middlesex P PhD/MPhil
Newcastle P PhD☆/MPhil☆
Salford U PhD/MPhil
Sheffield City P PhD/MPhil
South Bank P PhD/MPhil
Southampton U PhD/MPhil
Strathclyde U PhD☆/MLitt☆

Office communication & languages
Lancashire P PhD/MPhil

Interpreting, translating

Higher degrees by instruction

Advanced language studies
Salford U MA☆

Arabic for communicative purposes
Heriot-Watt U dip☆

Arabic-English translation & interpreting
Heriot-Watt U MSc☆/dip☆

Arabic-English/English-Arabic translation studies
Central London P dip☆

Bilingual executive assistant: French/German/Italian/Spanish
Lancashire P dip☆　　　　Bus

Comparative literary theory
Warwick U MA☆

Conference interpretation techniques
Central London P dip☆

French/English translation through contrastive linguistics
Keele U MA☆

General & technical translation
London S of Translation Studies cert☆/dip☆　　□

General interpreting
London S of Translation Studies dip☆

International studies
Salford U MA☆/cert☆

Interpretation (English/Arabic/ English)
Salford U MA☆/dip☆

Interpreting & translating (French, German, Russian)
Bradford U MA☆/dip☆

Language studies (interpreting & translating)
Bath U dip☆

Linguistics, special applications
Birmingham U MA

Proficiency in modern foreign languages
Newcastle U cert☆

Technical & specialised translation
Central London P dip☆

Theory & practice of literary translation
Essex U MA☆

Translation
Salford U MA☆/dip☆

Translation & interpreting
Salford U MA☆/dip☆

Translation & linguistics (Arabic/ English)
Bath U MA☆/dip☆

Translation (English/Arabic/ English)
Salford U MA☆/cert☆/dip☆

Translation (French, German, Norwegian or Swedish)
Surrey U MA☆/dip☆

Translation studies
Warwick U MA☆

Vocational techniques for career linguists
Kent U MA/dip

Higher degrees by research

Comparative literary studies
Kent U PhD/MA/MPhil

European languages
Swansea UC PhD☆/MA☆

Language studies
City of London P PhD☆/MPhil☆
Coventry P PhD/MPhil

Languages
Heriot-Watt U PhD☆/MPhil☆

Modern languages
Salford U PhD/MPhil

Translation theory
Central London P PhD☆/MPhil☆

Italian

Higher degrees by instruction

Applied European studies
South Bank P MA△/dip△

Comparative European literature
Buckingham U MA

Contemporary European culture
Exeter U MA☆

European languages & linguistics
East Anglia U MA☆

European literary & historical studies
London U King's C MA

European literature
East Anglia U MA☆

European literature (Medieval, Renaissance or modern literary studies)
Oxford U MPhil☆/MSt☆

European literature of the Middle Ages
Manchester U MA

Franco-Italian Renaissance studies
Exeter U MA

French & Romance linguists
Aberystwyth, UC of Wales MA☆

General & technical translation
London S of Translation Studies
cert☆/dip☆   ▢

Italian
Exeter U MA☆
Hull U MA☆

Italian studies
Reading U MA

Modern languages
Bristol U MA

Politics & modern languages
Aberystwyth, UC of Wales dip☆

Renaissance European literature
Glasgow U MPhil

Romance languages & literatures
London U Birkbeck C MA△
London U UC MA☆

Romance studies
Swansea UC MA

Sociology of literature
Essex U MA☆

Spanish & Italian
Durham U MA

Higher degrees by research

Comparative European literature
Buckingham U DPhil/MA/MPhil

Comparative literary studies
Kent U PhD/MA/MPhil
Manchester U PhD/MA

European languages
Aberystwyth, UC of Wales
PhD☆/MPhil☆
Swansea UC PhD☆/MA☆

European languages & linguistics
East Anglia U PhD☆/MPhil☆

European literature
East Anglia U PhD☆/MPhil☆

Italian
Belfast Queen's U PhD/MA
Bristol U PhD/MLitt
Cambridge U PhD☆/MLitt☆
Cardiff U of Wales C PhD☆/ MPhil☆
Central London P PhD☆/MPhil☆
Durham U PhD/MA/MLitt
Edinburgh U PhD/MLitt
Exeter U PhD/MPhil
Glasgow U PhD/MLitt
Hull U PhD/MPhil
Kent U PhD/MA/MPhil
Leicester U PhD/MPhil
London U Royal Holloway & Bedford New C PhD/MPhil
London U UC PhD☆/MPhil☆
Warwick U PhD☆/MA☆/MPhil☆

Italian language & literature
Birmingham U PhD/MLitt/MPhil
Leeds U PhD/MPhil

Italian studies
Lancaster U PhD/MPhil
Manchester U PhD/MPhil
Reading U PhD/MPhil

Language studies
Canterbury Christ Church C
PhD/MPhil

Medieval & modern languages
Cambridge U PhD☆/MLitt☆
Oxford U DPhil☆/MLitt☆

Modern languages
Bath U PhD☆/MPhil☆
Bristol U PhD/MPhil
East Anglia U PhD☆/MPhil☆
Exeter U PhD/MPhil
Salford U PhD/MPhil
Sheffield City P PhD/MPhil
South Bank P PhD/MPhil
Southampton U PhD/MPhil
Strathclyde U PhD☆/MLitt☆

Office communication & languages
Lancashire P PhD/MPhil

Romance languages & literatures
London U Queen Mary & Westfield C PhD☆/MPhil☆

Romance studies
Swansea UC PhD/MPhil

Linguistics, philology, phonetics

Higher degrees by instruction

Advanced language studies
Salford U MA☆

Applied linguistics
Bangor, U of Wales MA☆/dip☆
Birmingham U MA/BLitt/dip
Edinburgh U MLitt☆/MSc☆/Dip☆
Essex U MA☆
Exeter U MA/dip
Kent U MA
Reading U MA/MPhil☆
Salford U MA☆/dip☆
Sheffield U MA

Applied linguistics with special reference to English language teaching
Durham U MA☆

Aspects of Biblical interpretation
London Bible C MA

Clinical communication studies
City U dip☆

Cognitive science
Manchester U MSc☆   *Comp*

Cognitive science & natural language
Edinburgh U MSc☆/dip☆

Comparative European literature
Buckingham U MA

Comparative literary studies
St Andrews U MLitt/MPhil☆/dip☆

Comparative literary theory
Warwick U MA☆

Comparative literature
East Anglia U MA☆
Edinburgh U MSc☆
Sussex U MA

Critical theory
Nottingham U MA

Descriptive & applied linguistics
Essex U MA☆

English as a second or foreign language
Bangor, U of Wales MA☆/dip☆

English language & stylistics
London U Royal Holloway & Bedford New C MA

European languages & linguistics
East Anglia U MA☆

French & Romance linguists
Aberystwyth, UC of Wales MA☆

French language & French linguistics
Sheffield U MA

French language studies
Newcastle U MA△

French studies
Reading U MA

French/English translation through contrastive linguistics
Keele U MA☆

General linguistics
Edinburgh U MLitt☆/MSc☆/dip☆
Manchester U MA☆/dip☆

General linguistics & comparative philology
Oxford U MPhil☆/MSt☆

German descriptive linguistics
St Andrews U MLitt/MPhil☆/dip☆

German language & linguistics
Newcastle U MA☆

Human communication
City U MSc

Language & linguistics
Essex U dip☆

Language studies
Lancaster U MA

Languages & linguistics of Spain
Liverpool U MA☆

Linguistic studies
Essex U cert☆

Linguistics
Cambridge U MPhil☆
Central London P MA△/dip△
East Anglia U MA
Essex U MA☆
Exeter U MA☆/dip☆
Leeds U MA☆/dip☆
London U SOAS MA/dip
London U UC MA/MPhil/dip
Manchester U MA/MLing
Portsmouth P MA☆
Reading U MA/MPhil☆
Sussex U MA☆
York U MA☆

Linguistics & English language teaching
Leeds U MA☆
York U MA☆

Linguistics & foreign language teaching
Leeds U MA☆

Linguistics & information processing
Leeds U MA☆

Linguistics & modern English language
Nottingham U MA/cert/dip

Linguistics & phonetics
Essex U MA☆

Linguistics (TESOL)
Surrey U MA☆/dip☆

Linguistics (with special reference to its applications)
Hatfield P MA△/dip△

Linguistics for English language teaching
Lancaster U MA

Linguistics for the teaching of English language & literature
Strathclyde U MLitt☆/cert☆/dip☆

Linguistics of 2 modern languages
St Andrews U MPhil/dip

Linguistics, special applications
Birmingham U MA

Machine translation
Manchester UMIST MSc☆

Medieval languages
Edinburgh U MSc☆

Modern English language
London U UC MA☆

Modern English language & linguistics
Sheffield U MA

Oral tradition & ethnology
Edinburgh U MLitt☆

Philosophy of language & logic
Birmingham U MA

Phonetics
Edinburgh U MLitt☆/MSc☆/dip☆
Leeds U dip☆
London U SOAS MA/dip
London U UC MA/MPhil/dip

Phonetics of English
Leeds U dip☆

Proficiency in modern foreign languages
Newcastle U cert☆

Slavonic studies
Sheffield U MA

Theoretical linguistics
Bangor, U of Wales MA☆/dip☆
Essex U MA☆

Translation & linguistics (Arabic/ English)
Bath U MA☆/dip☆

Vocational techniques for career linguists
Kent U MA/dip

Higher degrees by research

Applied language studies
Swansea UC PhD/MPhil

Applied linguistics
East Anglia U PhD/MPhil
London U Birkbeck C PhD/MPhil
Reading U PhD

Applied linguistics & area studies
Manchester UMIST PhD/MSc

Behavioural & communication studies
Wales P PhD/MPhil

Clinical communication studies
City U PhD/MPhil

Communication studies
Sheffield City P PhD/MPhil
Ulster U DPhil/MPhil
York U DPhil/MPhil

Comparative European literature
Buckingham U DPhil/MA/MPhil

Comparative literary studies
Kent U PhD/MA/MPhil

Comparative literary theory & literary translation
Warwick U PhD☆/MPhil☆

Comparative literature
East Anglia U PhD☆/MPhil☆
Sussex U DPhil/MPhil

Comparative philology
London U UC PhD☆/MPhil☆

Computational linguistics
Manchester UMIST PhD/MSc

Critical theory
Nottingham U PhD/MPhil

Discourse in context
Aston U PhD/MPhil

English & communication studies
Birmingham P PhD/MPhil

English studies
Strathclyde U PhD/MLitt

European languages & linguistics
East Anglia U PhD☆/MPhil☆

European studies
Loughborough U PhD☆/MPhil☆

European studies & modern languages
Ulster U DPhil/MPhil

Human communication
London U UC PhD☆/MPhil☆

Language & linguistic science
York U DPhil/MPhil

Language & linguistics
Central London P PhD☆/MPhil☆
Essex U PhD/MPhil

Language (teaching & learning)
Southampton U PhD/MPhil

Language studies
City of London P PhD☆/MPhil☆
Coventry P PhD/MPhil
London U LSE PhD/MPhil

Languages
Heriot-Watt U PhD☆/MPhil☆
Newcastle U PhD/MLitt

Languages & linguistics
Brunel U PhD/MPhil
Kent U PhD/MPhil

Linguistic science
Reading U PhD/MPhil

Linguistics
Bradford U PhD/MPhil
Cambridge U PhD☆/MLitt☆
East Anglia U PhD/MPhil
Edinburgh U PhD/MLitt
Exeter U PhD/MPhil
Hatfield P PhD/MPhil
Manchester U PhD/MLing/BLing
Nottingham U PhD/MPhil
Southampton U PhD/MPhil
Sussex U DPhil/MPhil

Linguistics & international studies
Surrey U PhD/MPhil

Linguistics & modern English language
Lancaster U PhD/MPhil

Linguistics & phonetics
Leeds U PhD/MA/MPhil

Medieval & modern languages
Cambridge U PhD☆/MLitt☆
Oxford U DPhil☆/MLitt☆

Modern languages
Aston U PhD/MPhil
Bath U PhD☆/MPhil☆
East Anglia U PhD☆/MPhil☆
Exeter U PhD/MPhil
Salford U PhD/MPhil
Sheffield City P PhD/MPhil

Modern languages & linguistics
Bangor, U of Wales PhD☆/ MPhil☆

Philology & linguistics
Oxford U DPhil☆/MLitt☆

Phonetics & linguistics
London U SOAS PhD/MPhil
London U UC PhD☆/MPhil☆

Semantics & lexicology (especially with reference to Spanish)
Bristol P PhD△/MPhil△/dip△

Speech
Newcastle U PhD/MPhil

Speech pathology
Leicester P PhD/MPhil

Speech science
London U UC PhD☆/MPhil☆

Theoretical & applied linguistics
Central London P PhD☆/MPhil☆

Russian and East European

Higher degrees by instruction

Comparative European literature
Buckingham U MA

Comparative literary studies
St Andrews U MLitt/MPhil☆/dip☆

Comparative literature
Sussex U MA

Contemporary European culture
Exeter U MA☆

Critical theory
Nottingham U MA

Czech & Slovak language & literature
London U SSEES MA

European languages & linguistics
East Anglia U MA☆

European literary & historical studies
London U King's C MA

European literature
East Anglia U MA☆

Interpreting & translating (French, German, Russian)
Bradford U MA☆/dip☆

Medieval languages
Edinburgh U MSc☆

Modern languages
Bristol U MA

Politics & government of Russia
London U LSE MSc

Romance languages & literatures (Romanian)
London U SSEES MA

Russian
Durham U MA
Exeter U MA☆
Surrey U dip☆

Russian & Czech studies
Bristol U MA☆

Russian & East European studies
Birmingham U MA☆
Oxford U MPhil☆
Swansea UC MA☆/MSc(Econ)☆

Russian language
Strathclyde U dip☆

Russian language & literature
Birmingham U MA☆
London U SSEES MA
St Andrews U MLitt/MPhil☆/dip☆

Russian language for social scientists
Glasgow U dip

Russian or Slavonic studies
Edinburgh U MLitt☆

Russian studies
Bristol U MA☆
Manchester U MA☆
Sheffield U MA   □
Sussex U MA

Slavonic languages
Glasgow U MPhil

Slavonic studies
Oxford U dip☆
Sheffield U MA

Sociology of literature
Essex U MA☆

Soviet & East European studies
Glasgow U MPhil/dip

Soviet studies
Glasgow U MPhil/dip   Soc

Higher degrees by research

Comparative European literature
Buckingham U DPhil/MA/MPhil

Comparative literature
Sussex U DPhil/MPhil

East European languages & literatures
London U SSEES PhD/MPhil

European languages & linguistics
East Anglia U PhD☆/MPhil☆

European literature
East Anglia U PhD☆/MPhil☆

Language studies
London U LSE PhD/MPhil

Languages
Liverpool P PhD/MPhil
Newcastle U PhD/MLitt

Languages & area studies
Portsmouth P PhD☆/MPhil☆

Languages & European studies
Wolverhampton P PhD/MPhil

Medieval & modern languages
Cambridge U PhD☆/MLitt☆
Oxford U DPhil☆/MLitt☆

Modern languages
Bath U PhD☆/MPhil☆
Bristol U PhD/MPhil
East Anglia U PhD☆/MPhil☆
Exeter U PhD/MPhil
Newcastle P PhD☆/MPhil☆
Sheffield City P PhD/MPhil
Strathclyde U PhD☆/MLitt☆

Russian
Bangor, U of Wales PhD☆/MPhil☆
Bristol U PhD/MLitt
Durham U PhD/MA/MLitt
Edinburgh U PhD/MLitt
Exeter U PhD/MPhil
Glasgow U PhD/MLitt
Liverpool U PhD/MPhil
London U Queen Mary & Westfield C PhD☆/MPhil☆
St Andrews U PhD/MPhil

Russian & East European studies
Birmingham U PhD/MLitt/MPhil
Swansea UC PhD/MPhil

Russian & Slavonic studies
Sheffield U PhD/MPhil

Russian language & literature
Birmingham U PhD/MLitt/MPhil
London U SSEES PhD/MPhil

Russian studies
Keele U PhD/MA
Leeds U PhD/MA/MPhil
Manchester U PhD/MA/MPhil
Sussex U DPhil/MPhil

Slavonic & East European studies
Oxford U DPhil☆/MLitt☆

Slavonic languages (Czech, Polish)
Glasgow U PhD/MLitt

Slavonic studies
Belfast Queen's U PhD/MA
Cambridge U PhD☆/MLitt☆
Glasgow U PhD/MLitt
Nottingham U PhD/MPhil

Soviet & East European studies
Glasgow U PhD/MLitt   Soc

Spanish

Higher degrees by instruction

Advanced language studies
Salford U MA☆

Applied European studies
South Bank P MA△/dip△

Area studies (Latin American & the USA)
London U King's C MA

Comparative European literature
Buckingham U MA

Comparative literary studies
St Andrews U MLitt/MPhil☆/dip☆

Contemporary European culture
Exeter U MA☆

Critical theory
Nottingham U MA

English & Hispanic studies
Glasgow U MPhil

European literary & historical studies
London U King's C MA

European literature
East Anglia U MA☆

European literature (Medieval, Renaissance or modern literary studies)
Oxford U MPhil☆/MSt☆

European marketing & languages
Napier P dip☆

French & Romance linguists
Aberystwyth, UC of Wales MA☆

General & technical translation
London S of Translation Studies
cert☆/dip☆ □

Hispanic studies
Liverpool U MA☆
London U Birkbeck C MA△
London U King's C MA
London U Queen Mary &
Westfield C MA☆
London U UC MA☆

Languages & linguistics of Spain
Liverpool U MA☆

Latin American studies
Cambridge U MPhil☆
Glasgow U MPhil/dip☆
London U Inst of Latin American
Studies MA Soc

Marketing & a foreign language
Salford U MSc△

Medieval languages
Edinburgh U MSc☆

Modern languages
Bristol U MA
St Andrews U MLitt/MPhil☆/dip☆

Politics & modern languages
Aberystwyth, UC of Wales dip☆

Proficiency in modern foreign languages
Newcastle U cert☆

Romance languages & literature (Spanish)
London U Queen Mary &
Westfield C MA

Romance languages & literatures
London U Birkbeck C MA△
London U King's C MA☆
London U UC MA☆

Romance studies
Swansea UC MA

Sociology of literature
Essex U MA☆

Spanish
Birmingham P IL△
Exeter U MA☆
Leeds U MA
St Andrews U MLitt/MPhil☆/dip☆
Sheffield U MA

Spanish & Italian
Durham U MA

Spanish & Portuguese literature
Liverpool U MA

Spanish American literature
Aberystwyth, UC of Wales MA☆

Spanish literature
Liverpool U MA

Spanish literature & film since 1939
Newcastle U MA☆

Spanish poetry of the 19th & 20th centuries
Aberystwyth, UC of Wales MA☆

Spanish theatre & cinema studies
Aberystwyth, UC of Wales MA☆

Higher degrees by research

Applied linguistics & area studies
Manchester UMIST PhD/MSc

Comparative European literature
Buckingham U DPhil/MA/MPhil

European languages
Aberystwyth, UC of Wales
PhD☆/MPhil☆
Swansea UC PhD☆/MA☆

European literature
East Anglia U PhD☆/MPhil☆

European studies & modern languages
Ulster U DPhil/MPhil

Hispanic & Latin American studies
Bristol U PhD/MLitt

Hispanic studies
Belfast Queen's U PhD/MA
Birmingham U PhD/MLitt/MPhil
Cardiff U of Wales C PhD☆/
MPhil☆
Edinburgh U PhD/MLitt
Hull U PhD/MPhil
Nottingham U PhD/MPhil
Sheffield U PhD/MPhil

Hispanic studies (Spanish, Portuguese)
Glasgow U PhD/MLitt

Hispanic studies (Spanish, Portuguese, Catalan)
Liverpool U PhD/MPhil

Iberian studies
Keele U PhD/MA

Language
Napier P PhD/MPhil

Language studies
Canterbury Christ Church C
PhD/MPhil
Coventry P PhD/MPhil
London U LSE PhD/MPhil

Languages
Heriot-Watt U PhD☆/MPhil☆
Liverpool P PhD/MPhil
Manchester P PhD/MPhil

Languages & area studies
Portsmouth P PhD☆/MPhil☆

Languages & European studies
Wolverhampton P PhD/MPhil

Latin American studies
Cambridge U PhD☆ Arts
Glasgow U PhD/MLitt
London U Inst of Latin American
Studies PhD/MPhil

Medieval & modern languages
Cambridge U PhD☆/MLitt☆
Oxford U DPhil☆/MLitt☆

Modern languages
Bath U PhD☆/MPhil☆
Bristol U PhD/MPhil
Exeter U PhD/MPhil
Middlesex P PhD/MPhil
Newcastle P PhD☆/MPhil☆
Salford U PhD/MPhil
Sheffield City P PhD/MPhil
South Bank P PhD/MPhil
Southampton U PhD/MPhil
Strathclyde U PhD☆/MLitt☆

Office communication & languages
Lancashire P PhD/MPhil

Romance languages & literatures
London U Queen Mary &
Westfield C PhD☆/MPhil☆

Romance studies
Swansea UC PhD/MPhil

Semantics & lexicology (especially with reference to Spanish)
Bristol P PhD△/MPhil△/dip△

Spanish
Aberdeen U PhD☆/MLitt☆/
MPhil☆
Cambridge U PhD☆/MLitt☆
Central London P PhD☆/MPhil☆
Durham U PhD/MA/MLitt
Edinburgh U PhD/MLitt
Exeter U PhD/MPhil
Hatfield P PhD/MPhil
London U Birkbeck C PhD/MPhil
London U Queen Mary &
Westfield C PhD☆/MPhil☆
St Andrews U PhD/MPhil
Stirling U PhD/MLitt

Spanish & Latin American studies
London U UC PhD☆/MPhil☆
Newcastle U PhD/MLitt

Spanish & Portuguese languages & literature
Leeds U PhD/MPhil

Spanish & Portuguese studies
Manchester U PhD/MPhil

Spanish & Spanish American studies
London U King's C PhD☆/MPhil☆

Spanish politics & literature since 1936
Bristol P PhD△/MPhil△/dip△

Spanish, Portuguese & Latin American studies
Southampton U PhD/MPhil

Languages and literature: other European

Higher degrees by instruction

Anglo-Welsh literature, & other literatures written in English
Aberystwyth, UC of Wales MA

Applied European studies
South Bank P MA△/dip△

Arthurian literature
Bangor, U of Wales MA☆

Breton
St David's UC MA☆

Breton & Cornish
Aberystwyth, UC of Wales MA☆

Byzantine & modern Greek studies
London U King's C MA

Celtic studies
Aberystwyth, UC of Wales MA☆
Edinburgh U MLitt☆
Oxford U dip☆

Comparative European literature
Buckingham U MA

Comparative literary studies
St Andrews U MLitt/MPhil☆/dip☆

Dutch
London U UC MA

Dutch studies
Liverpool U MA☆

English & European Romanticism
Durham U MA☆

European & modern Dutch studies
Hull U MA☆/MPhil☆

European language & literature
London U Queen Mary & Westfield C MA ☐

European languages & linguistics
East Anglia U MA☆

European literary & historical studies
London U King's C MA

European literature
East Anglia U MA☆

European literature (Medieval, Renaissance or modern literary studies)
Oxford U MPhil☆/MSt☆

Greek
Durham U MA☆
St Andrews U MLitt/MPhil☆/dip☆

Greek & Latin
St Andrews U MLitt/MPhil☆/dip☆

Hispanic studies
London U King's C MA
London U UC MA☆

History & culture of the Dutch Golden Age
London U UC MA☆

Icelandic studies
Leeds U dip☆

Irish
Aberystwyth, UC of Wales MA

Medieval & Renaissance literature
Cambridge U MPhil☆

Medieval languages
Edinburgh U MSc☆

Modern French literature
Liverpool U MA
Stirling U MPhil△

Modern French studies
Ulster U MA△/dip△

Modern Welsh writing in English
Swansea UC MA☆

New Testament language, literature & theology
Edinburgh U MTh

Northern Renaissance studies
Sussex U MA

Ottoman studies
Birmingham U MA☆

Poetry in our time
Sheffield U MA

Politics & modern languages
Aberystwyth, UC of Wales dip☆

Politics, literature & culture in the German Democratic Republic
Reading U MA

Portuguese
London U King's C MA☆

Post war German studies
Loughborough U MA△

Proficiency in modern foreign languages
Newcastle U cert☆

Renaissance drama (including Shakespeare)
Exeter U MA☆

Renaissance European literature
Glasgow U MPhil

Romance languages & literatures
London U King's C MA☆

Scandinavian studies (Medieval & West Norse studies)
London U UC MA

Scandinavian studies (modern)
London U UC MA

Scottish literature
St Andrews U MLitt/MPhil☆/dip☆

Scottish studies
St Andrews U MLitt/dip☆

Spanish & Portuguese literature
Liverpool U MA

Viennese popular theatre
St Andrews U MLitt/MPhil☆/dip☆

Viking studies
Nottingham U MA☆

Welsh
Bangor, U of Wales MA☆/dip☆
Swansea UC MA☆

Welsh language & literature
Aberystwyth, UC of Wales MA☆

Welsh linguistic studies
Cardiff U of Wales C MA/dip

Western European social studies
Exeter U MA

Western European studies
Hull U dip☆

Women's studies & languages
Lancaster U MA

Higher degrees by research

Anglo Saxon, Norse & Celtic
Cambridge U PhD☆/MLitt☆

Applied language studies
Swansea UC PhD/MPhil

Applied linguistics & area studies
Manchester UMIST PhD/MSc

Area studies & languages
North London P PhD/MPhil

Breton & Cornish
Aberystwyth, UC of Wales
PhD☆/MPhil☆

Business studies & languages
East London P PhD/MPhil

Byzantine & modern Greek studies
London U King's C PhD☆/MPhil☆

Celtic
Aberdeen U PhD☆/MLitt☆/
MPhil☆
Belfast Queen's U PhD/MA
Glasgow U PhD/MPhil

Celtic studies
Aberystwyth, UC of Wales
PhD☆/MPhil☆
Edinburgh U PhD/MLitt
Manchester U PhD/MA/MPhil

Comparative European literature
Buckingham U DPhil/MA/MPhil

Comparative literature
East Anglia U PhD☆/MPhil☆

Dutch
Cambridge U PhD☆/MLitt☆
Liverpool U PhD/MPhil
London U UC PhD☆/MPhil☆

European languages
Aberystwyth, UC of Wales
PhD☆/MPhil☆

European languages & linguistics
East Anglia U PhD☆/MPhil☆

European literature
East Anglia U PhD☆/MPhil☆
Middlesex P PhD/MPhil

European studies
Bradford U PhD/MPhil
Central London P PhD☆/MPhil☆

European studies & modern languages
Ulster U DPhil/MPhil

French novels since 1940
Bristol P PhD△/MPhil△/dip△

German & Scandinavian studies
Newcastle U PhD/MLitt

Germanic studies
Sheffield U PhD/MPhil

Greek
Edinburgh U PhD/MLitt

Hellenic, Roman & Byzantine studies
Birmingham U PhD/MLitt/MPhil

Hispanic studies
Belfast Queen's U PhD/MA
Hull U PhD/MPhil
Nottingham U PhD/MPhil

Irish
Aberystwyth, UC of Wales
PhD☆/MA☆

Language studies
Canterbury Christ Church C
PhD/MPhil

Languages & European studies
Wolverhampton P PhD/MPhil

Literature
Essex U PhD/MPhil

Medieval & modern languages
Cambridge U PhD☆/MLitt☆
Oxford U DPhil☆/MLitt☆

Modern Dutch studies
Hull U PhD/MPhil

Modern graphics
Cambridge U PhD☆/MLitt☆

Modern Greek
Cambridge U PhD/MLitt

Modern languages
Bradford U PhD/MPhil
East Anglia U PhD☆/MPhil☆
St David's UC PhD☆/MA☆
Sheffield City P PhD/MPhil

Northern Renaissance studies
Sussex U DPhil/MPhil

Occitan
Cambridge U PhD☆

Portuguese
Bristol U PhD/MLitt
Cambridge U PhD☆/MLitt☆
London U King's C PhD☆/MPhil☆

Romance languages & literatures
London U Queen Mary &
Westfield C PhD☆/MPhil☆

Scandinavian
Edinburgh U PhD/MLitt

Scandinavian studies
Cambridge U PhD☆/MLitt☆
Hull U PhD/MPhil

London U UC PhD☆/MPhil☆

Scottish literature
Glasgow U PhD/MPhil

Scottish studies
Edinburgh U PhD/MLitt

Spanish & Portuguese languages & literature
Leeds U PhD/MPhil

Swedish
St David's UC PhD☆/MA☆

Welsh
St David's UC PhD☆/MA☆
Swansea UC PhD/MPhil

Welsh language & literature
Aberystwyth, UC of Wales
PhD☆/MPhil☆
Bangor, U of Wales PhD☆/
MPhil☆

Yugoslav studies
Bradford U PhD☆/MPhil☆

Languages and literature: other non European

Higher degrees by instruction

19th & 20th century English & United States literature
Essex U MA☆

African & Caribbean literature in English
Birmingham U MA△

African language (Hausa)
London U SOAS MA

African language (Swahili)
London U SOAS MA

African studies
Edinburgh U MSc☆/dip☆

American literature
Keele U MA
Leeds U MA☆

American literature since 1945
Aberystwyth, UC of Wales MA☆

American literature, film or culture
Exeter U MA☆

American poetry
Essex U MA☆

American studies
Manchester U MA
Nottingham U MA

Amerindian studies
St Andrews U MLitt☆/MPhil☆/
Dip☆

Anglo American literary relations
London U UC MA

Anglo American studies
Sussex U MA

Anglo-Welsh literature, & other literatures written in English
Aberystwyth, UC of Wales MA

Arabic
Durham U dip☆

Area studies (Afro American & Afro Caribbean)
London U SOAS MA

Area studies (the Commonwealth)
London U Inst of Commonwealth
Studies MA☆   Soc

Chinese
Durham U dip☆

Chinese studies
Oxford U MSt☆

Classical civilisation
London U Birkbeck C MA△

Commonwealth literature
Leeds U MA☆

Critical theory
Nottingham U MA

East Asian studies
Durham U MA☆

English & American literature of the 20th century
Newcastle U MA/MPhil☆

Hindi
London U SOAS MA

Hispanic studies
London U King's C MA

Icelandic studies
Leeds U MA☆

Islamic studies
Birmingham U dip☆

Japanese language
Sheffield U dip

Japanese studies
Sheffield U MA

Latin American literature
Essex U MA☆

Latin American studies
Liverpool U MA/dip
Newcastle U MA☆/MPhil☆
Oxford U MPhil☆

Literature of region and nation
Aberdeen U MLitt

Medieval languages
Edinburgh U MSc☆

Modern Chinese
Ealing C London dip☆

Modern literature (since 1850)
Kent U MA

Modern literature: theory & practice
Leicester U MA

Modern Middle Eastern studies
Durham U MA☆

Native American studies
Essex U MA☆

Old & Middle Iranian
London U SOAS MA

Oriental studies
Cambridge U MPhil☆

Oriental studies (Indian studies)
Oxford U MPhil☆/MSt☆

Persian studies
Edinburgh U MLitt☆

Poetry in our time
Sheffield U MA

Politics & modern languages
Aberystwyth, UC of Wales dip☆

Quechua studies
St Andrews U dip☆

Sanskrit
London U SOAS MA

Sociology of literature
Essex U MA☆

South East Asian studies
Kent U MA/dip

Southern African studies
York U MA☆

Spanish American literature
Aberystwyth, UC of Wales MA☆

Turn of the century: American & English fiction
York U MA☆

Urdu
London U SOAS MA

Women's studies & languages
Lancaster U MA

Higher degrees by research

Africa
London U SOAS PhD/MPhil

African studies
Sussex U DPhil/MPhil

American studies
Aberystwyth, UC of Wales
PhD☆/MPhil☆
East Anglia U PhD/MPhil
Hull U PhD/MPhil
Keele U PhD/MA
Manchester U PhD/MPhil
Nottingham U PhD/MPhil
Sussex U DPhil/MPhil

Amerindian studies
St Andrews U PhD☆/MPhil☆

Applied language studies
Swansea UC PhD/MPhil

Applied linguistics & area studies
Manchester UMIST PhD/MSc

Arabic
Central London P PhD☆/MPhil☆

Arabic & Islamic studies
Exeter U PhD/MPhil
Glasgow U PhD/MLitt

Area studies & languages
North London P PhD/MPhil

Business studies & languages
East London P PhD/MPhil

Canadian studies
Edinburgh U PhD/MPhil

Caribbean studies
Warwick U PhD/MA/MPhil

Chinese
Edinburgh U PhD/MLitt

Chinese studies
Central London P PhD☆/MPhil☆

Chinese, Japanese & North East Asian studies
Leeds U PhD/MA/MPhil

Comparative literary studies
Kent U PhD/MA/MPhil

English & American literature
East Anglia U PhD/MPhil
Kent U PhD/MA/MPhil

Far East
London U SOAS PhD/MPhil

Hispanic & Latin American studies
Bristol U PhD/MLitt

Hispanic studies
Belfast Queen's U PhD/MA
Nottingham U PhD/MPhil

Humanities
Thames P PhD/MPhil

Indology, modern languages & literatures of South Asia
London U SOAS PhD/MPhil

Japanese
Cardiff U of Wales C PhD☆/
MPhil☆

Japanese studies
Sheffield U PhD/MPhil

Languages
Heriot-Watt U PhD☆/MPhil☆

Languages & area studies
Portsmouth P PhD☆/MPhil☆

Latin American studies
Liverpool U PhD/MPhil
Oxford U DPhil☆/MLitt☆

Literature
Essex U PhD/MPhil

Medieval & modern languages
Oxford U DPhil☆/MLitt☆

Middle Eastern studies
Manchester U PhD/MPhil

Modern languages
Sheffield City P PhD/MPhil

Oriental studies
Cambridge U PhD☆/MLitt☆
Durham U PhD/MA/MLitt
Liverpool U PhD/MPhil
Oxford U DPhil☆/MLitt☆

Persian
Edinburgh U PhD/MLitt

Sanskrit
Edinburgh U PhD/MLitt

South Asian studies
Sussex U DPhil/MPhil

South East Asia & the Islands
London U SOAS PhD/MPhil

South East Asian studies
Kent U PhD/MPhil

Southern African studies
York U DPhil/MPhil

Spanish & Latin American studies
Newcastle U PhD/MLitt

Spanish & Spanish American studies
London U King's C PhD☆/MPhil☆

Third World studies
Liverpool U PhD/MPhil

Languages and literature: Semitic

Higher degrees by instruction

Advanced Arabic & English studies
Salford U dip☆

Advanced Jewish studies
Jews' C dip△
Leo Baeck C MA☆

Ancient Near Eastern & Mediterranean studies
Edinburgh U MLitt☆

Applied linguistics
Salford U MA☆/dip☆

Arabic
Durham U dip☆

Arabic & Islamic studies
Edinburgh U MLitt☆

Arabic for communicative purposes
Heriot-Watt U dip☆

Arabic studies
Leeds U MA
St Andrews U MLitt

Arabic-English/English-Arabic translation studies
Central London P dip☆

Biblical languages
Aberdeen U MTh☆

Hebrew & Jewish studies
Jews' C MA
London U SOAS MA
London U UC MA☆

Hebrew & Old Testament studies
Edinburgh U MSc☆/MTh☆

Interpretation (English/Arabic/English)
Salford U MA☆/dip☆

Islamic societies & cultures
London U SOAS MA

Islamic studies
Kent U MA/dip

Jewish studies
Jews' C dip☆

Jewish studies in the Graeco Roman period
Oxford U MSt☆

Judaism & Jewish-Christian relations
Birmingham U dip☆

Medieval languages
Edinburgh U MSc☆

Modern Arabic
St Andrews U MLitt/MPhil☆/dip☆

Modern Jewish studies
Oxford U MSt☆

Oriental studies (Islamic art & architecture)
Oxford U MPhil☆/MSt☆

Oriental studies (Medieval Arabic thought)
Oxford U MPhil☆/MSt☆

Oriental studies (modern Jewish studies)
Oxford U MPhil☆/MSt☆

Oriental studies (modern Middle Eastern studies)
Oxford U MPhil☆/MSt☆

Religious studies
Bangor, U of Wales MA☆

Syriac studies
Oxford U MSt☆

Teaching Arabic as a foreign language
St Andrews U MLitt☆/MPhil☆/
Dip☆

Translation & linguistics (Arabic/English)
Bath U MA☆/dip☆

Higher degrees by research

Arabic
Central London P PhD☆/MPhil☆
Edinburgh U PhD/MLitt

Arabic studies
St Andrews U PhD/MPhil

Hebrew
Glasgow U PhD/MLitt

Hebrew & Jewish studies
London U UC PhD☆/MPhil☆

Hebrew & Old Testament studies
Edinburgh U PhD/MPhil

Hebrew & Semitic languages
Aberdeen U PhD☆/MLitt☆/
MPhil☆

Islamic & Middle Eastern studies
Edinburgh U PhD/MLitt

Islamic studies
Kent U PhD/MPhil

Jewish studies
Birmingham U PhD☆/MPhil☆
Jews' C PhD☆/MPhil☆

Language studies
Canterbury Christ Church C
 PhD/MPhil

Middle Eastern studies
Central London P PhD☆/MPhil☆

Modern Arabic studies
Leeds U MA

Modern languages
Bath U PhD☆/MPhil☆
Salford U PhD/MPhil

Near & Middle East
London U SOAS PhD/MPhil

Near Eastern studies
Manchester U PhD/MA/MPhil

New Testament studies
Edinburgh U PhD/MPhil

Semitic studies
Belfast Queen's U PhD/MA

Classical studies

MA
1 year full time
2 years part time
Department of Classics, St
David's University College,
Lampeter, Dyfed SA48 7ED
Tel: 0570 422351

This course for the MA degree of the University of Wales offers opportunities for graduates in Classical Studies, Ancient History or Classics to undertake advanced study in two of the fields listed below, one as a main subject, one as a subsidiary.

Greek tragedy, Historiography, Literature and Society in the Hellenistic World, Menander and Terence, Roman Religion, Roman Africa, The Transformation of the Roman World, Etruscan Studies, Ancient Art.

This is a taught MA, examined by four papers and a dissertation of not more than 20,000 words. There is however provision for MPhil by research within most of these topic areas.

Computer speech & language processing

MPhil
1 year full time
20 places
Secretary (MPhil Computer
Speech & Language
Processing), University
Engineering Department,
University of Cambridge,
Trumpington Street,
Cambridge CB2 1PZ
Tel: 0223 332752

For students with backgrounds in computing, electronic engineering, psychology, or linguistics. Interdisciplinary course organised by Computer laboratory and Engineering department and involving Faculties from all the above areas. Aims to provide practical and theoretical expertise in information technology computer systems for speech and language understanding. Lectures, practical work, 3 months supervised project. Industrial support and collaboration.
Entrance requirements Good honours degree or equivalent: computing experience preferred.
Grants SERC studentships available.
Course directors Professor F Fallside (Engineering Department), Dr K Sparck Jones (Computer laboratory).

European language & literature

MA
1 year full time
2 years part time
Centre for Modern European
Studies, Queen Mary &
Westfield College, Mile End
Road, London E1 4NS
Tel: 081 975 5555

The course, the only one of its kind in London, is designed to give graduates from Britain and abroad the opportunity to deepen their understanding of European culture by studying in parallel the languages and literatures of the nations of Europe.

A further objective is to provide expertise in the literature of several major European nations - England, France, Germany, Russia and Spain -using the techniques and disciplines of critical theory, and linking literature to other fields, notably linguistics, philosophy and political theory.

While the main emphasis is on the living languages, and on the literature of the last 300 years, close study may also be made of the foundations of literary genres, and of the transmission of major themes from Classical antiquity to the present.

Entrance requirements A first degree, preferably with a literary and/or linguistic bias, and a native or near-native knowledge of English. Knowledge of another European language, while not essential, is desirable.

Grants British Academy awards.

Course co-ordinator Dr David Shepheard.

French studies

MA
1 year full time
2 years part time
Graduate Adviser,
Department of French,
University of Liverpool, , PO
Box 147, Liverpool L69 3BX
Tel: 051 794 2746

Ma in French autobiography, one year full time, two years part time. Consists of two courses (1, eighteenth & nineteenth centuries, 2, twentieth century). Authors studied include Rousseau, Constant, Senancour, Musset, Stendhal, Renan, Gide, Sarraute, Beauvoir, Aron, Cavanna & Rochefort. Full time candidates take both courses, part time candidates one course per year. Assessment is by one essay (approximately 5000 words) per course and a dissertation of 10,000 words.

Entrance requirements Normally a first or second class degree in French.

General & technical translation

cert
dip
1 year full time
Department of Translation
studies, London School of
Translation Studies,
University of London Union,
Malet Street, London WC1E
7HY
Tel: 071 580 6740

English plus one from: French, Spanish, Arabic, German, Italian. Designed to train students with appropriate language skills to become professional translators, the course consists of translation practice into both languages studied, translation theory , methodology and background studies in relevant areas eg: economics, government and politics, EEC studies, international law. Training is given for Institute of Linguists' examinations. Interpreting courses are also available. Courses in each language are subject to a minimum number of registrations.

Entrance requirements Degree or equivalent standard in the foriegn language.

Principal S C Eden BA(Hons) AIL RSA(Cert) TEFL.

Medieval French studies/ Modern French literature/ French language and education/Modern France: politics, society and culture

MA
Dr B J Levy, Department of French, University of Hull, Hull HU6 7RX

Our MA's are well-established, and the last named offers a postgraduate qualification unique in the UK. All courses consist of a blend of compulsory core elements and optional features which allow the student to pursue areas of specialisation. These courses are subject to assessment or examination; and an MA dissertation completes the student's submission for the degree.

Special facilities include school computer unit, regular seminars and funding for attendance at regional French colloquia.

Entrance requirements Candidates seeking admission to read for taught Masters degrees will normally be expected to possess an honours degree of upper second class honours, or better, from a university approved for the purpose by the Senate. Candidates from overseas will be expected to demonstrate competence in the English language. Admission to the MA in French Language and Education requires that the applicant be a qualified teacher.

Grants British Academy funding may be sought.

Russian studies

MA (Russian studies)
1 year full time
MA (Russian studies)
1 year full time
MA (Slavonic studies)
1 year full time
Mr A G Waring, Head of Department, Department of Russian Studies, University of Sheffield, Sheffield S10 2TN
Tel: 0742 768555

The Russian course leads to a 3 part written examination consisting of: essay in Russian; paper on a selected field of study in literature, language or another aspect of Russia or the Soviet Union (to be approved by the department); paper on the general background to the selected field. Dissertation in the selected field of study. Oral examination. Slavonic studies comprises: practical study of a modern Slavonic language (leading to a written and an oral examination): the comparative study of 3 other modern Slavonic languages; linguistics with special reference to the Slavonic languages; and a dissertation.

Entrance requirements Normally a good honours degree in Russian or an international equivalent. Graduates of other disciplines who can demonstrate a high level of Russian may be considered).

Head of Department Mr A G Waring.

Word & the visual imagination

MA
1 year full time
2 years part time
10 places
Dr William Marx, Course director, English Department, St David's University College, Dyfed SA48 7ED
Tel: 0570 422351 ext 303

This course is broadly conceived to explore the inter-relationships between literature and art. Students take two core courses: one on theories of representation; the other on research method, and the evolution of the illustrated book. Two options are selected from: text and film; the novel, art and artist; Hogarth and Rowlandson; landscape in 18th and 19th century literature; Elizabethan literature and renaissance painting; medieval poets and artists; medieval religious iconography. A dissertation is also written.

Teaching uses books and manuscripts from the Old Library. Students may also make a video, mount an exhibition, or offer their creative work.

Entrance requirements Good honours degree in English, art, communications, or cultural studies.

Grants UK applicants are eligible for a number of University of Wales studentships.

MBA – Masters of Business Administration

The Southampton MBA is a practical managerial qualification developing a student's ability to handle senior levels of responsibility in a competitive and turbulent environment.

The programme is designed in two parts (MBA Part 1 and MBA Part 2) and is constructed of compulsory and optional subject modules. The Southampton MBA student has the opportunity therefore to tailor a course of study appropriate to their own career objectives.

The flexible construction of the programme allows a choice of completion in one year's full-time intensive study or over a period of up to five years. This approach integrates the full-time student with part-time students working within the framework of their own company programmes of management development. In this way the Southampton MBA helps students to focus on real practical management issues taught through a mix of interactive group work, case studies, lectures and projects.

SOUTHAMPTON UNIVERSITY

MANAGEMENT SCHOOL

The Southampton Management School reflects its relevance and adaptability to the needs of the business community through a regular appraisal of its course materials and teaching approach. As well as maintaining strong links with Continental Europe, particular strengths at Southampton include: the Management of Risk and Uncertainty; International Finance; and Project Management.

Students already holding a DMS qualification are able to gain special entry to the MBA Part 2 programme.

For further details contact: The Director, Southampton University Management School, Enterprise Road, Chilworth, Southampton SO9 5NH, United Kingdom.

Postgraduate Programmes in Accounting, Management Science, and Finance.

The following programmes leading to Diploma or the degree of MSc (SocSci) are offered on a full-time (one year) or part-time day-release (at least two years) basis: Management Sciences; Financial Managerial Controls; International Banking and Financial Studies. A two year full-time programme in Accounting and Management Science, specially designed to meet the needs of holders of non-UK degrees or professional qualifications, is also offered.

Supervision of research leading to the degrees of MPhil or PhD on topics in accounting, management science or finance is offered on a full-time or part-time basis.

For further details contact: The Postgraduate Tutor, Department of Accounting & Management Science, The University, Southampton, SO9 5NH, United Kingdom.

MSc in International Banking and Financial Studies

The global integration of financial markets has made it increasingly important for multinational companies, banks, fund managers, securities firms and corporate financial advisers to have a clear understanding of the theory and practice of international banking and finance. With these needs in mind, this new MSc programme aims to develop students' existing skills in the areas of finance and banking, with particular emphasis on the international dimension.

The 12 month MSc programme (24 months for part-time students) is designed for those seeking or developing careers in commercial and central banking, securities business, fund management, investment analysis, or multinational corporate finance.

Candidates, who must have at least a good second class honours degree or equivalent professional qualification, should make early application for the course beginning in October.

For further details contact: Professor Richard Dale, Department of Accounting & Management Science, The University, Southampton, SO9 5NH, United Kingdom.

UNIVERSITY OF SOUTHAMPTON

2

Business/ education/ social sciences

Business, administration and management

Graduates considering business courses obviously do so hoping to improve their career prospects. But it is a good idea to discuss first with a careers adviser whether this is likely to be the case and which type of course to go for. Companies do not share the same opinion of postgraduate business courses. Some are happy with a range of qualifications while others prefer particular types of course. Some would rather take you on after your first degree and put you through their in-house management training, while others are definitely against recruiting students from postgraduate business courses of any description as they regard them as having inflated salary expectations.

Assuming however that you have passed this stage and are seriously considering courses, how do you choose one? 'Going to business school' is an American concept: there, business education is much more common, firms more receptive to business graduates, and business schools consequently have a more standard syllabus. In the UK the situation is different. We have some business schools but most courses are offered by the business departments of universities, colleges and polytechnics. Courses vary in content - and in title - according to the institution. Course names vary from management studies, business economics and business studies through to the more specialised hotel management, personnel, marketing and industrial relations courses.

The degree option

Courses fall into two categories: higher degrees and diploma or certificate courses. Higher degrees may be taught, or gained by research, and many - particularly the research ones - are only open to graduates in relevant subjects. Courses may lead to PhD, MPhil, MSc or MBA (Master in Business Administration) qualifications. Specialist schools such as the London Business School tend to offer MBA courses.

Some of the degrees are in specialist fields, for example MSc in industrial relations or MPhil in accountancy, but the MBA and the degrees in business studies, management studies, management and administrative studies normally provide a basic core of study, which includes accountancy and finance, economics, behavioural science, marketing and mathematics as applied to management (including

statistics and computing). Optional courses are then provided to cater for specific interests. These degree courses do not aim to replace work experience (indeed many insist on a period of experience before enrolment) but instead try to teach students how to approach and solve management problems. They demand very hard work, with papers, projects, exams and continuous assessment all playing a part. Many last for two years, but some are one-year intensive courses.

General business courses are usually taken by graduates in any subject wanting an introduction to business. Opinions on the value of such 'conversion courses' vary but although there is again no guarantee of employment, most students find that they do become more employable.

The MBA is without doubt the most prestigious management qualification. Increasingly recognised by employers, it is now more and more sought after by graduates. Places in business schools do not meet demand. The number of places is now approximately 3000, and ratios of 20 applicants to each place are quite common.

Most holders of the MBA degree can expect to move into management or management consultancy within two years. Courses vary in content however. Some are relevant to the needs of specific industries since they originally attracted older applicants with experience in different companies. These may not give you the same opportunity to move into more general administration and management as those which are more general in content. Many teach skills appropriate to a wide range of employment, making it easier for their holders to change from one employer or function to another and even have international relevance. It is therefore advisable, before investing time and often a great

deal of money, to ascertain which is likely to be the best course for you. This can be done by consulting the *Guide to Business Schools for Prospective Students and Employers* (price £10.45 from the Association of MBAs, 15 Duncan Terrace, London N1 8BZ *Tel:* 071 837 3375) or by attending one of their introductory courses for people considering business school.

Alternative qualifications

Diplomas and certificates are also available in specific areas, for example personnel management, hotel and catering, or general business. Most are of one year's duration but some, like Buckinghamshire College's diploma in European marketing management, take two.

Unlike higher degrees, diplomas are sometimes compulsory for entry to a profession (such as the diploma in accounting in Scotland which must be taken by non-relevant graduates wishing to qualify through the Institute of Chartered Accountants in Scotland), but most are taken because students hope to improve their employment prospects through gaining the additional qualifications. Graduates hoping to enter marketing, tourism, hotel management or personnel work often find that a specific postgraduate qualification enhances their attractiveness to employers, particularly if their first degree is in an unrelated discipline. But it must be remembered that no qualification is ever a guarantee of employment.

Since courses, both at degree and diploma level, vary so much in content, would-be applicants need to consider the options very carefully and research the different alternatives at an early stage. Early application, too, is advisable, since there are always several candidates for every place. Not only that, but some institutions have

adopted the American 'Graduate Management Admission Test', a multiple-choice test of verbal and quantitative skills, as an entrance requirement. Such courses may have an early closing date, after which the test may not be taken.

Obtaining finance for postgraduate courses is not easy. One recent change is that the Economic and Social Research Council (ESRC) no longer funds MBAs as it did until last year. All MBA studentships are now awarded on a competitive basis and details can only be obtained from each institution offering the course. Some students *may* be eligible for grants from the ESRC, LEAs in England and Wales or the Scottish Education Department. Some get low interest bank loans, and a very few scholarships are available.

Beryl Dixon

This listing contains **taught courses** (under the heading 'Higher degrees by instruction') and **research opportunities** (under the heading 'Higher degrees by research'). All study exceeds two terms or six months and is offered on both a full-time and part-time basis unless otherwise indicated. Post-experience and in-service courses are only included when advertised.

☐   This symbol indicates that the **taught course(s)** or **research opportunities** are advertised at the end of this listing.

Biol   An italic abbreviation indicates that an advertisement has been placed at the end of another chapter.

☆   This symbol indicates full-time study only.

△   This symbol indicates part-time study only.

For quick reference to advertisements, please use the 'Advertiser's course entry index'. For further information regarding the listing, please refer to page 53.

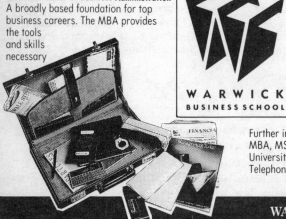

General

Higher degrees by instruction

Administrative science & development problems
York U MSc☆

Advanced recreation management
Salford U cert△

Banking & finance
Bangor, U of Wales MA☆/dip☆

Bilingual business administration: French/German/Spanish/Russian/Italian
Stradbroke C RSA dip☆ □

Business administration
Cranfield S of Management MBA☆
Manchester BS dip☆
Nottingham U MBA □
Sheffield U MBA □
Strathclyde U dip

Business administration (information technology)
Lancashire P MSc☆/dip☆ □

Business information technology systems
Strathclyde U MSc☆/dip☆

Business management systems
Warwick U MSc△

Business strategy
Bristol U MSc☆

Commercial law
Bristol U LLM☆

Construction management
Birmingham U MSc(Eng)

Continuing development programme
Brunel U MSc△

Corporate financing & control
Belfast Queen's U MSc△

Distribution technology & management
Cranfield IT MSc☆ □

Economic development & policy
Birmingham U PhD/MPhil/MSocSc/dip *Soc*

Energy resources management
South Bank P MSc△/dip△

Entrepreneurial studies
Stirling U MSc/dip □

Health management, planning & policy
Leeds U MA☆

Health planning & administration
Leeds U dip☆

Independent study
East London P MA/MSc/dip

Industrial mathematics
Glasgow C MSc☆/dip☆

Information & library studies
Strathclyde U MSc/dip

Information management
Strathclyde U MSc☆/dip☆

Internal auditing & management
City U MSc☆/dip☆

International business administration
Exeter U MBA

Management of technological change
Salford U MSc△

Management science & computer applications in management systems
Cranfield IT MSc☆ □

Management studies
Lancashire P cert☆ □
Staffordshire P DMS☆ □

Management studies (administrative)
Teesside P DMS☆

Management systems & sciences
Hull U MA☆/MSc☆/dip☆ □

Manufacturing
Open U MSc

Maritime studies
Cardiff U of Wales C MSc☆

Physical education & sports science
Loughborough U MSc☆/dip☆

Policy studies
Leeds P MA☆/dip☆

Port & shipping administration
Cardiff U of Wales C dip☆

Public management
Exeter U MA

Publishing & book production
South West P dip *Arts*

Regional development
Strathclyde U MSc/dip

Rural resource management
Bangor, U of Wales MSc☆/dip☆

Science, technology & industrialisation
Sussex U MSc☆

Secretarial & management studies
Ealing C London dip☆

Secretarial linguist: French/German/Spanish
Colchester Inst LCC dip☆ □

Urban & regional planning
Strathclyde U MSc/dip

Urban development
Strathclyde U MSc/dip

Higher degrees by research

Business & management
Birmingham P PhD/MPhil
Lancashire P PhD/MPhil

Business management
Dorset Inst PhD/MPhil/dip

Distribution studies
Cranfield IT PhD☆/MSc☆ □

Economic development & policy
Birmingham U PhD/MPhil/MSocSci

Economics & management sciences
Keele U PhD/MA/MSc

Independent study
East London P PhD/MPhil

Information management
Hull U PhD☆/MPhil☆ □

Management
Kent U PhD/Mphil☆/MPhil△

Management systems & sciences
Hull U PhD/MSc □

Accountancy, finance

Higher degrees by instruction

Accountancy
Aberdeen CC ACA☆/CIMA☆
Aberystwyth, UC of Wales dip☆
Belfast Queen's U MAcc/dip☆
Bell CT ACCA☆/CIMA☆
Dorset Inst ACCA△
Dundee U MAcc☆
Fife CT CIMA△/CIMA△
Glasgow C ACCA/CIMA
Glasgow U MAcc/dip
Gwent CHE ACCA☆/CIMA☆
Heriot-Watt U dip☆
Leicester P ACCA☆
Luton CHE ACCA☆/CIMA☆
Napier P ACCA☆
Norwich City C ACCA
Nottingham P ICAEW△
Sandwell CFHE ACCA/CIMA
South Bank P ACCA△/dip△
South West London C ACCA/
 CIMA
Southampton IHE ACCA/
 CDipAF△/CIMA
Stirling U dip☆
Strathclyde U dip☆
Thames Valley C ACCA☆
West Glamorgan IHE ACCA ☐

Accountancy & management studies
Aberdeen U cert☆

Accountancy(conversion)
Nottingham P cert△
West London IHE CIPFA△

Accountancy
Kilburn C ACCA☆

Accounting
Hull U MBA☆

Accounting & business finance
Manchester U MA(Econ)☆/dip☆

Accounting & development finance
Birmingham U MSocSc☆

Accounting & finance
Birmingham P MA△
Central London P dip△
City of London P MA△
Croydon C dip△
Doncaster C dip☆

Ealing C London ACA△
Lancaster U MA/dip☆
London U LSE MSc/dip
Nottingham P MA△/CdipAF△
Stirling U MSc/dip

Actuarial science
City U dip☆
Heriot-Watt U dip☆

Banking
City of London P cert△
Nottingham P ACIB△
West Glamorgan IHE dip△

Banking & finance
Bangor, U of Wales MA☆/dip☆

Business & accounting
Aberdeen U MBAcc☆/cert☆

Business administration
Sheffield U MBA ☐
Stirling U MBA/dip ☐

Business analysis
Leicester U MA

Business finance
Brunel U MSc

Business strategy
Bristol U MSc☆

Business studies
Salford U MBA☆/MSc☆

Chartered secretaries & administrators
West Glamorgan IHE ICSA

Chartered surveying (general practice - chattels option)
Southampton IHE RICS

Corporate financing & control
Belfast Queen's U MSc△

Development finance
Birmingham U MSocSc☆/dip△

Econometrics
Essex U MA☆
London U LSE dip
Manchester U MA(Econ)☆/dip☆

Econometrics & economics
Manchester U MA(Econ)☆

Econometrics & forecasting
City of London P MSc△/dip△

Econometrics & macroeconomic forecasting
Reading U MA☆

Economics & finance
Loughborough U MSc☆

Finance
Cambridge U MPhil☆
Lancaster U MSc☆/dip☆
Strathclyde U MSc☆/dip☆ ☐

Finance & accounting
Bristol U dip

Farnborough CT dip△

Finance & investment
Exeter U MA☆

Financial & business economics
Essex U MA☆

Financial accountancy
Ulster U dip☆

Financial managerial controls
Southampton U MSc/cert/dip

Financial studies
Glasgow U dip☆

Fiscal studies
Bath U MSc☆/dip☆

Health planning & financing
London U S of Hygiene &
 Tropical Med MSc☆

Health planning, finance & management
Wales U C of Med MSc☆

Internal auditing
South Bank P dip△

International accountancy & finance
London U LSE MSc

International banking & financial services
Reading U MA☆

International banking & financial studies
Heriot-Watt U MSc☆

International business & international financial management
Reading U MA☆

International business administration
Exeter U MBA

International finance
Glasgow U MPhil

International financial analysis
Newcastle U MA

International financial management
Glasgow U MAcc△

International trade & finance
Lancaster U MSc☆

Management accounting
Ulster U dip☆

Management sciences
Manchester UMIST MSc/dip

Money, banking & finance
Sheffield U MA☆/dip☆ ☐
Birmingham U MSocSc☆

Multinational accounting & financial management
Reading U MA☆

Professional accountancy
Stirling U dip

Project analysis, finance & investment
York U MSc☆

Property investment
City U MSc△

Public sector finance
Brunel U MSc

Quantitative international finance
Southampton U MSc/cert/dip

Taxation
South Bank P dip△

Valuation & auctioneering (fine arts & chattels)
Southampton IHE ISVA☆

Higher degrees by research

Accountancy
Aberdeen U PhD☆/MLitt☆/ MPhil☆
Aberystwyth, UC of Wales PhD☆/MPhil☆
Belfast Queen's U PhD/MA
Bristol P PhD/MPhil/dip
Edinburgh U PhD/MPhil
Hull U PhD/MPhil
Kent U PhD/MPhil
Leeds U MA
Liverpool U PhD/MPhil
Middlesex P PhD/MPhil
Napier P PhD/MPhil
Newcastle P PhD☆/MPhil☆
Staffordshire P PhD/MPhil

Accountancy & business finance
Dundee U PhD/LLM

Accountancy & business law
Stirling U PhD/MSc

Accountancy & economics
Dundee IT PhD/MPhil

Accountancy & finance
City of London P PhD☆/MPhil☆
East Anglia U PhD/MPhil/MSc☆
Heriot-Watt U PhD☆/MPhil☆
Huddersfield P PhD/MPhil
Strathclyde U PhD☆/MPhil☆/ MSc☆
Ulster U DPhil/MPhil

Accountancy & financial studies
Sheffield City P PhD/MPhil

Accountancy, business & finance
South Bank P PhD/MPhil

Accounting & business computing
Portsmouth P PhD☆/MPhil☆

Accounting & finance
Birmingham P PhD/MPhil
Birmingham U PhD/MPhil/ MSocSc
Cardiff U of Wales C PhD☆/ MPhil☆
Central London P PhD☆/MPhil☆
East London P PhD/MPhil
Glasgow U PhD/MAcc
Hatfield P PhD/MPhil
Lancashire P PhD/MPhil
Lancaster U PhD/MPhil
Leeds P PhD/MPhil/dip
Liverpool P PhD/MPhil
London U LSE PhD/MPhil
Manchester P PhD/MPhil
Manchester U PhD/MA(Econ)
Nottingham P PhD☆/MPhil☆

Accounting & financial management
Essex U PhD/MPhil

Accounting & insurance
Nottingham U PhD/MPhil

Accounting & management sciences
Southampton U PhD/MPhil

Accounting, banking & finance
Bangor, U of Wales PhD☆/ MPhil☆

Accounting, business & economics
Buckingham U DPhil/MPhil

Actuarial science
City U PhD/MPhil

Banking & commerce
Ulster U DPhil/MPhil

Banking & finance
Loughborough U PhD/MPhil

Banking & insurance
City of London P PhD☆/MPhil☆/ dip☆
Napier P PhD/MPhil

Banking & international finance
City U BS PhD☆/MPhil☆

Business & finance
South Bank P PhD/MPhil

Business & related studies
Manchester BS MBSc△

Business economics & operations management
Bath U PhD/MPhil

Business studies
London U London BS PhD
North London P PhD/MPhil

Computerised accountancy & business computing
East Anglia U PhD/MPhil

Econometrics
Leeds U PhD/MA/MPhil
Manchester U PhD/MA(Econ)
York U DPhil/MPhil

Economics & accounting
Leicester P PhD/MPhil

Economics & banking
City of London P PhD☆/MPhil☆

Economics & finance
Loughborough U PhD/MPhil

Economics, accounting & management
Newcastle U PhD/MPhil   *Soc*

Economics/econometrics
Southampton U PhD/MPhil

Enterprise & small business
Cranfield IT PhD☆/MPhil☆

Finance
Belfast Queen's U MSc☆
City U BS PhD☆/MPhil☆

Finance & accounting
Cranfield IT PhD☆/MPhil☆
Cranfield S of Management PhD/ MPhil
Oxford U DPhil☆/MLitt☆

Finance & Economics
Manchester BS PhD☆/MPhil☆

Finance & law
Dorset Inst PhD/MPhil/dip

Finance & strategy
Aston U PhD/MPhil

Financial management & control
Bath U PhD☆/MSc☆

Fiscal studies
Bath U PhD☆/MPhil☆

Information systems
East Anglia U PhD☆/MPhil☆/ MSc☆

International finance
Manchester BS PhD☆/MPhil☆

Administration

Higher degrees by instruction

Administration
New C ICSA△
Sandwell CFHE ICSA△

Administration studies
Leeds P dip☆

Administrative & legal studies
Ulster U MA☆/dip☆

Administrative & secretarial procedures
Croydon C RSA dip☆ □

Administrative management
Nottingham P dip☆
Sandwell CFHE dip

Administrative science & development problems
York U MSc☆

Administrative studies & practice
Bristol P dip☆

Applications of information technology in business & management
Middlesex P MSc☆

Archive administration
Aberystwyth, UC of Wales dip☆
Bangor, U of Wales dip☆

Arts administration
City U MA/dip
Roehampton I dip☆

Bilingual business administration: French/German/Spanish/Russian/Italian
Stradbroke C RSA dip☆ □

Business administration
Aberdeen U MBA△
Aston U dip
Birmingham U dip☆
Cardiff U of Wales C dip☆
Cranfield S of Management MBA☆
Edinburgh U dip
Heriot-Watt U MBA/dip BA □
Keele U MBA☆
Manchester BS dip☆
Manchester U dip
Open U dip△
Sheffield City P dip☆
Stirling U MBA/dip □
Strathclyde U dip

Business administration (information technology)
Lancashire P MSc☆/dip☆ □

Business administration (human resource management)
City U BS MBA

Business administration (information technology management)
City U BS MBA

Business management systems
Warwick U MSc△

Cadastre & land information management
East London P MSc☆/dip☆

Chartered secretaries & administrators
West Glamorgan IHE ICSA
Worcester TC ICSA△

Community education management
Sheffield U cert△/dip

Computer based administration systems
Glasgow C MSc☆/dip☆

Crime risk management
Cranfield IT MSc☆

Defence administration
Royal Military C of Science MDA☆

Development administration
Birmingham U MSocSc/dip
Manchester U dip☆

Development administration & management
Manchester U MA(Econ)☆

Educational & administrative management
Reading U MA△

Educational administration
London U Inst of Education MA

Educational administration & institutional management
Reading U MA△

Educational management & administration
Manchester U MEd☆

Educational statistics & educational administration
London U Inst of Education MA

Entrepreneurship & competitive strategy
Reading U MA☆

European business administration
Bristol P MA☆/dip☆

Facilities management
Strathclyde U MSc/dip

General management & industrial relations
Cardiff U of Wales C MSc(Econ)☆

Health planning, finance & management
Cardiff U of Wales C MSc☆
Wales U C of Med MSc☆

Hotel administration
Strathclyde U MSc☆/dip☆

Housing
Stirling U dip☆

Housing administration
Sheffield City P dip△

Human resource management
Newcastle U MA

Industrial & administrative sciences
City U MSc☆/dip☆

Industrial administration
Bell CT dip☆
Fife CT dip
Napier P dip☆

Industrial administration (marketing)
Scottish C of Textiles dip☆

Industrial administration (personnel)
Scottish C of Textiles dip☆

Information & systems in management
Sheffield City P MSc☆/Dip☆

Information systems design & management
Kingston P MSc△/Dip△

Intelligent management systems
South Bank P MSc☆/dip☆

International business administration
Exeter U MBA

Land administration
East London P cert△/dip△

Librarianship & arts administration
City U MA△

Management
Dundee CFE Dip☆
London U Imperial C MSc☆/dip☆
Portsmouth P MBA△

Management & administration in education
Bristol U MEd☆

Management & administration of higher education
Manchester U MEd☆

Management & implementation of development projects
Manchester UMIST MSc☆ ☐

Management & scientific aspects of water surveillance & water quality
Surrey U dip☆

Management sciences
Kent U MA
Southampton U MSc/cert/dip
Swansea UC dip☆

Management studies
Durham U MA☆/MSc☆
Lancashire P cert☆ ☐
North London P dip

Management studies (administrative)
Teesside P DMS☆

Management with manufacturing
Glasgow C MA☆ ☐

Museums & gallery administration
City U MA

Office information technology
City of London P dip☆

Office systems management
Humberside CHE MSc☆/dip☆

Operations management & manufacturing systems
Nottingham U MSc

Personnel administration
Robert Gordon's IT dip☆

Personnel management
Glasgow C dip(SCOTVEC)☆/
 IPM☆ ☐

Port & shipping administration
Cardiff U of Wales C dip☆

Port management/shipping management
Humberside CHE MSc☆

Public administration
Glasgow C MA☆ ☐

Public administration & management (developing countries)
Glasgow C dip

Public purchasing management
Ulster U MSc☆/cert☆/dip☆

Secretarial linguist: French/German/Spanish
Colchester Inst LCC dip☆ ☐

Technology management
Stirling U MSc☆/dip☆

Valuation & auctioneering (fine arts & chattels)
Southampton IHE ISVA☆

Higher degrees by research

Accounting & management sciences
Southampton U PhD/MPhil

Administration
City of London P PhD☆/MPhil☆
Strathclyde U PhD☆/MPhil☆/
 MSc☆

Administrative studies
Manchester U PhD

Advanced management development
Brighton P PhD/MPhil

Arts policy & management
City U PhD/MPhil

Building administration
South Bank P PhD/MPhil

Business & administrative studies
Wales P PhD/MPhil

Business & management
Anglia HEC PhD☆/MPhil☆

Business & management studies
Nottingham P PhD☆/MPhil☆
Salford U PhD/MSc
Wolverhampton P PhD/MPhil

Business administration
Manchester U PhD/MBSc/MPhil
Newcastle P PhD☆/MPhil☆
Thames P PhD/MPhil

Business studies
London U London BS PhD
North London P PhD/MPhil
South West P PhD/MPhil

Development policy & management
Manchester U PhD/MA(Econ)

Education management & administration
Sheffield City P PhD/MPhil

Estate management
East London P PhD/MPhil
South Bank P PhD/MPhil

General management
City U BS PhD☆/MPhil☆

Information management
Belfast Queen's U PhD/MA/MLS
Hull U PhD☆/MPhil☆ ☐

Management
Aston U PhD/MPhil
Bristol P PhD/MPhil/dip
East London P PhD/MPhil
Kingston P PhD/MPhil
Leicester P PhD/MPhil
Manchester P PhD/MPhil

Management & administration
Bradford U PhD/MPhil
Newcastle P PhD☆/MPhil☆

Management & administrative studies
Huddersfield P PhD/MPhil

Management & business studies
Oxford P PhD/MPhil
Portsmouth P PhD☆/MPhil☆

Management & economic studies
Sheffield U PhD☆

Management & organisational studies
Sheffield City P PhD/MPhil

Management sciences
City of London P PhD☆/MPhil☆
City U BS PhD☆/MPhil☆
Kent U PhD/MPhil
Lancashire P PhD/MPhil
London U Imperial C PhD/MPhil
Stirling U PhD/MSc

Management sciences/studies
St Andrews U PhD/MPhil

Management studies
Brunel U PhD/MPhil
Central London P PhD☆/MPhil☆
Coventry P PhD/MPhil
Durham U PhD/MPhil
Glasgow U PhD/MLitt
Hatfield P PhD/MPhil
Leeds U PhD/MA/MPhil
Liverpool P PhD/MPhil
Loughborough U PhD/MPhil
Napier P PhD/MPhil
Oxford U DPhil☆/MLitt☆/MPhil☆
South Bank P PhD/MPhil

Management systems & sciences
Hull U PhD/MSc ☐

Marine resource management
Cardiff U of Wales C PhD/MPhil

Office administration
Napier P PhD/MPhil

Office communication & languages
Lancashire P PhD/MPhil

DURHAM
UNIVERSITY BUSINESS SCHOOL

GRADUATE ASSOCIATE PROGRAMME (GAP)

The Programme is designed to encourage graduates under 25, of any degree discipline to build careers with small and medium sized enterprises in the North East. It provides:

* a career opportunity with a progressive employer
* regular off-the-job training at DUBS in management, technical and entrepreneurial skills
* a formal qualification – the Diploma in Enterprise Management on successful completion of the one-year programme.

Send S.A.E. to The Secretary, Graduate Associate Programme, Durham University Business School, Mill Hill Lane, Durham DH1 3LB. Tel: 091 374 3383.

THE MANAGEMENT SCHOOL
LANCASTER
UNIVERSITY

The Management School at the University of Lancaster is one of the largest and longest-established, with a reputation for broad-based strength across the subject range. Its postgraduate programme reflects innovation as well as building on proven success.

Master of Business Administration (MBA) (12 months full-time)
Diploma in Business Analysis
MSc in Information Management
MA or Diploma in Accounting and Finance
MSc or Diploma in Finance
MA in Organisational Analysis and Behaviour
MSc in International Trade and Finance
Diploma in Development Studies
MA in Management Learning (Full-time or part-time)
MA in Management Education
MSc in Operational Research
MSc or Diploma in Management Sciences (Operational Research)

In addition to the above taught programmes, there are extensive opportunities to study for MPhil and PhD by research. Subjects include all the above and also Marketing.

For further details, contact:

The Administrator (Dept. DG), The Management School, University of Lancaster, Lancaster LA1 4YW.
Telephone 0524 65201

Operations management
Cranfield IT PhD☆/MPhil☆
Newcastle P PhD☆/MPhil☆

Organisation & management
Middlesex P PhD/MPhil

Organisation studies
Lancashire P PhD/MPhil

Planning
Anglia HEC PhD☆/MPhil☆

Service sector management
Brighton P PhD/MPhil

Strategic management
Cranfield IT PhD☆/MPhil☆

Business studies

Higher degrees by instruction

Accountancy
Strathclyde U dip☆

Accounting & business finance
Manchester U MA(Econ)☆/dip☆

Administration studies
Leeds P dip☆

Administrative science & development problems
York U MSc☆

Administrative studies & practice
Bristol P dip☆

Advertising
Watford C dip☆

Agricultural communications
Loughry CAg & Food Technology dip☆

Agricultural economics (farm business management)
London U Wye C MSc☆

Agricultural policy analysis
Glasgow U MPhil

Analysis, design & management of information systems
London U LSE MSc

Applications of information technology in business & management
Middlesex P MSc☆

Bilingual executive assistant: French/German/Italian/Spanish
Lancashire P dip☆   □

Business & accounting
Aberdeen U MBAcc☆/cert☆

Business & public sector strategy
Kingston P MA△

Business administration
Aberdeen U MBA△
Aberystwyth, UC of Wales dip☆
Aston U dip
Birmingham U dip☆
Cardiff U of Wales C dip☆
Cranfield S of Management MBA☆
Edinburgh U dip
Gwent CHE dip△
Heriot-Watt U MBA/dip BA   □
Keele U MBA☆
Manchester BS dip☆
Manchester U dip
Open U dip△
Sheffield City P dip☆
Strathclyde U dip

Business administration (human resource management)
City U BS MBA

Business administration (information technology management)
City U BS MBA

Business analysis
Lancaster U dip☆

Business economics
Buckingham U MSc☆/dip☆
Reading U MA☆

Business information technology
Newcastle P dip☆
Nottingham P dip△

Business law
City of London P MA

Business linguist
South Bank P dip☆

Business management
Manchester BS MBM
Manchester U MBM△

Business management systems
Warwick U MSc△

Business research methods
Brighton P dip☆

Business science
Manchester U MBSc

Business studies
London U LSE dip
Salford U MBA☆/MSc☆

Careers guidance
Strathclyde U dip☆

Commerce
Birmingham U dip☆

Commercial law
Bristol U LLM☆

Digital & microcomputer systems engineering
East Anglia U MSc△

Econometrics & macroeconomic forecasting
Reading U MA☆

Economics
London U Queen Mary & Westfield C MSc(Econ)/dip

Education management
Anglia HEC MSc△

Educational management
Bath U MEd

Entrepreneurial studies
Stirling U MSc/dip   □

Entrepreneurship & competitive strategy
Reading U MA☆

European & international management
Derbyshire CHE dip☆

European business
South Bank P cert☆

European business & management
Portsmouth P dip☆

European business administration
Bristol P MA☆/dip☆

European business management & information systems
Anglia HEC dip☆

European enterprise management
Dorset Inst DETSUP☆/dip☆

Finance
Strathclyde U MSc☆/dip☆   □

Financial & business economics
Essex U MA☆

Financial managerial controls
Southampton U MSc/cert/dip

Foreign languages for business
Bristol P dip☆

Forest business management
Aberdeen U MSc☆/dip☆

Human resources management
Sheffield City P MSc/dip☆

Industrial relations
Strathclyde U MSc☆
Warwick U MA

Information & library studies
Strathclyde U MSc/dip

Information & systems in management
Sheffield City P MSc☆/dip☆

Information management
Strathclyde U MSc☆/dip☆

Information technology for management
Coventry P MSc

Information technology in business
Humberside CHE MSc/dip

International banking & financial services
Reading U MA☆

International business
Manchester UMIST MSc☆

International business & economic development
Reading U MA☆

International business & economic integration
Reading U MA☆

International business & industrial development
Ulster U MBA☆

International business & international financial management
Reading U MA☆

International business administration
Exeter U MBA

International business history
Reading U MA☆

International business law
Hull U dip☆/LLM☆

International financial management
Glasgow U MAcc△

International hotel management
Surrey U MSc☆/dip☆

International trade & finance
Lancaster U MSc☆

Labour studies
North London P dip☆

Law
London U King's C LLM

Management
London U Imperial C MSc☆/dip☆
Portsmouth P MBA△

Management & society
Newcastle U MA☆

Management (industrial relations)
Oxford U MSc☆

Management of information systems
London U LSE dip☆

Management science & operational research
Warwick U MSc

Management sciences
Kent U MA
London U LSE dip
Southampton U MSc/cert/dip
Swansea UC dip☆

Management studies
Blackburn C dip△
Canterbury C cert△
Doncaster C DMS△
Durham U MA☆/MSc☆
Leeds U MA☆
Manchester P dip△
Oxford U MPhil☆/cert☆

Management studies (administrative)
Teesside P DMS☆

Management, economics, politics
St Andrews U MLitt/MPhil☆/dip☆

Maritime studies
Cardiff U of Wales C MSc☆

Marketing
Strathclyde U MSc☆/dip☆
Watford C dip△

Marketing & product management
Silsoe C MSc☆/dip☆

Modular studies
Crewe & Alsager CHE MA△/
    MSc△

Money, banking & finance
Sheffield U MA☆/dip☆

Office systems management
Humberside CHE MSc☆/dip☆

Operational research
Lancaster U MSc☆/dip☆

Organisation development
Sheffield City P MSc☆/dip☆

Organisational analysis & behaviour
Lancaster U MA

Organisational behaviour
London U Birkbeck C MSc△

Personnel management
Strathclyde U MSc△/dip☆

Personnel management & industrial relations
Manchester UMIST MSc☆

Policy analysis
Ulster U MSc△

Port & shipping administration
Cardiff U of Wales C dip☆

Post graduate secretarial
Suffolk CHFE BTEC☆/RSA☆

Private & executive secretarial
St Godric's C, London dip☆

Private secretarial
Teesside P dip

Property development (project management)
South Bank P MSc△

Purchasing & supply
North London P dip△
Nottingham P △

Recreation management
Loughborough U MSc☆

Regional development
Strathclyde U MSc/dip

Statistical applications in business & government
Central London P MSc△

Teaching of economics or business studies
Sheffield U MA/dip

Technical change & industrial strategy
Manchester U MSc☆/dip☆

Tourism planning & development
Surrey U MSc☆/dip☆

Urban & regional planning
Strathclyde U MSc/dip

Urban development
Strathclyde U MSc/dip

Higher degrees by research

Accountancy & business law
Stirling U PhD/MSc

Accountancy & finance
East Anglia U PhD/MPhil/MSc☆

Accountancy, business & finance
South Bank P PhD/MPhil

Accounting & business computing
Portsmouth P PhD☆/MPhil☆

2 POSTGRADUATE OPPORTUNITIES

Accounting & finance
Manchester U PhD/MA(Econ)

Accounting & management sciences
Southampton U PhD/MPhil

Accounting, business & economics
Buckingham U DPhil/MPhil

Advanced management development
Brighton P PhD/MPhil

Behavioural & communication studies
Wales P PhD/MPhil

British policy studies
Sheffield U PhD

Business
Humberside CHE PhD/MPhil
Kingston P PhD/MPhil
Oxford P PhD/MPhil
Thames Valley C MPhil
West Glamorgan IHE PhD/MPhil

Business & administrative studies
Wales P PhD/MPhil

Business & finance
South Bank P PhD/MPhil

Business & management
Anglia HEC PhD☆/MPhil☆
Sunderland P PhD/MPhil

Business & management studies
Cardiff IHE PhD/MPhil/dip△
Nottingham P PhD☆/MPhil☆
Salford U PhD/MSc
Wolverhampton P PhD/MPhil

Business & professional studies
Teesside P PhD☆/MPhil☆

Business & related studies
Manchester BS MBSc△

Business administration
Glasgow U PhD
Manchester U PhD/MBSc/MPhil
Newcastle P PhD☆/MPhil☆
Thames P PhD/MPhil

Business analysis
Lancaster U PhD/MPhil
Newcastle P PhD☆/MPhil☆

Business economics
Cranfield S of Management PhD/MPhil

Business economics & operations management
Bath U PhD/MPhil

Business information technology
Manchester P PhD/MPhil

Business management
Leeds P PhD/MPhil/dip
Scottish C of Textiles PhD/MPhil

Business organisation
Heriot-Watt U PhD☆/MPhil☆

Business policy & strategy
Bath U PhD☆/MPhil☆

Business science
Manchester U MBSc

Business studies
Belfast Queen's U PhD/MA
Bristol P PhD/MPhil/dip
Central London P PhD☆/MPhil☆
City of London P PhD☆/MPhil☆
Coventry P PhD/MPhil
Dundee IT PhD/MPhil
Edinburgh U PhD/MPhil
Hatfield P PhD/MPhil
Lancashire P PhD/MPhil
Liverpool P PhD/MPhil
Liverpool U PhD/MPhil
London U London BS PhD
Manchester P PhD/MPhil
Middlesex P PhD/MPhil
Napier P PhD/MPhil
North London P PhD/MPhil
Portsmouth P PhD☆/MPhil☆
Robert Gordon's IT PhD/MPhil
Sheffield City P PhD/MPhil
South West P PhD/MPhil
Stirling U PhD/MSc

Business studies & languages
East London P PhD/MPhil

Business systems analysis
City U BS PhD☆/MPhil☆

Commercial law studies
London U Queen Mary & Westfield C PhD☆/MPhil☆

Communication studies
Ulster U DPhil/MPhil

Computer applications
Cranfield S of Management PhD/MPhil

Computerised accountancy & business computing
East Anglia U PhD/MPhil

Development policy & management
Manchester U PhD/MA(Econ)

Economics & commerce
Hull U PhD/MPhil

Economics & management
Paisley CT PhD/MPhil

Economics, accounting & management
Newcastle U PhD/MPhil   *Soc*

Enterprise & small business
Cranfield IT PhD☆/MPhil☆

Enterprise studies
Cranfield S of Management PhD/MPhil

European business
Leeds P PhD/MPhil/dip

Human resources
Cranfield IT PhD☆/MPhil☆
Cranfield S of Management PhD/MPhil

Industrial & business studies
Warwick U PhD/MA/MPhil/MSc

Industrial economics & business studies
Birmingham U PhD/MPhil/MSocSc☆

Information systems
Cranfield S of Management PhD/MPhil
East Anglia U PhD☆/MPhil☆/MSc☆

Management
Aston U PhD☆
Birmingham P PhD/MPhil
Bristol P PhD/MPhil/dip
Nottingham U PhD/MPhil

Management & administrative studies
Huddersfield P PhD/MPhil

Management & business studies
Oxford P PhD/MPhil
Portsmouth P PhD☆/MPhil☆

Management & economic studies
Sheffield U PhD☆

Management & legal studies
Wales P PhD/MPhil

Management & organisational studies
Sheffield City P PhD/MPhil

Management development
Cranfield S of Management PhD/MPhil

Management sciences
City of London P PhD☆/MPhil☆
City U BS PhD☆/MPhil☆
Kent U PhD/MPhil
Lancashire P PhD/MPhil
London U Imperial C PhD/MPhil
Stirling U PhD/MSc
Swansea UC PhD/MPhil   □

Management sciences/studies
St Andrews U PhD/MPhil

Management studies
Brunel U PhD/MPhil

Central London P PhD☆/MPhil☆
Coventry P PhD/MPhil
Durham U PhD/MPhil
Glasgow U PhD/MLitt
Hatfield P PhD/MPhil
Leeds U PhD/MA/MPhil
Liverpool P PhD/MPhil
Loughborough U PhD/MPhil
Napier P PhD/MPhil
Oxford U DPhil☆/MLitt☆/MPhil☆
Reading U PhD/MPhil
South Bank P PhD/MPhil

Management studies for tourism & hotel industry
Surrey U PhD/MPhil

Manufacturing
Cranfield IT PhD☆/MSc☆
Dorset Inst PhD/MPhil/dip

Marketing & business organisation
Ulster U DPhil/MPhil

Marketing & logistics
Cranfield IT PhD☆/MPhil☆

North West public sector research
Salford U PhD/MPhil/MSc

Office communication & languages
Lancashire P PhD/MPhil

Operational research & operations management
Lancaster U PhD/MPhil/MSc □

Operations management
Cranfield S of Management PhD/MPhil

Organisation, management & employment relations
Strathclyde U PhD☆/MPhil☆/MSc☆

Small businesses
Manchester BS PhD☆/MPhil☆

Strategic management
Cranfield IT PhD☆/MPhil☆
Cranfield S of Management PhD/MPhil

Diploma of Management Studies (DMS)

Administrative science & development problems
York U MSc☆

Business management systems
Warwick U MSc△

Business strategy
Bristol U MSc☆

International shipping
South West P   Eng

Management
Dundee CFE Dip☆

Management studies
Anglia HEC △
Birmingham P △
Brighton P
Bristol P
Buckinghamshire CHE △
Central London P
City of London P dip△
Crewe & Alsager CHE △
Croydon C △
Derbyshire CHE ☆
Dundee IT MSc☆/DMS
Ealing C London
Farnborough CT △
Huddersfield P △
Humberside CHE △
Kingston P
Lancashire P cert☆/DMS☆   □
Leeds P
Liverpool P △
Luton CHE
Middlesex P
Newcastle P ☆
North East Worcestershire C △
Nottingham P △
Portsmouth P
Robert Gordon's IT
South Bank P △
Southampton IHE △
Staffordshire P ☆   □
Sunderland P
Teesside P
Thames Valley C △
Ulster U △
Wales P
West Glamorgan IHE △
Worcester TC △

Management studies (administrative management)
Teesside P

Management studies (international management)
Teesside P

Management studies (leisure management)
Teesside P

Management studies (leisure)
North London P ☆

Management studies (marketing management)
Teesside P

Management studies (shipping)
South West P ☆   □

Management studies (administrative)
Teesside P ☆

Personal assistants/executive assistants
Luton CHE ☆

Port & shipping administration
Cardiff U of Wales C dip☆

Public management
Exeter U MA

Secretarial & management studies
Ealing C London ☆

Shipping & transport management
South West P ☆

Ergonomics, work study

Higher degrees by instruction

Business management systems
Warwick U MSc△

Ergonomics
London U S of Hygiene & Tropical Med MSc
London U Royal Free Hosp S of Med MSc
Loughborough U MSc

Ergonomics (human factors in work, design & production)
London U UC MSc☆   Soc

Human resources management
Sheffield City P MSc/dip☆

Interactive computing system design
Loughborough U MSc☆/dip△

Labour market studies
Loughborough U MA△

Occupational behaviour
Hatfield P MSc☆

Organisation development
Sheffield City P MSc☆/dip☆

Trading standards
Manchester P dip△

Work design & ergonomics
Birmingham U MSc(Eng)☆

Work study
West Glamorgan IHE cert△

Higher degrees by research

Cognitive performance & ergonomics
Aston U PhD/MPhil

Human sciences
Loughborough U PhD/MPhil

Occupational studies
Keele U PhD/MA

Occupational therapy & physiotherapy
Ulster U DPhil/MPhil

Strategic management
Cranfield S of Management PhD/MPhil

Work organisation
Aston U PhD/MPhil

Hotel and catering management

Higher degrees by instruction

Food & management science
London U King's C MSc☆

Food policy & commodity trade
Swansea UC MSc(Econ)☆

Hospitality management
Blackpool & The Fylde C
  HCIMA☆ □
Queen Margaret C dip☆/
  HCIMA☆ □
Westminster C London
  HCIMA☆ □

Hotel & catering administration
Manchester P dip☆

Hotel & catering management
Oxford P MSc☆/dip☆
Ulster U MSc☆/dip☆

Hotel administration
Strathclyde U MSc☆/dip☆

Hotel, catering & accommodation management
Queen's C Glasgow HCIMA☆ □

Hotel, catering & institutional management
Leeds P dip☆/HCIMA☆

International hospitality management/catering & applied nutrition
Huddersfield P dip☆

International hotel management
Surrey U MSc☆/dip☆

Tourism, food & hospitality management
Sheffield City P MSc☆

Higher degrees by research

Catering & home economics
Anglia HEC PhD☆/MPhil☆

Catering & hotel administration
Dorset Inst PhD/MPhil/dip

Catering & hotel management
Thames Valley C MPhil

Catering & hotel studies
Napier P PhD/MPhil

Food & accommodation studies
North London P PhD/MPhil

Food & catering management
Dorset Inst PhD/MPhil

Food & tourism management
Sheffield City P PhD/MPhil

Home economics
Robert Gordon's IT PhD/MPhil
Worcester CHE PhD/MPhil

Home economics & institutional management
Cardiff U of Wales C PhD☆/
  MPhil☆

Hospitality management
Leeds P PhD/MPhil/dip

Hospitality, food & product management
South Bank P PhD/MPhil

Hotel & catering management
Ulster U DPhil☆/MPhil☆

Hotel & institution administration
Robert Gordon's IT PhD/MPhil

Hotel, catering & accommodation management
Queen's C Glasgow PhD/MPhil

Hotel, catering & food studies
Oxford P PhD/MPhil

Hotel, catering & institutional management
Manchester P PhD/MPhil

Management studies for tourism & hotel industry
Surrey U PhD/MPhil

Scottish Hotel School
Strathclyde U PhD☆/MPhil☆/
  MSc☆

Service sector management
Brighton P PhD/MPhil

Industrial management

Higher degrees by instruction

Administrative management
Nottingham P dip☆

Advanced agricultural business management
Royal AgC dip☆

Advanced manufacturing management
Derbyshire CHE MSc☆

Advanced manufacturing systems
Brunel U MSc   *Eng*

Advanced manufacturing technology
Cranfield IT MSc☆

Agricultural economics (farm business management)
London U Wye C MSc☆

Agricultural management
Reading U MSc☆

Air transport management
Cranfield IT MSc☆

Architectural management
Nottingham U MA☆

Building economics & management
London U UC MSc

Building management & economics
Lancashire P dip☆

Building technology & management
Newcastle P dip☆

Business management systems
Warwick U MSc△

Concrete technology, construction & management
Dundee U MSc☆

Construction management
Birmingham U MSc(Eng)
Glasgow C of Building & Printing dip☆
Loughborough U MSc
Reading U MSc☆
Ulster U MSc☆/cert△/dip☆

Construction project management
Manchester UMIST MSc☆

Engineering construction project management
Cranfield S of Management MSc☆

Engineering management
Glasgow U MSc

Engineering production & management
Birmingham U MSc(Eng)☆

Environmental forestry
Bangor, U of Wales MSc☆/dip☆

European marketing management
Buckinghamshire CHE MA△

Farm business organisation & management
Aberdeen SAg dip☆

Farm management
South West P dip☆

Financial managerial controls
Southampton U MSc/cert/dip

Fisheries (fisheries management)
Humberside CHE dip☆

General management & industrial relations
Cardiff U of Wales C MSc(Econ)☆

Human resources management
Sheffield City P MSc/dip☆

Industrial administration
Bell CT dip☆
Fife CT dip

Industrial administration (marketing)
Scottish C of Textiles dip☆

Industrial administration (personnel)
Scottish C of Textiles dip☆

Industrial management
Sandwell CFHE dip△

Industrial relations
Brunel U MA   □

Information & systems in management
Sheffield City P MSc☆/dip☆

Irrigation water management
Silsoe C MSc☆/dip☆

Labour market studies
Loughborough U MA△

Land resource management & planning
Silsoe C MSc☆/dip☆

Management
Kent U MA
London U Imperial C MSc☆/dip☆

Management & economics for construction & design
Bristol P MSc

Management & scientific aspects of water surveillance & water quality
Surrey U dip☆

Management accounting
Ulster U dip☆

Management for agricultural development
Silsoe C MSc☆

Management of technological change
Salford U MSc△

Management of technology & operational research
Sussex U MSc☆

Management science & computer applications in management systems
Cranfield IT MSc☆   □

Management sciences
Kent U MA
Southampton U MSc/cert/dip
Swansea UC dip☆

Management studies
Doncaster C DMS△
Durham U MA☆/MSc☆
North London P dip

Management, economics, politics
St Andrews U MLitt/MPhil☆/dip☆

Manufacturing management
Cranfield IT MSc☆   □
Ulster U MSc△/dip△

Manufacturing systems
Nottingham U MSc   Eng

Manufacturing systems engineering
Leeds P MSc△

Maritime studies
Cardiff U of Wales C MSc☆

Marketing & product management
Silsoe C MSc☆/dip☆

Medical laboratory management
City of Westminster C FIMLS dip△

Mineral production management
London U Imperial C MSc☆/dip☆

Organisation development
Sheffield City P MSc☆/dip☆

Petroleum technology & management systems
Brunel U MSc☆

Plantation management
Silsoe C MSc☆

Production engineering & management
Strathclyde U dip☆

Production management & manufacturing technology
Strathclyde U MSc☆

Production methods & management
Lancaster U ☆

Project analysis, finance & investment
York U MSc☆

Project management
Brunel U MSc
Reading U MSc△

Property development (project management)
South Bank P MSc△

Public management
Exeter U MA

Public sector management
Aston U MSc/dip

Purchasing & supply
North London P dip△

Range management
Silsoe C MSc☆

Resource management
Edinburgh U MSc☆/dip☆

Structure & organisation of science & technology
Manchester U MSc☆/dip☆

Technical change & industrial strategy
Manchester U MSc☆/dip☆

Transport management
City U MSc

Transport planning & management
Central London P MSc

Valuation & auctioneering (fine arts & chattels)
Southampton IHE ISVA☆

Higher degrees by research

Accounting & management sciences
Southampton U PhD/MPhil

Agricultural economics & management
Reading U PhD/MPhil/MSc

Business & management
Anglia HEC PhD☆/MPhil☆
Sunderland P PhD/MPhil

Business & management studies
Nottingham P PhD☆/MPhil☆
Wolverhampton P PhD/MPhil

Business & related studies
Manchester BS MBSc△

Business economics & operations management
Bath U PhD☆

Business studies
North London P PhD/MPhil
South West P PhD/MPhil

Construction management
Reading U PhD/MPhil
South Bank P PhD/MPhil

Design, manufacturing & engineering management
Strathclyde U PhD☆/MPhil☆/MSc☆

Economics & management
Paisley CT PhD/MPhil

Engineering science & industrial management
Liverpool U PhD/MSc(Eng)

Enterprise studies
Cranfield S of Management PhD/MPhil

Estate management
South Bank P PhD/MPhil

Estate management & quantity surveying
Wales P PhD/MPhil

Finance & strategy
Aston U PhD/MPhil

Fisheries studies
Humberside CHE PhD/MPhil

General management
City U BS PhD☆/MPhil☆

Health services management
Birmingham U PhD☆/MPhil☆/MSocSc☆

Industrial & business studies
Warwick U PhD/MA/MPhil/MSc

Industrial & defence studies
Royal Naval Engineering C PhD☆/MSc☆

Industrial management
Newcastle U PhD/MSc

Industrial studies & social studies
Napier P PhD/MPhil

Innovation, design & operations management
Aston U PhD/MPhil

Labour economics
Leeds U PhD/MA/MPhil

Management
Bristol P PhD/MPhil/dip
Kingston P PhD/MPhil
Leicester P PhD/MPhil
Manchester P PhD/MPhil

Management & administration
Bradford U PhD/MPhil
Newcastle P PhD☆/MPhil☆

Management & administrative studies
Huddersfield P PhD/MPhil

Management & business studies
Oxford P PhD/MPhil

Management & industrial relations
City of London P PhD☆/MPhil☆

Management & organisational studies
Sheffield City P PhD/MPhil

Management development
Manchester BS PhD☆/MPhil☆

Management learning
Lancaster U PhD/MPhil

Management sciences
City of London P PhD☆/MPhil☆
City U BS PhD☆/MPhil☆
Kent U PhD/MPhil
Lancashire P PhD/MPhil
London U Imperial C PhD/MPhil
Stirling U PhD/MSc
Strathclyde U PhD☆/MPhil☆/MSc☆

Management sciences/studies
St Andrews U PhD/MPhil

Management studies
Brunel U PhD/MPhil
Central London P PhD☆/MPhil☆
Coventry P PhD/MPhil
Durham U PhD/MPhil
Glasgow U PhD/MLitt
Hatfield P PhD/MPhil
Leeds U PhD/MA/MPhil
Liverpool P PhD/MPhil
Loughborough U PhD/MPhil
Napier P PhD/MPhil
Oxford U DPhil☆/MLitt☆/MPhil☆
South Bank P PhD/MPhil

Marketing & business organisation
Ulster U DPhil/MPhil

Marketing & management
Silsoe C PhD/MPhil

Mining economics & management
Camborne S of Mines PhD/MPhil

Operations management
Newcastle P PhD☆/MPhil☆

Organisation & management
Middlesex P PhD/MPhil

Organisation studies
Lancashire P PhD/MPhil

Production engineering & production management
Nottingham U PhD/MPhil

Property valuation & management
City U PhD/MPhil

Self-organised learning
Brunel U PhD/MPhil

Service sector management
Brighton P PhD/MPhil

Social innovation
Aston U PhD/MPhil

Study of human learning
Brunel U PhD/MPhil

Systems science
City U PhD/MPhil

Technological management
Bradford U PhD/MPhil

Technology policy
Aston U PhD/MPhil

Textile industries
Leeds U PhD/MPhil/MSc(Eng)

Marketing

Higher degrees by instruction

Administration studies
Leeds P dip☆

Advertising
Watford C dip☆

Agricultural & food marketing marketing
Aberystwyth, UC of Wales MSc☆

Agricultural economics (agricultural marketing)
London U Wye C MSc☆

Beef, sheep production & marketing
Welsh AgC cert☆

Business administration
Stirling U MBA/dip   ☐

Business studies
Salford U MBA☆/MSc☆

Chartered surveying (general practice - chattels option)
Southampton IHE RICS

European management
Cranfield S of Management MA☆

European marketing
Staffordshire P dip☆

European marketing & languages
Napier P dip☆

European marketing management
Buckinghamshire CHE MA△

Export marketing
Buckinghamshire CHE dip☆

Fisheries biology
Buckingham U MSc☆

Industrial administration (marketing)
Scottish C of Textiles dip☆

Industrial administration (personnel)
Scottish C of Textiles dip☆

International agricultural marketing
Newcastle U MSc☆/dip☆   ☐

International hotel management
Surrey U MSc☆/dip☆

International marketing
Staffordshire P dip☆
Strathclyde U MSc/dip

Marketing
Bolton IHE dip△
Bristol P dip
Central London P MA△
Dorset Inst dip△
Ealing C London MA☆
Fife CT dip△
Kingston P dip☆
Manchester P dip△
Manchester UMIST MSc☆
Middlesex P dip☆
Newcastle P dip☆
Newcastle U MSc☆
Nottingham P dip△
Sandwell CFHE dip△
Silsoe C MSc☆/Dip☆
South Bank P dip△
Southampton IHE dip△
Staffordshire P MSc△
Strathclyde U MSc☆/dip☆
Ulster U dip△

Marketing & a foreign language
Salford U MSc△

Marketing & product management
Silsoe C MSc☆/dip☆

Marketing management
Liverpool P dip☆
Staffordshire P dip☆

Purchasing & supply
Nottingham P △

Social research methods
Surrey U MSc☆

Tourism marketing
Surrey U MSc☆/dip☆

World animal production
Bangor, U of Wales MSc☆/dip☆

Higher degrees by research

Agricultural economics & food marketing
Newcastle U PhD/MPhil

Applied consumer sciences
Newcastle P PhD☆/MPhil☆

Behavioural & communication studies
Wales P PhD/MPhil

Business & related studies
Manchester BS MBSc△

Business studies
London U London BS PhD

Communication studies
Ulster U DPhil/MPhil

Food marketing
Newcastle U PhD☆/MPhil☆

Home economics & consumer studies
South Bank P PhD/MPhil

Management development
Cranfield S of Management PhD/ MPhil

Management sciences
Manchester UMIST PhD/MSc
Stirling U PhD/MSc
Swansea UC PhD/MPhil   ☐

Marketing
Bath U PhD/MPhil
Bradford U PhD/MPhil
Central London P PhD☆/MPhil☆
City of London P PhD☆/MPhil☆
City U BS PhD☆/MPhil☆
Lancaster U PhD/MPhil
Liverpool P PhD/MPhil
Manchester BS PhD☆/MPhil☆
Middlesex P PhD/MPhil
Staffordshire P PhD/MPhil
Stirling U PhD/MPhil
Strathclyde U PhD☆/MPhil☆/ MSc☆

Marketing & business organisation
Ulster U DPhil/MPhil

Marketing & logistics
Cranfield IT PhD☆/MPhil☆
Cranfield S of Management PhD/ MPhil

Marketing & management
Silsoe C PhD/MPhil

Marketing & strategy
Cardiff U of Wales C PhD☆/ MPhil☆

Marketing & tourism management
Newcastle P PhD☆/MPhil☆

Marketing communications
Cranfield S of Management PhD/ MPhil

Retail marketing
Manchester P PhD/MPhil

Master of Business Administration (MBA)

Administrative science & development problems
York U MSc☆

Business administration
Aberystwyth, UC of Wales ☆
Anglia HEC △
Aston U
Bath U
Birmingham U ☆
Bradford U
Brunel U
Cardiff U of Wales C
Central London P △
City U BS
Cranfield S of Management ☆
Ealing C London △
East London P △
Edinburgh U
Exeter U
Glasgow C ☆ ☐
Glasgow U
Heriot-Watt U MBA/dip BA ☐
Huddersfield P △
Hull U ☆
Humberside CHE △
Kingston P △
Lancashire P △
Lancaster U
London U London BS
Manchester BS
Manchester U
Middlesex P
Newcastle U △
Nottingham U ☐
Open U △
Portsmouth P △
Sheffield City P
Sheffield U ☐
Stirling U MBA/dip ☐
Strathclyde U
Teesside P
Thames Valley C
Ulster U △
Warwick U

Business administration (finance)
City U BS ☆

Business administration (marketing)
City U BS

Business administration (information technology management)
City U BS

Business administration: Europe
Buckinghamshire CHE △

Business studies
Buckingham U ☆
Salford U ☆

Computer management
City U

Executive business administration
Cranfield S of Management △

Export management & international business
City U

Industrial relations & personnel management
City U

International business management (Paris, Oxford, Berlin)
European S of Management ☆

International business management (Paris, Oxford, Madrid)
European S of Management ☆

Interpreting
Salford U MA☆/dip☆

Management studies
Glasgow U △

Personnel management
Leeds P

Operational research

Higher degrees by instruction

Applied statistics & operational research
London U Birkbeck C MSc△

Decision theory
Manchester U dip☆

Industrial programming technology
Sheffield U MSc☆

Management of technology & operational research
Sussex U MSc☆

Management science & operational research
Warwick U MSc

Management sciences
Kent U MA
Southampton U MSc/cert/dip
Swansea UC dip☆

Management sciences (operational research)
Lancaster U MSc☆/dip☆

Management systems & sciences
Hull U MA☆/MSc☆/dip☆ ☐

Manufacturing systems engineering
Cranfield IT MSc☆ *Eng*

Military operational research
Royal Military C of Science MSc△

Operational research
Birmingham U MSc(Eng)☆
Exeter U MSc☆
Lancaster U MSc☆/dip☆ ☐
London U LSE MSc
Southampton U MSc☆/cert☆
Strathclyde U MSc/dip
Sussex U MSc/dip☆

Operational research & computer techniques
Southampton IHE dip☆ ☐

Operational research & information systems
London U LSE MSc

Organisational behaviour ➔
London U Birkbeck C MSc△

Production methods & management
Lancaster U ☆

Statistics & operational research
Essex U MSc☆/dip☆
Loughborough U MSc

Higher degrees by research

Accounting & management sciences
Southampton U PhD/MPhil

Applied statistics & operational research
Sheffield City P PhD/MPhil

Business & related studies
Manchester BS MBSc△

Business science
Manchester U MBSc

Computing/operational research
Silsoe C PhD/MPhil

Decision theory
Manchester U PhD/MA(Econ)

Ergonomics & operational research
Birmingham U PhD☆/MPhil☆ *Eng*

Information management
Hull U PhD☆/MPhil☆   □

Management development
Cranfield S of Management PhD/MPhil

Management sciences
City of London P PhD☆/MPhil☆
City U BS PhD☆/MPhil☆
Kent U PhD/MPhil

Management sciences/studies
St Andrews U PhD/MPhil

Management systems & sciences
Hull U PhD/MSc   □

Manufacturing & mechanical engineering
Birmingham U PhD/MPhil(Eng)   *Eng*

Mathematical sciences
Durham U PhD/MSc

Mathematical statistics & operational research
Cardiff U of Wales C PhD☆/MPhil☆

Mathematics, statistics & operational research
Nottingham P PhD☆/MPhil☆

Operational research
Brighton P PhD/MPhil
Hatfield P PhD/MPhil
London U LSE PhD/MPhil
Manchester BS PhD☆/MPhil☆
Sussex U DPhil/MPhil

Operational research & information systems
Leeds U PhD/MPhil/MSc

Operational research & operations management
Lancaster U PhD/MPhil/MSc   □

Organisational behaviour
Manchester BS PhD☆/MPhil☆

Statistics & operational research
Belfast Queen's U PhD/MSc
Coventry P PhD/MPhil

Technology policy
Aston U PhD/MPhil

Personnel, industrial relations, manpower studies

Higher degrees by instruction

Business studies
Salford U MBA☆/MSc☆

Careers guidance
Kent C for the Careers Service dip☆
Strathclyde U dip☆

Employment relations
Coventry P dip☆

Employment studies
Cardiff U of Wales C MSc(Econ)☆
Salford U MSc/dip

General management & industrial relations
Cardiff U of Wales C MSc(Econ)☆

Human resource development
Manchester U MSc☆

Human resources management
Gwent CHE dip△/IPM△
Sheffield City P MSc/dip☆

Industrial administration (personnel)
Scottish C of Textiles dip☆

Industrial relations
Glasgow U MPhil
Keele U MA△/dip△
Stirling U MSc/dip
Strathclyde U MSc☆
Warwick U MA

Industrial relations & personnel management
East London P dip△
London U LSE MSc

Industrial relations with labour law
Manchester P dip△

Labour studies
North London P dip☆

Labour studies & industrial relations
Central London P dip△

Management (industrial relations)
Oxford U MSc☆

Management sciences
Manchester UMIST MSc/dip

Management studies
Lancashire P cert☆   □

Management, economics, politics
St Andrews U MLitt/MPhil☆/dip☆

Manpower studies
Central London P MA
Ealing C London MA△
Portsmouth P MA△
Ulster U MSc△

Occupational behaviour
Hatfield P MSc☆

Occupational psychology
London U Birkbeck C MSc△

Organisation & manpower studies
Belfast Queen's U MSSc△

Organisation development
Sheffield City P MSc☆/dip☆

Organisational analysis & behaviour
Lancaster U MA   □

Organisational behaviour
London U Birkbeck C MSc△

Personnel administration
Robert Gordon's IT dip☆

Personnel management
Bristol P dip☆
Doncaster C dip/IPM
Dundee CFE dip☆
Ealing C London dip
Fife CT dip☆
Glasgow C dip(SCOTVEC)☆/IPM☆   □
Gwent CHE dip☆
Leeds P dip
Leicester P IPM☆
Manchester P dip
Middlesex P dip
Napier P IPM☆
Portsmouth P dip
Sandwell CFHE IPM△
South West London C dip☆
Southampton U MSc
Strathclyde U MSc△/dip☆
Teesside P dip☆
Thames Valley C dip☆
Ulster U dip☆
Wales P IPM△
West Glamorgan IHE IPM△

Personnel management & business administration
Aston U MSc/dip

Personnel management & industrial relations
Manchester UMIST MSc✫

Personnel supply
Sandwell CFHE IPS△

Public administration
Glasgow C MA✫ □

Public management
Exeter U MA

Public purchasing management
Ulster U MSc✫/cert✫/dip✫

Public relations
Stirling U MSc✫/Dip✫
Watford C dip✫

Work study
West Glamorgan IHE cert△

Higher degrees by research

Advanced management development
Brighton P PhD/MPhil

Applied economics & human resource management
Ulster U DPhil/MPhil

Behaviour in organisations
Lancaster U PhD/MPhil

Behavioural sciences
Central London P PhD✫/MSc✫

Business studies
North London P PhD/MPhil

Employment & human resources
Bath U PhD✫/MSc✫

Employment relations
Anglia HEC PhD/MPhil

Human resource management
Cardiff U of Wales C PhD✫/MPhil✫

Human resources
Cranfield IT PhD✫/MPhil✫
Cranfield S of Management PhD/MPhil

Industrial relations
Glasgow U PhD/MLitt
Keele U PhD✫/MA✫
Kent U PhD/MPhil
Leeds U MA
London U LSE PhD/MPhil
Manchester U PhD/MA(Econ)
Oxford U DPhil✫/MLitt✫

Industrial relations & personnel management
City U BS PhD✫/MPhil✫

Industrial studies & social studies
Napier P PhD/MPhil

Innovation, design & operations management
Aston U PhD/MPhil

International relations
Keele U PhD/MA

Management & industrial relations
City of London P PhD✫/MPhil✫

Management development
Cranfield S of Management PhD/MPhil

Management learning
Lancaster U PhD/MPhil

Management sciences/studies
St Andrews U PhD/MPhil

Management studies
Central London P PhD✫/MPhil✫

Manpower studies
Ulster U DPhil/MPhil

North West public sector research
Salford U PhD/MPhil/MSc

Occupational studies
Keele U PhD/MA

Organisation & management
Middlesex P PhD/MPhil

Organisation behaviour
Bath U PhD/MPhil

Organisation, management & employment relations
Strathclyde U PhD✫/MPhil✫/MSc✫

Organisational change & development
Bath U PhD/MSc

Public relations
Cranfield IT PhD✫/MPhil✫

Service sector management
Brighton P PhD/MPhil

Safety and hygiene

Higher degrees by instruction

Crime risk management
Cranfield IT MSc✫

Design of energy efficient systems
Cranfield IT MSc✫/dip✫

Environmental health
Nottingham P dip✫

Management & scientific aspects of water surveillance & water quality
Surrey U dip✫

Occupational hygiene
London U S of Hygiene & Tropical Med MSc
Manchester U MSc
Newcastle U MSc✫ □

Public health
Glasgow U MPH

Safety & reliability
Bradford U MSc△

Higher degrees by research

Biological sciences & environmental health
Thames P PhD/MPhil

Construction & environmental health
Bristol P PhD/MPhil/cert/dip

Environmental health
Bristol P PhD/MPhil/dip△

Industrial & environmental health & safety
Surrey U PhD/MPhil

Industrial safety & health
South Bank P PhD/MPhil

Occupational health
London U S of Hygiene & Tropical Med PhD/MPhil
Manchester U PhD/MSc

Occupational health & hygiene
Newcastle U PhD/MPhil

Occupational psychology
London U Birkbeck C PhD/MPhil

Public health
Glasgow U PhD

Secretarial linguist

Bilingual executive assistant: French/German/Italian/Spanish
Lancashire P dip☆ ☐

Bilingual private secretarial Welsh
Ceredigion CFE cert☆

Bilingual secretarial
Chichester CT RSA dip☆
Chippenham TC RSA dip☆
Crawley CT RSA cert☆/RSA dip☆

Bilingual secretarial administration
Newcastle P dip☆

Bilingual secretarial studies
Brighton CT RSA dip☆

Bilingual secretarial: French/German/Spanish
Salford CFE RSA dip☆

Business linguist
South Bank P dip☆

Executive secretarial (bilingual)
Cassio C RSA cert☆/RSA dip☆

Executive secretarial with languages
Bradford & Ilkley Community C IL☆

Graduate secretarial (with languages)
Aberdeen CC dip☆/RSA dip☆

Information administration for linguists
Leeds P dip☆

Intensive secretarial
Lewisham C LCCI dip☆/RSA dip☆ ☐

Language secretary: French, German, Spanish
Guildford CT Cert☆

Office technology & languages
Ealing C London dip☆

Personal assistants/senior secretaries
West Glamorgan IHE LCCI☆/RSA ☐

Secretarial linguist: French
Institut Francais du Royaume-Uni dip☆

Secretarial linguist: French/business studies
Weymouth C RSA dip☆

Secretarial linguist: French/German
Cardiff IHE RSA dip☆
Clarendon CFE IAM☆/RSA dip☆
Shrewsbury CAT RSA dip☆
York CAT RSA dip☆

Secretarial linguist: French/German/Italian
West Glamorgan IHE dip☆/LCCI cert☆/RSA cert☆

Secretarial linguist: French/German/Italian/Spanish
Anglia HEC cert☆/RSA dip☆
Buckinghamshire CHE dip☆
Manchester CT LCCI dip☆/RSA dip☆
North East Worcestershire C RSA dip☆
West London IHE dip☆/IL☆/RSA cert☆/RSA dip☆

Secretarial linguist: French/German/Spanish
Colchester Inst LCC dip☆ ☐
New C dip☆
Somerset CAT RSA dip☆

Secretarial linguist: French/Spanish
Millbrook C RSA dip☆

Secretarial studies: RSA dip

Administrative & secretarial procedures
Abingdon C ☆
Manchester CT ☆ ☐
Croydon C ☆ ☐
Salisbury CT ☆
West Cheshire C RSA Higher dip☆ ☐

Administrative procedures
Bromley CT ☆ ☐
Chichester CT ☆
Chippenham TC ☆
Colchester Inst ☆
Norwich City C ☆
Parson Cross C ☆
Salford CFE ☆

Somerset CAT ☆
Stoke-on-Trent C ☆
Worcester TC ☆

Advanced executive secretarial
North East Wales IHE ☆

Bilingual secretarial: French/German/Spanish
Belfast C of Bus Studies ☆

Executive secretarial
Llandrillo TC ☆

Executive secretarial with languages
Bradford & Ilkley Community C ☆

Graduate secretarial
Reading CT ☆

Graduate secretarial/personal assistants
Northbrook CDT ☆

Graduate secretaries
Dundee CFE ☆

Intensive office technology
HWLC cert△/RSA dip△

Intensive secretarial
Brighton CT ☆
Exeter C ☆
Lewisham C LCCI dip☆/RSA dip☆ ☐
North East Worcestershire C ☆
Stoke-on-Trent C ☆

Personal assistants
Anglia HEC ☆
Belfast C of Bus Studies ☆
Brighton CT ☆
Brooklands TC ☆
Canterbury C ☆
Cardiff IHE ☆
Cassio C ☆
Ceredigion CFE ☆
Clarendon CFE ☆
Coventry TC ☆
Harlow TC ☆
Millbrook C ☆
New C ☆
North West CT ☆
Solihull CT ☆

Personal assistants/advanced secretarial
Crawley CT LCCI△/RSAdip△/RSA dip☆

Personal assistants/executive assistants
Luton CHE ☆

Personal assistants/senior secretaries
West Glamorgan IHE LCCI☆/RSA ☐

Post graduate secretarial
Suffolk CHFE BTEC☆/RSA☆

Private secretarial
Crawley CT ☆

Secretarial
Filton C ☆
Loughborough C

Secretarial & administrative procedures
North Cheshire C ☆

Secretarial & European language studies (French/German/Spanish)
Ealing C London ☆

Secretarial & office procedures
Guildford CT RSA☆

Secretarial linguist: French/German
Llandrillo TC RSA dip☆/RSA△

Secretarial linguist: French/German/Spanish
Coventry TC ☆
New C ☆

Secretarial linguist: French/German
Northbrook CDT ☆

Secretarial procedures
Matthew Boulton C ☆

Secretarial studies: LCCI cert/dip

Advanced executive secretarial
North East Wales IHE ☆

Advanced secretarial
Erith CT ☆

Business administration
North Lincolnshire C ☆

Executive secretarial
Llandrillo TC ☆

Executive secretarial with management
Bradford & Ilkley Community C ☆

Executive secretary
Somerset CAT ☆

Graduate secretarial
Blackburn C ☆

Intensive secretarial
Hendon C ☆

Personal assistants
Weymouth C LCCI dip☆/LCCI cert☆

Personal assistants/advanced secretarial
Crawley CT ☆

Personal assistants/senior secretaries
West Glamorgan IHE LCCI☆/RSA ☐

Private & executive secretarial
Armagh CFE LCCI☆
Blackpool & The Fylde C ☆
Cornwall C ☆
Hendon C ☆
Sandwell CFHE ☆
Stockport C ☆
West London IHE ☆

Private secretarial
Chichester CT cert☆/LCCI☆
Crawley CT ☆
Teesside P

Secretarial
Salisbury CT ☆

Secretarial linguist: French/German/Italian/Spanish
Manchester CT LCCI dip☆/RSA dip☆ ☐

Secretarial linguist: French/German/Spanish
Coventry TC ☆

Other secretarial qualifications

Higher degrees by instruction

Administrative & secretarial procedures
Worcester TC dip☆

Administrative procedures
Shrewsbury CAT dip☆

Executive secretarial
Anglia HEC cert☆

Executive secretarial & office systems
Strathclyde U dip☆

Graduate secretarial
Fife CT dip

Information management
Pitman Education & Training cert

Intensive secretarial
HWLC cert☆
Lewisham C LCCI dip☆/RSA dip☆ ☐
North East Worcestershire C dip☆
Pitman Education & Training cert☆
St Godric's C, London dip☆

Intensive senior secretarial
Mid Kent CHFE ☆

International secretarial
Salisbury CT cert☆

Medical secretarial
North East Worcestershire C AMS☆

Office technology
Pitman Education & Training cert ☐

Office technology & languages
Ealing C London dip☆

Post graduate secretarial
Suffolk CHFE BTEC☆/RSA☆

Private & executive secretarial
Farnborough CT dip☆

Private secretarial
Teesside P dip

Secretarial
Aberdeen CC cert☆/dip☆
Bell CT dip☆

Secretarial & management studies
Ealing C London dip☆

Secretarial administration
Newcastle P dip☆

Secretarial studies
Napier P dip☆

Higher degrees by research

Business studies
York CAT RSA Higher Dip☆ ☐

Accountancy

ACCA
2 years full time
(levels 2 & 3)
Department of Management
and Professional Studies,
West Glamorgan Institute of
Higher Education, Mt
Pleasant, Swansea SA1 6ED
Tel: 0792 469004

The Institute offers postgraduate courses in Accountancy leading to the examinations of ACCA.

The course is broadly based and leads to a rewarding career in accountancy.

Entrance requirements Any degree.
Grants Discretionary.
Head of department T B Williams.

Administrative and secretarial procedures

RSA dip
9 months full time
W J Davison, Faculty of
Business Studies, Central
Manchester College of
Technology, St Johns
Centre, Lower Hardman
Street, Manchester M3 3ER
Tel: 061 831 7791

In this course the College aims to meet the needs of graduates seeking senior secretarial posts or administrative positions in industry and commerce. Students take advanced level examinations in shorthand, audio typewriting and word processing and RSA Higher Diploma in administrative and secretarial procedures.

Grants Discretionary.
Head of faculty W J Davison.

Administrative procedures

Higher diploma
1 year full time
20 places
Marilyn Macdonald,
Department SLCS, Bromley
College of Technology,
Rookery Lane, Bromley,
Kent BR2 8HE
Tel: 081 462 6331

This course provides an integrated approach to acquiring business knowledge and practical business skills. It prepares graduates for executive and management careers, covering information and office technology, personnel, finance, administration, supervision and delegation. There is also a European foreign language route to this qualification. Work experience is an important assessed element of the course.

Entrance requirements University degree or equivalent.
Head of section Marilyn Macdonald.

Bilingual business administration

RSA dip
9 months full time

25 places
Patricia Bull, Department of
Business Studies,
Stradbroke College,
Richmond Centre, Spinkhill
Drive, Sheffield S13 8FD
Tel: 0742 392621

This course combines commercial languages, bilingual business administration and bilingual office skills. A wide range of commercial languages is offered including Russian, Italian, German, French and Spanish. International marketing, modern office technology and desk top publishing ensure that students are equipped for the very latest developments in business administration. A two week placement where commercial language skills can be used is an integral part of the course.

The course leads to RSA Diploma for Bilingual Secretaries and the University of Sheffield Certificate in Bilingual Business Administration.

BUSINESS/EDUCATION/SOCIAL SCIENCES 2

Bilingual executive assistant

dip
1 year full time
25 places
Department of Business & Management, Lancashire Polytechnic, Preston PR1 2TQ
Tel: 0772 201201

This is a postgraduate vocational course for those wishing to obtain bi-lingual positions as executive or personal assistants, secretaries or administrators, either in this country or abroad.

The course provides a balanced programme of two languages for business (French and German or Spanish) with an integrated office communication studies component of office technology, office organisation, management appreciation, business communications, word processing, notetaking, typing and audio. A two-week placement forms an integral part of the course. All elements are examined on a continuous on-course assessment basis together with final examinations and successful completion will result in the award of a polytechnic diploma.
Entrance requirements Degree or equivalent in French, German or Spanish.
Grants LEA discretionary.
Head of school Angela Murphy.

Bilingual secretaryship

LCCI dip
9 months full time
W J Davison, Faculty of Business Studies, Central Manchester College of Technology, City Centre Campus, Manchester M3 3ER
Tel: 061 831 7791

An intensive course for grduates in modern languages, combining a training in business methods and secretarial skills with an extension of language studies (preferably in two foreign languages) to the fields of industry and commerce, leading to LCCI secretarial linguist examination.
Grants Discretionary.

Business administration

MBA/dipBA
1 year full time
25 places
2 years part time
(1 day per week)
35 places
MBA Programme Director, Heriot-Watt Business School, Heriot-Watt University, Riccarton, Edinburgh EH14 4AS
Tel: 031 449 5111
Fax: 031 451 3190

This is a postgraduate post experience course available full-time, on a part-time day release basis or by distance learning. It is especially suitable for engineers, scientists, accountants and other specialists wishing to broaden into general management. There is a wide choice of elective modules which include Health Service Management; Law; Finance; Business Management Information Systems; Investment Analysis; Career Development; Small Business Management.
Entrance requirements Honours degree or equivalent professional qualifications plus 2 years' minimum management experience plus GMAT.
Grants Scottish Education Department for DipBA.
Programme director Dr W N Shaw.

Business administration

MBA
1 year full time
4 years part time
Admissions Tutor MBA, Institute of Management Studies, University of Nottingham, University Park, Nottingham NG7 2RD
Tel: 0602 484848

The MBA degree programme and the MBA in Financial Studies are designed to enhance the managerial abilities of the participants and prepare them for leading careers in industry and commerce in the private and public sectors. They offer a combination of conceptual knowledge, technical skills, problem analysis and personal development appropriate to the modern business environment.
Entrance requirements Normally a good honours degree or equivalent professional qualifications, experience and GMAT.
Admissions tutors Dr V G Gilgeous (MBA Programme), Professor I R Davidson (MBA in Financial Studies).

Business administration

MBA/diploma Business
Administration
MBA 1 year full time
3 years part time
Diploma
1 year full time
3 years part time
Dr D G Jacobs, Sheffield
University Management
School, University of
Sheffield, Sheffield S10 2TN
Tel: 0742 768555

The internationally recognised one-year Sheffield University MBA/Diploma is offered with nine specialist options: general management, marketing management, accounting and financial management, financial services management, European business management, information systems management, production and design management, sports management, and housing management. All students take seven core courses in the first semester: marketing management, accounting and financial management, business policy, organisational behaviour, operations management, business economics, and business statistics. In the second semester, they choose four career-relevant options to suit their chosen specialism. Almost 50 option courses are usually offered. Students qualifying to proceed to the MBA do dissertation work on an empirical topic within their area of interest, and are expected to complete the dissertation within 3-6 months.
Entrance requirements A good honours degree (or overseas equivalent), or equivalent professional qualifications; a minimum GMAT score of 500 (required of all candidates); for candidates whose native language is not English, a minimum TOEFL score of 540.
Course tutor Dr D G Jacobs.

Business administration

MBA
1 year full time
Ian Bird, Director MBA
Programmes, University of
Stirling, Stirling, Scotland
FK9 4LA
Tel: 0786 73171

The MBA comprises nine months coursework followed by three months project. The nine months coursework qualifies for a diploma. Students may study for a general MBA or for a specialist variant currently available in industrial relations and personnel management, retail studies, management information systems, banking, finance, marketing or international business.
Entrance requirements A good honours degree or equivalent professional qualifications; exceptionally candidates' management work experience may qualify them for entry.
Director of programmes Mr Ian Bird.

Business administration (information technology)

MSc
1 year full time
dip
School of Business
Information Management,
Lancashire Polytechnic,
Preston PR1 2TQ
Tel: 0772 201201

This intensive course is primarily a conversion route for science-related or business graduates who wish to acquire a sound IT background with a managerial dimension. Part 1 (25 weeks) will lead to a postgraduate Diploma and on its successful completion the part 2 (25 weeks) Masters' course will be undertaken and this includes a 12 week in-company consultancy project. Credit Accumulation: Part 1 25 credits minimum, Part 2 50 credits minimum.
Entrance requirements Honours degree balanced with relevant industrial experience.
Grants LEA discretionary. Training agency funded.
Course leader David Walters.

Diploma in shipping & transport management

Diploma
9 months full time
Faculty Administrator,
Institute of Marine Studies,
Plymouth: Polytechnic South
West, Drake Circus,
Plymouth PL4 8AA
Tel: 0752 232405 Fax: 0752
232293

A nine month post graduate/post experience course intended to improve the managerial skills of practicing managers in the shipping and transport sector and provide an entry pass to the MSc programme in International Shipping & International Distribution. The course covers the management skills and specialised knowledge required for operational management in an international environment including the use of information technology and operational research methods.
Entrance requirements 23 years of age or over. Degree, HND/C and/or relevant work experience.
Head of department Professor D H Moreby ExC PhD FNI.

Distribution technology

MSc
1 year full time
PhD
full time
and part time
Alan Rushton, Distribution
Studies Unit, Cranfield
Institute of Technology,
Cranfield, Bedford MK43
0AL
Tel: 0234 752768

The MSc programme is academically demanding and also highly relevant to practical career development. It covers all important aspects of logistics and distribution including transport, warehousing, inventory, strategy and information technology. Half the study year may be spent in working with companies on industrial projects. PhD research may also be undertaken.
Entrance requirements A good first degree or an equivalent qualification with appropriate industrial experience.
Course director A S Rushton.

Entrepreneurial studies

MSc
1 year full time
2 years distance learning
dip
9 months full time
Scottish Enterprise
Foundation, University of
Stirling, Stirling, Scotland
FK9 4LA
Tel: 0786 73171
Fax: 0786 50201

This programme provides a focussed study of subjects such as entrepreneurship, the enterprise, venture management and links this to company based project work. Potential students are: (a) those planning to work in support agencies; (b) those wishing to undertake further study prior to research or teaching and (c)those aiming to start their own small businesses.
Entrance requirements Degree or equivalent industrial/ commercial experience.
Grants SED (Full time programme).
Course director Frank Martin.

Finance

MSc
1 year full time
dip
9 months full time
Departments of Economics &
Accounting & Finance,
University of Strathclyde,
Curran Building, 100
Cathedral Street, Glasgow
G4 0LN
Tel: 041 552 4400 ext 3710

The programme in Finance is offered jointly by the Departments of Accounting & Finance and Economics. It is open to ambitious graduates or professionals interested in furthering their careers in finance and accounting. Students take core classes in finance, accounting, and computing, and may select options from a wide range of available courses such as security analysis, finance of multi-national business, project management, accounting theory, financial markets & institutions, money & capital in developing countries, and computer based financial systems.
Entrance requirements Degree or professional qualification in appropriate subject.
Course director J R Davies.

HCIMA Professional qualification (Exceptional entry)

HCIMA
1 year full time
Faculty Secretary, Faculty of Business, Food and Management, Blackpool & The Fylde College, Ashfield Road Campus, Bispham, Blackpool FY2 0HB
Tel: 0253 52352 ext 2201

A full time conversion course which will lead to licentiate membership of the hospitality industry's principal professional body (HCIMA). The programme is concerned with the development of management competencies for today's managers within the industry. The course is of an intensive nature and is designed to equip the graduate to make a successful career in any section of the industry. Major areas of study will concentrate on Food and Beverage, Accommodation, Financial, Human Resource and Operational Management. Each student will be expected to complete the equivalent of 300 hours of appropriate work experience before the completion of the programme. An industry based in-depth project will be undertaken.

Entrance requirements Applicants must hold a university CNAA degree (awarded in the UK in a non-hospitality discipline). Holders of a BTEC Higher National Diploma, for example in Business Studies, who have an appropriate academic profile will be considered. Other degrees or professional qualifications will be considered on an individual basis.

Grants Discretionary awards available from many LEA's. Training agency grants available.

Higher diploma for administrative and secretarial procedures

Higher diploma
1 year full time
20 places
Croydon Business School, Croydon College, Croydon CR9 1DX
Tel: 081 686 5700

This challenging and demanding course leads to the RSA Higher Diploma in Administrative and Secretarial Procedures, which provides training for a responsible role in administration and management. The course also provides the student with a high degree of competence in secretarial skills and also includes practical aspects of information processing. The award of the diploma is based on continual assessment and a one month period of work experience forms a valuable part of the course.

Entrance requirements Degree or equivalent.
Grants LEA Discretionary.
Course Director Mrs Marian Webb.

Hospitality management

HCIMA
dip
Course Leader, Department of Hospitality Studies, Queen Margaret College, Edinburgh, Clerwood Terrace, Edinburgh EH12 8TS
Tel: 031 317 3585 or 031 317 3000 (switchboard)

This is a new 35 week postgraduate diploma course for graduates from other fields which will open doors to a management career in the many sectors of the hotel and catering industry.

Non standard entry qualifications may be considered & special grants are available for women returning to work who require retraining, women requiring training to facilitate a job move, mature students & disabled students.

The two semester course includes a four week industrial placement & provides exemption from HCIMA parts 'A' and 'B' examinations. After successful completion of the course & one year's relevant industrial experience, graduates are eligible for licentiate membership of the HCIMA (Hotel, Catering & Institutional Management Association).

Semester 1 comprises 3 modules: Hospitality practice and operations, Financial & business operations & Marketing to the hospitality consumer.

Semester 2 comprises 3 further modules: Hospitality management, Financial & business management & a Hospitality management project.

Hospitality management

HCIMA
1 year full time
Department of Hotel and
Catering Studies,
Westminster College,
London, Vincent Square,
London SW1P 2PD
Tel: 071 828 1222

This is a conversion course for those with entrepreneurial flair; leading to management careers in only one year in applications ranging from hotels, restuarants, directors dining rooms, business conventions and public and private institutions.

Undertake your year of study in the UK's long established and famous hotel school, situated within easy access of London's major hotels and other catering outlets.

Course subjects: food and beverage management, accommodation management and manpower studies, a feasibility case study.

Entrance requirements A first degree in any faculty other than hospitality management.

Grants This course comes under the category of 'discretionary awards ' but the college plays an active part in assisting students to obtain an award from their local authorities.

Head of department B E G Puxley FHCIMA FCFA.

Hotel, catering & accommodation management

dip
1 year full time
Mr J Bance, Recruitment &
Publicity Officer, The
Queen's College, Glasgow, 1
Park Drive, Glasgow G3 6LP
Tel: 041 334 8141

This course provides vocational training for graduates seeking a career in management within the hotel, catering and accommodation industry. In this growing industry - in which career opportunities are good and varied - there are two main sectors. The institutional or welfare sector includes hospitals, halls of residence, homes for the elderly or handicapped, the armed forces and the Civil Service. The commercial sector includes hotels, motels, restaurants, airport and industrial catering, touring and sports centres. The industry is expanding and larger organisations welcome properly trained applicants to their management programme. The course content- which is college based - includes catering studies, accommodation studies, management studies, finance and accountancy, legal studies, social studies, personnel studies and marketing lectures and includes five weeks industrial placement.

Entrance requirements The course is open to UK and overseas graduates in any discipline and to those with an equivalent qualification - eg: diploma.

Grants This course is approved by the Scottish Education Department for the purpose of awarding a student grant and the qualification has HCIMA recognition.

Course leader Mrs M Biggam.

Industrial relations

MA
1 year full time
(2 full days per week)
2 years part time
(1 full day per week)
25 places
Convenor, MA Industrial
Relations, Department of
Human Sciences, Brunel
University, Uxbridge,
Middlesex UB8 3PH
Tel: 0895 56461

This multi-disciplinary programme combines an overview of different theoretical perspectives on industrial relations with an analysis of contemporary industrial relations issues and problems. There are course units in industrial relations, industrial sociology, labour law and research methods. Students also write a dissertation on a topic relevant to their interests.

Entrance requirements Applicants should possess a degree or equivalent qualifications and experience.

Course convenor Peter Seglow.

Intensive secretarial & information technology

RSA dip
5 months full time
22 places
Mrs V Gibb, Department of
Business, North East Surrey
College of Technology,
Reigate Road, Ewell, Epsom,
Surrey KT17 3DS
Tel: 081 394 1731

This course is a preparation for administrative executive positions in industry and commerce. Subjects studied are: note-taking, keyboarding, typewriting, transcription, marketing, business background, communications, law, information technology and word-processing.

Language graduates study commercial languages in French, German, Spanish, Italian, Russian. RSA and Pitman examinations are available and you will learn modern techniques on up to date equipment.

Entrance requirements Degree or equivalent.
Grants LEA.
Course tutor Mrs V Gibb.

International agricultural marketing

MSc
1 year full time
20 places
dip
Ms E Oughton, (Course
Director), Department of
Agricultural Economics &
Food Marketing, University
of Newcastle upon Tyne,
Newcastle upon Tyne NE1
7RU

A diploma course of nine months or an advanced course of 12 or 24 months for the MSc depending upon qualifications and experience. Four courses are studied, the two core courses, marketing principles and international agricultural and food markets are obligatory. Two options to be chosen from agricultural marketing in less developed countries, international trade, quantiative-methods for marketing and agricultural development. Subject to satisfactory exam performance students for the MSc undertake a three month dissertation project.

Entrance requirements Honours degree in relevant subject or professional qualifications and appropriate experience.
Head of Department Professor C Ritson.

Management & implementation of development projects

MSc
1 year full time
15 places
The Postgraduate
Admissions Officer,
Department of Civil &
Structural Engineering,
UMIST - The University of
Manchester Institute of
Science and Technology, PO
Box 88, Manchester M60
1QD

There are six core modules, human and organisational management, decision process and techniques, design for management I and II, project implementatiron, research methodology and two optional modules from, irrigation I and II, water supply and sanitation, infrastructure development, environmental impact. A dissertation project follows this.

Entrance requirements Good honours degree or equivalent.
Course director Professor P A Thompson.

Management science

PhD
2 years full time
3 years part time
MPhil
Postgraduate Admissions
Tutor, European Business
Management School,
University College of
Swansea, Singleton Park,
Swansea, West Glamorgan
SA2 8PP
Tel: 0792 205678

Supervision available for research (leading to the degree of PhD or MPhil) in the areas of operational research (especially distribution, inventory and production control and micro-computer solutions), statistical computing, applied statistics, information systems, marketing, tourism, finance, economic forecasting and human resource management.

Entrance requirements Good honours degree.
Head of department Professor R B Gravenor.

Management science & computer applications in management systems

PhD/MPhil
2-3 years full time
MSc
1 year full time
25 places
Mrs S Hyde, College of Manufacturing, Cranfield Institute of Technology, Cranfield, Bedford MK43 0AL
Tel: 0234 752771

This MSc programme has two options (1) Management science studies (2) Computer applications in management systems and is designed as a one year programme for applicants with a good honours degree.

A preliminary year's course of study is available for those students whose entry qualifications do not meet those required for direct entry.

Entrance requirements Good honours degree or equivalent.
Grants Bursaries and industrial sponsorship.

Management studies

cert
1 year part time
20 places
DMS
R Armstrong, Course Leader, School of Business, Lancashire Polytechnic, Preston PR1 2TQ
Tel: 0772 201201

The aim is to provide an advanced course of study for students who are already well qualified by education and experience; it is principally concerned with the wider development of a person as a manager. It is particularly well suited to those changing careers or returning to employment.

Stage I (first three months) may be taken as a polytechnic certificate without any work experience, and the DMS completed later.
Entrance requirements Degree, HND/C and/or relevant work experience.
Grants LEA discretionary.
Head of school Professor Graham Kelly.

Management studies

DMS
1 year full time
Dr O Gaafar, Course Tutor, Management Centre, Staffordshire Polytechnic, College Road, Stoke on Trent ST4 2DE
Tel: 0782 412143

This course offers a challenging opportunity for the senior manager of the future to equip himself or herself with a wide range of relevant knowledge and skills. Stage 1 provides an introduction to a range of management disciplines including accounting, economics, quantitative methods, marketing, operations management, management of organisations. Stage 11 develops many of the disciplines the foundations of which were laid in Stage 1 although new disciplines are introduced. The areas covered include, financial management, management information, marketing, planning, management of people, business strategy.
Entrance requirements A degree of the CNAA or a UK university equivalent or a higher award of BTEC or SCOTVEC together with appropriate experience, or at least 4 years substantial management experience.
Admissions tutor Dr O Gaafar.

Management systems & sciences

MA
1 year full time
MSc
1 year full time
35 places
Mr P Keys, Department of Management Systems & Sciences, University of Hull, Hull HU6 7RX
Tel: 0482 465779

The MA course will enhance a student's knowledge of problem-solving and decision making in organisations. It includes organisational and social science inputs as well as a strong core of systems concepts and information technology.

MSc Management Science provides training in principles and application of important management science techniques, MSc Information Management provides training in the management of information resources and information systems. Both MSc programmes place particular emphasis on microcomputer based information and decision support technologies. All MA/Msc courses involve a six month taught programme followed by a dissertation/project.

Entrance requirements Normally an honours degree or equivalent. HND/HNC or professional qualifications may also be considered.

Grants Available from various sources.

Head of department Professor R L Flood.

Management with manufacturing or marketing

dip (SCOTVEC)
1 year full time
The Admissions Officer, Glasgow College, Cowcaddens Road, Glasgow G4 0BA
Tel: 041 331 3000

Designed for those wishing a career in industrial or service-based organisations. The course offers students the opportunity to supplement their first degree with vocational study in depth of either Manufacturing Management or Marketing. Core subjects include personal effectiveness, management of people and functional activities, analysis of organisation environment.

Grants Limited number available from SED.

Head of Department Mr P O'Donnell.

Manufacturing management

MSc
1 year full time
Mrs S Hyde, College of Manufacturing, Cranfield Institute of Technology, Cranfield, Bedford MK43 0AL
Tel: 0234 752771

Primarily designed for Women Graduates with Work Experience who want to retrain or update their knowledge. The course involves modern Manufacturing Technologies, the development of interpersonal skills and Management Techniques. Each student will carry out a high level supervised project of real practical value upon which their MSc thesis will be based. The first six months are based at Cranfield, the second six months spent mainly in industry. Fees: Will be paid by the Training Agency for all returners. Participating companies will provide a nominal salary for the students.

Master of Business administration

MBA
Admissions Officer, Department of Management Studies, Glasgow College, Cowcaddens Road, Glasgow G4 0BA
Tel: 041 331 3000

This masters course is part of an Integrated Management Development Programme designed for experienced managers who both implement policy and participate in its formulation.

Entrance requirements : to DMS Foundation Year - degree or postgraduate diploma. Direct entry to MBA Year 2 - honours degree and 3 years'relevant management experience.

Head of department W Elder MA MSc MPhil MIProdE CEng.

Money, banking & finance

MA/dip Money, Banking and
Finance
MA 1 year full time
2 years part time
Dip
9 months full time
18 months part time
Mr Robert D Sedgwick,
Sheffield University
Management School,
University of Sheffield,
Sheffield S10 2TN
Tel: 0742 768555

This internationally recognised MA/Diploma in Money, Banking and Finance is designed both for those seeking to enhance their qualifications to pursue careers in banking, finance, commerce, or industry and for those wishing to use the rigorous training as a foundation for academic work or further research. All students take courses in Econometric Theory and The Theory of Finance, and have a choice of two option courses chosen according to personal background and objectives. Current options include Money and Banking, International Money and Finance, Finance and Financial Markets, and Advanced Econometric Methods. Students qualifying to proceed to the MA do a dissertation/research project on a topic within the degree subject area.
Entrance requirements An upper second class honours degree (main subject normally economics) or the overseas degree equivalent, or if the qualification is of a lower standard or is not sufficiently related to the subject of study, a pass in a qualifying examination.
Director of programme Mr Robert D Sedgwick.

Occupational hygiene

MSc
1 year full time
Administrative Assistant, The
Medical School, University of
Newcastle upon Tyne,
Newcastle upon Tyne NE2
4HH
Tel: 091 222 6000

The aim of the course is to produce a hygienist who is well grounded in the theory of occupational hygiene and competent in its practice. Studies in occupational hazards caused by chemical, biological and physical agents, hazard evaluation, and environmental control are complemented by practical field exercises in all types of industry. Additionally, a four-month research project is required.
Entrance requirements Graduate in pure or applied science, medicine, or specially approved qualifications.
Head of department Dr J Steel.

**Office technology,
information management,
secretarial training &
foreign language training**

Pitman, LCCI & RSA
Examinations
full time
part time, day, evening
day release and Seminar
Programmes
Pitman Secretarial Colleges,
Department of Secretarial
studies, Pitman Education &
Training, 154 Southampton
Row, London WC1B 5AX
Tel: 071 837 4481

PITMAN offer you a choice of business/secretarial courses to complement your academic qualifications. Special intensive courses run year round and during the Summer vacation period. Our Information Management, Office Technology, Secretarial, Computing and specialised courses lead to qualifications for immediate employment. Pitman Colleges in Central London, Leeds, Oxford and Cambridge.

Operational research

PhD
3 years full time
MSc
1 year full time
MSc/dip
1 year full time
Postgraduate Admissions
Tutor, Department of
Operational Research &
Operations Management,
Lancaster University,
Lancaster LA1 4YX
Tel: 0524 65201

The department's international reputation is based on applying operational research and operations management to real problems of purchasing, production, marketing, distribution and finance in industrial, commercial and public sector organisations. Research supervision is available in these areas and on associated relevant techniques, such as forecasting and simulation.

The MSc course is designed to produce the operational research professional. Lecture courses in the above areas of application complement those on mathematical techniques and on the methodology of problem solving. There is a four month consultancy study for the top management of an organisation.

The MSc/diploma has a similar orientation.

Entrance requirements A good honours degree with a numerate background is normally required. The MSc/diploma is for less numerate students, whose degree depends solely on performance at Lancaster.

Grants In excess of 20 SERC awards are available for the MSc.

Head of department Professor Alan Mercer.

Operational research & computer techniques

Advanced Diploma
(University of Southampton)
1 year full time
20 places
Mr C Crutchley, Information
Systems Division,
Southampton Institute of
Higher Education, East Park
Terrace, Southampton SO9
4WW
Tel: 0703 229381

This course is designed for those with some industrial or commercial experience but who have had no formal training in operational research. It will have a practical bias and the students will be expected to carry out project work and industrial case studies using the Institute's facilities which include a VAX 11/780, and networked IBM P.C.'s.

The vocational nature of this course cannot be stressed too highly, for careers in Operational Research, Scientific Computing, and Systems Analysis, and can also be used to gain entry to Master's Programmes. The Advanced Diploma is the official preparatory year for the MSc in Operational Research at the University of Southampton.

Entrance requirements Applicants must be at least 20 years of age and possess either a degree of a recognised university or an HND/HNC or a professional qualification. Alternatively, applicants over 27 years of age with relevant commercial or industrial experience will be considered on merit. Mathematics to A level standard is desirable.

Grants LEA discretionary.

Head of Division Mr D E Heffer.

Organisational analysis & behaviour

MA
1 year full time
2 years part time
Postgraduate Admissions
Officer, Department of
Behaviour in Organisations,
Lancaster University,
University House, Lancaster
LA1 4YX
Tel: 0524 65201

Designed for graduates of a social science, also for those with managerial or administrative experience and for personnel or industrial relations staff. The course provides an overview of the major concepts and theories relevant to an understanding of organisational behaviour and reviews their practical implications. It includes a three month project placement.

Entrance requirements Normally a first or second class honours degree in psychology, sociology or a related social science subject.

Head of department A Whitaker.

Personal assistant

Dip RSA
1 year full time
Computing & Office
Technology Section, West
Cheshire College , Eaton
Road, Handbridge, Chester
CH4 7ER
Tel: 0244 677677

Higher diploma in administrative and secretarial procedures:
This highly acclaimed advanced diploma course is designed for men and women seeking executive secretarial posts in the private and public sectors of industry and commerce in Britain and overseas. This is a fully integrated, task-based course, using a practical approach to the training of personal assistants/senior secretaries, and leading to advanced administrative and secretarial qualifications.
Entrance requirements Degree or equivalent qualification.
Grants Discretionary.
Course tutor Mrs M Ellwood.

Personal assistant

RSA Higher dip
9 months (36 weeks) full
time
50 places
Mrs D Curley, School of
Business Studies, York
College of Arts &
Technology, Dringhouses,
York Y02 1UA
Tel: 0904 704141

However serious the unemployment situation may be there are usually jobs for personal assistants. Our intensive course leading to the RSA Higher Diploma in Administrative Procedures equips graduates with secretarial and administrative skills for a rewarding career and the potential for moving into management. The course includes secretarial skills, management appreciation, communicaton in a commercial environment, word processing information technology and a bilingual secretarial option. Work experience is an integral part of the course.
Entrance requirements Degree or equivalent qualification.
Grants LEA, Discretionary.

Personal assistants/senior secretaries

RSA/LCCI NVQ Stages 3
and 4 in business
administration and
secretarial procedures
1 year full time
20 places
Head of Department of
Business Studies,
Department of Business,
West Glamorgan Institute of
Higher Education, Mt
Pleasant, Swansea SA1 6ED
Tel: 0792 469114 ext 2240

An intensive training and development programme is provided for graduates who wish initially to pursue a career as a personal assistant or a private secretary to senior management, but who later may themselves seek careers in management. The bilingual programme language options are German, French, Spanish and Welsh.
Entrance requirements Degree or equivalent qualification.
Grants Students may be eligible for an LEA grant.
Course tutor Mrs P M Waymark.

Personnel management

dip(SCOTVEC)
1 year full time
IPM
Admissions Officer,
Department of Management
Studies, Glasgow College,
Cowcaddens Road, Glasgow
G4 0BA
Tel: 041 331 3000

This course is designed for graduates wanting to follow a career in personnel management. The course consists of two stages. Stage I covers personnel management, personnel information and decision making, introducton to organisational behaviour. Stage II covers the applied subjects of employee relations, employee resourcing and employee development and a practical personnel skills input.
Grants SED.
Head of Department W Elder MA MSc MPhil MIProdE CEng.

Postgraduate administrators/linguists

RSA/Dip
32 weeks full time
The Director, Department of
Secretarial studies,
Colchester Institute,
Sheepen Road, Colchester,
Essex CO3 3LL
Tel: 0206 761660

Integrated course of a highly practical nature including managerial and administrative tasks, law, economics, information processing, secretarial skills and work experience. Language options also available. Students prepared initially for Administrative and PA roles, with management as ultimate objective. RSA Higher Diploma in Administrative procedures (course assessment); RSA examinations in secretarial skills etc.
Course tutor Miss J S Blockley.

Public administration

dip (SCOTVEC)
3 years part time
Admissions Officer,
Department of Law & Public
Administration, Glasgow
College, Cowcaddens Road,
Glasgow G4 0BA
Tel: 041 331 3000

Designed as a final professional qualification for administrators in the Public Sector. Course includes government administration, law, economics, finance, information systems, project.
Entrance requirements Degree or equivalent, or 5 years' appropriate experience.
Grants SED or Employer.
Head of department Mrs J Charlton.

Secretarial course for graduates

RSA
18 weeks full time
40 places
RSA
8 months part time
40 places
Office Studies Department,
Lewisham College,
Tressillian Building,
Lewisham Way, Lewisham,
London SE4 1UT
Tel: 081 692 0353

Intensive 18 weeks' secretarial course concentrating on office skills to enable students to achieve employment quickly. Background lectures in office administration and management. Very well-equipped department for all apects of information technology and word processing. Bilingual option available.

A part time secretarial course is also available. This is intended for unemployed graduates who are able to study for up to 21 hours a week for the eight months of the course.
Entrance requirements Degree, any discipline.
Fees on application.
Head of department Mrs M D Drew MA BEd(Hons) Dip RSA FSBT.

Education

Education has been making a lot of headlines recently: the new National Curriculum, controversy over the spread of TVEI, cuts in higher education, new city technical schools, talk of low morale and declining standards. Are we witnessing a profession in decline or the start of a new Golden Age?

If you want to take an active part in the education debate by training to teach, there are one-year Postgraduate Certificate of Education (PGCE) courses offered by institutions all over the country, as well as the new, two-year conversion course leading to a PGCE in the shortage areas of mathematics, physics and CDT (craft, design and technology). If your interest is more academic there are courses in the philosophy of education, child development and the history of education in the pages that follow. Many non-PGCE courses, however, are designed for those already in teaching posts. To reflect the fact that nearly all first-degree graduates studying education are training to teach, I shall concentrate on the PGCE.

Variety of courses

There are many different kinds of PGCE courses run by education departments in universities, polytechnics and colleges. Some will qualify you to teach the younger child - infant, junior, primary - and others the older child and young adult - middle, secondary and further education. For primary schools, PGCE courses train you to teach right across the curriculum, while most secondary PGCEs train you in a specialist subject, plus a subsidiary. Unlike many postgraduate courses, grants for PGCEs are mandatory.

Two recent initiatives in teacher-training - the articled and licensed teachers' schemes - are worth noting. The articled teachers' scheme enables graduates to undertake a predominantly school-based two-year training course while being paid a bursary from the LEA where they are studying and teaching. The licensed teachers' scheme enables graduates and non-graduates of 26 or over, who have completed at least two years in higher education, to teach in schools while following a two year part-time course of teacher training.

Nearly all applications are made through a central clearing house, the Graduate Teacher Training Registry (GTTR). The exceptions are the four further education training courses at Bolton College, Garnett College, Huddersfield Polytechnic and Wolverhampton Polytechnic and the course for teachers of the deaf at Manchester University. Also outside the GTTR are Art Teachers Certificate/Diploma courses which have their own clearing house (Penn House, 9 Broad Street, Hereford HR4 9AP) and teacher training courses in Scottish and Northern Irish institutions (TEACH, PO Box 165, Holyrood Road, Edinburgh EH8 8AT or Department of Education, Rathgael House, Balloo Road, Bangor, County Down,respectively).

West Sussex Institute
of Higher Education

The Dome
Upper Bognor Road
Bognor Regis
West Sussex PO21 1HR
Telephone (0243) 865581

Incorporating:
Bishop Otter College, Chichester
Bognor Regis College

Postgraduate Study

Education

PGCE (Primary): 5-8 or 7-12 year olds.
PGCE (Secondary): English, History or Mathematics.
PGCE Secondary Mathematics: 2 year course.

The Secondary PGCE is for English, History or Mathematics graduates. The two year secondary Mathematics course is for non-mathematics graduates whose degree has some mathematical content.

- Practical Approach: extensive classroom experience.
- Small group work in seminars and workshops.
- Continuous assessment based on development and performance (no written exam)

Articled Teachers Scheme (leading to PGCE)

- 2 year, school based programme.
- In West Sussex, Hampshire, or Isle of Wight LEA schools.
- A bursary is available which is in excess of the standard grant.

Applications for PGCE and Articled Teachers Scheme through:
Graduate Teacher Training Registry
3 Crawford Place, London W1H 2BN

In-Service Courses for Teachers

MA (ED) (Validated by the University of Southampton)

- 2 year, part time, for experienced teachers.
- Focusses on quality of pupil learning .
- Full use of your own teaching experience.
- Four inter related modules.
- Individual research and dissertation.

Regional Credit Transfer Scheme (leading to Diploma in Advanced Educational Study)

- Adult and Community Education (6 Certificates)
- Dance (6)
- Early childhood education (4)
- Mathematics (9)
- Mentorship
- Science (7)
- Special Educational Needs (4)

Applications for In Service Courses to the Admissions Office
at the main Institute address above.

Research Opportunities

West Sussex Institute offers opportunities for Postgraduate research leading to MPhil or PhD.

- Education and Teaching Studies, Arts, Humanities, Social Sciences.

Suitably qualified graduates should enquire in the first instance to:
Dr JT Brighton, Deputy Director (Academic)
West Sussex Institute of Higher Education
Bishop Otter College, College Lane, Chichester, West Sussex PO19 4PE

Applying for entry

If you intend to apply through the GTTR you can request application forms from 1 September in the year preceding entry by sending a 10 x 7 inch self-addressed envelope stamped for a weight of 100g to GTTR, 3 Crawford Place, London W1H 2BN. As well as the application form you will also be sent a G1 Booklet which will explain how to apply and which also lists all institutions in England and Wales that offer PGCE courses. Those who apply early stand a much better chance of being accepted on the course.

On the form you will be asked to list four institutions in order of preference. Course prospectuses are available from the institutions themselves or from your careers service so try to choose the four courses that best meet your needs. An Association of Graduate Careers Advisory Services (AGCAS) survey - *Selection Procedures and Criteria for PGCE Courses* - is also available in your careers service and contains a lot of useful information about how and when courses recruit and what they look for. Most candidates are accepted by their first choice institution, so spend most of your time choosing your number one.

The application form is fairly straightforward but has several key questions, the answers to which may determine whether or not you will be given an interview. Two relate specifically to the experience you have had with young people - 'Any teaching experience' and 'Other work with young people' - and one (and this is the largest blank space on the form) asks you your reasons for wanting to enter the profession. All courses would like individuals who have thought clearly about why they want to teach and what they can offer in terms of skills, experience and commitment. If you haven't had much contact with children before, try to get some before you fill in the form. At the very least, arrange with a local school to do some observation of lessons.

Interviews

PGCE interviews can vary widely from institution to institution but typically they will last about half an hour and you will be interviewed by a panel of people. As well as the course tutors, local headmasters are frequently co-opted onto the panel. Don't be too surprised, however, if you find yourself involved in a more complex selection process: group discussions, role play and written exercises are all used in some places.

It is possible, and advisable, to do some simple preparation before your interview. Your careers service will have an AGCAS leaflet, *Preparing for Interview for PGCE Courses*, and might be able to offer you a practice interview. Read the education press so that you are aware of any big issues around - new exams, pay disputes, curriculum developments -because the interviewers will not only be interested in you as a person but also as someone who has a general interest in the future of education.

As for the kind of personal qualities they will be looking for at interview, a recent Department of Education and Science (DES) circular expressed this particularly well: 'Institutions should look in particular for a sense of responsibility, a robust but balanced outlook, awareness, sensitivity, enthusiasm and facility in communication.' I would add a couple of others to this list: stamina, because it's an exhausting job, and an ability to form relationships with children, which is central to the work.

Recently there has been some controversy about which degree

courses are 'relevant' for admission to a PGCE. The DES would like all applicants to be studying a first degree subject which is 'relevant' to (ie appears on) the school curriculum. Each institution, however, is responsible for its own interpretation of DES guidelines so if you find yourself studying a non relevant subject, contact the places where you would like to take a PGCE before completing the application form, and see what their policy is. Stress that you have compensatory qualities like commitment, enthusiasm and extensive experience with young children, and highlight those parts of your degree course that are most 'relevant' in curriculum terms.

Finding work

When you have completed the PGCE your chances of finding a post quickly depend very largely on your willingness to consider jobs all over the country, your specialist subject and, of course, your teaching practice report. You will be cheered to know that nearly all graduates who want a teaching job do in fact get one, although some are forced to accept short-term contracts. The DES is, of course, keenest of all to recruit specialists in shortage subjects like maths, physics, chemistry, and CDT and offers graduates of these disciplines a bursary, currently £1300, in addition to their grant. The Stock Exchange, the EITB and the Society of Chemical Industries are also offering bursaries to those training to teach physics, maths and chemistry at secondary level.

I'm as confused as anyone, including the DES, about predicting the numbers studying for PGCEs in the future but it does seem as though there will be a fairly large increase in the number of primary PGCE places in the next three years and a much smaller one in the number of secondary places.

Chris Phillips

This listing contains **taught courses** (under the heading 'Higher degrees by instruction') and **research opportunities** (under the heading 'Higher degrees by research'). All study exceeds two terms or six months and is offered on both a full-time and part-time basis unless otherwise indicated. Post-experience and in-service courses are only included when advertised.

☐   This symbol indicates that the **taught course(s)** or **research opportunities** are advertised at the end of this listing.

Biol   An italic abbreviation indicates that an advertisement has been placed at the end of another chapter.

☆   This symbol indicates full-time study only.

△   This symbol indicates part-time study only.

Postgraduate study listed under 'General' is intended for those who do not wish to become qualified teachers but who are nevertheless interested in studying the academic and peripheral applications of education. 'Curriculum studies' lists courses and research opportunities intended for those wishing to study a specific subject area. Courses listed under 'PGCE......' are training courses leading to a graduate teacher training qualification. The PGCE conversion course leads to the same qualification but is listed as PGCE......(conversion) under 'PGCE other categories'. The subheadings 'PGCE (art/languages/music/physical education/ science/other categories)'list secondary teacher training courses only. Further information regarding PGCE courses can be obtained either from the institutions' prospectuses or by writing to Graduate Teacher Training Registry (GTTR), 3 Crawford Place, London W1H 2BN (please enclose a stamped addressed envelope). The National Association of Teachers in Further and Higher Education (NATFHE) handbook lists all PGCE courses in England and Wales, and is available from GTTR.

For quick reference to advertisements, please use the 'Advertiser's course entry index'. For further information regarding the listing, please refer to page 53.

General (excluding post experience courses)

Higher degrees by instruction

Access studies to higher education
South Bank P dip

Adult education
Hull U MA☆/MEd☆

Adult education & learning
Durham U MA☆

Advanced educational & social research methods
Open U MSc△

Advanced educational studies
Aberystwyth, UC of Wales
  MEd☆/dip☆
Belfast Queen's U dip☆
Newcastle U dip☆

Advanced educational studies (communicative modern language teaching)
Stirling U MEd/dip   □

Agricultural education
Reading U MSc☆/dip☆

Applied linguistics
Birmingham U MA/BLitt/dip

Applied research in education
East Anglia U MA/MEd

Art & design in education
London U Inst of Education MA

Arts management in education
City U MA

Assessment
Bristol U MEd☆

Careers guidance
Kent C for the Careers Service
  dip☆

Chemistry & chemical education
Glasgow U MSc(SciEduc)

Child development
London U Inst of Education MA/
  MSc

Child development & philosophy of education
London U Inst of Education MA/
  MSc

Christian education
Edinburgh U dip☆

Communicative modern language teaching
Stirling U MEd/Dip

Community education
Edinburgh U MSc/dip

Community education management
Sheffield U cert△/dip

University of Reading
Faculty of Education and Community Studies

POSTGRADUATE STUDIES

The Faculty of Education and Community Studies was established in April 1989 with the merger of Bulmershe College of Higher Education and the University of Reading. The Faculty is sited on the purpose-built campus of the former Bulmershe College, one mile from the main University Whiteknights campus and two miles from the centre of Reading (London Paddington 23 mins).

The Faculty offers the following opportunities for postgraduate studies:

Research – part-time or full-time, in areas of education and training of people of all ages in the UK, EEC and throughout the world, with special attention being paid to developing countries – leading to M.Phil or Ph.D.

Taught Masters Courses – part-time or full-time higher degree courses covering a wide area of arts and science education and education management.

PGCE Courses – full-time, one-year specialisms in nursery/infant or junior teaching, primary music, and a wide range of arts and science subjects at secondary level.

Applications for the PGCE courses should be made through the GTTR.
Applications for other courses should be made direct to the Sub-Dean, Faculty of Education and Community Studies, University of Reading, Bulmershe Court, Earley, Reading, Berks. RG6 1HY. Tel. (0734) 318816.

INSTITUTE OF EDUCATION
UNIVERSITY OF LONDON

The Institute offers a full range of courses: initial teacher training for graduates; advanced diplomas and BEd degree courses; Master's degrees (MA, MSc, MEd); Research degrees (MPhil, PhD); Associateship, Special and Short Courses.

Further information:

The Deputy Registrar, Institute of Education, University of London, 20 Bedford Way, London WC1H 0AL.

Teaching and research cover the following areas:

- Foundation disciplines — Philosophy, Psychology, Sociology, History, Economics of education.
- Curriculum studies — subjects of the school curriculum.
- Comparative education.
- Education of children with special needs.
- Education in developing countries.
- English for speakers of other languages.
- Educational policy and administration.
- Child development.
- Statistical methods.
- Health and welfare education.
- Educational media.
- Computer applications in education.

Comparative education
London U Inst of Education MA/
MEd

Computers in education
London U King's C MA

Continuing education
Leeds U MEd

Early childhood studies
Roehampton I dip☆

Economics of education
London U Inst of Education MA

Education
Aberdeen U MEd/dip
Bangor, U of Wales MEd☆
Belfast Queen's U MEd
Bristol U MEd☆
Cambridge U MPhil☆
Cardiff U of Wales C MEd☆
Dundee U MEd/dip△
East Anglia U MA
East London P MEd△
Glasgow U MEd
Lancaster U MA
Leicester U MA△/diploma△   ☐
Goldsmiths' C London U MA☆
Nottingham P MEd△
Open U MA△
Southampton U MA(Ed)/cert/dip
Ulster U dip

Education & the mass media
Manchester U MEd☆

Education (special educational needs)
Lancaster U MA

Education for primary health care
Manchester U MEd☆

Education in developing countries
London U Inst of Education MA/
MEd
Manchester U MEd☆

Education in multicultural urban areas
London U Inst of Education MA

Education management
Sheffield City P MSc/cert/dip
Wales P dip△

Education marketing
Manchester U MEd☆

Education studies
Durham U MA(Ed)/MA/dip
Loughborough U MA△

Educational administration
Dundee U dip△
London U Inst of Education MA

Educational guidance for adults
Goldsmiths' C London U MA☆

Educational management
Bath U MEd

Educational management & administration
Manchester U MEd☆

Educational management & planning
Cardiff U of Wales C dip☆

Educational media & technology
Hull U dip☆

Educational policy & management
Brunel U MA

Educational psychology
Brunel U MSc
Edinburgh U MSc☆/dip☆
London U Inst of Education MA/
MSc
Manchester U MEd☆/MSc☆
Moray House CE MSc☆
Newcastle U MEd☆/MSc☆
Southampton U MSc
Strathclyde U MSc

Educational statistics & child development
London U Inst of Education MA/
MSc

Educational statistics & educational administration
London U Inst of Education MA

Educational studies
Glasgow U MPhil
Hull U dip☆
Hull U MA/MEd/dip   ☐
Lancaster U dip
Manchester U MEd☆
Newcastle U BPhil☆/dip☆
Roehampton I MA☆
Sheffield U MEd/dip
Surrey U MSc/dip△   ☐
York U MA

Educational technology
Aberystwyth, UC of Wales MEd☆
Bath U MEd

Energy & buildings
Cranfield IT MSc☆   *Eng*

Equal opportunities in education
Manchester U MEd☆

Film & TV studies for education
London U Inst of Education MA

French
Hull U MA☆

Further & adult education
Manchester P cert△
Salford CFE cert△

Further & higher education
Nottingham P cert△

Geography in education
London U Inst of Education MA

Health care ethics
Manchester U MA☆

Health education & health promotion studies
Manchester U MSc/dip

Health promotion & health education
Wales U C of Med MSc

Higher & further education
London U Inst of Education MA

History of education
London U Inst of Education MA

History of English education
Manchester U MEd☆

Independent study
East London P MA/MSc/dip

Language in education
Aberystwyth, UC of Wales dip☆

Language teaching to adults
Goldsmiths' C London U MA△

Management & administration in education
Bristol U MEd☆

Management & administration of higher education
Manchester U MEd☆

Management in higher education
Surrey U MSc☆

Mathematical education
Roehampton I dip☆

Mathematical, statistical & computing education
London U Inst of Education MSc

Mathematics education
Southampton U cert☆

Media in educational development
Stirling U MPhil/dip

Media technology for teaching English as a foreign language
Newcastle U MA☆

Methodology of TEFL
Stirling U dip☆

Music education
Roehampton I MA☆/dip☆

Organisation, planning & management in education
Reading U MA☆

PGCE primary
Craigie CE PGCE☆   ☐

PGCE teaching of English as a 2nd language
Aberystwyth, UC of Wales
  PGCE☆

Philosophy of education
London U Inst of Education MA
Manchester U MEd☆

Population for family life education
Manchester U MEd

Post-compulsory education
Sheffield U MEd/dip

Practice of higher education
Surrey U MSc△/dip△

Preclinical science & education
Glasgow U MSc(MedSci)☆

Professional studies in education
Leicester U MA/cert/dip

Professional studies in education (computing)
South Bank P dip☆

Psychology & education of children with special needs
London U Inst of Education
  MA△/MSc☆

Psychology of education
London U Inst of Education MA/
  MSc

Psychology of education & philosophy of education
London U Inst of Education MA

Psychology of education & primary education
London U Inst of Education MA

Race & education
Birmingham U MSocSc/dip

Race relations & community studies
Bradford U MSc/dip☆

Recreation management
Loughborough U MSc☆

Rights in education
London U Inst of Education MA

Social learning theory & practice
Leicester U dip△

Sociology (with special reference to education)
London U Inst of Education MSc

Sociology of education
London U Inst of Education MA/
  MSc
Manchester U MEd☆
Warwick U MA/dip

Special education
Sheffield U MEd/dip

Special education (international)
Manchester U MEd☆

Teacher education
Manchester U MEd☆

Teaching
Manchester P MA△

Teaching English for specific purposes
St Mark & St John C MEd☆

Urban education
London U King's C MA

Women & education
Sussex U MA△

Women's studies & education
Lancaster U MA

Higher degrees by research

Adult & community education
Liverpool P PhD/MPhil

Adult & continuing education
Keele U PhD△/MA△

Applied research in education
East Anglia U PhD☆/MPhil☆

Art & design education
Brighton P PhD/MPhil

Community education
Liverpool U PhD/MPhil
Open U PhD/MPhil/BPhil

Computer assisted learning
Open U PhD/MPhil
Surrey U PhD/MPhil

Continuing education
Warwick U PhD/MA/MPhil

Development in education overseas
Newcastle U PhD/MPhil

Education
Aberdeen U PhD☆/MLitt☆/
  MPhil☆
Aberystwyth, UC of Wales
  PhD☆/MPhil☆
Anglia HEC PhD☆/MPhil☆
Bangor, U of Wales PhD☆/
  MEd☆/MPhil☆
Bath U PhD/MPhil
Belfast Queen's U PhD/MA(Ed)
Birmingham U PhD
Bradford U PhD/MPhil
Brighton P PhD/MPhil
Bristol P PhD/MPhil/dip

Bristol U PhD☆/MEd☆
Brunel U PhD/MPhil
Cambridge U PhD☆/MLitt☆/
  MSc☆/dip☆
Canterbury Christ Church C
  PhD/MPhiL☆/MPhil△
Cardiff IHE PhD/MPhil/dip△
Cardiff U of Wales C PhD☆/
  MPhil☆
Cheltenham & Gloucester CHE
  PhD☆/MPhil☆
Durham U PhD/MA/MEd
East Anglia U PhD/MEd/MPhil
Exeter U PhD/MPhil
Glasgow U PhD/MLitt
Hatfield P PhD/MPhil
Huddersfield P PhD/MPhil
King Alfreds C PhD☆/MPhil☆
Kingston P PhD/MPhil
Leeds P PhD/MPhil/dip
Leeds U PhD/MEd/MPhil
Leicester P PhD/MPhil
Leicester U PhD/MEd
Liverpool P PhD/MPhil
Liverpool U PhD/MPhil
London U Inst of Education PhD/
  MPhil
Loughborough U PhD/MPhil
Manchester P PhD/MPhil/dip
Middlesex P PhD/MPhil
Newcastle U PhD/MPhil
Nottingham P PhD☆/MPhil☆
Nottingham U PhD/MEd/MPhil
Reading U PhD/MPhil
St Mark & St John C MPhil△
St Mary's C Strawberry Hill PhD/
  MPhil
Sheffield City P PhD/MPhil
Sheffield U PhD/MPhil
South Bank P PhD/MPhil
South West P PhD/MPhil
Stirling U PhD/MSc
Sunderland P PhD/MPhil
Sussex U DPhil/MPhil
Swansea UC PhD/MPhil
Ulster U DPhil/MPhil
Warwick U PhD/MA/MPhil/MSc
West Glamorgan IHE PhD/MPhil
West London IHE MPhil☆
West Sussex IHE PhD△/MPhil△
Wolverhampton P PhD☆/MPhil☆
Worcester CHE PhD☆/MPhil
York U DPhil/MA/MPhil

Education & teaching studies
Westminster C Oxford PhD△/
  MPhil△

Education & the mass media
Manchester U PhD/MPhil

Education development
Ulster U DPhil/MPhil

Education in developing countries
Manchester U PhD/MPhil

Education management & administration
Sheffield City P PhD/MPhil

Education marketing
Manchester U PhD/MPhil

Educational development & training
Manchester P PhD/MPhil

Educational guidance
Manchester U PhD/MPhil

Educational management & administration
Manchester U PhD/MPhil

Educational policy
Bristol P PhD/MPhil

Educational policy management
Open U PhD/MPhil/BPhil

Educational psychology
Manchester U PhD/MPhil

Educational psychology & child guidance
Glasgow U PhD/MSc

Educational research
Lancaster U PhD/MPhil

Educational science
Manchester U PhD/MSc

Educational studies
East London P PhD/MPhil
Hull U PhD/MEd/MPhil
London U King's C PhD/MPhil
Manchester U PhD✫/MPhil✫
Newcastle P PhD✫/MPhil✫
Oxford U DPhil✫/MLitt✫/MSc✫
Southampton U PhD/MPhil
Surrey U PhD/MPhil   ☐
Thames P PhD/MPhil

Educational technology
Open U PhD/MPhil/BPhil

English language teaching
Warwick U PhD/MPhil

English studies
Strathclyde U PhD/MLitt

Equal opportunities in education
Manchester U PhD/MPhil

History of English education
Manchester U PhD/MPhil

Human development & learning
Open U PhD/MPhil/BPhil

Independent study
East London P PhD/MPhil
Lancaster U PhD/MPhil

Language in education
Bristol P PhD△/MPhil△

Management
East London P PhD/MPhil

Medical & dental education
Wales U C of Med PhD✫/MSc✫

Medical education
Dundee U PhD/MSc
Glasgow U PhD/MSc(MedSci)

Microcomputers in education
Bristol P PhD△/MPhil△

Philosophy of education
Bristol P PhD△/MPhil△
Manchester U PhD/MPhil

Physical & outdoor education
Liverpool P PhD/MPhil

Professional education
Canterbury Christ Church C PhD/MPhil

Psychology
London U UC PhD✫/MPhil✫   Soc

School technology, craft & design
Nottingham P PhD✫/MPhil✫

Science education
Glasgow U PhD/MSc

Sociology & social research in education
Open U PhD/MPhil/BPhil

Sociology of education
Bristol P PhD△/MPhil△
Manchester U PhD/MPhil

Special education
Manchester U PhD/MPhil

Special educational needs
Bristol P PhD△/MPhil△

Speech
Newcastle U PhD/MPhil

Sports science
Brighton P PhD/MPhil

Teaching of English overseas
Manchester U PhD/MPhil

Teaching studies
North London P PhD/MPhil

Youth & adult studies
Open U PhD/MPhil/BPhil

Youth studies
Manchester U PhD/MPhil

Curriculum studies

Higher degrees by instruction

Adult education
Glasgow U MEd/dip
Hull U MA✫/MEd✫

Adult education & literature for rural development
Manchester U MEd✫

Advanced training in art therapy
Hertfordshire CAD dip△

Advanced training in dramatherapy
Hertfordshire CAD dip△

Aesthetic education
Manchester U MEd✫

Applied educational research & assessment
Manchester U MEd✫

Art & design (extension studies)
Bristol P dip

Art & design in education
London U Inst of Education MA

Art education
Cardiff IHE MEd   ☐

Art teachers
Goldsmiths' C London U cert✫

Art therapy
Hertfordshire CAD MA△/dip
Sheffield U dip

Assessment
Bristol U MEd✫

Audiology
Manchester U MSc✫

Computer education
Stirling U dip✫

Computers in education
London U King's C MEd△

Continuing education
Sheffield U MEd/dip
Warwick U dip△

Curriculum development in schools
Sussex U MA✫

Curriculum studies
London U Inst of Education MA
Loughborough U MA△
Manchester U MEd✫

Dance movement therapy
Hertfordshire CAD dip△

Dance/movement therapy
Laban Centre for Movement &
Dance MA

Dramatherapy
Hertfordshire CAD MA△/dip

Education & local history
Leeds U MA

Education management
Anglia HEC MSc△

Education of adults
Surrey U cert

Education of teachers overseas
Manchester U cert✩

**Educational & administrative
management**
Reading U MA△

Educational studies
London U Inst of Education MA△
Roehampton I MA✩
Surrey U MSc/dip△ ☐

**Educational technology for
speakers of other languages**
Manchester U MEd

**English as a second or foreign
language**
Bangor, U of Wales MA✩/dip✩
Manchester U cert✩

English language teaching
Reading U dip✩
Warwick U MA

**English language teaching &
administration**
Warwick U dip✩

Further & technical education
Manchester U MEd✩/cert✩

Further education
Bolton IHE cert✩
Cardiff U of Wales C cert✩
Wolverhampton P cert✩

Health education
London U King's C MSc/dip△

**Health education & health
promotion**
Leeds P MSc/dip

Higher education
Manchester U MEd✩

Humanities in the curriculum
London U Inst of Education MA

Industrial education & training
Manchester U MEd✩

**Language & literature in
education**
London U Inst of Education MA

**Linguistics & English language
teaching**
Leeds U MA✩
York U MA✩

**Linguistics & foreign language
teaching**
Leeds U MA✩

**Linguistics for the teaching of
English language & literature**
Strathclyde U MLitt✩/cert✩/dip✩

Mathematical education
Edinburgh U MSc/dip
South Bank P MSc△/dip△

**Mathematical education &
mathematics**
Leeds U MSc△

Mathematics education
Bristol U MEd✩
London U King's C MA

Medical education
Wales U C of Med MSc✩

Microcomputers in education
Manchester U MEd✩

Modern languages & education
Lancaster U MA

Modular studies
Crewe & Alsager CHE MA△/
MSc△

Music education
London U Inst of Education MA
Reading U MA
Roehampton I MA✩/dip✩

**Organisation & planning of
education**
Manchester U MEd✩

Physical education
Leeds U MEd
Manchester U MEd✩

**Physical education & exercise
studies**
Glasgow U MEd/MPhil

**Physical education & sports
science**
Loughborough U MSc✩/dip✩

Physics
Liverpool U dip✩

Physics education
Liverpool U MSc✩

Primary science education
Cheltenham & Gloucester CHE
dip△

Reading
Manchester U MEd✩

Religious education
Cheltenham & Gloucester CHE
MA

Lancaster U MA
London U Inst of Education MA
London U King's C MA
S Martin's C MA✩

**Science & mathematics for
education in the primary &
middle years of schooling**
Canterbury Christ Church C
MA✩/dip✩

Science & science education
Glasgow U MSc

Science education
Bristol U MEd✩
London U Inst of Education MA
London U King's C MA/MEd△/
dip✩
Warwick U MSc/dip✩

**Science, mathematics &
technology education**
Manchester U MEd✩

Special education
Manchester U MEd✩

Special educational needs
Stirling U MEd

Sport & exercise sciences
Birmingham U MA✩

Teacher education
Leicester U MA(Ed)✩

Teachers of the deaf
Manchester U cert✩

**Teaching Arabic as a second
language**
Salford U MA✩

**Teaching English as a foreign
language**
Brighton P dip
Bristol U MEd✩
Cardiff U of Wales C dip✩
Manchester CT dip△
Cheltenham & Gloucester CHE
RSA Cert✩/TEFL✩
East Anglia U MA✩/dip✩
Essex U MA✩
Swansea UC dip✩
Ulster U dip✩

**Teaching English as a foreign
or second language**
Birmingham U MA/dip
Cheltenham & Gloucester CHE
Cert✩

**Teaching Italian as a foreign
language**
Warwick U MA✩/cert✩

**Teaching of economics or
business studies**
Sheffield U MA/dip

Teaching of English overseas
Manchester U MEd☆

Technology in education
Salford U MSc△

Youth studies
Manchester U MEd☆

Higher degrees by research

Adult & continuing education
Hull U PhD/MEd/MPhil
Leeds U PhD/MEd/MPhil
Ulster U DPhil/MPhil

Adult & higher education
Manchester U PhD/MPhil

Adult education
Glasgow U PhD☆/MLitt☆
Leicester U PhD/MEd

Art & design education
Birmingham P PhD/MPhil

Art education
Bristol P dip
Warwick U PhD/MA/MPhil

Arts & technology in education
Thames P PhD/MPhil

Audiological medicine
Manchester U PhD/MPhil

Continuing education
City U PhD/MPhil
Dundee U PhD/MEd/MPhil
Sheffield U PhD/MPhil

Curriculum & educational methods
Manchester U PhD/MPhil

Curriculum & professional studies
Open U PhD/MPhil/BPhil

Curriculum studies
Bristol P PhD△/MPhil△
Middlesex P PhD/MPhil

Design education
Royal CA PhD☆/MA☆

Education
Edinburgh U PhD/MPhil
Keele U PhD/MA
Goldsmiths' C London U PhD/ MPhil

Education development
Ulster U DPhil/MPhil

Education of the deaf
Manchester U PhD/MPhil

Educational studies
Birmingham P PhD/MPhil

Oxford P PhD/MPhil

Exercise sciences
Birmingham U PhD/MSc

Further education
Thames P PhD☆/MPhil☆

Language & education
Liverpool U PhD/MPhil

Language (teaching & learning)
Southampton U PhD/MPhil

Mathematical education
Nottingham U PhD/MPhil

Mathematics education
Open U PhD/MPhil/BPhil

Medical education
Warwick U PhD☆/MSc☆

Physical education
Belfast Queen's U PhD
Birmingham U PhD/MLitt/MPhil
Leeds U PhD/MEd/MPhil
Liverpool U PhD/MPhil
Manchester U PhD/MPhil
St Andrews U PhD/MSc
Warwick U PhD☆/MSc☆

Physical education & recreation
Glasgow U PhD/MSc

Physical education & sport
Newcastle U PhD/MPhil

Physical education & sports science
Loughborough U PhD☆/MPhil☆

Primary education
West Glamorgan IHE MEd

Professional & continuing education
Surrey U PhD/MPhil

Science education
Liverpool U PhD/MPhil
Manchester P PhD/MPhil

Social & environmental education
Thames P PhD/MPhil

Special needs in education
Liverpool U PhD/MPhil

Sports & recreation studies
Birmingham U PhD/MSc

Sports science
Birmingham U PhD/MSc
Brighton P PhD/MPhil

Teaching English as a foreign language
East Anglia U PhD/MPhil

PGCE: first, infants

PGCE early primary years
Brighton P ☆

PGCE early years
East Anglia U ☆

PGCE first
Bradford & Ilkley Community C ☆
Kingston P ☆
West Sussex IHE ☆

PGCE first, infants
Charlotte Mason CE ☆
Derbyshire CHE ☆

PGCE infant, junior
Cardiff U of Wales C ☆
Craigie CE ☆

PGCE infants
Bath CHE ☆
Cheltenham & Gloucester CHE ☆
Durham U ☆
Edge Hill CHE ☆   □
Hatfield P ☆
La Sainte Union CHE ☆
Liverpool IHE ☆
Liverpool U ☆
Manchester P ☆
Manchester U ☆
Nene C ☆
Newcastle P ☆
Nottingham P ☆
South West P ☆
Warwick U ☆
Wolverhampton P ☆
Worcester CHE ☆
York C of Ripon & York St John ☆

PGCE lower
St Mark & St John C ☆

PGCE nursery
North Riding C ☆

PGCE nursery, first
Oxford P ☆

PGCE nursery, infant
Bangor Normal C ☆
Bristol P ☆
Crewe & Alsager CHE ☆
Leicester U
Reading U ☆
South Bank P ☆

PGCE primary
West Sussex IHE ☆   □

PGCE primary (lower)
Homerton C ☆

PGCE: primary, middle

PGCE junior
Bristol P ☆
Canterbury Christ Church C ☆
Charlotte Mason CE ☆
Crewe & Alsager CHE ☆
Derbyshire CHE ☆
Durham U ☆
Edge Hill CHE ☆
Liverpool U ☆
Manchester U ☆
Nene C ☆
Nottingham P ☆
Reading U ☆
South West P ☆
Warwick U ☆
Westminster C Oxford ☆
Wolverhampton P ☆
Worcester CHE ☆
York C of Ripon & York St John
☆ ☐

PGCE junior, middle
Bangor Normal C ☆ ☐
Oxford P ☆

PGCE later primary years
Brighton P ☆

PGCE middle
East Anglia U ☆
Kingston P ☆
Roehampton I ☆

PGCE primary
Aberystwyth, UC of Wales ☆
Anglia HEC ☆
Bangor, U of Wales ☆
Bath CHE ☆ ☐
Bedford CHE ☆
Belfast Queen's U ☆
Birmingham P ☆
Bishop Grosseteste C ☆
Bradford & Ilkley Community C ☆
Cardiff IHE ☆
Cheltenham & Gloucester CHE ☆
Chester CHE ☆
Craigie CE ☆ ☐
Exeter U ☆
Hatfield P ☆

PGCE (primary)
Jordanhill CE Cert☆

PGCE primary
Jordanhill CE ☆
King Alfreds C ☆
Leeds P ☆
Leeds U ☆
Leicester U

Liverpool IHE ☆
Goldsmiths' C London U ☆
London U Inst of Education ☆
Loughborough U ☆
Manchester P ☆ ☐
Moray House CE ☆
Newcastle P ☆
Newcastle U ☆
Newman & Westhill C ☆
North London P
North Riding C ☆
Northern CE ☆
Reading U ☆
Roehampton I ☆
St Andrew's CE ☆
S Martin's C ☆
St Mary's C Belfast ☆
St Mary's C Strawberry Hill ☆ ☐
Sheffield City P ☆
Stranmillis C ☆
Strathclyde U ☆
Sussex U ☆
Swansea UC ☆
Thames P ☆
Trinity & All Saints' C ☆
Trinity C Carmarthen ☆
West London IHE ☆
West Sussex IHE ☆ ☐
Wolverhampton P ☆

PGCE primary (bilingual Welsh)
Trinity C Carmarthen ☆

PGCE primary (upper)
St Mark & St John C ☆
Homerton C ☆

PGCE primary, middle
La Sainte Union CHE ☆ ☐

PGCE primary/middle
Bretton Hall ☆

PGCE secondary
St Mary's C Strawberry Hill ☆

PGCE: secondary

PGCE primary
West Sussex IHE ☆ ☐

PGCE secondary
Crewe & Alsager CHE ☆

PGCE (secondary)
Jordanhill CE Cert☆

PGCE secondary
Roehampton I ☆
St Andrew's CE ☆
S Martin's C ☆
St Mary's C Strawberry Hill ☆

PGCE secondary (English, maths, history & geography)
Northern CE ☆

PGCE secondary (English & maths only)
Homerton C ☆
Kingston P ☆
Liverpool U ☆
London U King's C ☆
Loughborough U ☆
Manchester U ☆
Thames P ☆
Warwick U ☆
Worcester CHE ☆

PGCE secondary (English only)
Bretton Hall ☆
Edge Hill CHE ☆
Trinity & All Saints' C ☆
Westminster C Oxford ☆

PGCE secondary (English, geography & maths only)
Keele U ☆
Goldsmiths' C London U ☆
Sheffield City P ☆
Southampton U ☆

PGCE secondary (English, history & maths only)
Bath U ☆
Reading U ☆
West Sussex IHE ☆

PGCE secondary (English, history, geography, maths)
Aberystwyth, UC of Wales ☆
Belfast Queen's U ☆
Birmingham U ☆
Bristol U ☆
Cardiff U of Wales C ☆
Durham U ☆
East Anglia U ☆
Exeter U ☆
Hull U ☆
Jordanhill CE ☆
Leeds U ☆
Leicester U
Liverpool IHE ☆
London U Inst of Education ☆
Manchester P ☆
Moray House CE ☆
Newcastle U ☆
Nottingham U ☆
Oxford U ☆
St Andrew's CE ☆
Sheffield U ☆
Sussex U ☆
Swansea UC ☆

PGCE secondary (history & maths only)
York U ☆

PGCE secondary (history, geography & maths only)
Bangor, U of Wales ☆

PGCE secondary (maths only)
Bristol P ☆
Canterbury Christ Church C ☆
Hatfield P ☆
Nottingham P ☆
St Mark & St John C ☆
St Mary's C Strawberry Hill ☆
Wolverhampton P ☆

PGCE: art

PGCE art
Bretton Hall ☆
Cardiff IHE ☆ □
Exeter U ☆
Manchester P ☆ □

PGCE art & design
Birmingham P ☆
Bretton Hall ☆
Brighton P ☆
Leicester P ☆
Liverpool P ☆
Goldsmiths' C London U ☆
London U Inst of Education ☆
Manchester P ☆
Middlesex P ☆
Northern CE ☆
Reading U ☆
St Andrew's CE ☆
Ulster U ☆

PGCE: languages

English
Edge Hill CHE ☆

PGCE languages
Aberystwyth, UC of Wales ☆
Bangor, U of Wales ☆
Bath U ☆
Belfast Queen's U ☆
Birmingham P ☆
Birmingham U ☆
Bristol U ☆
Cardiff U of Wales C ☆
Durham U ☆
East Anglia U ☆
Exeter U ☆
Hull U ☆
Jordanhill CE ☆
Keele U ☆
Leeds U ☆

Leicester U
Liverpool U ☆
Goldsmiths' C London U ☆
London U Inst of Education ☆
London U King's C ☆
Manchester P ☆
Manchester U ☆
Moray House CE ☆
Newcastle U ☆
Northern CE ☆
Nottingham U ☆
Oxford U ☆
Reading U ☆
St Andrew's CE ☆
S Martin's C ☆
Sheffield City P ☆
Sheffield U ☆
Southampton U ☆
Swansea UC ☆
Trinity & All Saints' C ☆
Warwick U ☆
Westminster C Oxford ☆
York U ☆

PGCE languages (French & German)
Homerton C ☆

PGCE languages - classics
Belfast Queen's U ☆
Durham U ☆
Jordanhill CE ☆
London U King's C ☆
Nottingham U ☆
St Mary's C Strawberry Hill ☆

PGCE modern languages
Canterbury Christ Church C ☆

PGCE: music

PGCE music
Aberystwyth, UC of Wales ☆
Bath CHE ☆
Birmingham P ☆
Birmingham U ☆
Bretton Hall ☆
Cardiff U of Wales C ☆
Durham U ☆
Homerton C ☆
Jordanhill CE ☆
Kingston P ☆
Leeds U ☆
Liverpool IHE ☆
Goldsmiths' C London U ☆
London U Inst of Education ☆
Manchester P ☆
Middlesex P ☆
Northern CE ☆
Reading U ☆
Roehampton I ☆

St Andrew's CE ☆
Ulster U ☆

PGCE: physical education

PGCE physical education
Bedford CHE ☆
Belfast Queen's U ☆
Birmingham U ☆
Brighton P ☆
Cardiff IHE ☆ □
Exeter U ☆
Hull U ☆
Leeds P ☆
Liverpool P ☆
Loughborough U ☆
Manchester U ☆
West London IHE ☆

PGCE physical education with humanities
Sheffield U ☆

PGCE: science

PGCE geology
Aberystwyth, UC of Wales ☆

PGCE physics
S Martin's C ☆

PGCE physics & science (conversion)
Sheffield City P ☆

PGCE physics (conversion)
Birmingham U ☆
Roehampton I ☆
Sunderland P ☆

PGCE physics with technology (conversion)
Brunel U ☆

PGCE primary science
Liverpool U ☆

PGCE science (biological or physical)
Canterbury Christ Church C ☆

PGCE sciences
Aberystwyth, UC of Wales ☆
Bangor, U of Wales ☆
Bath U ☆
Belfast Queen's U ☆
Birmingham U ☆
Bolton IHE ☆
Bristol U ☆
Cardiff U of Wales C ☆
Crewe & Alsager CHE ☆

Durham U ☆
East Anglia U ☆
Exeter U ☆
Homerton C ☆
Hull U ☆
Jordanhill CE ☆
Keele U ☆
Kingston P ☆
Leeds U ☆
Leicester U
Liverpool U ☆
Goldsmiths' C London U ☆
London U Inst of Education ☆
London U King's C ☆
Loughborough U ☆
Manchester P ☆   ☐
Manchester U ☆
Moray House CE ☆
Newcastle P ☆
Newcastle U ☆
Northern CE ☆
Nottingham P ☆
Nottingham U ☆
Oxford U ☆
Reading U ☆
St Andrew's CE ☆
S Martin's C ☆
St Mary's C Strawberry Hill ☆
Sheffield City P ☆
Sheffield U ☆
Southampton U ☆
Sussex U ☆
Swansea UC ☆
Thames P ☆
Warwick U ☆
Wolverhampton P ☆
Worcester CHE ☆
York U ☆

PGCE sciences (biology or chemistry)
Roehampton I ☆

PGCE technology
Northern CE ☆

PGCE: other categories

Higher degrees by instruction

Modern studies
Northern CE ☆

PGCE art & design
Birmingham P ☆
Bretton Hall ☆

Brighton P ☆
Leicester P ☆
Liverpool P ☆
Goldsmiths' C London U ☆
London U Inst of Education ☆
Manchester P ☆
Middlesex P ☆
Moray House CE ☆
Reading U ☆
Ulster U ☆

PGCE art & Design (further education)
Bolton IHE ☆

PGCE business studies
Bolton IHE ☆
Crewe & Alsager CHE ☆
Jordanhill CE ☆
London U Inst of Education ☆
Moray House CE ☆
Northern CE ☆
Nottingham P ☆
Roehampton I ☆
Sheffield City P ☆
Wolverhampton P ☆

PGCE business subjects
Bristol P ☆

PGCE communication studies
Leicester U

PGCE computer science
Manchester U ☆

PGCE computer studies
Belfast Queen's U ☆
Birmingham U ☆
Keele U ☆
Leeds U ☆

PGCE computing
Jordanhill CE ☆
Northern CE ☆
St Andrew's CE ☆

PGCE craft
Middlesex P ☆

PGCE craft design & technology
Bristol P ☆

PGCE craft, design & technology
Bristol P ☆

PGCE craft design & technology
Crewe & Alsager CHE ☆
Leeds P ☆
Goldsmiths' C London U ☆
Loughborough U ☆
Newcastle P ☆
Nottingham P ☆
Sheffield City P ☆
Thames P ☆
Wolverhampton P ☆

PGCE dance
Bedford CHE ☆

Brighton P ☆

PGCE design & technology
Brighton P ☆
Brunel U ☆
Middlesex P ☆
St Mark & St John C ☆
York C of Ripon & York St John ☆

PGCE drama
Aberystwyth, UC of Wales ☆
Birmingham P ☆
Bretton Hall ☆
Jordanhill CE ☆
Goldsmiths' C London U ☆
Manchester P ☆
Middlesex P ☆
Northern CE ☆
Reading U ☆

PGCE economics
Hull U ☆
Jordanhill CE ☆
London U Inst of Education ☆
Moray House CE ☆
St Andrew's CE ☆
Trinity & All Saints' C ☆
Warwick U ☆
Worcester CHE ☆

PGCE economics & business studies
Manchester U ☆

PGCE economics with social studies
Edge Hill CHE ☆

PGCE educational computing
Moray House CE ☆

PGCE engineering
Bolton IHE ☆

PGCE English & drama
Exeter U ☆
Homerton C ☆
Liverpool U ☆
London U Inst of Education ☆
Nottingham U ☆
Sheffield U ☆

PGCE English & media studies
London U Inst of Education ☆

PGCE English (including drama)
Bangor, U of Wales ☆

PGCE English as a second or foreign language
Leicester U ☆

PGCE English for speakers of other languages
London U Inst of Education ☆

PGCE further education
Cardiff U of Wales C ☆
Huddersfield P ☆

PGCE Gaelic
Northern CE ☆

PGCE general studies
Bolton IHE ☆

PGCE geology
Aberystwyth, UC of Wales ☆

PGCE history & politics
London U Inst of Education ☆

PGCE home economics
Cardiff U of Wales C ☆
Jordanhill CE ☆
Leeds P ☆
Liverpool P ☆
Manchester P ☆
Moray House CE ☆
Newcastle P ☆
Roehampton I ☆
Worcester CHE ☆

PGCE home economics in design & technology
Bath CHE ☆

PGCE humanities
Sussex U ☆

PGCE information technology
Liverpool IHE ☆

PGCE integrated humanities
Leicester U
London U Inst of Education ☆

PGCE mathematical education
Thames P

PGCE maths & computing
London U Inst of Education ☆

PGCE maths (conversion)
Homerton C ☆
Hull U ☆
Keele U ☆
Nottingham U ☆
S Martin's C ☆
Sheffield City P ☆

PGCE modern studies
Jordanhill CE ☆
Moray House CE ☆
St Andrew's CE ☆

PGCE outdoor activities
Bangor, U of Wales ☆

PGCE physics (conversion)
Swansea UC ☆

PGCE physics with technology (conversion)
Brunel U

PGCE religious education
Durham U ☆
Northern CE ☆

PGCE religious studies
Aberystwyth, UC of Wales ☆
Bangor, U of Wales ☆
Belfast Queen's U ☆
Birmingham U ☆
Bristol U ☆
Canterbury Christ Church C ☆
Cardiff U of Wales C ☆
Edge Hill CHE ☆
Exeter U ☆
Hull U ☆
Jews' C ☆
Jordanhill CE ☆
Liverpool IHE ☆
London U Inst of Education ☆
London U King's C ☆
Manchester P ☆
Roehampton I ☆
St Andrew's CE ☆
S Martin's C ☆
St Mary's C Strawberry Hill ☆
Swansea UC ☆
Trinity C Carmarthen ☆
West London IHE ☆
Westminster C Oxford ☆

PGCE religious studies/personal & social education
Homerton C ☆

PGCE rural & environmental science with integrated science
Bath CHE ☆

PGCE secondary
St Mary's C Strawberry Hill ☆

PGCE secondary maths (conversion)
West Sussex IHE ☆

PGCE secretarial studies
Bolton IHE ☆

PGCE social sciences
Keele U ☆
Leeds U ☆
Leicester U
Manchester P ☆   ☐
York U ☆

PGCE social studies
Goldsmiths' C London U ☆
London U Inst of Education ☆
Sussex U ☆

PGCE social studies (economics, politics & sociology)
Birmingham U ☆

PGCE sociology
Liverpool IHE ☆

PGCE speech & drama
Jordanhill CE ☆

PGCE technological education
Moray House CE ☆

PGCE technology
Leeds U ☆
Manchester U ☆
St Mary's C Belfast ☆

PGCE textiles & dress
Bretton Hall ☆

PGCE three dimensional studies
Gwent CHE ☆

Higher degrees by research

Higher education
Surrey U PhD/MPhil

Art education

MEd
1 year full time
2 years part time
Adv dip
2 years part time
Department of Arts
Education, Cardiff Institute of
Higher Education, Cyncoed
Road, Cardiff CF2 6XD
Tel: 0222 551111 ext 3338

The taught courses of MEd and AdvDip are part of the INSET provision at this, one of the largest departments of art education in the UK.

Action research for primary, secondary and tertiary teachers and lecturers is promoted through these distinctive courses. Multi media engagements and research of curriculum issues & studio processes in art & design education provide the impetus for individual and/or shared investigations. MPhil and PhD are also available as research programmes.

Entrance requirements For Phd graduates who have achieved Masters level in research in Art & Design Education. For MEd and MPhil, normally graduates with Art & Design teaching experience at appropriate level. For AdvDip, graduates & non-graduates with relevant teaching experience.

Head of department Raymond Ellis.

Education

**MA and Diploma in
Professional Studies**
1 year full time
or 2-5 years part time
The Secretary (INSET),
School of Education,
University of Leicester, 21
University Road, Leicester
LE1 7RP

These are modular courses covering a wide variety of professional topics, eg assessment, management, special needs, multi-ethnic education, TVEI, curriculum studies. Successful completion of 4 standard modules in a related area qualifies for a Certificate, 8 (plus 8-10,000 words study) for a Diploma. Candidates for the MA must complete 5 advanced modules plus a dissertation; those already holding a Diploma may be eligible for remission of up to two advanced modules.

Entrance requirements Diploma - Qualified teachers; MA - 1st or 2nd class honours degree or Advanced Diploma in Education.

Education

**MEd/diploma of Advanced
Educational Studies**
University of Stirling
1 year full time
2 1/2 years part time
dip
1 year full time
2 years part time
Director MEd Programmes,
Department of Education,
University of Stirling, Stirling,
Scotland FK9 4LA
Tel: 0786 73171

The programme provides full and part-time programmes with a range of routes. General, educational research, computer education, TEFL/TESL and special education are available for full-time students. Guidance, management in education, curriculum and language, physical recreation, sport and leisure, educational research and special education are available for part-timers. Special education is in collaboration with Moray House College, Edinburgh.

Entrance requirements Graduate of approved university, or equivalent qualification and a teaching qualification. For Special Education a diploma in special education or equivalent is required.

Head of department Professor Sally Brown.

Educational studies

Advanced diplomas, Higher degrees, PGCE
Secretary to Education, School of Education, University of Hull, Cottingham Road, Hull HU6 7RX
Tel: 0482 465402

The University offers taught courses leading to advanced diplomas in Educational Studies, Mathematical Education, the teaching of Mathematics and Educational Media and Technology, an advanced diploma/Master of Education (modular) in Applied Educational Studies, and higher degrees (BPhil, MA, MEd). Higher degrees may also be awarded by thesis.

In addition to the one year PGCE (Primary and Secondary), a two year conversion course for graduates in subjects other than mathematics taught jointly with the School of Mathematics and Statistics leads to a PGCE and an advanced diploma in Mathematics.

Entrance requirements Advanced diplomas: approved Certificate in Education and teaching experience; Higher degrees: normally an approved degree. Advanced diploma acceptable in some circumstances.

Grants LEA.

Dean Professor V A McClelland.

Educational studies

MSc
1 year full time
20 places
MSc
2 years part time
25 places
dip
part time
Course Secretary (MSc), Department of Educational Studies, University of Surrey, Guildford, Surrey GU2 5XH
Tel: 0483 571281 ext 3125

The purpose of the course is to give teachers, administrators and others the opportunity of studying particular aspects of the education system and process. For example: developments in the education and training of the 16-19 age group; issues in continuing and adult education; national curriculum developments; planning and managing education.

Entrance requirements Degree or other appropriate professional qualifications, and at least three years relevant experience.

Grants LEA.

Course co-ordinator Athalinda McIntosh.

PGATC

PGCE
1 year full time
40 places
Department of Arts Education, Cardiff Institute of Higher Education, Cyncoed Road, Cardiff CF2 6XD
Tel: 0222 551111 ext 3303

The Postgraduate Art Teacher's Certificate course is a core element of the largest specialist Department of Art Education in the UK. Art & Design graduates undertake innovative, experimental and sustained teaching contacts/practice in secondary schools, museums, galleries, special education units, community arts centres & with schemes involving Artists in Residence projects, TVEI, CPVE & GCSE. Theory and practice cohere through child development studies involving the studio processes of drawing, painting, etching, screen printing: textiles, photography, video computers, design & craft, ceramics, sculpture & performance.

Entrance requirements Degree in art & design or equivalent.

Grants LEA mandatory.

Course director John O'Neil.

PGCE

PGCE
1 year full time
39 places
Department of Education,
Bangor Normal College,
Bangor, Gwynedd LL57 2PX
Tel: 0248 370171

It is a Primary course which can be studied in either English or Welsh. The course focuses on early childhood 3-8, and junior 7-12. Professional studies include all curriculum areas and education. In addition to 15 weeks' block teaching practice in different primary schools, students have regular contact with children in workshop sessions and visits to special units and schools.
Entrance requirements Maths and English O level and degree.
Grants LEA.
Course director Mrs A E Elliott.

PGCE

PGCE (CNAA)
1 year (36 weeks) full time
80 places
The Registrar, Department
of Education, Bath College
of Higher Education, Newton
Park, Newton St Lowe, Bath
BA2 9BN
Tel: 0225 873701 Fax: 0225
874123

The College offers a course in Primary Education with opportunities to focus upon either the early years (4-7) or the later years (8-11) of the primary age phase, and courses for intending secondary teachers of music, home economics and rural and environmental science with integrated science.All the PGCE courses have a strong practical focus involving working with children in schools for at least 16 weeks of course time. The College is well resourced for teaching and learning in both the primary and secondary areas of the curriculum.
Entrance requirements Degree or equivalent in relevant subjects.
Grants LEA mandatory.
Course director Mrs L Fursland.

PGCE

PGCE
1 year full time
Admissions Officer,
Department of Education,
Edge Hill College of Higher
Education, Ormskirk,
Lancashire L39 4QP
Tel: 0695 575171

Edge Hill College of Higher Education offers a general course for primary teachers with options in education of disadvantaged children or education of minority groups. There are secondary specialist courses for teachers of English with drama and English as a second or foreign language, social studies with economics.
Entrance requirements Degree or degree equivalent.
Grants LEA.
Head of department M W Wilkinson MA MEd.

PGCE

PGCE
9 months full time
The Registrar, Department
of Education, La Sainte
Union College of Higher
Education, The Avenue,
Southampton SO9 5HB
Tel: 0703 228761

La Sainte Union College of Higher Education offers a long established one year course leading to the Post Graduate Certificate in Education or an MSc in Educational Computing of the University of Southampton. The former course is specifically designed for graduates (in any suitable subject) wishing to teach children in schools covering the age ranges 4-12 years, with an option in nursery education.
Distinctive features include opportunities to specialise in English, maths, creative arts, environmental studies, French, science, RE and a broad range of curriculum studies and options; 15 weeks' school experience over three terms of the academic year. A nursery school on the campus offers special opportunities in nursery education.
Entrance requirements Degree.
Grants Mandatory.
Head of Department Miss P M Trosh BA MA(Ed) Cert ED DipEd.

PGCE

PGCE
1 and 2 years full time
2 years part time
The Postgraduate Office,
Manchester Polytechnic,
Didsbury School of
Education, 799 Wilmslow
Road, Didsbury, Manchester
M20 8RR
Tel: 061 247 2006/7

Manchester Polytechnic's Didsbury School of Education has one of the country's largest PGCE courses, featured in the TASC video "Don't smile before Christmas" at your careers office. There is a primary (3-11 years) and a secondary course (art, biology, chemistry, drama, English, French, German, geography, history, home economics, maths, music, physics, RE, social studies). There are also special initiative courses - a 2 year part time (1 day per week) and a 2 year full time (for graduates in other subjects) in maths, physics and chemistry and a 2 year articled teacher course.
Course administration officer Dr Heather Spiro.

PGCE

PGCE
Director of Course, St
Mary's College, Strawberry
Hill, Twickenham, Middlesex
TW1 4SX
Tel: 081 892 0051

St Mary's College offers a one year course leading to the Post Graduate Certificate in Education of the University of Surrey for intending teachers in both primary and secondary education. The course for primary teachers concentrates in the study of the curriculum of the primary school and appropriate methodologies. Secondary students follow specialist courses in the teaching of either physical sciences or mathematics or religious studies or classics as main subjects. Subsidiary subjects include biology, history and drama. A course leading to the certificate in religious education is available.
Entrance requirements Degree.
Grants Mandatory.
Director of courses Secondary: Mrs T O'Donovan BA MA. Primary: Mr J Hart BEd MPhil.

PGCE

PGCE primary
1 year full time
PGCE secondary: English,
History, Mathematics
1 year full time
PGCE Mathematics
secondary
2 years full time
The Admissions Office, West
Sussex Institute of Higher
Education, The Dome, Upper
Bognor Road, Bognor Regis,
West Sussex PO21 1HR
Tel: 0243 865581 ext. 202

Primary courses are for teaching the 5-8 or 7-12 age ranges. Secondary courses are available for graduates who wish to teach English, Mathematics or History in secondary schools and tertiary colleges. West Sussex Institute has been selected to pilot the Articled Teachers Scheme, a school based graduate teacher training programmme leading to PGCE. This is for Primary or Mathematics secondary teachers. The English, History and Mathematics staff have developed a national reputation in the academic subjects and in their application in the classroom. The Mathematics Centre at the Institute is a centre for DES sponsored research into a wide range of mathematics teaching issues, particularly dealing with problems of under-achievers. The secondary courses are lively and classroom centred, and place an emphasis on group discussion and close tutorial contact. The two years full time Mathematics Secondary PGCE is intended for graduates who do not have a Mathematics degree but who have an identifiable mathematical study of at least one year post A level. The institute also offers the MA (Ed) and other In Service Postgraduate education.
Entrance requirements Degree or degree equivalent (in related subject for secondary).
Grants LEA mandatory.
Programme co-ordinators Dr V Hanley (PGCE). Nigel Bufton (Articled Teachers Scheme).

PGCE

PGCE
1 year full time
50 places
The Registrar (Admissions),
Department of Education,
York: College of Ripon &
York St John, Lord Mayor's
Walk, York YO3 7EX
Tel: 0904 656771

The programme is designed to provide initial professional preparation for graduates interested in teaching children within the age range of five to twelve years. There is a particular emphasis on professional experience through work with children and students are required to link the theory and the practice of education in their wide range of curriculum courses as well as in their school based work. These courses offer a workshop approach and teachers as well as tutors work alongside students.
Entrance requirements Degree or recognised equivalent.
Grants LEA.
Director of course Mrs P C Scott.

PGCE physical education

PGCE
1 year full time
35 places
Head of Department,
Physical Education and
Human Movement Studies,
Cardiff Institute of Higher
Education, Cyncoed Road,
Cardiff CF2 6XD
Tel: 0222 551111 ext 3316

Professional training designed specifically to equip graduates as specialist teachers of physical education at secondary level is offered. The course comprises: school placement, education and curriculum studies, specialist subject teaching and second subject teaching. A varied school experience programme will be provided: evaluation will be by continuous assessment.
Entrance requirements A recognised degree.
Grants LEA mandatory.

PGCE primary

PGCE: special infant
qualification; special
remedial qualification
9 months full time
30 places
The Vice Principal, Craigie
College of Education, Ayr
KA8 0SR
Tel: 0292 260321

The college offers a one year certificate course in primary education for graduates. Practical teaching in schools is part of each course. BEd courses are also available.
Entrance requirements Degree of a British university or equivalent. Normal closing date for applications, 15th December of preceeding session although late entries may be considered if places are available.
Grants SED, LEA.
Director for preservice course Mr A MacCallum.

Practice of education

MSc/diploma
Self-paced
(average 2 years Diploma
plus 1-2 years MSc)
Course Administrator (DPE),
Department of Educational
Studies, University of Surrey,
Guildford, Surrey GU2 5XH
Tel: 0483 571281 ext 3170
or 0483 509198

The course is for practising teachers/trainers/managers in Adult Education, Continuing Professional Education, Further Education, Higher Education, Training in Industry and Commerce, Youth and Community Education. It is modular in design and is primarily taught by distance learning and is based on practice. It seeks to produce reflective practitioners and to increase participants' knowledge, awareness and skills in the process of teaching and learning in education and work.
Entrance requirements Degree or other equivalent qualification and at least two years teaching experience at the appropriate level.
Course co-ordinator Dr Peter Jarvis.

UNIVERSITY OF BRISTOL

The FACULTY OF SOCIAL SCIENCES offers a wide range of taught courses, by full-time or extended-study, at M.Sc., Master's and Diploma level as well as M.Phil. or Ph.D. by Research. Normal entrance: II.i Hons. or equivalent.

RESEARCH: M.Phil., Ph.D.: Opportunities to undertake research are available in the Departments of ADVANCED URBAN STUDIES, ECONOMICS, ECONOMIC HISTORY, EDUCATION, GEOGRAPHY, PSYCHOLOGY, SOCIAL POLICY, SOCIAL WORK AND SOCIOLOGY.

TAUGHT COURSES: M.Ed.: specialist and individually constructed programmes; M.Sc. in: Economics, Gender and Social Policy, Policy Studies and Race Relations. Diplomas in: Advanced Studies in Education, Gender and Social Policy, Social Policy, Race Relations and in Social Work in Work with Young Children and Families. Also the Certificate in Applied Social Studies (MSW in 1991) and Personal Social Service Fellowships.

NEW COURSES: M.Ed. in Teaching English as a Foreign Language (TEFL); M.Sc. in: Counselling, the Economics of Public Policy, Comparative Development and International Policy Studies, and Organizational Psychology.

ENGLISH LANGUAGE AND STUDY SKILLS COURSES, specifically related to a proposed area of study or research, are available during August and September to any student about to commence postgraduate studies anywhere.

FURTHER DETAILS available from: Ref: FSS/PG/DOG, University of Bristol, Senate House, Bristol, BS8 ITH. Tel (0272) 303030 Ext: 4032.

THE UNIVERSITY OF HULL

SCHOOL OF SOCIAL AND POLITICAL SCIENCES
GRADUATE PROGRAMMES

The School of Social and Political Sciences offers a full range of graduate tuition within a lively and expanding academic environment. The School incorporates the Department of Politics, Social Policy and Professional Studies and Sociology and Social Anthropology. Members of the School have a high reputation for research in their chosen areas; particular specialisms are provided for through the Centres of Criminology and Criminal Justice, Defence and Disarmament Studies, Developing Area Studies and South East Asian Studies, the European Community Research Unit and the Institute for Health Studies.

*　　*　　*　　*

Taught Masters courses (full-time and part-time)

Criminology
Defence and Disarmament Studies
Developing Area Studies
European Integration and Cooperation
European Political Economy
Health Administration & Research
International Law and Politics
International Politics
MBA: Europe

MBA: Military Management
Modern British Politics
Political Philosophy
*Social Work Studies
　(*CCETSW and Home Office funded)
Sociology of Developing Societies
South East Asian Studies
Third World Politics

Research Supervision for M.Phil./Ph.D. (full-time and part-time)

Supervision of appropriately qualified candidates is offered in all the main areas covered by the School's Departments and associated Centres, listed above. A limited number of University of Hull awards are available, including special Bursaries for Overseas Postgraduates.

*　　*　　*　　*

Application forms and further details are available from

**The Postgraduate Office,
University of Hull,
Hull HU6 7RX
Tel. 0482-465568.**

Social sciences

Social sciences is a term which covers such a wide variety of courses that it is difficult to find a coherent theme of postgraduate study. Yet, although at first sight economics and librarianship may seem to have very little in common, all the social sciences are in fact concerned, to a greater or lesser extent, with the way people behave. After all, a good librarian has to be something of an economist and a psychologist too.

You can begin to classify the courses available in two basic ways; those which are academic - based on deeper study and research into the subject - and those which are vocational - leading to a qualification for a specific career. It is easy to distinguish between a diploma in housing that exempts you from the exams of the Institute of Housing, and an MA in paleopathology and funerary archaeology, but there are many careers outside the academic world which demand a further academic qualification, which might not at first sight appear vocational. This is particularly true of many of the best career opportunities for economists, in the Treasury for example, or some of the economic forecasting groups, which prefer to recruit people with higher degrees. Academic careers in any social science require, of course, substantial evidence of research and study, and some original thought, as well as a genuine interest in the subject.

If you are thinking of taking one of the very specific vocational qualifications, you need to be sure that it is to do with a career you really want. A diploma in health administration, though based on much useful information and knowledge, is not a very marketable qualification outside the health service. There are, however, plenty of subjects to study that can be both intellectually satisfying and a useful preparation for a variety of jobs.

Qualifying for a course

Postgraduate courses in the social sciences are available at most colleges and universities, the largest number being in different branches of economics and in politics and government. For degrees by research you would normally need a first-class honours degree or a 2i in a relevant subject. Vocational courses usually ask for a second class degree, or equivalent professional qualification. Sometimes the degree subject is specified, as for most psychology courses, otherwise any good degree may be acceptable. An important consideration is that many vocational courses now insist that students have some practical experience before taking the course. For example, all students wishing to take a one-year course for the Certificate of Qualification in Social Work (CQSW) now have to have at least one year's relevant experience. If you plan far enough ahead, you may be able to acquire some of the necessary work experience during vacations.

Grants

The main source of grants for postgraduate social science work is the Economic and Social Research Council (ESRC), which funds both research degrees and degrees by instruction. Competition for its awards is very keen. The DSS, the Home Office, and other branches of the Civil Service may offer grants for some courses. The college providing the course should be able to give you details of where to apply for a grant. Some colleges can occasionally offer studentships. Local education authorities will not normally give grants if there is an alternative source of funding, and their generosity in making grants available for postgraduate study varies from one area to another. If you are taking a vocational course, some employers may be prepared to take you on and contribute towards the cost. However, there is no point in disguising the fact that it can be very difficult to get a grant for postgraduate work in the social sciences. Small local charities can sometimes help, if you apply early enough. Look them up in the *Charities Digest* in the library.

Pros and cons

When you are considering the possibility of continuing to study after your degree, you need to weigh up very carefully the advantages and disadvantages. Are you good enough to succeed in a very competitive field? Would you be prepared to settle for a teaching job outside higher education, if you were not lucky enough to get one of the scarce university or polytechnic lectureships?

If you have a particular career in mind, check with potential employers to see if they prefer you to take a vocational course immediately after your first degree, or would like you to have some work experience first. This might solve the financial problem, as you are then more likely to get financial help from your employer, especially if you decide to study part time. The social sciences are, after all, about people and the real world, and there is a limit to what can be learned theoretically.

Felicity Taylor

This listing contains **taught courses** (under the heading 'Higher degrees by instruction') and **research opportunities** (under the heading 'Higher degrees by research'). All study exceeds two terms or six months and is offered on both a full-time and part-time basis unless otherwise indicated. Post-experience and in-service courses are only included when advertised.

☐   This symbol indicates that the **taught course(s)** or **research opportunities** are advertised at the end of this listing.

Biol   An italic abbreviation indicates that an advertisement has been placed at the end of another chapter.

☆   This symbol indicates full-time study only.

△   This symbol indicates part-time study only.

For quick reference to advertisements, please use the 'Advertiser's course entry index'. For further information regarding the listing, please refer to page 53.

General

Higher degrees by instruction

Applied policy analysis for developing countries
Nottingham U MA☆/dip☆

Applied research methods
Ealing C London dip☆

Applied social studies
Lancashire P dip☆   □

Area studies (the Commonwealth)
London U Inst of Commonwealth Studies MA☆   □

Business administration
Hull U MBA☆

Contemporary sociology
Lancaster U MA   □

Crime risk management
Cranfield IT MSc☆

Development economics
Kent U MA

Development studies
Sussex U MPhil☆

Early childhood studies
Roehampton I dip☆

Economic development & policy
Birmingham U PhD/MPhil/ MSocSc/dip   □

Entrepreneurial studies
Stirling U MSc/dip   Bus

Equal opportunities studies
Southampton U MSc△

Facilities management
Strathclyde U MSc/dip

Gender & social policy
Bristol U MSc/dip

Geographical information systems
Edinburgh U MSc☆/dip☆   Env

Housing studies
South Bank P dip△
York U MA△

Independent study
East London P MA/MSc/dip

Industrial relations
Brunel U MA   Bus

Information technology systems
Strathclyde U MSc☆/dip☆

International business law
Hull U dip☆/LLM☆

International studies
Southampton U MSc(SocSci)/ cert☆/dip   □

Latin American studies
London U Inst of Latin American Studies MA   □

Law
London U King's C LLM

Librarianship & information studies
Robert Gordon's IT dip☆

Medical anthropology
Brunel U MSc   □

Modern Middle Eastern studies
Durham U MA☆

Organisational analysis & behaviour
Lancaster U MA   Bus

Pathological sciences
Sheffield City P MSc☆

Physical education
Sheffield U Cert☆

Physical habilitation
Liverpool U MSc☆

Physiotherapy
Teesside P dip☆

Public sector economics
Salford U MSc/dip

Race relations & community studies
Bradford U MSc/dip☆

Science & technology studies
Brunel U MA   □

Science, technology & society
Brunel U MA

Socio legal studies
Brunel U MA/dip   □

Sociology
Belfast Queen's U MMedSc
Manchester U dip☆

Sociology of contemporary culture
York U MA☆   □

Sociology of scientific knowledge
Edinburgh U MSc☆/dip☆   □

South East Asian studies
Hull U MA/dip

Soviet studies
Glasgow U MPhil/dip   □

Special studies
Birmingham U MSocSc☆

Urban & regional studies
Birmingham U PhD/MPhil/ MSocSc/dip   Env

Women's studies
Exeter U MA☆

Higher degrees by research

Economic development & policy
Birmingham U PhD/MPhil/ MSocSci

Geographical information systems
Edinburgh U PhD☆

Geography
Bristol U PhD/MPhil/MSc
London U UC PhD☆/MPhil☆
Sheffield U PhD/MPhil   Env

Housing
Cardiff U of Wales C PhD☆/ MPhil☆

Housing studies
Glasgow U PhD/MLitt

Human & environmental sciences
West London IHE MPhil☆

Humanities
Liverpool P PhD/MPhil

Independent study
East London P PhD/MPhil
Lancaster U PhD/MPhil

Interdisciplinary human studies
Bradford U PhD/MPhil

Interdisciplinary studies
Aston U PhD/MPhil

Interdisciplinary studies in social sciences
Kent U PhD/MPhil

Psychology
London U UC PhD☆/MPhil☆   ☐

Social & economic aspects of information & communication technologies
Newcastle U PhD☆

Social innovation
Aston U PhD/MPhil

Social sciences
Sunderland P PhD/MPhil

Social statistics
Southampton U PhD/MPhil

Sociology
Lancaster U PhD/MPhil

Urban & regional development studies
Newcastle U PhD/MLitt/MPhil

Urban & regional studies
Birmingham U PhD/MPhil/
    MSocSc   ☐, Env

Anthropology

Higher degrees by instruction

Anthropological archaeology
Oxford U MSt☆

Anthropology
Durham U MA☆/dip☆
Goldsmiths' C London U MA

Anthropology & community & youth work
Goldsmiths' C London U MA

Applied anthropology
Belfast Queen's U MA

Applied computing in social anthropology
Kent U PhD☆

Biological anthropology
Cambridge U MPhil☆
Durham U MSc☆
London U UC MSc

Community studies in Western Europe
Belfast Queen's U MA

Early man & the environment
Durham U MA☆

Ethnology & museum ethnography
Oxford U MPhil☆/MSt☆

Ethnomusicology
Bangor, U of Wales MA☆
Belfast Queen's U MA☆
Durham U MA☆
Goldsmiths' C London U MMus△

Funerary archaeology & human skeletal studies
Sheffield U MSc

History & anthropology
London U UC MA

Medical anthropology
Brunel U MSc   ☐

Medical social anthropology
Keele U MSc☆

Oral tradition & ethnology
Edinburgh U MLitt☆

Osteology, palaeopathology & funerary archaeology
Bradford U MSc☆

Race & ethnic relations
Bristol U MSc/dip

Rural development
Manchester U MA(Econ)☆

Social anthropology
Belfast Queen's U MA
Cambridge U MPhil☆
Durham U MA☆/dip☆
Edinburgh U MSc☆/dip☆
Kent U MA/dip
London U LSE MSc
London U SOAS MA
London U UC MSc
Manchester U MA(Econ)☆/dip☆
Oxford U MPhil☆/MSt☆
St Andrews U MLitt/MPhil☆/dip☆
Sussex U MA

Social anthropology & computing
Kent U MA/dip

Social anthropology & linguistics
St Andrews U MLitt/dip☆

Social anthropology of development
London U SOAS MA

Sociology & anthropology of travel & tourism
Roehampton I MA☆

Sociology & social anthropology
Hull U MA☆/MSc☆   ☐

South East Asian studies
Hull U MA/dip

Visual anthropology
Manchester U MA(Econ)☆

Higher degrees by research

Anthropology
Durham U PhD/MA/MPhil/MSc
Goldsmiths' C London U PhD/
    MPhil
London U LSE PhD/MPhil
London U UC PhD☆/MPhil☆

Anthropology & sociology
London U SOAS PhD/MPhil

Applied computing in social anthropology
Kent U PhD

Biological anthropology
Cambridge U PhD☆/MSc☆
Oxford U DPhil☆/MSc☆

Development studies
East Anglia U MPhil☆
Salford U PhD/MSc

Ethnology & prehistory
Oxford U DPhil☆/MLitt☆

Evolution of human environments
Durham U PhD/MA/MPhil/MSc

Medical social anthropology
Keele U PhD/MA

Social anthropology
Aberdeen U PhD☆/MLitt☆/
    MPhil☆
Belfast Queen's U PhD/MA
Cambridge U PhD☆/MSc☆
Edinburgh U PhD/MPhil
Kent U PhD/MPhil
Manchester U PhD/MA(Econ)
Oxford U DPhil☆/MLitt☆
St Andrews U PhD/MPhil
Sussex U DPhil/MPhil

Sociology
Glasgow U PhD/MLitt
Kent U PhD/MPhil
Ulster U DPhil/MPhil

Sociology & anthropology
Salford U PhD/MPhil/MSc
Swansea UC PhD/MPhil

Sociology & social anthropology
Brunel U PhD/MPhil
Hull U PhD/MPhil ☐

Sociology/social anthropology
Liverpool U PhD/MPhil ☐

Third World studies
Liverpool U PhD/MPhil

Visual anthropology
Manchester U PhD/MPhil

Careers work

Higher degrees by instruction

Careers guidance
Birmingham P dip☆
Bristol P dip☆
East London P dip☆
Kent C for the Careers Service dip☆
Manchester P dip☆
Napier P dip☆
Newcastle P dip☆
Nottingham P dip☆
Paisley CT dip☆
South Bank P dip☆
Strathclyde U dip☆
Wales P dip☆

Careers guidance & employment counselling
Strathclyde U MSc☆

Educational guidance for adults
Goldsmiths' C London U MA☆

Industrial relations
Strathclyde U MSc☆
Warwick U MA

Personnel management
Strathclyde U MSc△/dip☆

Vocational guidance
Reading U dip☆

Higher degrees by research

Careers education & counselling
Hatfield P PhD/MPhil

Occupational research
Hatfield P PhD/MPhil

Occupational studies
Newcastle P PhD☆/MPhil☆

Economics

Higher degrees by instruction

Agricultural development economics
East Anglia U dip☆

Agricultural economics
Aberdeen SAg MSc/dip
Aberdeen U MSc☆/dip☆
Aberystwyth, UC of Wales MSc☆/dip☆ ☐
East Anglia U MSc☆
London U Wye C dip☆
Manchester U MA(Econ)☆/dip☆
Oxford U MSc☆
Reading U MSc☆/dip☆

Agricultural economics (agrarian development overseas)
London U Wye C MSc☆

Agricultural economics (agricultural policy)
London U Wye C MSc☆

Applied economics
Ulster U MSc△/cert△/dip△

Banking & finance
Bangor, U of Wales MA☆/dip☆

Building economics & management
London U UC MSc

Building management & economics
Lancashire P dip☆

Business & economic forecasting
Kingston P MSc△

Business analysis
Leicester U MA

Business economics
Buckingham U MSc☆/dip☆
Reading U MA☆

Business finance
Brunel U MSc

Cadastre & land information management
East London P MSc☆/dip☆

Development economics
East Anglia U MA☆/dip☆
Essex U MA☆/dip☆

Keele U dip☆
Kent U MA
Manchester U dip☆
Oxford U MSc☆
Sussex U MA☆

Development finance
Birmingham U MSocSc☆/dip△

Development policy
Glasgow U dip☆

Development policy & planning
Swansea UC dip☆

Development studies
Bath U MSc☆/dip☆
Cambridge U dip☆
Lancaster U dip☆
Manchester U MA(Econ)☆/dip☆

Development studies with special reference to co-operatives
Surrey U MSc☆/dip☆

Diplomatic studies
Central London P MA/dip

East West trade studies
Central London P dip△

Econometrics
Essex U MA☆
London U LSE dip
Manchester U MA(Econ)☆/dip☆

Econometrics & economics
Manchester U MA(Econ)☆

Econometrics & forecasting
City of London P MSc△/dip△

Econometrics & macroeconomic forecasting
Reading U MA☆

Econometrics & mathematical economics
London U LSE MSc

Econometrics & social statistics
Kent U MA
Manchester U dip☆

Economic & social history
Birmingham U MSocSc☆

Economic & social policy analysis
York U MSc☆

Economic analysis
Salford U cert

Economic development
Glasgow U MPhil
Leicester U MA☆
Manchester U dip☆ ☐
Oxford U dip☆
Salford U MSc/dip ☐

Economic development & international trade
Reading U MA☆

Economic development & policy
Birmingham U PhD/MPhil/
MSocSc/dip □

Economic development planning
Keele U MSc☆/dip☆

Economic geography
London U LSE dip

Economic history
Swansea UC MSc (Econ)☆/dip☆

Economic planning
Glasgow U MPhil

Economic policy & planning
Sussex U MA

Economic statistics & national accounts
East Anglia U dip☆

Economics
Aberystwyth, UC of Wales dip☆□
Belfast Queen's U MSc(Econ)
Birmingham U MSocSc☆
Bradford U dip☆
Bristol U MSc☆
Cambridge U MPhil☆/dip☆
Cardiff U of Wales C
　MSc(Econ)☆　　　　　　　□
Dundee U dip☆
Durham U MA☆
East Anglia U MA☆/dip☆
Essex U MA☆/dip☆
Kent U MA
Leicester U dip☆
London U Birkbeck C MSc/cert
London U LSE MSc/dip
London U Queen Mary &
　Westfield C MSc(Econ)/dip
Manchester U MA(Econ)☆
Nottingham P MA△
Oxford U MPhil☆
Reading U MA☆
Salford U MSc/dip
Southampton U MSc/cert/dip
Sussex U MA/dip
Swansea UC MA☆/MSc(Econ)☆
Warwick U MA/dip
York U MSc☆/cert☆

Economics & commerce
Hull U MSc(Econ)

Economics & econometrics
Kent U MA
Southampton U MSc/cert/dip □

Economics & finance
Loughborough U MSc☆

Economics & labour economics
Hull U dip

Economics & politics of development
Cambridge U MPhil☆

Economics (Asia & the Pacific region)
London U SOAS MSc☆/dip☆

Economics (monetary)
Glasgow U MPhil

Economics of education
London U Inst of Education MA

Economics of energy & development
Surrey U dip☆

Economics of Latin America
London U Queen Mary &
　Westfield C MSc

Economics of public policy
East Anglia U dip☆
Leicester U MA☆

Economics of the European community
Exeter U MA☆

Employment studies
Cardiff U of Wales C
　MSc(Econ)☆
Salford U MSc/dip

Energy economics
Surrey U MSc

Entrepreneurship & competitive strategy
Reading U MA☆

Finance
Cambridge U MPhil☆
Strathclyde U MSc☆/dip☆　　Bus

Finance & accounting
Bristol U dip

Finance & investment
Exeter U MA☆

Financial & business economics
Essex U MA☆

Fiscal studies
Bath U MSc☆/dip☆

Fisheries economics
Portsmouth P cert☆

Health economics
York U MSc☆/dip☆

Industrial relations
Glasgow U MPhil

International agricultural marketing
Newcastle U MSc☆/dip☆　　Bus

International business & economic development
Reading U MA☆

International business & economic integration
Reading U MA☆

International business & international financial management
Reading U MA☆

International business history
Reading U MA☆

International economics
Essex U MA☆
Sussex U MA☆

International economics & banking
Cardiff U of Wales C
　MSc(Econ)☆

International finance
Glasgow U MPhil

International financial analysis
Newcastle U MA

International political economy
Swansea UC MSc☆

International shipping
South West P MSc　　　　　Eng

International studies
Salford U MA☆/cert☆
Warwick U MA/dip　　　　　□

Land economy
Aberdeen U MLE☆/dipLE☆

Law & employment relations
Leicester U cert△/dip△/LLM△

Law, society & the economy in England, 1450-1660
Birmingham U MA☆

Macroeconomics
Liverpool U MA　　　　　　□

Management & economics for construction & design
Bristol P MSc

Management sciences
Manchester UMIST MSc/dip

Management, economics, politics
St Andrews U MLitt/MPhil☆/dip☆

Money, banking & finance
Sheffield U MA☆/dip☆　　　Bus

Multinational accounting & financial management
Reading U MA☆

Negotiated studies
Loughborough U MA/MSc

Police studies
Exeter U MA

Political economy
Essex U MA☆

Political economy & political culture: Britain & France
Nottingham U MA

Politics of the world economy
London U LSE MSc

Pollution & environmental control
Manchester UMIST MSc☆

Project analysis, finance & investment
York U MSc☆

Public policy & administration
Manchester U MA(Econ)☆

Public sector economics
Bristol U MSc☆
Salford U MSc/dip

Public sector finance
Brunel U MSc

Quantitative development in economics
Warwick U MA/dip

Quantitative economics
Edinburgh U MSc☆/dip☆

Regional development planning
Swansea UC MSc(Econ)☆

Rural development
Manchester U MA(Econ)☆

Science, technology & industrialisation
Sussex U MSc☆

Sea use law, economics & policy
London U LSE MSc

Social & economic development
Essex U MA

Soviet studies
Glasgow U MPhil/dip ☐

Strategic studies
Aberdeen U MLitt☆

Structure & organisation of science & technology
Manchester U MSc☆/dip☆

Teaching of economics or business studies
Sheffield U MA/dip

Technical change & industrial strategy
Manchester U MSc☆/dip☆

Tourism planning & development
Surrey U MSc☆/dip☆

Trade & development
Lancaster U MSc☆

Trading standards
Manchester P dip△

Transport economics
Leeds U MA

Transport in developing countries
Central London P MSc☆/dip☆

Transport planning & management
Central London P MSc

Urban & regional studies
Birmingham U PhD/MPhil/
MSocSc/dip   Env

Valuation & auctioneering (fine arts & chattels)
Southampton IHE ISVA☆

Western European political co-operation & economic integration
Durham U MA☆

Higher degrees by research

Accountancy & economics
Dundee IT PhD/MPhil

Accounting, business & economics
Buckingham U DPhil/MPhil

Agricultural economics
Aberdeen SAg PhD☆/MSc☆
Aberdeen U PhD☆/MPhil☆/MSc☆
Bangor, U of Wales PhD☆/
MPhil☆
Edinburgh U PhD/MPhil
Glasgow U PhD/MSc
London U Wye C PhD☆/MPhil☆
Manchester U PhD/MA(Econ)
Newcastle U PhD/MPhil
Oxford U DPhil☆/MLitt☆/MSc☆
West of Scotland C PhD☆/MSc☆

Agricultural economics & management
Reading U PhD/MPhil/MSc

Agricultural economics & marketing
Aberystwyth, UC of Wales
PhD☆/MPhil☆

Agriculture & food economics
Belfast Queen's U PhD/MAgr/
MSc

Applied economic studies
East London P PhD/MPhil

Applied economics & human resource management
Ulster U DPhil/MPhil

Banking & finance
Loughborough U PhD/MPhil

British local government
Birmingham U PhD☆/MPhil☆/
MSocSc☆

British policy studies
Sheffield U PhD

Building economics
South Bank P PhD/MPhil

Business & related studies
Manchester BS MBSc△

Business economics
Cranfield S of Management PhD/
MPhil

Business economics & operations management
Bath U PhD△/MPhil

Business studies
North London P PhD/MPhil
Sheffield City P PhD/MPhil

Development administration
Birmingham U PhD☆/MPhil☆/
MSocSc☆

Development policy & management
Manchester U PhD/MA(Econ)

Development studies
Bath U PhD☆/MPhil☆
East Anglia U PhD☆/MPhil☆
Glasgow U PhD/MLitt
Leeds U PhD/MPhil
Manchester U PhD/MA(Econ)
Salford U PhD/MSc
Sussex U DPhil/MPhil
Swansea UC PhD/MPhil

Econometrics
East Anglia U PhD☆/MPhil☆
Leeds U PhD/MA/MPhil
Manchester U PhD/MA(Econ)
York U DPhil/MPhil

Econometrics & social statistics
Kent U PhD/MPhil

Economic & political studies
London U SOAS PhD/MPhil

Economic & social history
Birmingham U PhD/MPhil/
MSocSc

Economic & social policy
Aberdeen U PhD☆/MLitt☆/
MPhil☆

Economic development
Glasgow U PhD/MLitt

Economic development & policy
Birmingham U PhD/MPhil/
MSocSci

Economic geology
Camborne S of Mines PhD/
MPhil☆

Economic history
Exeter U PhD/MPhil

Economic statistics
Leeds U PhD/MA/MPhil

Economic studies
Leeds U PhD/MA/MPhil

Economic theory
Leeds U PhD/MA/MPhil

Economics
Aberdeen U PhD☆/MLitt☆/
MPhil☆
Aberystwyth, UC of Wales
PhD☆/MPhil☆
Bangor, U of Wales PhD☆/
MPhil☆
Bath U PhD☆/MPhil☆
Belfast Queen's U PhD/
MSc(Econ)
Birmingham U PhD☆/MPhil☆/
MSocSc☆
Bradford U PhD/MPhil
Bristol U PhD/MPhil
Brunel U PhD/MPhil
Cambridge U PhD☆/MSc☆
Cardiff U of Wales C PhD☆/
MPhil☆
Central London P PhD☆/MPhil☆
City of London P PhD☆/MPhil☆
City U PhD/MPhil
Coventry P PhD/MPhil
Dundee U PhD/MPhil
Durham U PhD/MA/MPhil
East Anglia U PhD☆/MPhil☆
Edinburgh U PhD/MPhil
Essex U PhD/MPhil
Exeter U PhD/MPhil
Glasgow U PhD/MLitt
Heriot-Watt U PhD☆/MPhil☆
Kent U PhD/MPhil
Lancashire P PhD/MPhil
Lancaster U PhD/MPhil
Leicester U PhD/MPhil
Liverpool U PhD/MPhil
London U Birkbeck C PhD/MPhil
London U LSE PhD/MPhil
London U Queen Mary &
Westfield C PhD☆/MPhil☆/
MSc(Econ)☆
London U UC PhD☆/MPhil☆
Manchester U PhD/MA(Econ)☆
Middlesex P PhD/MPhil
Newcastle P PhD☆/MPhil☆
Nottingham U PhD/MPhil
Open U PhD/MPhil/BPhil
Oxford U DPhil☆/MLitt☆
Reading U PhD/MPhil
St Andrews U PhD/MPhil
Salford U PhD/MSc
Staffordshire P PhD/MPhil
Stirling U PhD/MSc

Strathclyde U PhD☆/MPhil☆/
MSc☆
Sunderland P PhD/MPhil
Surrey U PhD/MPhil
Sussex U DPhil/MPhil
Swansea UC PhD/MPhil
Ulster U DPhil/MPhil
Warwick U PhD/MA/MPhil
York U DPhil/MPhil

Economics & accounting
Leicester P PhD/MPhil

Economics & banking
City of London P PhD☆/MPhil☆

Economics & commerce
Hull U PhD/MPhil

Economics & economic history
Manchester P PhD/MPhil
Portsmouth P PhD/MPhil

Economics & finance
Loughborough U PhD/MPhil

Economics & industrial studies
Leeds U PhD/MA/MPhil

Economics & management
Paisley CT PhD/MPhil

**Economics & management
sciences**
Keele U PhD/MA/MSc

Economics & politics
Kingston P PhD/MPhil

**Economics & public
administration**
Nottingham P PhD☆/MPhil☆

Economics & public policy
Leeds P PhD/MPhil/dip

Economics & social science
Bristol P PhD/MPhil/cert/dip

Economics & social studies
Wolverhampton P PhD☆/MPhil☆

Economics (monetary)
Glasgow U PhD/MLitt

Economics (public policy)
Glasgow U PhD/MLitt

**Economics, accounting &
management**
Newcastle U PhD/MPhil ☐

Economics/econometrics
Southampton U PhD/MPhil

European population studies
Liverpool U PhD/MPhil

European studies
Central London P PhD☆/MPhil☆

Family research
Open U PhD/MPhil/BPhil

Finance & accounting
Cranfield S of Management PhD/
MPhil

Finance & Economics
Manchester BS PhD☆/MPhil☆

Fiscal studies
Bath U PhD☆/MPhil☆

Government & economics
Birmingham P PhD/MPhil

Health economics
York U DPhil☆/MPhil☆

Health economics research
Brunel U PhD/MPhil

Housing studies
Glasgow U PhD/MLitt

Industrial economics
Nottingham U PhD/MPhil

**Industrial economics & business
studies**
Birmingham U PhD/MPhil/
MSocSc☆

Industrial relations
Glasgow U PhD/MLitt

International politics
Sheffield U PhD☆/MPhil☆

Labour economics
Leeds U PhD/MA/MPhil

Labour studies
Sussex U DPhil/MPhil

Land economics
Paisley CT PhD/MPhil

Land economy
Aberdeen U PhD☆/MPhil☆/MSc☆

Local economic development
Cranfield IT PhD☆/MPhil☆

**Local government &
development**
Birmingham U PhD☆/MPhil☆/
MSocSc☆

Macroeconomics
Liverpool U PhD/MPhil

**Management & economic
studies**
Sheffield U PhD☆/MPhil☆

Management sciences
Manchester UMIST PhD/MSc

Management studies
South Bank P PhD/MPhil

**Modern social & economic
history**
Bath U PhD☆/MPhil☆

Police studies
Exeter U PhD/MPhil

Political theory
Sheffield U PhD☆/MPhil☆

Public & industrial economics
Newcastle U PhD/MA

210

Public sector management
Aston U PhD/MPhil

Scottish economy research
Strathclyde U PhD☆/MPhil☆

Social & economic studies
Bradford U PhD/MPhil

Social sciences
Thames P PhD/MPhil

Social, economic & environmental studies
Middlesex P PhD/MPhil

Transport economics
Leeds U PhD/MA/MPhil

Urban & regional development studies
Newcastle U PhD/MLitt/MPhil

Urban & regional studies
Birmingham U PhD/MPhil/
  MSocSc   ☐, Env

Urban economics
Glasgow U PhD/MLitt

Government, politics

Higher degrees by instruction

Analysis of decision processes
Huddersfield P MSc△

Britain & the European community
Brunel U MA△

British government
Leeds U MA

British government & politics
Essex U MA☆

Business & public sector strategy
Kingston P MA△

Comparative development & international policy studies
Bristol U MSc

Comparative European studies
Sussex U MA

Comparative government
London U LSE MSc

Comparative politics
Glasgow U MPhil

Contemporary East European studies
Sussex U MA☆

Contemporary Japan
Essex U MA☆

Contemporary sociology
Lancaster U MA   ☐

Contemporary West European studies
Sussex U MA

Criminal justice
Reading U MA

Cultural studies: discourse, power & political economy
Lancaster U MA

Defence & internal security studies
Reading U MA

Defence & security analysis
Lancaster U MA☆

Development studies
Bath U MSc☆/dip☆
East Anglia U MA☆/cert☆
Leeds U MA
Manchester U MA(Econ)☆/dip☆

Diplomacy
Lancaster U MA☆

Diplomatic studies
Central London P MA/dip
Keele U MA/dip

Domestic politics & foreign policy
Bristol U MSc☆

East West trade studies
Central London P dip△

Economics & politics of development
Cambridge U MPhil☆

Economics of public policy
Leicester U MA☆

Educational policy & management
Brunel U MA

European area studies
Surrey U MA☆/dip☆

European law & government
Aberystwyth, UC of Wales dip☆

European politics
Manchester U MA(Econ)☆
Manchester UMIST MA△

Government
Manchester U MA(Econ)☆/dip☆

History & philosophy of social & political science
Essex U MA☆

History & politics of the United States
Manchester U MA☆

Housing policy & practice
Birmingham U PhD/MPhil/
  MSocSc/dip   ☐

Human rights
Essex U LLM☆   ☐

Ideology & discourse analysis
Essex U MA☆

Industrial development
East Anglia U MA☆

International & comparative politics
London U LSE dip

International business & economic development
Reading U MA☆

International business & economic integration
Reading U MA☆

International business law
Hull U dip☆/LLM☆

International conflict analysis
Kent U MA

International political economy
Swansea UC MSc☆

International relations
Cambridge U MPhil☆
East Anglia U MA☆
Keele U MA△/dip
Kent U MA
Lancaster U dip☆
London U LSE MSc
Nottingham U MA☆/dip☆
Oxford U MPhil△
Southern California U MA
Sussex U MA☆

International relations & strategic studies
Lancaster U MA☆

International studies
Birmingham U MSocSc/dip
Reading U MA
Salford U MA☆/cert☆
Southampton U MSc(SocSci)/
  cert☆/dip   ☐
Warwick U MA/dip   ☐

Irish political studies
Belfast Queen's U MSSc

Labour politics
Manchester P MA△

Latin American government & politics
Essex U MA☆

Leisure services & tourism
Birmingham U PhD/MPhil/
MSocSc/dip ☐

Local government & health service studies
Birmingham U MSocSc

Management, economics, politics
St Andrews U MLitt/MPhil☆/dip☆

Middle East politics
Exeter U MA

Modern British politics
London U LSE MSc

Modern historical & political studies
Coventry P MA△/dip△

Modern international studies
Leeds U MA☆

Modern political studies
Aberystwyth, UC of Wales
MSc(Econ)☆/dip☆

Moral philosophy
St Andrews U MLitt/MPhil☆/dip☆

Peace studies
Bradford U MA/dip
Lancaster U MA☆
Ulster U MA/dip

Philosophy (socialist studies)
Kent U MA

Police studies
Exeter U MA

Policy studies
Coventry P dip△

Political behaviour
Essex U MA☆

Political development
Manchester U MA(Econ)☆

Political economy
Essex U MA☆
Middlesex P MA△

Political economy & political culture: Britain & France
Nottingham U MA

Political philosophy
York U MA☆

Political philosophy, political ideology & the history of political thought
Durham U MA☆

Political philosophy: the idea of toleration
York U MA☆

Political science
Birmingham U MSocSc
Buckingham U MA

Essex U cert☆

Political sociology
Kent U MA/dip
Leeds U MA
London U LSE MSc

Political sociology of development
Leeds U MA

Political theology
Bristol U MA☆

Political theory
London U LSE MSc
Manchester U MA(Econ)☆
Warwick U MA△

Political theory & government
Swansea UC MA☆/MscEcon☆

Political theory & philosophy
Glasgow U MPhil

Political thought
Kent U MA

Politics
Exeter U MA
Hull U MA☆/dip☆
Oxford U MPhil☆
Swansea UC MA☆
Warwick U MA
York U MA☆

Politics & administration
London U Birkbeck C MSc

Politics & administration of the modern state
Nottingham P MA△

Politics & contemporary history
Salford U MA☆

Politics & culture
Southampton U MSc(SocSci)/
cert☆/dip

Politics & government
City of London P MA△/dip△
London U SOAS MSc

Politics & government of Russia
London U LSE MSc

Politics & government of Western Europe
London U LSE MSc

Politics & modern languages
Aberystwyth, UC of Wales dip☆

Politics & policy in Britain
Warwick U MA△

Politics & sociology
London U Birkbeck C MSc

Politics, literature & culture in the German Democratic Republic
Reading U MA

Politics of international resources & development
Leeds U MA

Politics of rights
London U Inst of Education MSc

Politics of the world economy
London U LSE MSc

Population policies & programmes
Cardiff U of Wales C
MSc(Econ)☆

Public administration & policy analysis
Warwick U dip☆

Public administration & public policy
London U LSE MSc

Public law
Bristol U LLM☆

Public policy & administration
Manchester U MA(Econ)☆
Southampton U MSc(SocSci)/
cert☆/dip

Race & ethnic relations
Bristol U MSc/dip

Regional development planning
Swansea UC MSc(Econ)☆

Science, technology & industrialisation
Sussex U MSc☆

Science, technology & international affairs
Lancaster U MA☆

Scottish government & administration
Glasgow U MPhil

Sea use law, economics & policy
London U LSE MSc

Social & political theory
Cambridge U MPhil☆

Social & political thought
Sussex U MA

Social & public policy
Leeds U MA△/dip△

Social change in modern Europe
London U Inst of Historical
Research/US Studies MA

Social policy & administration
Swansea UC dip☆

Social policy & politics in Western industrial societies
Birmingham U MSocSc

Social policy & professional studies
Hull U MA☆/MSc☆

Social science data analysis
Essex U MA△/dip△

Socialist theories & movements
Glasgow U MPhil/dip

South East Asian studies
Hull U MA/dip

Soviet government & politics
Essex U MA☆

Soviet studies
Glasgow U MPhil/dip ☐

State, policy & social change
Portsmouth P MA△/dip△

Statistical applications in business & government
Central London P MSc△

Strategic studies
Aberdeen U MLitt☆
Aberystwyth, UC of Wales MSc(Econ)☆/dip☆
Salford U MA

Structure & organisation of science & technology
Manchester U MSc☆/dip☆

The rise of the modern state
St Andrews U MPhil☆

United States government & politics
Essex U MA☆

United States history & politics
Keele U MA☆

Urban & regional studies
Sussex U MA

War studies
London U King's C MA/dip

Western European political co-operation & economic integration
Durham U MA☆

Western European politics
Essex U MA☆

World politics
London U LSE dip

Higher degrees by research

Agricultural economics
London U Wye C PhD☆/MPhil☆

British local government
Birmingham U PhD☆/MPhil☆/ MSocSc☆

British policy studies
Sheffield U PhD

British political studies
Sheffield U PhD☆/MPhil☆

Contemporary European studies
Sussex U DPhil/MPhil

Contemporary French & German studies
Aston U PhD/MPhil

Cultural studies
East London P PhD/MPhil

Defence studies
Aberdeen U PhD☆/MLitt☆/ MPhil☆

Development administration
Birmingham U PhD☆/MPhil☆/ MSocSc☆

Development studies
Bath U PhD☆/MPhil☆
East Anglia U PhD☆/MPhil☆
Glasgow U PhD/MLitt
Manchester U PhD/MA(Econ)
Sussex U DPhil/MPhil
Swansea UC PhD/MPhil

Developments in Spanish politics in the Franco era
Bristol P PhD△/MPhil△/dip△

East Asian studies
Newcastle U MA

Economic & political studies
London U SOAS PhD/MPhil

Economics & politics
Kingston P PhD/MPhil

European & international studies
Reading U PhD/MPhil

European governmental studies
Edinburgh U PhD/MPhil

European policies research
Strathclyde U PhD☆/MPhil☆/ MSc☆

European population studies
Liverpool U PhD/MPhil

European studies
Central London P PhD☆/MPhil☆

German, Austrian & Swiss affairs
Nottingham U PhD/MPhil

Government
Brunel U PhD/MPhil
Central London P PhD☆/MPhil☆
Essex U PhD/MPhil
London U LSE PhD/MPhil
Manchester U PhD☆/MA(Econ)☆
Newcastle P PhD☆/MPhil☆

Government & economics
Birmingham P PhD/MPhil

Government & law
Manchester U PhD/MPhil

Government & politics
Open U PhD/MPhil/BPhil
Sunderland P PhD/MPhil

Housing & housing policy
Birmingham U PhD/MPhil/ MSocSci

Humanities
Huddersfield P PhD/MPhil
Leicester P PhD/MPhil
Teesside P PhD☆/MPhil☆
Thames P PhD/MPhil

Industrial & defence studies
Royal Naval Engineering C PhD☆/MSc☆

International politics
Aberystwyth, UC of Wales PhD☆/MPhil☆
Sheffield U PhD☆/MPhil☆

International relations
Keele U PhD/MA
Kent U PhD/MPhil
London U LSE PhD/MPhil
Oxford U DPhil☆/MLitt☆
St Andrews U PhD/MPhil
Sussex U DPhil/MPhil

International relations & politics
Staffordshire P PhD/MPhil

International studies
Birmingham U PhD/MPhil
Warwick U PhD☆/MPhil☆

Law & government
South Bank P PhD/MPhil

Leisure services & tourism
Birmingham U PhD/MPhil/ MSocSci

Linguistics & international studies
Surrey U PhD/MPhil

Local government & development
Birmingham U PhD☆/MPhil☆/ MSocSc☆

Military studies
Manchester U PhD/MPhil

North West public sector research
Salford U PhD/MPhil/MSc

Peace studies
Bradford U PhD/MPhil
Middlesex P PhD/MPhil/dip△

Philosophy & politics
Ulster U DPhil/MPhil

Police studies
Exeter U PhD/MPhil

Policy studies
Brunel U PhD/MPhil
North London P PhD/MPhil

Political economy
Glasgow U PhD/MLitt

Political science
Aberystwyth, UC of Wales
PhD☆/MPhil☆
Belfast Queen's U PhD/MSSc
Birmingham U PhD/MPhil/
MSocSc
Buckingham U DPhil/MA/MPhil

Political science & social policy
Dundee U PhD/MPhil

Political studies
London U Queen Mary &
Westfield C PhD☆/MPhil☆

Political theory
Sheffield U PhD☆/MPhil☆

Political theory & government
Swansea UC PhD/MPhil

Politics
Bath U PhD☆/MPhil☆
Bradford U PhD/MPhil
Bristol P PhD/MPhil/dip
Bristol U PhD/MPhil
Brunel U PhD/MPhil
Cardiff U of Wales C PhD☆/
MPhil☆
Central London P PhD☆/MPhil☆
Durham U PhD/MA/MPhil
Edinburgh U PhD/MPhil
Exeter U PhD/MPhil
Glasgow U PhD/MLitt
Hull U PhD/MPhil
Keele U PhD/MA
Leeds U PhD/MA/MPhil
Leicester U PhD/MPhil
Liverpool U PhD/MPhil
London U Birkbeck C PhD/MPhil
Middlesex P PhD/MPhil
Newcastle U PhD/MPhil
Nottingham U PhD/MPhil
Oxford U DPhil☆/MLitt☆
Paisley CT PhD/MPhil
Reading U PhD/MPhil
Sheffield U PhD/MPhil
Southampton U PhD/MPhil
Strathclyde U PhD☆/MPhil☆/
MSc☆
Sussex U DPhil/MPhil
Warwick U PhD☆/MPhil☆
York U DPhil/MA/MPhil

Politics & contemporary history
Salford U PhD/MPhil/MSc

Politics & government
City of London P PhD☆/MPhil☆/
dip☆
Kent U PhD/MPhil

Politics & history
Coventry P PhD/MPhil

Politics & international relations
Aberdeen U PhD☆/MLitt☆/
MPhil☆
Lancaster U PhD/MPhil

Politics/international relations
East Anglia U PhD/MPhil

Public administration
Ulster U DPhil/MPhil

Public policy
Strathclyde U PhD☆/MPhil☆/
MSc☆

Public sector administration & law
Sheffield City P PhD/MPhil

Public sector management
Aston U PhD/MPhil

Science & technology studies
Manchester U PhD/MSc

Scottish government & administration
Glasgow U PhD/MLitt

Social & political sciences
Cambridge U PhD☆/MSc☆

Social & political studies
South West P PhD/MPhil

Social & political thought
Sussex U DPhil/MPhil

Social & public policy studies
Kent U PhD/MPhil

Social policy & professional studies
Hull U PhD/MPhil

Socialist studies
Middlesex P PhD/MPhil/dip△

Socialist theories & movements
Glasgow U PhD/MLitt

Sociology
Lancaster U PhD/MPhil

Spanish politics & literature since 1936
Bristol P PhD△/MPhil△/dip△

Study of conflict
Ulster U DPhil/MPhil

Systems science
City U PhD/MPhil

Technology policy
Open U PhD/MPhil/BPhil

The Institute of local government studies
Birmingham U PhD☆/MPhil☆/
MSocSc☆

Urban policy
Glasgow U PhD/MLitt

War studies
London U King's C PhD/MPhil

Librarianship, information science

Higher degrees by instruction

Analysis, design & management of information systems
London U LSE MSc

Archive studies
London U UC MA/dip

Bibliography & textual criticism
Sheffield U MA

Business information technology systems
Strathclyde U MSc☆/dip☆

Computer science (conversion)
Aberystwyth, UC of Wales
MSc☆/dip☆   Comp

Design & evaluation of information systems
Aberystwyth, UC of Wales MLib☆

Information & library studies
Liverpool P dip☆
Newcastle P MA/dip☆
Strathclyde U MSc/dip

Information & systems in management
Sheffield City P MSc☆/dip☆

Information administration
Leeds P dip☆

Information engineering
City U MSc/dip

Information management
Belfast Queen's U cert△
Central London P dip△
Sheffield U MSc
Strathclyde U MSc☆/dip☆

Information science
City U MSc/dip

Information studies
Belfast Queen's U MSSc
Birmingham P MA☆/MSc☆/dip☆
Loughborough U MSc
North London P MA△/dip△
Sheffield U MA☆/MSc☆/dip☆

Information systems
Portsmouth P MSc☆/dip☆

Librarianship
Aberystwyth, UC of Wales
MLib☆/DipLib☆
Leeds P MA
Sheffield U MA

Librarianship & arts administration
City U MA△

Librarianship & information studies
Birmingham P MA/MSc/dip
Robert Gordon's IT dip☆

Librarianship & information work
Leeds P dip

Library & information studies
Belfast Queen's U MLS
Brighton P MA/dip
Ealing C London MA△/dip
London U UC MA/dip
Loughborough U MA/MSc
North London P dip

Management of information systems
London U LSE dip☆

Overseas records management & archive administration
London U UC MA

Periodical press in Britain 1580-1900
Aberystwyth, UC of Wales MA☆

Research methodology
Birmingham P dip△

School librarianship
Loughborough U MA

Science, technology & society
Brunel U MA

Higher degrees by research

Conflict & peace research
Lancaster U PhD/MPhil

Information management
Belfast Queen's U PhD/MA/MLS

Information media & technology
Hatfield P PhD/MPhil

Information resources
Anglia HEC PhD☆/MPhil☆

Information science
City U PhD/MPhil
Strathclyde U PhD☆/MPhil☆/MSc☆

Information studies
Sheffield U PhD/MPhil
West Glamorgan IHE PhD/MSc

Information systems
East Anglia U PhD☆/MPhil☆/MSc☆

Information technology
Central London P PhD☆/MPhil☆

Librarianship
Aberystwyth, UC of Wales PhD/MPhil

Librarianship & information studies
Birmingham P PhD/MPhil
Liverpool P PhD△/MPhil△
Newcastle P PhD☆/MPhil☆
North London P PhD☆/MPhil☆
Robert Gordon's IT PhD/MPhil

Library & information studies
Brighton P PhD/MPhil
Leeds P PhD/MPhil/dip
Loughborough U PhD/MPhil
Manchester P PhD/MPhil

Library, archive & information studies
London U UC PhD☆/MPhil☆

Psychology

Higher degrees by instruction

Abnormal psychology
Belfast Queen's U MSc☆

Addiction behaviour
London U Inst of Psychiatry dip☆

Advanced training in art therapy
Hertfordshire CAD dip△

Advanced training in dramatherapy
Hertfordshire CAD dip△

Analysis of decision processes
Huddersfield P MSc△

Applied psychology
Bolton IHE MSc☆
Cardiff U of Wales C MSc☆/dip☆
Cranfield IT MSc☆

Manchester U MSc☆
Nottingham U dip☆

Art therapy
Hertfordshire CAD MA△/dip
Sheffield U dip

Behavioural sciences
Liverpool U MSc☆

Child development
London U Inst of Education MA/MSc

Child development & philosophy of education
London U Inst of Education MA/MSc

Child psychology
Nottingham U MA☆

Clinical & community psychology
Exeter U MSc☆

Clinical psychology
Belfast Queen's U MSc☆
Birmingham U PhD/MSc
East London P MSc△
Edinburgh U MPhil☆
Glasgow U MAppSci/MSc
Leeds U MSc☆
Leicester U MSc☆
London U Inst of Psychiatry MSc☆
Manchester U MSc☆
Newcastle U MSc☆
South West P MSc
Surrey U MSc☆

Cognition, computing & psychology
Warwick U MSc   □

Cognitive neuropsychology
London U Birkbeck C MSc△

Cognitive science
London U Birkbeck C MSc△
Manchester U MSc☆   *Comp*

Cognitive science & natural language
Edinburgh U MSc☆/dip☆

Counselling
Brighton P dip△
Goldsmiths' C London U MSc△/dip△

Counselling in formal & informal settings
Roehampton I cert△

Criminal justice
Brunel U MA   *Arts*

Dance movement therapy
Hertfordshire CAD dip△

Decision making
City of London P MSc△/dip△

Developmental & educational psychology
Belfast Queen's U MSc☆

Developmental psychology
Manchester U MSc☆

Dramatherapy
Hertfordshire CAD MA△/dip

Educational psychology
Brunel U MSc
Edinburgh U MSc☆/dip☆
London U Inst of Education MA/ MSc
Manchester U MEd☆/MSc☆
Moray House CE MSc☆
Newcastle U MEd☆/MSc☆
Sheffield U MSc☆
Southampton U MSc
Strathclyde U MSc

Educational statistics & child development
London U Inst of Education MA/ MSc

Educational statistics & psychology of education
London U Inst of Education MA/ MSc

Environmental psychology
Surrey U MSc☆

Ergonomics (human factors in work, design & production)
London U UC MSc☆   □

Experimental psychology
Sussex U MSc☆

Family therapy
London U Birkbeck C MSc△

Health psychology
London U United Med & Dent S, Guys's & St Thomas's MSc△
Surrey U MSc☆/dip☆

Human communication
City U MSc

Information technology systems
Strathclyde U MSc☆/dip☆

Intelligent systems
Brunel U MSc
South West P MSc

Interactive computing system design
Loughborough U MSc☆/dip△

Mental health
Belfast Queen's U dip△

Neurophysical basis of behaviour
City of London P MSc△

Neuropsychology
St Andrews U dip☆

Occupational & organisational psychology
East London P MSc△

Occupational psychology
Belfast Queen's U MSc
Hatfield P MSc
London U Birkbeck C MSc△
Nottingham U MA☆
Sheffield U MSc

Organisational behaviour
London U Birkbeck C MSc△

Organisational psychology
Bristol U MSc☆
Manchester UMIST MSc☆

Philosophy
Liverpool U MA☆

Philosophy & psychology
St Andrews U MLitt/dip☆

Police studies
Exeter U MA

Political behaviour
Essex U MA☆

Psychoanalytic studies
Kent U MA

Psychological counselling
Roehampton I MSc☆/dip☆

Psychological research methods
Southampton U MSc☆/dip☆

Psychology
Cardiff U of Wales C dip☆
City of London P dip
Hull U MSc☆/dip☆
Liverpool U MA☆/MSc☆
London U Birkbeck C cert△
Nottingham U MA☆
St Andrews U dip☆
Stirling U MSc
Surrey U MSc☆/dip☆
Warwick U MSc/dip

Psychology & education of children with special needs
London U Inst of Education MA△/MSc☆

Psychology & health
Middlesex P MSc△/dip△

Psychology of education
London U Inst of Education MA/ MSc

Psychology of education & philosophy of education
London U Inst of Education MA

Psychology of education & primary education
London U Inst of Education MA

Psychotherapy
Aberdeen U MMedSci☆/dip△
Belfast Queen's U MMedSc△

Research methods in developmental & social psychology
Strathclyde U MSc☆

Research methods in psychology
London U UC MSc☆
Reading U MSc/dip

Social learning theory & practice
Leicester U dip△

Social psychology
London U LSE MSc/dip

Social studies
Belfast Queen's U dip

Higher degrees by research

Applied psychology
Aston U PhD/MPhil

Behaviour in organisations
Lancaster U PhD/MPhil

Behavioural & communication studies
Wales P PhD/MPhil

Behavioural science
Newcastle P PhD☆/MPhil☆

Behavioural sciences
Central London P PhD☆/MSc☆
Huddersfield P PhD/MPhil

Child & adolescent psychology
Glasgow U PhD/MSc(MedSci)

Clinical communication studies
City U PhD/MPhil

Clinical psychology
Glasgow U PhD/MPhil
Leeds U PhD/MPhil
Liverpool U PhD
London U Inst of Psychiatry PhD☆/MPhil☆

Cognitive studies
Edinburgh U PhD/MLitt/MPhil
Sussex U DPhil/MPhil

Communication studies
Liverpool U PhD/MPhil
York U DPhil/MPhil

Educational psychology & child guidance
Glasgow U PhD/MSc

Experimental psychology
Cambridge U PhD☆
Oxford U DPhil☆/MLitt☆/MSc☆
Sussex U DPhil/MPhil

Family research
Open U PhD/MPhil/BPhil

Human cognition research
Open U PhD/MPhil/BPhil

Human communication
London U UC PhD☆/MPhil☆

Human development & learning
Open U PhD/MPhil/BPhil

Human movement
Brighton P PhD/MPhil

Management sciences
Manchester UMIST PhD/MSc

Mental health
Belfast Queen's U PhD

Occupational psychology
London U Birkbeck C PhD/MPhil

Occupational research
Hatfield P PhD/MPhil

Occupational studies
Keele U PhD/MA

Police studies
Exeter U PhD/MPhil

Psychoanalytic studies
Kent U PhD/MA/MPhil

Psychological medicine
Glasgow U PhD/MSc(MedSci)
London U King's C S of Med &
Dentistry PhD☆/MPhil☆
London U St Bartholomew's
Hosp Med C PhD/MPhil

Psychology
Aberdeen U PhD☆/MLitt☆/
MPhil☆/MSc☆
Bangor, U of Wales PhD☆/
MPhil☆
Bath U PhD☆/MPhil☆
Belfast Queen's U PhD☆/MSc☆
Birmingham U PhD/MSc
Bolton IHE PhD/MPhil
Bradford U PhD/MPhil
Bristol U PhD/MPhil/MSc
Brunel U PhD/MPhil
Cardiff U of Wales C PhD☆/
MPhil☆
City of London P PhD☆/MPhil☆
City U PhD/MPhil
Dundee U PhD/MPhil
Durham U PhD/MA/MPhil/MSc
East London P PhD/MPhil
Edinburgh U PhD/MPhil
Exeter U PhD/MPhil
Glasgow U PhD/MLitt   □
Hatfield P PhD/MPhil
Hull U PhD/MSc
Keele U PhD/MA
Lancashire P PhD/MPhil
Lancaster U PhD/MPhil
Leeds U PhD/MPhil/MSc☆

Leicester U PhD/MPhil
Liverpool U PhD/MPhil/MSc
London U Birkbeck C PhD/MPhil
Goldsmiths' C London U PhD/
MPhil
London U Imperial C PhD☆/
MPhil☆
London U Inst of Psychiatry
PhD☆/MPhil☆
London U Royal Holloway &
Bedford New C PhD/MPhil
London U UC PhD☆/MPhil☆   □
London U St George's Hosp
Med S PhD/MPhil
Manchester U PhD/MA/MSc
Middlesex P PhD/MPhil
Newcastle U PhD/MPhil
Nottingham U PhD/MPhil
Open U PhD/MPhil/BPhil
Paisley CT PhD/MPhil
Portsmouth P PhD/MPhil
Reading U PhD/MPhil
St Andrews U PhD/MPhil/MSc
Sheffield U PhD/MPhil
South West P PhD/MPhil
Southampton U PhD/MPhil
Stirling U PhD/MSc
Strathclyde U PhD☆/MPhil☆/
MSc☆
Surrey U PhD/MPhil
Sussex U DPhil/MPhil
Swansea UC PhD/MPhil
Ulster U DPhil/MPhil
Warwick U PhD☆/MPhil☆/MSc☆
York U DPhil/MPhil

Psychology & speech pathology
Manchester P PhD/MPhil

**Psychology as applied to
medicine**
London U United Med & Dent S,
Guys's & St Thomas's PhD☆/
MPhil☆

Self-organised learning
Brunel U PhD/MPhil

Social & applied psychology
Kent U PhD/MPhil
Sheffield U PhD/MPhil

Social psychology
London U LSE PhD/MPhil

Study of human learning
Brunel U PhD/MPhil

Public and social administration

Higher degrees by instruction

Administration
New C ICSA△
Sandwell CFHE ICSA△

**Administrative social planning &
national development**
Bristol U dip

Administrative studies
Liverpool U dip☆

**Adult education & literature for
rural development**
Manchester U MEd☆

**Business & public sector
strategy**
Kingston P MA△

**Comparative development &
international policy studies**
Bristol U MSc

Contemporary sociology
Lancaster U MA   □

Development administration
Birmingham U MSocSc/dip
Manchester U dip☆

**Development administration &
management**
Manchester U MA(Econ)☆

Development finance
Birmingham U MSocSc☆/dip△

Development policy
Glasgow U dip☆

Development policy & planning
Swansea UC dip☆

Development studies
Cambridge U dip☆
Lancaster U dip☆
Manchester U MA(Econ)☆/dip☆

Economics of public policy
Bristol U MSc☆
East Anglia U dip☆
Leicester U MA☆

Educational administration
Dundee U dip△

**Educational policy &
management**
Brunel U MA

Epidemiology & health planning
Swansea UC MSc(Econ)☆

Equal opportunities
Birmingham P MA△/dip△

Gender & social policy
Bristol U MSc/dip

Health administration & research
Hull U MSc☆/dip☆

Health facility planning
North London P MA/dip☆

Health management, planning & policy
Leeds U MA☆

Health planning & administration
Leeds U dip☆

Health planning & financing
London U S of Hygiene & Tropical Med MSc☆

Health planning, finance & management
Cardiff U of Wales C MSc☆

Health promotion
Birmingham P MSc△/dip△

Health service management
New C dip△

Health services management
Manchester U MA(Econ)☆/dip☆

Health services studies
Leeds U MA   *Biol*

Hospital management in primary health care
Leeds U dip☆

Housing
Birmingham P MA△/dip
Bristol U dip☆
Cardiff U of Wales C dip☆
Middlesex P dip△
New C dip△
Salford U dip☆

Housing administration
Sheffield City P dip△

Housing management & administration
Humberside CHE dip△

Housing policy & management
Newcastle U dip

Housing policy & practice
Birmingham U PhD/MPhil/
MSocSc/dip   ☐

Housing studies
Bristol P dip

Human resource development
Manchester U MSc☆

Human resource management
Newcastle U MA

Industrial relations
Brunel U MA   *Bus*

International studies
Southampton U MSc(SocSci)/
cert☆/dip   ☐

Labour studies
North London P dip☆

Leisure services & tourism
Birmingham U PhD/MPhil/
MSocSc/dip   ☐

Local government & health service studies
Birmingham U MSocSc

Management in higher education
Surrey U MSc☆

Methods & applications of social research
Cardiff U of Wales C
MSc(Econ)△

Planning studies
Newcastle U MA☆

Policy analysis & development
Bath U MSc/dip
Bristol U MA☆

Politics & administration
London U Birkbeck C MSc

Politics & administration of the modern state
Nottingham P MA△

Public administration
Bell CT dip△
Glasgow C MA☆   *Bus*
Liverpool U MPA☆

Public administration & management (developing countries)
Glasgow C dip

Public administration & policy analysis
Warwick U dip☆

Public administration & public policy
London U LSE MSc

Public policy & administration
Manchester U MA(Econ)☆
Southampton U MSc(SocSci)/
cert☆/dip

Public sector economics
Bristol U MSc☆
Salford U MSc/dip

Public sector management
Aston U MSc/dip

Public sector planning & management
Hull U dip☆

Public service management
Birmingham U MSocSc/dip

Race relations & community studies
Bradford U MSc/dip☆

Road safety studies
Middlesex P cert☆

Rural development
East Anglia U MA☆/MSc☆

Scottish government & administration
Glasgow U MPhil

Social & public policy
Leeds P MA☆

Social administration
Birmingham U MSocSc
Bristol U dip☆
Oxford U dip☆
York U dip☆

Social planning
Swansea UC MSc(Econ)☆

Social planning in developing countries
London U LSE MSc☆/dip☆

Social policy
Goldsmiths' C London U cert△/
dip△
York U MA☆

Social policy & administration
Nottingham U MA/dip
Swansea UC dip☆

Social policy & planning
London U LSE MSc

Social policy & politics in Western industrial societies
Birmingham U MSocSc

Social policy & social work studies
London U LSE MSc☆

Social policy, planning & administration
Ulster U MSc△

Social research
Surrey U MSc/dip

Social research & social policy
Oxford U MSc☆

Social sector planning & management
Swansea UC MSc(Econ)☆

Social service planning
Bristol U MSc
Essex U MA

Social services management
Birmingham U MSocSc/dip
Lancaster U MSc△

Social studies
Belfast Queen's U dip

Social welfare & social planning
Kent U MA☆

Social work
Bangor, U of Wales MA☆/dip△

Socio legal studies
Sheffield U MA☆   □

Sociology & social policy
North London P MA☆
Southampton U MSc/dip

Tourism planning & development
Surrey U MSc☆/dip☆

Trade & development
Lancaster U MSc☆

Training & development for the public sector
Manchester U dip☆

Urban policy
Glasgow U MPhil/dip☆   *Env*

Urban studies
Salford U MSc△

Welfare administration
East Anglia U cert☆

Higher degrees by research

Administrative & social studies
Teesside P PhD☆/MPhil☆

Administrative studies
Manchester U PhD

Applied social sciences & public administration
Leicester P PhD/MPhil

British local government
Birmingham U PhD☆/MPhil☆/
  MSocSc☆

Business studies
North London P PhD/MPhil

Development administration
Birmingham U PhD☆/MPhil☆/
  MSocSc☆

Development policy
Glasgow U PhD/MLitt

Development studies
East Anglia U PhD☆/MPhil☆
Manchester U PhD/MA(Econ)
Salford U PhD/MSc
Sussex U DPhil/MPhil
Swansea UC PhD/MPhil

Economic & social policy
Aberdeen U PhD☆/MLitt☆/
  MPhil☆

Economics & public administration
Nottingham P PhD☆/MPhil☆

Evaluation & planning for health care
London U S of Hygiene &
  Tropical Med PhD/MPhil

Finance & strategy
Aston U PhD/MPhil

Government & economics
Birmingham P PhD/MPhil

Health planning & management
Keele U PhD/MSc

Health services management
Birmingham U PhD☆/MPhil☆/
  MSocSc☆
Manchester U PhD/MA(Econ)

Housing & housing policy
Birmingham U PhD/MPhil/
  MSocSci

Housing administration
Stirling U PhD/MSc

Housing studies
Glasgow U PhD/MLitt

Leisure services & tourism
Birmingham U PhD/MPhil/
  MSocSci

Local government & development
Birmingham U PhD☆/MPhil☆/
  MSocSc☆

Management
East London P PhD/MPhil

Planning
Anglia HEC PhD☆/MPhil☆
Central London P PhD☆/MPhil☆

Planning & landscape
Birmingham P PhD/MPhil

Policy studies
Bristol U PhD/MPhil
Brunel U PhD/MPhil

Political science & social policy
Dundee U PhD/MPhil

Population & housing
Anglia HEC PhD/MPhil

Public administration
Bath U PhD☆/MPhil☆
Liverpool U PhD/MPhil
Ulster U DPhil/MPhil

Public policy
Strathclyde U PhD☆/MPhil☆/
  MSc☆

Public policy & administration
Lancashire P PhD/MPhil

Public relations
Cranfield IT PhD☆/MPhil☆

Public sector administration & law
Sheffield City P PhD/MPhil

Public sector management
Aston U PhD/MPhil

Public service management
Birmingham U PhD/MSocSc

Scottish government & administration
Glasgow U PhD/MLitt

Scottish local authorities management
Strathclyde U PhD☆/MPhil☆

Social & administrative studies
Cardiff U of Wales C PhD☆/
  MPhil☆
Oxford U PhD☆/MLitt☆

Social & public policy
Kent U PhD/MPhil

Social & public policy studies
Kent U PhD/MPhil

Social administration
Bath U PhD☆/MPhil☆
Birmingham U PhD/MPhil/
  MSocSc
Bristol U PhD/MPhil
Lancaster U PhD/MPhil
Stirling U PhD/MSc

Social administration & policy
Ulster U DPhil/MPhil

Social administration & social work
Glasgow U PhD/MSc

Social policy
Bath U PhD☆/MPhil☆
Cranfield IT PhD/MSc
Durham U PhD/MA/MPhil
Edinburgh U PhD/MPhil
Leeds U PhD/MA/MPhil
Newcastle U PhD/MPhil
Open U PhD/MPhil/BPhil
York U DPhil/MPhil

Social policy & administration
Nottingham U PhD/MPhil

Social policy & professional studies
Hull U PhD/MPhil

Social policy & social science
London U Royal Holloway &
  Bedford New C PhD/MPhil

Social policy & social work
Manchester U PhD/MA(Econ)

Social policy administration
Brighton P PhD/MPhil

Social science & administration
Goldsmiths' C London U PhD/
  MPhil
London U LSE PhD/MPhil

Social studies
Belfast Queen's U PhD/MSSc

Sociology
Exeter U PhD/MPhil
Lancaster U PhD/MPhil

**Sociology & social
administration**
Southampton U PhD/MPhil

Sociology/social anthropology
Liverpool U PhD/MPhil □

Technology policy
Aston U PhD/MPhil

Urban & regional studies
Sheffield City P PhD/MPhil

Social work: CQSW

Applied social studies
Aberdeen U
Croydon C ☆
Liverpool P ☆
Liverpool U ☆
Goldsmiths' C London U ☆
Nottingham P ☆
Sheffield U ☆
South Bank P ☆
Southampton U ☆
Swansea UC ☆
Warwick U

**Health & social sciences
management**
Ulster U MSc☆/dip☆

Psychiatric social work
Manchester U

**Social policy & social work
studies**
London U LSE ☆

Social work
Bangor, U of Wales ☆
Belfast Queen's U
Birmingham U
Bristol U ☆
Cardiff U of Wales C ☆
Dundee U ☆
Edinburgh U ☆
Exeter U ☆
Keele U ☆
Lancaster U ☆

Leeds P ☆
London U Royal Holloway &
  Bedford New C ☆
Manchester P ☆
Middlesex P ☆
Newcastle P ☆
Nottingham U ☆
Queen's C Glasgow ☆
Robert Gordon's IT ☆
Stirling U ☆
Sussex U ☆
Ulster U ☆
York U ☆

Social work studies
Hull U CQSW☆/dip☆
London U LSE ☆

Sociology
Belfast Queen's U MMedSc

Social work, youth and community work

Higher degrees by instruction

Advanced social work
Belfast Queen's U cert△

Advanced social work studies
Edinburgh U MSc/dip

Alcohol studies
Paisley CT cert☆/dip☆

**Anthropology & community &
youth work**
Goldsmiths' C London U MA

Applied social studies
Aberdeen U cert
Bristol U MSW☆
Croydon C dip☆
Lancashire P dip☆ □
Liverpool P dip☆
Liverpool U dip☆
Goldsmiths' C London U dip☆
Nottingham P dip☆
Oxford U MSc☆
Sheffield U MA☆/dip☆
South Bank P dip☆
Southampton U MSc/dip
Warwick U MA

**Applied social studies
(community work)**
Swansea UC MSc(Econ)☆/dip☆

**Applied social studies (social
work)**
Swansea UC MSc(Econ)☆/dip☆

Art therapy
Goldsmiths' C London U MA△/
  dip

Community education
Edinburgh U MSc/dip
Northern CE cert☆

Community health
Incorporated Liverpool S of
  Tropical Med MCommH☆

**Community studies in Western
Europe**
Belfast Queen's U MA

Counselling
Brighton P dip△
Goldsmiths' C London U MSc△/
  dip△

Dance/movement therapy
Laban Centre for Movement &
  Dance MA

Gerontology
Keele U MA△

**Health & social sciences
management**
Ulster U MSc☆/dip☆

**Health administration &
research**
Hull U MSc☆/dip☆

Health visiting
South Bank P dip☆

Mission studies
Birmingham U dip☆

Practitioner research
Manchester P MSc△

Psychiatric social work
Manchester U MSc/dip

**Race relations & community
studies**
Bradford U MSc/dip

Rehabilitation studies
Southampton U MSc/dip

**Social & community work
studies**
Bradford U MA

Social & pastoral theology
Manchester U MA(Theol)/dip

Social policy
Manchester U MA(Econ)/dip

Social policy & administration
Goldsmiths' C London U MA△

Social policy & social work studies
London U LSE MSc☆

Social sector planning & management
Swansea UC MSc(Econ)☆

Social services management
Birmingham U MSocSc/dip
Lancaster U MSc△

Social welfare & social planning
Kent U MA☆

Social work
Aberdeen U MSc/dip
Bangor, U of Wales MA☆/dip△
Belfast Queen's U MSW
Birmingham U MSocSc/dip
Brunel U MPhil△
Cardiff U of Wales C dip☆
Dundee U MSW☆/dip☆
East Anglia U MA☆/MSW☆
Edinburgh U dip☆
Exeter U BPhil☆/dip☆
Keele U dip☆
Lancashire P CQSW☆/dip☆
Lancaster U dip☆
Leeds P dip☆
Leicester U MA☆/CQSW☆
London U Royal Holloway & Bedford New C MSc☆
Manchester P dip☆
Middlesex P dip☆
Newcastle U CQSW☆/dip☆
Nottingham U MA☆
Queen's C Glasgow dip☆
Stirling U dip☆
Sussex U MSW☆
Ulster U dip☆
York U MSW☆/dip☆

Social work administration
Kent U MA

Social work studies
Hull U CQSW☆/dip☆
London U LSE MSc☆

Sociology
Belfast Queen's U MMedSc

Welfare law
Liverpool P dip△

Youth & community studies
Crewe & Alsager CHE dip☆
St Mark & St John C dip☆

Youth & community work
Brunel U cert△
Jordanhill CE cert☆
Manchester P cert/dip☆
Moray House CE cert☆
S Martin's C dip☆
Thames P dip☆

Higher degrees by research

Applied community studies
Manchester P PhD/MPhil

Applied social sciences
Anglia HEC PhD☆/MPhil☆
Newcastle P PhD☆/MPhil☆

Applied social sciences & public administration
Leicester P PhD/MPhil

Applied social studies
Bradford U PhD/MPhil
Bristol U PhD/MPhil
Coventry P PhD/MPhil
North London P PhD/MPhil
Paisley CT PhD/MPhil
Sheffield City P PhD/MPhil
Ulster U DPhil/MPhil

Community dental health
London U King's C S of Med & Dentistry PhD☆/MPhil☆

Community education
Liverpool U PhD/MPhil
Open U PhD/MPhil/BPhil

Community health
Bristol U PhD☆/MSc☆

Community medicine
Cambridge U PhD☆/MSc☆
Dundee U PhD/MSc

Community medicine & medical statistics
Southampton U PhD/MPhil

Community studies
Brighton P PhD/MPhil
Lancashire P PhD/MPhil

Councelling & interpersonal skills
Brighton P PhD/MPhil

Epidemiology & community studies
Manchester U PhD/MSc

Gender & social policy
Bristol U PhD/MPhil

Health & community studies
Teesside P PhD☆/MPhil☆

Health & social welfare
Open U PhD/MPhil/BPhil

Health & social work
North London P PhD/MPhil

Personal social services
Kent U PhD/MPhil

Public policy & administration
Lancashire P PhD/MPhil

Rehabilitation studies
Southampton U PhD/MPhil

Social & administrative studies
Oxford U PhD☆/MLitt☆

Social administration & policy
Ulster U DPhil/MPhil

Social administration & social work
Glasgow U PhD/MSc

Social gerontology
Keele U PhD/MA

Social policy
St Mark & St John C MPhil△

Social policy & social planning
Bristol U PhD/MPhil

Social policy & social work
Manchester U PhD/MA(Econ)

Social studies
Belfast Queen's U PhD/MSSc
Humberside CHE PhD/MPhil

Social work
Aberdeen U PhD☆/MLitt☆/ MPhil☆
Bristol U PhD/MSc
East Anglia U PhD/MPhil
Keele U PhD/MA
Kent U PhD/MPhil
Kingston P PhD/MPhil
Leicester U PhD/MPhil
Liverpool P PhD/MPhil
Liverpool U PhD/MPhil
Middlesex P PhD/MPhil
Nottingham U PhD/MPhil
Stirling U PhD/MSc
Sussex U DPhil/MPhil
York U DPhil/MPhil

Social work & social policy
Newcastle P PhD☆/MPhil☆

Social work studies
Hatfield P PhD/MPhil
Southampton U PhD/MPhil

Social work, health & community studies
South West P PhD/MPhil

Sociology
Exeter U PhD/MPhil

Sociology & anthropology
Swansea UC PhD/MPhil

Sociology & applied social studies
Birmingham P PhD/MPhil

Study of conflict
Ulster U DPhil/MPhil

Sociology, social studies

Higher degrees by instruction

Advanced educational & social research methods
Open U MSc△

Advanced sociology
Salford U cert△

Analysis of decision processes
Huddersfield P MSc△

Applied population analysis
Glasgow U MPhil

Applied social research
Manchester U MA(Econ)/dip
Stirling U MSc△/dip△

Applied social studies
Aberdeen U cert
Croydon C dip☆
Lancashire P dip☆　　　　　　　☐
Liverpool U dip☆
Goldsmiths' C London U dip☆
Nottingham P dip☆
Oxford U MSc☆
Sheffield U MA☆/dip☆
South Bank P dip☆
Southampton U MSc/dip
Warwick U MA

Applied social studies (community work)
Swansea UC MSc(Econ)☆/dip☆

Applied social studies (social work)
Swansea UC MSc(Econ)☆/dip☆

Communication & information studies
Brunel U MA　　　　　　　　　　☐

Communication studies (conversion)
Sunderland P MA△/dip△

Communications policy studies
City U MA

Comparative British & European social history
Warwick U MA

Comparative development & international policy studies
Bristol U MSc

Comparative labour history
Warwick U MA

Comparative regional analysis
Glasgow U MPhil

Computing & social statistics
Kent U MA

Contemporary sociology
Lancaster U MA　　　　　　　　☐

Criminal justice
Brunel U MA　　　　　　　　*Arts*

Criminology
Cambridge U MPhil☆
Cardiff U of Wales C
　MSc(Econ)☆/dip☆
Hull U MA☆/dip☆
Keele U MA
Middlesex P MA△/dip△
Nottingham U MA☆/dip☆

Cultural studies
Birmingham U MA
Ealing C London MA△
Leeds U MA

Culture, communication & society
Goldsmiths' C London U MA△

Defence & internal security studies
Reading U MA

Demography
London U LSE MSc

Development studies
Bath U MSc☆/dip☆
East Anglia U MA☆/cert☆
Leeds U MA
Manchester U MA(Econ)☆/dip☆
Sussex U MPhil☆

Development studies with special reference to co-operatives
Surrey U MSc☆/dip☆

Econometrics & social statistics
Kent U MA
Manchester U dip☆

Economic & social policy analysis
York U MSc☆

Economic development & policy
Birmingham U PhD/MPhil/
　MSocSc/dip　　　　　　　　☐

Employment & planning
Middlesex P MA△/dip△

Employment studies
Salford U MSc/dip

Ethnic studies
Liverpool U MA　　　　　　　☐

European culture & society
Birmingham U MA

European social policy
London U LSE MSc

Film & television studies
Sunderland P MA△/dip△

Food resources related to community development
London U King's C dip☆

Gender & development
Sussex U MA☆

Gender & social policy
Bristol U MSc/dip

General sociology
Reading U dip

Health & social sciences management
Ulster U MSc☆/dip☆

Health administration & research
Hull U MSc☆/dip☆

Health care ethics
Manchester U MA☆

History, philosophy & social relations of science
Kent U MA

Housing policy & practice
Birmingham U PhD/MPhil/
　MSocSc/dip　　　　　　　　☐

Housing studies
South Bank P dip△

Human rights
Essex U LLM☆　　　　　　　☐

Humour & society
Reading U MA☆

Industrial development
East Anglia U MA☆

Information management
Sheffield U MSc

Interdisciplinary women's studies
Warwick U MA

Labour studies
North London P dip☆

Labour studies & industrial relations
Central London P dip△

Latin American studies
Cambridge U MPhil☆

Law, society & the economy in England, 1450-1660
Birmingham U MA☆

Leisure services & tourism
Birmingham U PhD/MPhil/
　MSocSc/dip　　　　　　　　☐

Local history, literature & cultural tradition
Sheffield U MA☆

Local social studies
Sunderland P MA△

Mass communication
Leicester U MA☆

Medical demography
London U S of Hygiene &
  Tropical Med MSc/dip

Medical social anthropology
Keele U MSc☆

**Methods & applications of
social research**
Cardiff U of Wales C
  MSc(Econ)△

Occupational behaviour
Hatfield P MSc☆

Peace studies
Bradford U MA/dip

Police studies
Exeter U MA

Policy analysis & development
Bath U MSc/dip

Policy studies
Hatfield P MA△/dip△

Political sociology
Kent U MA/dip
Leeds U MA
London U LSE MSc

**Political sociology of
development**
Leeds U MA

Politics & sociology
London U Birkbeck C MSc

Population studies
Exeter U MA☆

Psychiatry
Manchester U MSc△

Race & education
Birmingham U MSocSc/dip

Race & ethnic relations
Bristol U MSc/dip
London U Birkbeck C MSc△

Race & ethnic studies
Warwick U MA/dip

Race relations
Lancaster U dip☆

**Race relations & community
studies**
Bradford U MSc/dip

Research methodology
Birmingham P dip△

**Research methods in
developmental & social
psychology**
Strathclyde U MSc☆

**Research methods in the social
sciences**
Middlesex P dip△

**Research techniques &
methods**
Ulster U cert△

Rights in education
London U Inst of Education MA

Rural social development
Reading U MA☆/dip☆

Science, technology & society
Brunel U MA

Social & economic development
Essex U MA

Social & political theory
Cambridge U MPhil☆

Social & political thought
Sussex U MA

Social & public policy
Leeds P dip☆
Leeds U MA△/dip△

Social administration
York U dip☆

Social anthropology
Cambridge U MPhil☆
Durham U MA☆/dip☆
London U UC MSc

Social ethics
Cardiff U of Wales C MA☆

Social gerontology
Aberdeen U MLitt△

Social justice
Stirling U MPhil

Social planning
Swansea UC MSc(Econ)☆

Social policy
Goldsmiths' C London U cert△/
  dip△
Manchester U MA(Econ)/dip
York U MA☆

Social policy & administration
Goldsmiths' C London U MA△
Nottingham U MA/dip

Social policy & planning
London U LSE MSc

**Social policy & professional
studies**
Hull U MA☆/MSc☆

Social policy & social research
East London P MA△/dip△

**Social policy & social work
studies**
London U LSE MSc☆

Social policy history
Liverpool U MA△

Social research
Surrey U MSc/dip

Social research & social policy
Oxford U MSc☆

Social research methods
Surrey U MSc☆

Social science data analysis
Essex U MA△/dip△

Social sciences (sociology)
Bristol U dip☆

Social service planning
Essex U MA

Social statistics
Kent U MA

Social studies
Belfast Queen's U dip
Oxford U dip☆

Social work
Bangor, U of Wales MA☆/dip△
Lancashire P CQSW☆/dip☆

Social work studies
Hull U CQSW☆/dip☆

Society & culture
Salford U MA△/MSc△

Socio legal studies
Birmingham U MSocSc/dip
Brunel U MA/dip   □
Ealing C London MA△/dip△
Sheffield U MA☆   □

Sociological method
Aberdeen U MLitt☆

**Sociological research in health
care**
Warwick U MA/dip

Sociological studies
Sussex U MA

Sociology
Belfast Queen's U MMedSc
Birmingham U MSocSc
Essex U MA/cert/dip
Glasgow U dip☆
Leeds U MA/dip☆
Goldsmiths' C London U MA△
London U LSE MSc/dip
Manchester U dip☆
Oxford U MPhil☆/MSc☆
Salford U MSc△
South Bank P MSc△

**Sociology & anthropology of
travel & tourism**
Roehampton I MA☆

**Sociology & community mental
health**
Essex U MA☆

Sociology & religion
Lancaster U MA☆

Sociology & social anthropology
Hull U MA☆/MSc☆   □

Sociology & social policy
Durham U MA△
North London P MA☆

Sociology & social research
Kent U MA/dip

Sociology & statistics
London U LSE MSc

Sociology (with special reference to education)
London U Inst of Education MSc

Sociology as applied to medicine
London U Royal Holloway & Bedford New C MSc

Sociology of contemporary culture
York U MA☆ □

Sociology of development
Essex U MA

Sociology of education
London U Inst of Education MA/MSc
Manchester U MEd☆
Warwick U MA/dip

Sociology of gender divisions
Essex U MA

Sociology of labour
Warwick U MA/dip

Sociology of literature
Essex U MA☆

Sociology of scientific knowledge
Edinburgh U MSc☆/dip☆ □

Sociology of sport
Leicester U MA

South East Asian studies
Hull U MA/dip

Sport, culture & society
Warwick U MA△

State, policy & social change
Portsmouth P MA△/dip△

Technology & information studies
Brunel U MA

Technology & society
Salford U MSc△

Urban & regional studies
Birmingham U PhD/MPhil/
MSocSc/dip *Env*
Sussex U MA

Urban history
Leicester U MA

Women's studies
Anglia HEC MA△
Cardiff U of Wales C MSc(Eng)△
Central London P dip△
Kent U MA
Loughborough U MA△
Strathclyde U MLitt☆

York U MA☆

Women's studies & English
Lancaster U MA

Women's studies & sociology
Lancaster U MA

Women's studies (applied)
Bradford U MA/dip

Youth & community studies
St Mark & St John C dip☆

Higher degrees by research

Administrative & social studies
Teesside P PhD☆/MPhil☆

Administrative studies
Manchester U PhD

Advanced studies in the humanities
Edinburgh U PhD/MLitt

Anthropology & sociology
London U SOAS PhD/MPhil

Applied social research
Manchester U PhD/MA(Econ)
Stirling U PhD/MSc

Applied social sciences
Newcastle P PhD☆/MPhil☆

Applied social sciences & public administration
Leicester P PhD/MPhil

Applied social studies
Bradford U PhD/MPhil
Coventry P PhD/MPhil
North London P PhD/MPhil
Paisley CT PhD/MPhil
Sheffield City P PhD/MPhil
Swansea UC PhD/MPhil
Ulster U DPhil/MPhil
Warwick U PhD/MA/MPhil

Behaviour in organisations
Lancaster U PhD/MPhil

Behavioural & communication studies
Wales P PhD/MPhil

Behavioural science
Newcastle P PhD☆/MPhil☆

Behavioural sciences
Huddersfield P PhD/MPhil

British policy studies
Sheffield U PhD

British political studies
Sheffield U PhD☆/MPhil☆

Communication studies
Liverpool U PhD/MPhil

York U DPhil/MPhil

Communications policy
City U PhD/MPhil

Contemporary cultural studies
Birmingham U PhD/MLitt/MPhil

Criminal justice studies
Leeds U PhD/MA/LLM

Criminological & socio legal studies
Sheffield U PhD/MPhil

Criminology
Cambridge U PhD☆/MLitt☆/MSc☆
Keele U PhD/MA

Criminology & social & philosophical study of law
Edinburgh U PhD/MPhil

Cultural studies
East London P PhD/MPhil

Development policy & practice
Open U PhD/MPhil/BPhil

Development studies
East Anglia U PhD☆/MPhil☆
Leeds U PhD/MPhil
Manchester U PhD/MA(Econ)
Sussex U DPhil/MPhil
Swansea UC PhD/MPhil

Economic development & policy
Birmingham U PhD/MPhil/MSocSci

Economics & social studies
Wolverhampton P PhD☆/MPhil☆

Ethnic relations
Warwick U PhD☆/MPhil☆

Family research
Open U PhD/MPhil/BPhil

Film & television studies
Central London P PhD☆/MPhil☆

Health & community studies
Leeds P PhD/MPhil/dip

Health services studies
Leeds U PhD/MPhil

Health studies
Lancashire P PhD/MPhil

History of science & technology
Keele U PhD/MA/MSc☆

History, philosophy & social relations of science
Kent U PhD/MPhil

Housing & housing policy
Birmingham U PhD/MPhil/MSocSci

Housing administration
Stirling U PhD/MSc

Housing studies
Glasgow U PhD/MLitt

Human movement
Brighton P PhD/MPhil

Humanities
Bristol P PhD/MPhil/dip
Huddersfield P PhD/MPhil
Teesside P PhD☆/MPhil☆
West London IHE MPhil☆

Humanities, social & cultural studies
Wolverhampton P PhD/MPhil

Humanity
Edinburgh U PhD/MLitt

Industrial studies & social studies
Napier P PhD/MPhil

Information & communication policy
Central London P PhD☆/MPhil☆

Labour studies
Sussex U DPhil/MPhil

Latin American studies
Cambridge U PhD☆   *Arts*
London U Inst of Latin American Studies PhD/MPhil

Leisure services & tourism
Birmingham U PhD/MPhil/MSocSci

Literary & cultural studies
Keele U PhD/MA

Management
East London P PhD/MPhil

Mass communication
Leicester U PhD/MPhil

Mass media
Central London P PhD☆/MPhil☆

Medical demography
London U S of Hygiene & Tropical Med PhD/MPhil

Modern social & economic history
Bath U PhD☆/MPhil☆

North West public sector research
Salford U PhD/MPhil/MSc

Nursing health & applied social studies
Bristol P PhD△/MPhil△/dip△

Occupational therapy & physiotherapy
Ulster U DPhil/MPhil

Organisation & social studies
Brunel U PhD/MPhil

Peace studies
Bradford U PhD/MPhil

Police studies
Exeter U PhD/MPhil

Policy studies
Bristol U PhD/MPhil

Politics
London U Birkbeck C PhD/MPhil

Population studies
Exeter U PhD/MPhil

Population studies/demography
London U LSE PhD/MPhil

Race relations
Bradford U PhD/MPhil

Rural sociology/social history
Open U PhD/MPhil/BPhil

Science studies
Bath U PhD☆/MPhil☆
Edinburgh U PhD/LLM

Social & administrative studies
Cardiff U of Wales C PhD☆/MPhil☆

Social & economic studies
Bradford U PhD/MPhil

Social & environmental education
Thames P PhD/MPhil

Social & political sciences
Cambridge U PhD☆/MSc☆

Social & political studies
South West P PhD/MPhil

Social & political thought
Sussex U DPhil/MPhil

Social & public policy
Kent U PhD/MPhil

Social analysis
Bradford U PhD/MPhil

Social gerontology
Keele U PhD/MA

Social implications of technical change
Sussex U DPhil/MPhil

Social policy
Cranfield IT PhD/MSc
Leeds U PhD/MA/MPhil
Liverpool P PhD/MPhil
Newcastle U PhD/MPhil
Open U PhD/MPhil/BPhil
St Mark & St John C MPhil△
York U DPhil/MPhil

Social policy & professional studies
Hull U PhD/MPhil

Social policy & social science
London U Royal Holloway & Bedford New C PhD/MPhil

Social research
North London P PhD/MPhil

Social science & administration
Goldsmiths' C London U PhD/MPhil
London U LSE PhD/MPhil

Social sciences
Birmingham U PhD☆/MSocSc☆
London U SSEES PhD/MPhil
Loughborough U PhD/MPhil
Manchester P PhD/MPhil
Manchester U PhD/MA(Econ)
South Bank P PhD/MPhil
Thames P PhD/MPhil
Worcester CHE PhD/MPhil

Social sciences studies
Hatfield P PhD/MPhil

Social statistics
City U PhD/MPhil
Manchester U PhD/MA(Econ)
Southampton U PhD/MPhil

Social studies
Belfast Queen's U PhD/MSSc
Humberside CHE PhD/MPhil
Lancashire P PhD/MPhil
Leeds P PhD/MPhil/dip
Nottingham P PhD☆/MPhil☆
Oxford P PhD/MPhil
Portsmouth P PhD/MPhil
Robert Gordon's IT PhD/MPhil
St David's UC PhD☆/MA☆

Social theory & institutions
Bangor, U of Wales PhD☆/MPhil☆

Social, economic & environmental studies
Middlesex P PhD/MPhil

Socio legal studies
Exeter U PhD/MPhil
Oxford U DPhil☆/MLitt☆

Sociological studies
Sheffield U PhD/MPhil
Sussex U DPhil/MPhil

Sociology
Aberdeen U PhD☆/MLitt☆/MPhil☆
Bath U PhD☆/MPhil☆
Birmingham U PhD/MPhil/MSocSc
Bolton IHE PhD△/MPhil△
Bradford U PhD/MPhil
Bristol P PhD/MPhil/dip
Bristol U PhD/MPhil
Cardiff U of Wales C PhD☆/MPhil☆
City of London P PhD☆/MPhil☆/dip☆
City U PhD/MPhil
East London P PhD/MPhil
Edinburgh U PhD/MPhil
Essex U PhD/MPhil

Exeter U PhD/MPhil
Glasgow U PhD/MLitt
Kent U PhD/MPhil
Kingston P PhD/MPhil
Lancaster U PhD/MPhil
Leeds U PhD/MA/MPhil
Leicester U PhD/MPhil
London U Birkbeck C PhD/MPhil
Goldsmiths' C London U PhD/MPhil
London U LSE PhD/MPhil
Manchester U PhD/MA(Econ)
Middlesex P PhD/MPhil
Nottingham U PhD/MPhil
Open U PhD/MPhil/BPhil
Oxford U DPhil☆/MLitt☆
Paisley CT PhD/MPhil
Reading U PhD/MA/MPhil
Staffordshire P PhD/MPhil
Strathclyde U PhD☆/MPhil☆/MSc☆
Surrey U PhD/MPhil
Ulster U DPhil/MPhil
Warwick U PhD☆/MA☆/MPhil☆
York U DPhil/MPhil

Sociology & anthropology
Salford U PhD/MPhil/MSc
Swansea UC PhD/MPhil

Sociology & applied social studies
Birmingham P PhD/MPhil
Central London P PhD☆/MPhil☆

Sociology & social administration
Southampton U PhD/MPhil

Sociology & social anthropology
Brunel U PhD/MPhil
Hull U PhD/MPhil   □
Keele U PhD/MA

Sociology & social policy
Durham U PhD/MA/MPhil
Stirling U PhD/MSc

Sociology & social research in education
Open U PhD/MPhil/BPhil

Sociology applied to medicine
London U London Hosp Med C PhD☆/MPhil☆

London U St Bartholomew's Hosp Med C PhD/MPhil

Sociology as applied to medicine
London U United Med & Dent S, Guys's & St Thomas's PhD☆/MPhil☆

Sociology/social anthropology
East Anglia U PhD/MPhil
Liverpool U PhD/MPhil   □

Urban & regional studies
Birmingham U PhD/MPhil/MSocSc   □, Env

Urban policy
Glasgow U PhD/MLitt

Urban studies
Liverpool U PhD/MPhil

Women's studies
Lancaster U PhD/MPhil
York U DPhil/MPhil

Work & gender studies
Bradford U PhD/MPhil

Applied social studies

dip
School of Community Studies, Lancashire Polytechnic, Preston PR1 2TQ
Tel: 0772 201201

This is a postgraduate vocational course in social work leading to the professional qualification - the diploma in applied social studies (CQSW).

It is organised around a generic conceptualisation of social work practice. The aim is to provide an integrating framework by which students can investigate, evaluate and gain proficiency in various modes of intervention in social situations.

Entrance requirements Degree in social administration and policy and at least twelve months experience of social work practice.
Grants CCETSW.
Head of School Chris Jones.

Cognition, computing & psychology

MSc
1 year full time
18 places
Dr George Dunbar,
Department of Psychology,
University of Warwick,
Coventry CV4 7AL
Tel: 0203 523096

A cognitive science course which integrates psychology and computing and functions as a conversion course in either direction. The course addresses the following topics: cognition; computing; artificial intelligence; human computer interaction; ergonomics; knowledge-based systems; language; expert systems; neuropsychology; artificial intelligence; non-numeric programming (LISP, PROLOG); and a project.
Assessed by exams, essays, programming exercises, project.
Entrance requirements First degree or equivalent.
Grants SERC studentships.
Course director Professor G V Jones.

Commonwealth studies

MA
1 year full time
2 years part time
Ms R Kochanowska,
Institute of Commonwealth
Studies, 28 Russell Square,
London WC1B 5DS
Tel: 071 580 5876 Fax: 071
252 2160

This course offers an opportunity to explore primarily political and economic dimensions of British "imperial" rule and the process of decolonisation and at the same time to examine the Commonwealth as a unique type of international organisation. Courses are offered in the following subjects: History, International Relations, Law, Literature and Politics. Students take three three-hour written papers and do a 10,000 word dissertation.

The Institute also registers students for the MA in Area Studies (Australia), organised by the Sir Robert Menzies Centre for Australian Studies.

Entrance requirements A good first degree (preferably an upper second class or equivalent) and fluency in English.
Grants Home students: ESRC awards.
Overseas students: ORS and ODASS awards.

In addition the ICS offers a limited number of fellowships to both home and overseas students to cover part of the tuition fees.

Communications & Technology

MA
1 year full time
2 years part time
25 places
Dr D Morley, Convenor,
Department of Human
Sciences, Brunel University,
Uxbridge, Middlesex UB8
3PH
Tel: 0895 56461

This course addresses the issues posed by the convergence of communications and information technologies and offers an advanced training in the social study of new technology, in relation to issues of communications and cultural policy and technolgical and social change. Students take a core course in Communications and Technology, a research course resulting in a dissertation and two optional courses from a range comprising Cultural Industries and Popular Culture; Technology, Communications and Society; Broadcasting and IT Policy; Intellectual Knowledge; Expertise and Society; Television Technology and Everyday Life.
Entrance requirements Applicants should possess a degree or equivalent qualifications and experience.
Convenor Dr D Morley.

Contemporary sociology

MA
1 year full time
2 years part time
Graduate Admissions
Officer, Department of
Sociology, Lancaster
University, Lancaster LA1
4YL

An introduction to the latest debates, and research finding in contemporary sociology. Students take a core course, four options (out of medical, city and regions, interactionism, development, culture and language, gender relations, social theory, late capitalism, computer techniques, economic sociology etc), and a dissertation. Departmental booklet available.
Entrance requirements Good honours degree in social science or equivalent.
Head of department Dr Nick Abercrombie.

Criminology

MA/Diploma
1 year full time
2 years part time
(1 day per week)
Postgraduate Secretary,
Department of Social Policy
& Professional Studies,
University of Hull, Hull HU6
7RX
Tel: 0482 465569

This newly revised course (full-time or part-time) provides a comprehensive and varied study of criminology and criminal justice. The part-time course is particularly suitable for those employed in the criminal justice or penal services. It is based on a modular system comprising four compulsory elements, covering theories of crime, criminal justice and research methodology, and a further five optional modules, including gender and ethnic issues, policing, juvenile justice, victims of crime and quantitative/qualitative research skills. Assessment is by a combination of course work, written papers and a 12,000-15,000 word dissertation.
Entrance requirements Second Class Honours degree in social sciences, law, psychology etc. or an equivalent professional qualification.
Course director Professor A K Bottomley.

Economic development

MSc
1 year full time
2 years part time
15 places
dip
1 year full time
2 years part time
15 places
The Postgraduate Secretary,
Department of Economics,
University of Salford, The
Crescent, Salford M5 4WT
Tel: 061 745 5724

The programme caters for two streams of students: one is concentrated exclusively on economic issues and the alternative stream is provided with exposure to historical aspects of economic development and to other social science disciplines.
One of the greatest challenges presently facing mankind is the eradication of widespread poverty in the Third World. Exposure to the postgraduate discipline of Economic Development helps to further individual career prospects in this expanding field and enables students to grasp a clear understanding of the complexity of the issues. The course at Salford has been running successfully over a number of years and the staff offer a great deal of individual encouragement and close personal supervision.
Entrance requirements Good honours degree or equivalent.
Head of department Professor N Topham.

Economic development/ housing/leisure services & tourism/urban & regional studies

PhD/MPhil (2 years)
MSocSc/dip (1 year)
(double/part-time)
20-25 places
Graduate Admissions Tutor,
Centre for Urban & Regional
Studies, J G Smith Building,
University of Birmingham,
Birmingham B15 2TT
Tel: 021 414 6372

The Centre offers a wide range of opportunities to study for postgraduate degrees by research, course work or both. Specialisms include: housing; economic development; leisure and tourism, and policy in relation to these.
Entrance requirements Good honours degree in an appropriate subject, or professional qualification and experience.
Grants ESRC awards.
Head of centre C J Watson.

Economics

MSc(Econ) in international
economics and banking
1 year full time
Assistant Registrar,
Department of Economics,
University of Wales College
of Cardiff, PO Box 68,
Cardiff CF1 3XA

This one year taught course offers students, who have already had a substantial economics background, an advanced programme of study in the essential aspects of international economics and banking. The nature of the course is deliberately designed to be relevant to a wide range of students from both developed and developing countries. The courses covered during the programme are, international banking, international trade, international finance and development economics. Having completed these courses, students are required to carry out a project and submit a dissertation which gives them the opportunity to test the applicability of their new learning whilst under close supervision.
Entrance requirements Good honours degree or equivalent.
Head of department Professor R Mansfield.

Economics

PhD
MPhil
Department of Economics,
University of Newcastle upon
Tyne, Newcastle upon Tyne
NE1 7RU
Tel: 091 222 6000

The department offers research degrees in a wide range of economics subjects, with particular emphasis on policy and decision making, portfolio behaviour, risk and financial markets, international debt and economic reform, environmental economics, the labour market, monetary and business economics, including econometric modelling and business forecasting. The Department offers excellent research facilities including computing and the appropriate software resources, regular workshops etc.
Entrance requirements Good honours degree in a relevant discipline.
Grants Some ESRC awards.
Head of department Professor Michael Jones-Lee.

Economics

MSc
1 year full time
2 years part time
cert
1 year full time
2 years part time
dip
9 months full time
21 months part time
Graduate Admissions
Officer, Department of
Economics, University of
Southampton, Highfield,
Southampton SO9 5NH
Tel: 0703 559122

The department offers masters courses in Economics, Quantitative International Finance and in Economics and Econometrics. These courses are designed for students seeking careers as professional economists. There are core courses in economic theory and econometrics, and options include open economy macro, labour, industrial, international trade, development, monetary theory, and topics in econometrics. In addition, a dissertation is submitted.
Entrance requirements Good honours degree in economics or equivalent.
Grants Some University scholarship awards and students are eligible for ESRC awards.
Head of department Professor J Malcomson.

Economics & agricultural economics

MSc
1 year full time
MPhil/PhD
2-3 years full time
Postgraduate admissions
tutor, Department of
Economics and Agricultural
Economics, University
College of Wales,
Aberystwyth, Aberystwyth
SY23 3DB
Tel: 0970 623111

Opportunities are available for postgraduate studies in economics and agricultural economics for *MSc* by examination, *MPhil* and *PhD* by research. A wide range of topics are available including development economics, macro-economic modelling, international economics, issues in agricultural economics including rural development and the environment, economic history, industrial relations and organisational theory. Also a 9 month postgraduate diploma is offered for graduates in other disciplines. Applications also invited from graduates in economics or related disciplines to read for the 1 year MSc in Agricultural Economics/Marketing by coursework and dissertation. All courses are full time, but part time regulations may be applied.
Entrance requirements Honours degree in appropriately related subject.
Head of department Professor D A Peel.

Economics, economic development

MA(Econ)
1 year full time
Department of Economics,
University of Manchester,
Manchester M13 9PL
Tel: 061 275 4823

The MA (Econ) by coursework and dissertation is designed to provide the training in analysis and empirical methods required by an entrant contemplating a career as a professional economist. Separate programmes are offered in Economics and Development Economics. Each comprises eight course units: four core units in theory and quantitative techniques and four cours units from a wide range of options. The supervised dissertation, prepared on an agreed research topic in the final three months, provides an introduction to research experience.

Other postgraduate courses offered by the department include research degrees at MA and PhD level and diplomas in Economics and Development Economics.

Entrance requirements A good UK honours degree in Economics or equivalent qualification. Students who do not qualify for direct entry may be offered admission to a two year programme of study.

Human Rights

LLM/MA
1 year full time
25 places
Professor Kevin Boyle,
Director of Centre, Human
Rights Centre, University of
Essex, Wivenhoe Park,
Colchester C04 3SQ
Tel: 0206 873333 Fax: 0206
873598

The Human Rights Centre, Essex University, is an inter-disciplinary centre for the study of the theory and practice of international human rights. It embraces Law, Philosophy, Government and Sociology Departments. It offers a well established one year LLM in international human rights protection, and will offer an MA from October 1991. The Masters degrees include seminars on global protection, regional protection (including European), a seminar on human rights and armed conflicts, and a seminar on the philosophy of human rights. Course requirements include a thesis and internship with an international human rights organisation.

Entrance requirements A good honours degree in law, social science or humanities.

Director of Centre Professor Kevin Boyle.

International studies

MA
1 year full time
20 places
dip
Dr Barry Buzan, Room 11,
Department of International
Studies, University of
Warwick, Coventry CV4 7AL

The MA consists of taught courses and a dissertation; the diploma is a taught course. The diploma can serve as basis for entry into the MA if a suitable standard is attained. Fields of research are: international political economy, strategic studies, EEC, transnational corporations, the law of the sea. Suitably qualified candidates for the MA may take relevant advanced options taught in Law, Race, Industrial and Business Studies, Politics, Sociology, and History. There is a three-month exchange arrangement with the Universidad Autonoma in Madrid is under negotiation.

Entrance requirements Diploma: an honours degree. MA: normally an upper second class honours degree.

Grants None.

Head of group Barry Buzan.

International studies/public policy and administration/ politics and culture/equal opportunities

PhD
3 years full time
Dr D M Hill, Department of Politics, University of Southampton, Highfield, Southampton SO9 5NH
Tel: 0703 595000

The department offers four Diploma/MSc(Soc Sci) programmes: International studies; Public policy & administration, Politics & culture and Equal Opportunities plus supervision for research students in linked areas. On each of the Diploma/MSc(Soc Sci) programmes two terms of course work lead to qualifying exams for either the award of the Diploma or permission to prepare a dissertation for the MSc(Soc Sci).
Entrance requirements Normally an upper second class honours degree or overseas equivalent. Post experience entrants considered. Overseas students seeking admission must possess an English language qualification acceptable to the university.
Grants ESRC eligible.
Head of department Professor R Plant BA PhD.

Latin American studies

MA in Area Studies (Latin America)
1 year full time
2 years part time
Institute of Latin American Studies, University of London, 31 Tavistock Square, London WC1H 9HA
Tel: 01 387 5671

Interdisciplinary study in the humanities and social sciences with specialisation in two or three of the following disciplines: anthropology, archaeology, economics, geography, history, international relations, literature, politics, sociology, and multidisciplinary topics. Three taught courses and a dissertation (or four courses) from a range of twenty-six courses, drawing on the intercollegiate resources of the schools and colleges of the University of London.
Entrance requirements normally at least upper second class honours degree or equivalent. Reading knowledge of Spanish or Portuguese.
Grants ESRC/British Academy.
Director Professor Leslie Bethell.

Macroeconomics

MA
1 year full time
2 years part time
A P L Minford, Department of Economics & Accounting, University of Liverpool, PO Box 147, Liverpool L69 3BX
Tel: 051 794 3032

The MA course provides comprehensive training in modern macroeconomic analysis and applications; backed by resources of a leading centre for macroeconomic modelling and forecasting, Liverpool Research Group in macroeconomics; course content: advanced macroeconomics, microeconomics, econometrics and two options from monetary, international macroeconomics, applied time-series and forecasting, applied macro-modelling; opportunities to work with Liverpool models and complete range of modelling software available on excellent microcomputer and mainframe facilities. Candidates with a good pass in the MA exams may then undertake the MPhil/PhD thesis in macroeconomics, including modelling, forecasting, monetary, international, and rational expectations.
Entrance requirements Good honours degree in economics.
Contact Professor A P L Minford.

Medical anthropology

MSc
1 year full time
2 full days per week
2 years part time
1 full days per week
25 places
Convenor, MSc Medical Anthropology, Department of Human Sciences, Brunel University, Uxbridge, Middlesex UB8 3PH
Tel: 0895 56461

This academic course centers on the range of complex cultural processes associated with the definition, genesis and the management of sickness and disease. The main objective of the course is to introduce key issues in medical anthropology; to equip students with the skills in the critical analysis of relevant issues and problems using an anthropological perspective; and to encourage the development of research expertise using anthropological techniques. Students take two core courses: The Social Anthropology of Health and Healing and Research Methods in Medical Anthropology; and a range of options.
Entrance requirements Applicants should possess a degree in a related area or equivalent qualifications and experience.
Course convenor Ian Robinson.

Psychology

MLitt/PhD Psychology
MSc/PhD
Cognitive Science and Psycholinguistics
Dr S Garrod, Department of Psychology, University of Glasgow, Glasgow G12 8QQ
Tel: 041 339 8855 ext 5033

Psychology: MLitt/PhD supervision available, interests: cognitive science especially HCI, natural language understanding, cognitive development. Applied social gambling and addiction, cross cultural communication, child abuse. Cognitive science/psycholinguistics: in league with the Human Communications Research Centre the department also offers a joint Glasgow/Edinburgh MSc/PhD course involving one year in the Edinburgh Cognitive Science programme followed by two year's PhD supervision in psycholinguistics at Glasgow.
Entrance requirements Open to UK and overseas students holding a good degree in Psychology or a relevant discipline such as linguistics, A I or Philosophy.
Grants Studentships are regularly available for UK students from ESRC and SERC.

Psychology

MPhil/PhD Psychology
Clinical Psychology - MSc 3 years
Educational Psychology - MSc 1 year
Ergonomics - MSc 1 year
Experimental Methods - MSc 1 year
Department of Psychology, University College London, Gower Street, London WC1E 6BT
Tel: 071 387 7050 ext 2679

Psychology: MPhil/PhD; supervision available, research interests: *experimental psychology*: especially visual and auditory perception, information processing, skills, psychology of language, speech, thinking and reading; math models of choice and reaction time; AI and computational studies of psychological processes; pharmacological studies of stress and anxiety in animals, human studies of electrical activity of brain, gen investigations of animal behaviour and its evolution; *developmental psychology* with special reference to cognitive processes, handicap and deviant behaviour; *clinical psychology and neuro-psychology*, psychological studies of stress and anxiety; research into problems of social psychology and personality; psychoanalytic research; human factors in industry esp complex control processes; cognitive ergonomics of information technology.
Entrance requirements A good first degree in psychology or a related subject.
Clinical psychology: contact Dr P Fonagy
Educational psychology:contact Dr I O M Morin
Ergonomics:contact Professor J B Long
Experimental methods:contact Dr H C Plotkin.

Science & technology studies

MA
1 year full time
(2 full days per week)
2 years part time
(1 full day per week)
25 places
Convenor, MA Science and Technology Studies, Department of Human Sciences, Brunel University, Uxbridge, Middlesex UB8 3PH
Tel: 0895 56461

This programme focuses on the generation and impact of science and technology in its social, political and cultural contexts. There is a core course in Innovation Studies and a course in Research Methods which lead to the production of a dissertation. In addition, students choose from electives such as 'science, technology and society', 'culture, technology and modernity' and 'knowledge, expertise and society'. Particular emphasis is given throughout the programme to the relation between the practice of science and technology, and theories and methods in Science and Technology Studies.
Entrance requirements Applicants should possess a degree or equivalent qualifications and experience.
Course convenor Dr Steve Woolgar.

Socio legal studies

MA
1 year full time
12-15 places
Secretary for Postgraduate Admissions, Faculty of Law, University of Sheffield, Crookesmoor Building, Conduit Road, Sheffield S10 1FL
Tel: 0742 768555

Law is explored through the social sciences. The concern is with how it is possible to gain knowledge of the role of law in society, and attempts to do so by social scientists. The operation of law in distinct social settings is also examined. Subjects include: the sociology of law and the emergence of the modern state, philosophy of inquiry and conduct of inquiry, methods and research strategies, law and social policy, feminism, women and the law and contemporay issues in criminology.

Applications are acceptable from: 1 January 1991. Starting date: October 1991. Closing date for applications: 1 March 1991 (all students requiring grants), 31 July 1991 (self-financing students).
Entrance requirements Good honours degree or equivalent.
Grants ESRC committee and competition awards.
Head of department Professor John Birds.

Socio-legal studies

MA
1 year full time
2 years part time
25 places
Convenor, MA Socio-Legal Studies, Department of Law, Brunel University, Uxbridge, Middlesex UB8 3PH
Tel: 0895 56461

A taught course which combines sociological and legal perspectives, both theoretically and in the examination and analysis of current issues, such as child abuse, social welfare, delinquency and the administration of justice. The course also provides an introduction to the carrying out and evaluation of social research projects. Students will be required to undertake a small-scale research project for a dissertation.
Entrance requirements A good honours degree, normally in law or sociology. Applicants with other qualifications will also be considered.
Grants Full-time students may be eligible to apply for an ESRC award.
Course convenor Dr. Jill Peay.

Sociology and social anthropology

PhD
3 years full time research
4 years part time
MPhil
2 years full time
3 years part time
MA in Sociology of Developing Societies
MA in South-East Asian Studies
MA in Developing Area Studies
MA in Defence and Disarmament Studies
1 year full time
2 years part time
Dr D Booth, Postgraduate Admissions Tutor, Department of Sociology and Social Anthropology, University of Hull, Hull HU6 7RX
Tel: 0482 46311

This combined department of sociology/anthropology offers research training and taught courses in association with inter-disciplinary centres of Developing Area Studies, South East Asian Studies and Defence and Disarmament Studies. Staff research interests include industry and employment, war and militarism, family and gender, urban community studies and religion as well as sociology and social anthropology of parts of Africa, Latin America and South East Asia. Research students initially take a taught course in the planning and conduct of research, and subsequently participate in regular workshops. MA students take compulsory core courses plus specialist options and dissertation. Recognised institution for ESRC training and coursework studentships.
Entrance requirements First or second class honours degree in appropriate subject.
Head of department H C Creighton.

Sociology of contemporary culture

MA
1 year full time
Dr B Sandywell, Department of Sociology, University of York, Heslington, York YO1 5DD
Tel: 0904 430000

MA This one-year taught MA covers a range of topics in contemporary cultural theory and analysis (including film, aesthetics, language, science, religion); applications are invited from students with relevant academic background (social sciences, literature, English, communications, history, etc). Workshops in empirical cultural analysis are a special feature of the course.
Degree is awarded on the basis of course-essays and dissertation project in a specialist area of culture of the students choice.
Doctoral research Supervision is available for MPhil/DPhil research in conjunction with current research projects and areas in sociology.
Entrance requirements First or upper second class honours degree.
Grants ESRC.
Head of department Andrew Tudor.

Sociology of scientific knowledge

MSc
dip
1 year full time
Secretary, Science Studies Unit, University of Edinburgh, 34 Buccleuch Place, Edinburgh EH8 9JT
Tel: 031 667 1011

This course offers a systematic introduction to the extensive literature in the sociology of scientific knowledge, and to its ideas, perspectives, resources and achievements. It is particularly suited to students with a good first degree in the natural sciences, and/or in history, sociology, social anthropology or philosophy, especially those who have had some contact with the history, sociology or philosophy of science - but such specific qualifications are not a requirement.
The first term covers a 'core syllabus'; in the second and third terms, more specialised topics are discussed. The diploma is awarded after examinations in June: the MSc after the submission of a dissertation in September.
Entrance requirements First/second class honours degree.
Grants Apply to ESRC, before the 1st of May.
Director Mr B Barnes.

Sociology, social policy and social anthropology

MA Sociology/Social Policy
MA/dip Ethnic Relations
PhD negotiable
Professor Robert Moore,
Department of Sociology,
Social Policy and Social
Work, University of
Liverpool, The University,
Liverpool L69 3BX
Tel: 051 794 2985

Possibilities in ethnic and race relations, industrial and labour studies, leisure studies, social administration, sociology of health and medicine, political sociology. Research is also available in Third World Studies, especially Africa and Latin America; special areas include gender relations and gender policy; agrarian transformation and development policy; migration and urban studies; culture, social history and political movements. The University provides TEFL courses and research students will find colleagues in the Institute for Latin American Studies and the Centre for African studies.
Entrance requirements Degree or equivalent.
Course director Professor Robert Moore.

Soviet & East European studies

MPhil
2 years full time
(exceptionally 1 year)
3 years part time
MLitt/PhD
2-3 years full time
3-4 years part time
dip
1 year full time
2 years part time
Professor W V Wallace,
Institute of Soviet & East
European Studies, University
of Glasgow, 29 Bute
Gardens, Glasgow G12 8RS
Tel: 041 339 8855

MPhil provides language training and choice of four out of twelve courses plus dissertation. Courses and MLitt/PhD research cover economics, politics, foreign policy, sociology and history.
Special research projects in comparative economic/political development, policy-making, East-West relations, environment, public health and nationality questions.
Academic co-operation in research with corresponding institutes in Soviet Union, Eastern Europe and China. Chinese option available. First class specialist library. Regular visiting scholars.
Entrance requirements First/second class honours degree in social sciences/arts.
Grants Apply to ESRC.
Director Professor W Wallace.

2

Engineering/ technology/ environment

The University of Liverpool
Faculty of Engineering
Postgraduate Study

The Faculty of Engineering, which has over 200 postgraduates, enjoys a high reputation for postgraduate teaching and research, with excellent facilities and a wide range of topics for study. Higher degrees may be obtained either wholly by research or by a combination of taught courses and research.

The University is sited on a single modern campus, close to the city centre, which contains postgraduate halls of residence and a large sports centre. The city is noted for its cultural, recreational and shopping facilities.

Postgraduate research degrees
Facilities to study by research for the M.Phil, the M.Sc. (Eng.) or the Ph.D degree are available in the Departments of the Faculty which are:
(a) Civil Engineering
(b) Electrical Engineering and Electronics
(c) Industrial Studies
(d) Materials Science and Engineering
(e) Mechanical Engineering

There are also associated facilities in Building Engineering within the School of Architecture and Building Engineering.

The research topics currently being studied in all these Departments are widespread and are continually developing. Only an indication is given by the coverage of the taught courses listed below. Further details of these research subjects are available from the Heads of the above Departments.

The submission of a thesis and, in the case of the Ph.D. and the part-time M.Sc. (Eng.) an oral examination are required for the award of the degree.

Postgraduate courses
Courses of one calendar year duration lead to the degree of M.Sc. (Eng.). These course are:
(1) Maritime Civil Engineering
(2) Structural Engineering (Civil Engineering)
(3) Environmental Civil Engineering
(4) Microelectronics Systems and Telecommunications
(5) Power Plants and Energy Related Studies (Mechanical Engineering)
(6) Mechanical Systems Engineering
(7) Advanced Engineering Materials
(8) Advanced Manufacturing Systems and Technology

The last of these courses is provided jointly by departments (b), (c) and (e) above.
All these courses next start on 8th October 1990.
Each course includes six months of lectures and laboratory work, assessed by written examination and continuous assessment. The remainder of the year is spent on a supervised research project leading to a dissertation.

Integrated Graduate Development Scheme (joint with Liverpool Polytechnic)
A series of residential one-week modules for those employed in the process or manufacturing industries lead to the award of a Postgraduate Diploma or, with dissertation. M.Sc.

Grants
Studentships for research studies or for the above courses are currently available from all the above departments.

Part-time study
Provision, in certain instances, can be made for part-time study.

Application
All initial applications for post-graduate study should be addressed to:
The Sub-Dean (Postgraduate Admissions)
Faculty of Engineering, The University of Liverpool,
P.O. Box 147, Liverpool L69 3BX, England.
Telephone: 051 794-4924. Telex: 627095. Fax: 051 794 4848
Applicants should indicate their interest in either the research school of one of the above Departments or in one of the above courses. Application can be made at any time in the year.

Computer studies

Although there are many jobs available in computing, the computer science graduate would be advised to consider a further degree before starting full-time work, or after a few years' work experience. A further degree is often the most effective way, too, for graduates from other disciplines to change to computing, offering a quick and unbiased introduction to the field. Usually, the problem is choosing the right course.

Most of the jobs in computing are in business, commercial or administrative applications. The majority of computer science courses are aimed at scientific, engineering or mathematical uses of computers. This mismatch means that, to be useful, computer science graduates are usually as much in need of a conversion course as graduates from other disciplines.

Logical approach

Many people think that mathematical ability is needed to use computers. That is quite wrong; it is true that *numeracy* is important, but it is a methodical and logical approach, rather than knowledge of maths, that is essential. For many jobs, getting on with people and a sympathetic understanding of their problems are also essential too. For this reason graduates in classics, music and Anglo-Saxon can be just as successful after a conversion course as their colleagues who studied maths, physics or computer science.

To help you decide if a further degree makes sense for you, you must review the jobs available, and the types of courses you can choose.

The jobs...

Jobs in computing are usually in management, systems analysis and programming. Management is very unlikely to be open to a graduate without considerable experience. Until recently, there were no courses to prepare graduates for management tasks in computing, as there have been for many years in other fields, but MBA degrees in information management are now appearing.

The systems analyst is the 'bridge' between the user, who knows the tasks to be done but does not understand the computer, and the computer expert, who knows how to instruct the computer, but does not understand the user's problems. Again, this job needs experience -preferably in a user-related field - and a liking for people and their problems.

Programmers tend to be at their best when young (although there are many exceptions to that rule), so a typical career path might include some years' programming, followed by training as a systems analyst or manager. There are three major divisions of programming - applications, systems and software. Applications programmers write programs to carry out specific tasks in the company they work for. The systems programmer becomes skilled in using and sometimes amending the

Queen Mary and Westfield College

UNIVERSITY OF
LONDON

POSTGRADUATE COMPUTER SCIENCE

PhD/MPhil by Research

The department currently has 50 research students and is continuing to expand its PhD programme. Applications are invited both for full-time and for part-time research. On acceptance, all research students will be registered initially for the MPhil degree, with conversion to PhD normally occurring after one year in the event of satisfactory progress. During the first year, research students are expected to attend a small number of MSc courses (see below) with the aim of extending their education and broadening their background for research. Also, a small preliminary research project is to be carried out and written up during the first year of study.

Research in a wide variety of areas can be considered, provided that it has some connection with the interests of one or more of the department's research groups which are as follows: Advanced Computing Environments, Automated Reasoning, Computer Vision, Distributed Systems, Human-Computer Interaction and Programming Foundations. We also have a strong association with the Centre for Parallel Computing.

MSc in Advanced Methods in Computer Science

A one year taught course with specialisation in any one of the following four programmes of study:

Artificial Intelligence and Automated Reasoning — covers the detailed understanding of cognitive tasks like reasoning, decision making and perception, using computational models to allow the construction of systems with new automated capabilities.

Distributed and Parallel Systems — aims to provide an understanding of the concepts and principles used in the design and implementation of distributed systems, parallel systems and computer architectures.

Formal Methods in Software Engineering — reflects the growing role of formal methods in all aspects of the process of designing and implementing software systems, covering both the relevant theoretical ideas and their practical applications.

Human-Computer Interaction — covers the design, implementation and evaluation of state-of-the-art user interfaces using the theory and methods from computer science, psychology, ergonomics and artificial intelligence.

These streams match the department's major research strengths. Students acquire a detailed understanding of relevant theoretical work from staff actively working in the area, and are then able to test out this understanding by working on practical coursework assignments.

Teaching is predominantly in small groups, emphasising participation and two-way communication. After the exams at Easter, the second half of the year is spent on a substantial project in one of the areas covered by the course.

Some SERC quota awards are available for all types of study.

For further information please apply to the Postgraduate Admissions Officer (D91), Department of Computer Science, Queen Mary and Westfield College, Mile End Road, London E1 4NS. Telephone 071-975 5200.

programs provided by the computer manufacturer to control the computer, and to carry out tasks that are often repeated such as copying data from one device to another. The software programmer generally works in a team preparing programs that will be useful to many users, such as production control or stock management systems.

...and the courses

Appropriate higher degrees include PhDs, MPhils, MScs and MBAs (you may also meet a few MA degrees in computer-related subjects). Research degrees in this field are very specialised, and should not be pursued except as an end in themselves; only if you wish to enter academic life, or unless you want to tackle a particular problem that interests you -although research does provide excellent training in thinking and applying techniques. Bear in mind, however, that as many PhDs have led to the formation of companies to exploit the results of the research, a PhD may turn out to be its own reward.

Master's courses may provide specialist knowledge in a specific area, such as computer management, systems analysis or expert systems, or they may cover the ground of a first degree in computer science. Many of these courses can be regarded as conversions from some other field, and few of them demand a first degree in computer science as a prerequisite.

One-year conversions to a 'standard' computer science syllabus should be viewed with suspicion, as most computing jobs require additional knowledge over and above that covered in a typical computer science syllabus. All the other courses available should lead to a wider range of possibilities; research should be seen as a long-term investment, however.

In choosing a postgraduate course, think carefully about what you want; do you want to be a researcher, an expert in the computer department, a 'bridge' between computer experts and the user, a manager of a computer installation or an 'educated' user? When you have made your mind up about this, you will be ready to choose a course - or not, if that is your decision.

Study the available courses, remembering that computers are *tools* and that you must always bear in mind the needs of the people these tools are there to serve. You may wish to take a course now, or your aims may be best served by getting some work experience first. In London, you can work and study, as there are evening MSc/postgraduate diploma courses in computer science (at Birkbeck) and business systems analysis (at City University). In some cases, and particularly if you intend to join a computer manufacturer, you may decide to rely on the training provided and do without a further degree. If you are undecided, consult someone you trust who works with computers; if you still cannot decide, a further course may be just what you need!

Course funding

More types of support are available for computer courses than for most others. The Science & Engineering Research Council (SERC) accepts some courses as suitable for the tenure of its advanced and research studentships, others are supported by the IT studentship scheme, and a few courses can offer Economic & Social Research Council (ESRC) support. For those unable to get grants, low-interest loans may be available from banks. These loans are not made available through local branches, so do not talk to your own bank manager or you will be offered a normal commercial loan. If

 **CITY** University **COURSES IN BUSINESS COMPUTING, 1991-92**

Places are available on the following courses starting in September 1991.

BUSINESS SYSTEMS ANALYSIS AND DESIGN
MSc/Postgraduate Diploma

These courses are run both full time in one year, and in evenings plus study schools in two years. Candidates should have a good honours degree or equivalent professional qualifications, and preferably some relevant experience. The Science and Engineering Research Council has accepted the full time MSc course as suitable for the tenure of its Advanced Course Studentships.

BUSINESS DATA PROCESSING
Undergraduate Diploma

This is a one year full time course. Candidates should have qualifications such as the BCS Part 1 by examination, IDPM Part IV, HND plus at least two years' experience, a third class honours degree or equivalent. Students who achieve good results may be able to join the MSc in the following year.

RESEARCH DEGREES – Phd/MPhil

Suitably qualified candidates are invited to join a strong research programme. Major projects include database design, systems design methodologies, human factors in systems design and the application of artificial intelligence to business problems. Sponsors include SERC, DTI, ESPRIT and public companies.

For further information and application forms contact:
The Courses Officer,
Room CM415 D,
Department of Business Systems Analysis,
City University, Northampton Square,
London, EC1V 0HB.
Telephone: 071 253-4399, Ext. 3405/6 Fax: 071-608 1270

THE UNIVERSITY OF WARWICK
MSc INFORMATION TECHNOLOGY FOR MANUFACTURE

THE UNIVERSITY OF WARWICK IS AT THE FOREFRONT OF
Information Technology research and teaching. The Warwick course has been jointly developed by academics and specialists from industry.

CONTENT: The course covers fields vital to the development of Information Technology and its application to manufacturing activities including:

Computer Languages and Systems
Information Technology
Computer Integrated Manufacture
Automation and Robotics

Artificial Intelligence and Expert Systems
Quantitative Techniques and Decision Analysis
Manufacturing Control
Financial Management and Risk Analysis
Technology and Management of Integration

Subject to approval by Course Manager, candidates having relevant experience and/or recent qualification which includes significant Information Technology may opt for the advanced information technology modules.

STRUCTURE: This is a full-time one-year taught course and a modular system is adopted for couse work, which is continuously assessed. In addition, an industrially oriented research project, assessed by dissertation and oral examination, is undertaken.

FACILITIES: The University has excellent research facilities including the largest academic CAD/CAM CENTRE in Western Europe; extensive Computer facilities; and Robotics, Control, FMS and Manufacturing Simulation laboratories.

The normal minimum entry requirement is a second class honours degree or equivalent qualification and SERC studentships are available.

Candidates not satisfying these requirements will be considered for either the MSc or Post Graduate Diploma depending on their qualifications and experience.

For further details please contact:

Postgraduate Admissions Tutor, Information Technology for Manufacture,
Department of Engineering, University of Warwick, Coventry CV4 7AL

the course you choose is eligible for low-interest loans, they can usually only be arranged through the course administration, and you should discuss the various ways of financing your studies when you are interviewed for the course.

Owen Hanson

This listing contains **taught courses** (under the heading 'Higher degrees by instruction') and **research opportunities** (under the heading 'Higher degrees by research'). All study exceeds two terms or six months and is offered on both a full-time and part-time basis unless otherwise indicated. Post-experience and in-service courses are only included when advertised.

☐   This symbol indicates that the **taught course(s)** or **research opportunities** are advertised at the end of this listing.

Biol   An italic abbreviation indicates that an advertisement has been placed at the end of another chapter.

☆   This symbol indicates full-time study only.

△   This symbol indicates part-time study only.

For quick reference to advertisements, please use the 'Advertiser's course entry index'. For further information regarding the listing, please refer to page 53.

General

Higher degrees by instruction

Applied artificial intelligence
Aberdeen U MSc☆/dip☆

Applied mathematics
Bangor, U of Wales MSc☆/dip☆

Business information technology systems
Strathclyde U MSc☆/dip☆

Business systems analysis & design
City U MSc/dip

Computational science
Belfast Queen's U MSc☆

Computer aided engineering
Cranfield IT MSc☆   ☐

Computer applications for history
London U Inst of Historical Research/US Studies MA

Computer applications in engineering
Robert Gordon's IT dip☆

Computer based administration systems
Glasgow C MSc☆/dip☆

Computer integrated manufacturing
Loughborough U MSc☆
Leeds P dip☆

Computer science
Birmingham U MSc☆
Cambridge U dip☆   ☐
East Anglia U MSc/dip
London U UC MSc☆   ☐
Manchester U MSc☆/dip☆

Computer science education
Ulster U MSc☆/cert☆/dip☆

Computer studies
Birmingham P dip△
Essex U MSc   ☐
Teesside P dip☆

Computer studies (cognitive science)
Essex U MSc☆

Computer studies (specialist)
Essex U MSc☆

Computer technology in manufacture
Sussex U MSc☆

Computer-based electronic music techniques
Bangor, U of Wales dip☆

Computing
Ulster U dip
Wales P dip☆

Computing & social statistics
Kent U MA

Computing in design
Middlesex P MA☆

Computing science
London U Imperial C MSc☆/
dip☆ □
Newcastle U MSc☆/dip☆

Computing science (conversion)
Staffordshire P MSc☆/dip☆ □

Computing software & systems design
Newcastle U MSc☆

Data communications networks & distributed systems
London U UC MSc☆ □

Decision sciences
Central London P MSc△

Digital & microcomputer systems engineering
East Anglia U MSc△

Digital image processing
Cranfield IT MSc☆/dip☆ □

Educational media & technology
Hull U dip☆

Engineering computation
Belfast Queen's U MSc☆/
dip☆ *Eng*

Engineering mechanics
Cranfield IT MSc☆

Exchange & membrane technology
Cranfield IT MSc☆

History & computing
Glasgow U MPhil

Human factors in manufacturing systems
Nottingham U MSc

Independent study
East London P MA/MSc/dip

Industrial applications of computers
Open U MSc/dip

Industrial programming technology
Sheffield U MSc☆

Information & library studies
Strathclyde U MSc/dip

Information management
Strathclyde U MSc☆/dip☆

Information systems
Leeds P MSc△

Information technology
Dundee IT dip☆
Glasgow U MSc/dip □
London U UC MSc☆/dip☆ □

Instrumentation & analytical science
Manchester UMIST MSc☆

Intelligent knowledge based systems
Essex U MSc☆ □

Intelligent management systems
South Bank P MSc☆/dip☆

Knowledge based systems
Heriot-Watt U MSc☆

Laser communications
Essex U MSc☆

Management of new technology with modern languages
Newcastle P MSc☆/dip☆

Mathematical astronomy & computation
London U Queen Mary & Westfield C MSc

Mathematical computation
London U Queen Mary & Westfield C MSc

Mathematics, statistics & computing
Teesside P dip☆

Microelectronics & computer technology
Birmingham P dip☆

Occupational psychology
Hatfield P MSc

Office systems management
Humberside CHE MSc☆/dip☆

Operational research & computer techniques
Southampton IHE dip☆ *Bus*

Real time systems (conversion)
Nottingham P MSc△

Science & technology studies
Brunel U MA *Soc*

Signal processing & machine intelligence
Surrey U MSc☆

Software engineering
Dundee IT dip☆

Software engineering with applications
Aston U MSc/dip □

Software systems technology
Sheffield U MSc □

Higher degrees by research

Accounting & business computing
Portsmouth P PhD☆/MPhil☆

Architecture
Dundee U PhD/MSc *Env*

Biomedical engineering
Sussex U DPhil/MPhil *Eng*

Cognitive studies
Edinburgh U PhD/MLitt/MPhil

Computer assisted learning
Open U PhD/MPhil

Computer integrated manufacture
Cranfield IT PhD☆

Computer science
Essex U PhD/MPhil/MSc
Hull U PhD/MSc
London U UC PhD☆/MPhil☆
London U UC PhD☆/MPhil☆ □
Manchester U PhD/MSc

Computer studies & mathematics
Bristol P PhD△/MPhil△/dip△

Computer systems & information technology
Warwick U PhD/MSc

Computers in medicine
Kent U PhD☆/MPhil☆

Computing
Birmingham P PhD/MPhil
London U Imperial C PhD/
MPhil □
Middlesex P PhD☆/MPhil/PhD△

Computing science
East Anglia U PhD☆/MPhil☆
Newcastle U PhD/MPhil

Computing studies
Leicester U PhD/MPhil

Control theory
Salford U PhD☆/MSc☆

Electrical, electronic & systems engineering
Cardiff U of Wales C PhD☆/ MPhil☆ *Eng*

Engineering design for manufacture
Cranfield IT PhD☆

Human communication
London U UC PhD☆/MPhil☆

Image processing
London U UC PhD☆/MPhil☆

Independent study
East London P PhD/MPhil

Instrumentation & analytical science
Manchester UMIST PhD/MSc

Mathematical compilation
London U Queen Mary & Westfield C PhD☆/MPhil☆

Microcomputer centre
Dundee U PhD/MSc

Operations management
Cranfield IT PhD☆/MPhil☆

Quality assurance
Cranfield IT PhD☆/MPhil☆/MSc☆

Science, mathematics & computing
Cheltenham & Gloucester CHE PhD/MPhil

Computer engineering

Higher degrees by instruction

Advanced manufacturing systems & technology
Liverpool U MSc(Eng) *Eng*

Advanced production engineering
Edinburgh U MSc/dip

Computational modelling & finite elements in engineering mechanics
Swansea UC MSc☆/cert☆

Computer aided design & manufacture of production machines & systems
Cranfield IT MSc☆

Computer aided engineering
Coventry P MSc☆/dip☆

Liverpool P MSc☆/dip☆ ☐
Nottingham P MSc△/dip△
Teesside P MSc

Computer aided engineering & automation technology
Leicester P dip

Computer applications in engineering
Robert Gordon's IT dip☆

Computer based engineering systems
Dundee IT dip☆

Computer integrated engineering
Loughborough U MSc☆

Computer integrated manufacturing
Loughborough U MSc☆
Cranfield IT MSc☆
Strathclyde U MSc

Computer modelling of molecular & biological processes
London U Birkbeck C MSc△

Computer related industrial design
Royal CA MDes☆

Computer science
East Anglia U MSc/dip
Manchester U MSc☆/dip☆

Computer science (new generation computing)
Exeter U MSc☆

Computer studies
Essex U MSc ☐

Computer studies (conversion)
Brunel U dip☆

Computer studies (specialist)
Essex U MSc☆

Computer-aided engineering design
Strathclyde U MSc

Computing
Ulster U dip

Computing software & systems design
Newcastle U MSc☆

Computing systems
Cranfield IT MSc☆ *Eng*

Data engineering
Keele U MSc☆

Design & economic manufacture
Swansea UC MSc☆

Design of integrated systems
South Bank P MSc△

Design systems in production
Warwick U MSc

Digital systems
Brunel U MSc

Digital systems & instrumentation
Central London P MSc△

Digital techniques for information technology
Heriot-Watt U MSc☆/dip☆

Electronic engineering
Cardiff U of Wales C MSc☆/ dip☆ *Eng*

Electronic manufacture
Birmingham P dip☆

Engineering mechanics
Cranfield IT MSc☆

Formal methods in software engineering
London U Queen Mary & Westfield C MSc

Information engineering
City U MSc/dip
Manchester UMIST MSc☆/dip☆
Robert Gordon's IT dip☆

Information systems engineering
South Bank P MSc/dip

Information technology (computer aided engineering)
Napier P dip☆

Information technology: computer systems engineering
Edinburgh U MSc/dip

Information technology: knowledge based systems
Edinburgh U MSc/dip

Instrument design
Aberdeen U MSc☆

Instrumental methods of analysis
Strathclyde U MSc/dip☆

Manufacturing systems engineering
Cranfield IT MSc☆ *Eng*
Leeds P MSc△
Warwick U MSc

Microelectronics
Durham U MEng☆/MSc☆ *Eng*

Microelectronics & computer engineering
Surrey U MSc

Microelectronics & microcomputer application
Ulster U dip△

Radio frequency & microwave engineering
Newcastle P MSc☆/dip☆

Scientific & engineering software technology
Thames P MSc/dip

Software engineering
Birmingham P dip☆
Brunel U MSc
Dundee IT dip☆
Liverpool U MSc
Manchester UMIST MSc☆/dip☆
Newcastle P MSc☆

Systems engineering (automatic control & computer engineering)
Surrey U MSc/dip

Telematics
Surrey U MSc/dip

Theoretical foundations for software engineering
Central London P MSc△

Three dimensional computer aided graphical technology applications
Teesside P MSc☆

Tribology in machine design
Leeds U MSc(Eng)☆

Higher degrees by research

Computer & communication engineering
Teesside P PhD☆/MPhil☆

Computer aided engineering
Central London P PhD☆/MPhil☆

Computer science
Essex U PhD/MPhil/MSc
Manchester U PhD/MSc

Computer systems & information technology
Warwick U PhD/MSc

Computer systems engineering
Bristol U PhD☆/MSc☆
Kent U PhD☆/MPhil☆

Computing
Nottingham P PhD☆/MPhil☆

Data & knowledge engineering
Keele U PhD/MSc

Electrical & electronic engineering
Bristol U PhD☆/MSc☆

Electronic engineering
Hull U PhD/MSc

Kent U PhD/MPhil/MSc

Electronic engineering & computer science
Sussex U DPhil/MPhil   Eng

Electronic engineering science
Bangor, U of Wales PhD☆/
  MPhil☆

Electronic instrumentation & on line computing
Newcastle U PhD/MSc

Electronics
East Anglia U PhD/MSc

Information engineering
City U PhD/MPhil

Information systems analysis
Bradford U PhD/MPhil

Mechanical & computer aided engineering
Staffordshire P PhD/MPhil

Microelectronics applications research
Newcastle U PhD/MSc

Self-organised learning
Brunel U PhD/MPhil

Signal processing
Central London P PhD☆/MPhil☆
Kent U PhD☆/MPhil☆

Signal processing & electronics
Royal Naval Engineering C
  PhD☆/MSc☆

Study of human learning
Brunel U PhD/MPhil

Computer science

Higher degrees by instruction

Advanced computer studies
Scottish C of Textiles dip☆

Advanced methods in computer science
London U Queen Mary &
  Westfield C MSc☆

Advanced production engineering
Edinburgh U MSc/dip

Analysis, design & management of information systems
London U LSE MSc

Applied artificial intelligence
Aberdeen U MSc☆/dip☆

Applied computing in social anthropology
Kent U PhD☆

Applied statistics & computing
Bangor, U of Wales dip☆

Artificial intelligence
Kingston P MSc

Artificial intelligence & automated reasoning
London U Queen Mary &
  Westfield C MSc

Biological computation
York U MSc☆/dip☆

Business information technology
Newcastle P dip☆

Cognitive science
Manchester U MSc☆   □

Computation
Manchester UMIST MSc☆/dip☆
Oxford U MSc☆   □

Computational methods in medical science
Manchester U MSc△

Computational science
Belfast Queen's U MSc☆

Computer & information technology
Dundee U MSc☆

Computer aided building design
Strathclyde U MSc/dip

Computer aided engineering & automation technology
Leicester P dip

Computer communications & networks
Leeds P Dip☆

Computer graphics
Middlesex P MSc△

Computer integrated manufacturing
Strathclyde U MSc

Computer science
Birmingham U MSc☆
Brunel U MSc   □
Cambridge U dip☆   □
City U MSc△
Dundee U MSc☆/dip☆
Durham U MSc
East Anglia U MSc/dip
Hatfield P MSc/dip△
Hull U MSc☆
London U Birkbeck C MSc
London U UC MSc☆   □
Manchester U MSc☆/dip☆

Salford U MSc☆/dip☆
South Bank P dip
Wales P MSc△/dip△

Computer science & applications
Belfast Queen's U MSc/dip

Computer science (conversion)
Aberystwyth, UC of Wales
  MSc☆/dip☆ □
Kent U MSc☆
Swansea UC MSc/dip

Computer science (new generation computing)
Exeter U MSc☆

Computer science education
Ulster U MSc☆/cert/dip☆

Computer speech & language processing
Cambridge U MPhil☆, □ Lang,
Eng

Computer studies
Bell CT dip☆
Essex U MSc □
Glasgow C MSc
Leicester P dip☆
Sheffield City P MSc/dip
Teesside P dip☆

Computer studies (conversion)
Brunel U dip☆

Computer studies in musicology
Nottingham U MA

Computer systems
Glasgow C MSc☆/dip☆

Computing
Bradford U MSc/dip
Cardiff U of Wales C MSc☆/dip☆
Essex U dip☆
Leicester P MSc☆
North London P dip
Robert Gordon's IT dip☆
Ulster U dip

Computing & artificial intelligence
South Bank P dip

Computing & information systems
Ulster U MSc/dip

Computing & statistics
Cardiff U of Wales C MSc☆/dip☆

Computing science
Glasgow U MAppSci
London U Imperial C MSc☆/
  dip☆ □
Newcastle U MSc☆/dip☆
Stirling U dip☆

Computing science (conversion)
Staffordshire P MSc☆/dip☆ □

Database & information systems
London U Birkbeck C MSc

Decision sciences
Central London P MSc△

Digital & microcomputer systems engineering
East Anglia U MSc△

Digital electronics (computers, communications & instrumentation)
London U King's C MSc☆

Digital image processing
Cranfield IT MSc☆/dip☆ □

Electronic engineering & microcomputer systems
Dundee U dip☆

Electronics
Southampton U MSc   Eng

Fifth generation computing systems
St Andrews U MSc

Foundations of advanced information technology
London U Imperial C MSc☆/dip☆

Human computer interaction
London U Queen Mary &
  Westfield C MSc

Information & communication technologies
Sussex U MSc

Information processing: computers & the man machine interface
York U MSc☆

Information systems
East London P MSc
Portsmouth P MSc☆/dip☆

Information technology
Dundee IT dip☆
Kingston P MSc☆
Leicester P MSc☆/dip☆
London U Queen Mary &
  Westfield C MSc☆/dip☆ □
London U UC MSc☆/dip☆ □
Loughborough U MSc
Nottingham U MA/MSc
Teesside P MSc☆
Ulster U MSc

Information technology (medical physics)
Aberdeen U MSc☆ □

Information technology for management
Coventry P MSc

Information technology for manufacture
Warwick U MSc

Information technology: computer aided manufacturing technology
Edinburgh U MSc/dip

Information technology: computer systems engineering
Edinburgh U MSc/dip

Information technology: knowledge based systems
Edinburgh U MSc/dip

Intelligent knowledge - based systems
Essex U MSc☆

Intelligent management systems
South Bank P MSc☆/dip☆

Intelligent systems
Brunel U MSc
South West P MSc

Interactive computing system design
Loughborough U MSc☆/dip△

Knowledge based systems
Heriot-Watt U MSc☆
Sussex U MSc☆

Machine translation
Manchester UMIST MSc☆

Management computer systems
Leicester P MSc

Management of information systems
London U LSE dip☆

Mathematical computation
London U Queen Mary &
  Westfield C MSc

Mathematical logic & the theory of computation
Bristol U MSc☆

Mathematical modelling & computer simulation
Coventry P MSc△/dip△
Sunderland P MSc△

Mathematical sciences
Aberdeen U dip☆

Mathematical, statistical & computing education
London U Inst of Education MSc

Mathematics
Dundee U dip☆

Mathematics, statistics & computing
Teesside P dip☆

Medical computing
Wales U C of Med MSc☆/dip☆

Medical physics
Aberdeen U MSc☆/dip   Phy

Medical statistics & information technology
Leicester P MSc☆/dip☆

Microelectronic & information engineering
Liverpool P MSc☆/dip☆

Microelectronics system design
Southampton U MSc   Eng

Microelectronics systems design
Brunel U MSc

Modular studies
Heriot-Watt U MSc/dip

Numerical analysis & computing
Manchester U MSc☆/dip☆

Numerical analysis & programming
Dundee U MSc

Office systems management
Humberside CHE MSc☆/dip☆

Optimisation & computing
Loughborough U MSc

Parallel computer systems
Bristol P MSc☆/dip☆

Science, technology & mathematics education
East Anglia U MSc☆

Scientific & engineering software technology
Thames P MSc/dip

Scientific computing & scientific information technology
South Bank P MSc/dip☆

Signal processing & machine intelligence
Surrey U MSc☆

Social anthropology & computing
Kent U MA/dip

Software design in English as a foreign language
Newcastle U MA☆

Software engineering
Dundee IT dip☆
Stirling U MSc☆

Software engineering with applications
Aston U MSc/dip   □

Software systems technology
Sheffield U MSc   □

Software techniques for computer aided engineering
Cranfield IT MSc   □

Software technology (conversion)
Stirling U MSc☆/dip☆

Statistical & computational modelling
Liverpool U MSc

Statistics
Dundee U dip☆

Structural engineering & computational technology
Heriot-Watt U MSc☆/Dip☆

Technology management
Stirling U MSc☆/dip☆

Theory & applications of computation
Loughborough U MSc

Higher degrees by research

Applied computing & information technology
Teesside P PhD☆/MPhil☆

Applied computing & mathematics
Cranfield IT PhD☆/MPhil☆/MSc☆

Applied computing in social anthropology
Kent U PhD

Applied sciences
Staffordshire P PhD/MPhil

Artificial intelligence
Aberdeen U PhD☆/MPhil☆/MSc☆
Edinburgh U PhD/MPhil

CAD for VLSI
Kent U PhD☆/MPhil☆

Communication studies
Sheffield City P PhD/MPhil

Computation
Manchester UMIST PhD/MSc

Computation in medicine
Manchester U PhD/MPhil

Computational linguistics
Manchester UMIST PhD/MSc

Computational science
St Andrews U PhD/MSc

Computer aided design
Teesside P PhD☆/MPhil☆
Ulster U DPhil/MPhil

Computer applications
Cranfield S of Management PhD/MPhil

Computer applications in engineering
Cardiff U of Wales C PhD☆/MPhil☆

Computer assisted learning
Surrey U PhD/MPhil

Computer science
Aberystwyth, UC of Wales PhD☆/MPhil☆
Aston U PhD/MPhil   □
Bangor, U of Wales PhD☆/MPhil☆/dip☆
Belfast Queen's U PhD/MSc
Bristol U PhD☆/MSc☆
Brunel U PhD/MPhil
Buckingham U DPhil/MPhil
Cambridge U PhD☆/MSc☆
Central London P cert☆
City U PhD/MPhil
Coventry P PhD/MPhil
Dundee U PhD☆/MSc☆
Durham U PhD/MSc
Edinburgh U PhD/MPhil
Essex U PhD/MPhil/MSc
Exeter U PhD/MPhil
Hatfield P PhD/MPhil
Heriot-Watt U PhD☆/MPhil☆
Hull U PhD/MSc
Keele U PhD/MSc
Liverpool U PhD/MSc
London U Birkbeck C PhD/MPhil
Goldsmiths' C London U PhD/MPhil
London U Royal Holloway & Bedford New C PhD/MPhil
London U UC PhD☆/MPhil☆
London U UC PhD☆/MPhil☆   □
Manchester U PhD/MSc
Nottingham U PhD/MPhil   □
Reading U PhD/MPhil
Salford U PhD☆/MSc☆
Sheffield U PhD/MPhil
Strathclyde U PhD☆/MPhil☆/MSc☆
Sussex U DPhil/MPhil
Swansea UC PhD/MPhil
Teesside P PhD☆/MPhil☆
Warwick U PhD☆/MSc☆   □
West Glamorgan IHE PhD/MPhil
York U DPhil/MPhil

Computer science & statistics
London U Queen Mary & Westfield C PhD☆/MPhil☆

Computer sciences
Leeds U MSc☆

Computer studies
Leeds U PhD/MPhil
Loughborough U PhD☆/MPhil☆
Napier P PhD/MPhil
Sheffield City P PhD/MPhil
Sunderland P PhD/MPhil

Computer studies & mathematics
Huddersfield P PhD/MPhil

Computers & fluids
Salford U PhD☆/MSc☆

Computers in medicine
Kent U PhD☆/MPhil☆

Computing
Anglia HEC PhD☆/MPhil☆
Bath U PhD☆/MPhil☆
Bradford U PhD/MPhil
Brighton P PhD/MPhil
City of London P PhD☆/MPhil☆
Kent U PhD/MPhil/MSc
Kingston P PhD/MPhil
Lancashire P PhD/MPhil
Lancaster U PhD/MPhil
Liverpool P PhD/MPhil
London U Imperial C PhD/
MPhil   □
London U King's C PhD☆/MPhil☆
Manchester P PhD/MPhil
Open U PhD/MPhil/BPhil
South West P PhD/MPhil

Computing & computing science
Birmingham U PhD☆/MSc☆

Computing & informatics
Newcastle P PhD☆/MPhil☆

Computing & information technology
Thames P PhD/MPhil
Wolverhampton P PhD/MPhil

Computing & mathematics
Royal Naval Engineering C
PhD☆/MSc☆

Computing applications
Glasgow U PhD/MSc

Computing mathematics
Cardiff U of Wales C PhD☆/
MPhil☆

Computing science
Aberdeen U PhD☆/MPhil☆/
MSc☆   □
East Anglia U PhD☆/MPhil☆
Glasgow U PhD/MSc
Leeds P PhD/MPhil/dip
Leicester P PhD/MPhil
Newcastle U PhD/MPhil
Paisley CT PhD/MPhil
Staffordshire P PhD/MPhil
Stirling U PhD/MSc
Ulster U DPhil/MPhil

Computing/operational research
Silsoe C PhD/MPhil

Control & electrical engineering
Sussex U DPhil/MPhil

Cybernetics
Reading U PhD/MPhil   Eng

Data processing
Leeds U MSc☆

Digital communication
Salford U PhD/MSc

Electrical & electronic engineering
Bath U PhD/MSc   Eng

Electronics & computer science
Southampton U PhD/MPhil   Eng

Human cognition research
Open U PhD/MPhil/BPhil

Information & communication technologies
Sussex U DPhil/MPhil

Information systems
East Anglia U PhD☆/MPhil☆/
MSc☆
London U LSE PhD/MPhil
Middlesex P PhD/MPhil

Information systems design
Kingston P PhD/MPhil

Information technology studies
City of London P PhD☆/MPhil☆

Mathematical sciences & computer studies
Robert Gordon's IT PhD/MPhil

Mathematical sciences & computing
South Bank P PhD/MPhil

Mathematics
Dundee U PhD△
Oxford U DPhil☆/MSc☆

Mathematics & computer science
Salford U PhD/MSc
Wales P PhD/MPhil

Mathematics & computer studies
Dundee IT PhD/MPhil

Mathematics & computing
Canterbury Christ Church C
PhD/MPhil

Mathematics, statistics & computing
Leicester P PhD/MPhil
North London P PhD/MPhil
Oxford P PhD/MPhil
Thames P PhD/MPhil

Medical computing & statistics
Edinburgh U PhD/MPhil

Neural networks
Manchester UMIST PhD/MSc

Numerical analysis
Oxford U DPhil☆/MSc☆

Parallel distributed processing
Manchester UMIST PhD/MSc

Physical sciences & scientific computing
South Bank P PhD/MPhil

Physics
Kent U PhD/MPhil/MSc

Programming research
Oxford U DPhil☆/MSc☆

Robotics & automated systems
London U Imperial C PhD/MPhil

Software reliability studies
City U PhD/MPhil

Statistics & computational mathematics
Liverpool U PhD/MPhil

Systems & computing studies
East London P PhD/MPhil

Information technology

Higher degrees by instruction

Administration & information processing
North East Surrey CT RSA
dip☆   Bus

Advanced methods in computer science
London U Queen Mary &
Westfield C MSc☆

Advanced production engineering
Edinburgh U MSc/dip

Applications of information technology in business & management
Middlesex P MSc☆

Business administration (information technology)
Lancashire P MSc☆/dip☆   Bus

Business information technology
Newcastle P dip☆
Nottingham P dip△

Business information technology systems
Strathclyde U MSc☆/dip☆

Cognition, computing & psychology
Warwick U MSc   Soc

Cognitive science
Manchester U MSc☆   □

Computer & information technology
Dundee U MSc☆

Computer aided design & manufacture of production machines & systems
Cranfield IT MSc☆

Computer aided engineering & automation technology
Leicester P dip

Computer based information systems
Sunderland P MSc△/dip△

Computer science
Birmingham U MSc☆
Manchester U MSc☆/dip☆

Computer science (conversion)
Aberystwyth, UC of Wales
MSc☆/dip☆   □

Computer speech & language processing
Cambridge U MPhil☆□ Lang, Eng

Computer studies
Birmingham P dip△
Glasgow C MSc
Teesside P dip☆

Computing
Robert Gordon's IT dip☆
Ulster U dip

Computing & artificial intelligence
South Bank P dip

Computing science
Newcastle U MSc☆/dip☆

Computing science (conversion)
Staffordshire P MSc☆/dip☆   □

Computing software & systems design
Newcastle U MSc☆

Control systems
Sheffield U MEng/MScTech

Data communications networks & distributed systems
London U UC MSc☆   □

Database & information systems
London U Birkbeck C MSc

Decision sciences
Central London P MSc△

Digital systems
Brunel U MSc

Electronic engineering & microcomputer systems
Dundee U dip☆

Electronics
Southampton U MSc   Eng

Electronics systems design (aviation electronics)
Cranfield IT MSc

Electronics with computing applications
London U King's C dip☆

Engineering information technology
Sheffield City P MSc△

Foundations of advanced information technology
London U Imperial C MSc☆/dip☆

Geographic information systems
Silsoe C dip☆

Geographical information systems
Edinburgh U MSc☆/dip☆   Env
Leeds U MA
Nottingham U MSc☆

Human factors in manufacturing systems
Nottingham U MSc

Industrial robotics & manufacturing automation
London U Imperial C MSc☆/dip☆   Eng

Information & communication technologies
Sussex U MSc

Information & systems in management
Sheffield City P MSc☆/dip☆
Sheffield City P MSc☆/Dip☆

Information engineering
Belfast Queen's U dip
Manchester UMIST MSc☆/dip☆
Robert Gordon's IT dip☆

Information management
Belfast Queen's U cert△
Birmingham P MSc△
Central London P dip△
Lancaster U MSc☆
Pitman Education & Training cert

Information processing: computers & the man machine interface
York U MSc☆

Information science
City U MSc/dip

Information studies
Loughborough U MSc

Information systems
Brighton P MSc☆/dip☆
Leeds P MSc△

Information systems & technology
City U MSc△

Information systems design & management
Kingston P MSc△/Dip△

Information technology
Aston U MSc☆   □
Bristol P MSc☆/dip☆
Dundee IT dip☆
Glasgow U MSc/dip   □
Keele U dip
Leicester P MSc☆/dip☆
Leicester U MSc☆/Dip☆
London U Queen Mary & Westfield C MSc☆/dip☆   □
Loughborough U MSc
Nottingham U MA/MSc
Paisley CT dip☆
Sheffield U MSc(Eng)/MSc(Tech)
Silsoe C MSc☆
Staffordshire P MSc☆/dip☆
Stirling U MSc/dip

Information technology (computer aided engineering)
Napier P dip☆

Information technology (medical physics)
Aberdeen U MSc☆   □

Information technology for management
Coventry P MSc

Information technology for manufacture
Warwick U MSc

Information technology for non electrical graduates
Heriot-Watt U MSc☆/dip☆   □

Information technology for the rural sector
Silsoe C MSc☆

Information technology in business
Humberside CHE MSc/dip

Information technology systems
Strathclyde U MSc☆/dip☆

Information technology: computer aided manufacturing technology
Edinburgh U MSc/dip

Information technology: computer systems engineering
Edinburgh U MSc/dip

Information technology: design & manufacture of microelectronic systems
Edinburgh U MSc/dip

UNIVERSITY OF STRATHCLYDE
Postgraduate Conversion Courses in Information Technology

MSc/Diploma in Business Information Technology Systems (BITS)
This is a conversion course for social science graduates who are interested in a management career with a strong IT emphasis. Graduates are not expected to be numerate and no prior knowledge of business or computing is required.

MSc/Diploma in Information Technology Systems (ITS)
This is a conversion course for graduates in science or in engineering interested in applying IT in design, manufacturing or in administration. It requires a numerate background, but excludes those already qualified in either electronic engineering or computer science.

Diploma courses last for 9 months and MSc courses for 12 months. A project must be completed by MSc candidates. Projects normally last for 3 months.

Grants are available for suitably qualified applicants either from the SED or from the SERC.

For further information contact:
The Registry — Postgraduate
University of Strathclyde
Richmond Street
Glasgow G1 1XQ
Tel: 041-552 4400
Telex: 77472 UNSLIB G
Fax: 041-552 0775

UNIVERSITY OF MANCHESTER
Postgraduate Courses in the Department of Computer Science

Course Work and Research: MSc by Method I
There are two one-year courses. One assumes no prior knowledge of Computer Science, and provides an introduction for Science or Engineering graduates whose careers would benefit from an understanding of computers. The other, for Computer Science graduates, teaches System Design, and includes hardware and software topics particularly relevant to Information Technology. Both Method I courses conclude with a six-month research project. The Department of Computer Science is also heavily involved in the one-year MSc course in Cognitive Science administered by the Department of Psychology.

Full-time Research: MSc by Method II and PhD
Excellent facilities exist for research into the design, construction and use of computer systems, hardware and software. Novel architectures, formal methods, software engineering, artificial intelligence, information systems and computer design of VLSI are particularly active areas. Much of the work is undertaken in collaboration with industry.

Applications
For further details and application forms write to:
The Postgraduate Admissions Officer, Department of Computer Science
(Ref: DOG), University of Manchester, Oxford Road, Manchester M13 9PL.

The SERC has accepted these courses as suitable for the tenure of its advanced course and research studentships.

Information technology: knowledge based systems
Edinburgh U MSc/dip

Intelligent knowledge - based systems
Essex U MSc☆

Intelligent knowledge based systems in manufacturing
Cranfield IT MSc☆

Intelligent systems
South West P MSc

Interactive computing system design
Loughborough U MSc☆/dip△

Knowledge based systems
Heriot-Watt U MSc☆

Linguistics & information processing
Leeds U MA☆

Machine translation
Manchester UMIST MSc☆

Management computer systems
Leicester P MSc

Management science & operational research
Warwick U MSc

Management systems & sciences
Hull U MA☆/MSc☆/dip☆   *Bus*

Mathematics of modern control systems
Loughborough U MSc☆

Media technology for teaching English as a foreign language
Newcastle U MA☆

Medical physics
Aberdeen U MSc☆/dip   *Phy*

Medical statistics & information technology
Leicester U MSc☆/dip☆

Microelectronics & computer engineering
Surrey U MSc

Microelectronics system design
Southampton U MSc   *Eng*

Microelectronics systems design
Brunel U MSc

Microprocessor technology & applications
Brighton P MSc☆/dip☆   □

Music information technology
City U dip

Numerical analysis & programming
Dundee U MSc

Office information technology
City of London P dip☆

Operational research & computer techniques
Southampton IHE dip☆   *Bus*

Optical data recording
Keele U MSc☆

Optoelectronic & laser devices
Heriot-Watt U MSc

Optoelectronics & optical information processing
Belfast Queen's U MSc☆

Science, technology & society
Brunel U MA

Scientific & engineering software technology
Thames P MSc/dip

Scientific computing & scientific information technology
South Bank P MSc/dip☆

Signal processing & machine intelligence
Surrey U MSc☆

Software engineering
Dundee IT dip☆

Software engineering with applications
Aston U MSc/dip   □

Software techniques for computer aided engineering
Cranfield IT MSc   □

Spatial information technology
Reading U MSc☆/dip☆

Structural engineering & computational technology
Heriot-Watt U MSc☆/Dip☆

System design
Manchester U MSc☆/dip☆

Systems engineering
Cardiff U of Wales C MSc   *Eng*

Technology management
Stirling U MSc☆/dip☆

Telecommunication & information systems
Essex U MSc

Telematics
Surrey U MSc/dip

Higher degrees by research

Applied computing & information technology
Teesside P PhD☆/MPhil☆

Artificial intelligence
Aberdeen U PhD☆/MPhil☆/MSc☆

Business information technology
Lancashire P PhD/MPhil
Manchester P PhD/MPhil

Business systems analysis
City U BS PhD☆/MPhil☆

Computer science
Hull U PhD/MSc
London U UC PhD☆/MPhil☆
Manchester U PhD/MSc

Computer systems & information technology
Warwick U PhD/MSc

Computerised accountancy & business computing
East Anglia U PhD/MPhil

Computing & information technology
Thames P PhD/MPhil

Computing science
Newcastle U PhD/MPhil

Cybernetics
Reading U PhD/MPhil   *Eng*

Electronic & electrical engineering
London U UC PhD☆/MPhil☆

Electronic engineering
Kent U PhD/MPhil/MSc

Electronic systems
Cranfield IT PhD☆/MSc☆

Electronics
York U DPhil/MPhil

Electronics & computer science
Southampton U PhD/MPhil   *Eng*

Fault detection & supervisory control
Manchester UMIST PhD/MSc

Geographical information systems
Edinburgh U PhD☆

Information & communication technologies
Sussex U DPhil/MPhil

Information science
City U PhD/MPhil
Portsmouth P PhD☆/MPhil☆

Information studies
Sheffield U PhD/MPhil

Information systems
Cranfield IT PhD☆/MPhil☆
Cranfield S of Management PhD/ MPhil
Dorset Inst PhD/MPhil/dip
Leeds P PhD/MPhil/dip

Middlesex P PhD/MPhil
Ulster U DPhil/MPhil

Information technology
Brighton P PhD/MPhil
Bristol U PhD☆/MSc☆
Central London P PhD☆/MPhil☆
Edinburgh U PhD/MPhil
Lancashire P PhD/MPhil
London U Queen Mary &
   Westfield C PhD☆/MPhil☆
Manchester BS PhD☆/MPhil☆
North London P PhD/MPhil
Salford U PhD/MSc

Information technology in transport
Cardiff U of Wales C PhD/MPhil

Knowledge based systems
South Bank P PhD/MPhil

Medical biophysics
Manchester U PhD/MSc   *Phy*

Opto-electronics & optical information processing
Kent U PhD☆/MPhil☆

Self-organised learning
Brunel U PhD/MPhil

Social & economic aspects of information & communication technologies
Newcastle U PhD☆

Study of human learning
Brunel U PhD/MPhil

Systems
Central London P PhD☆/MPhil☆
Open U PhD/MPhil/BPhil

Systems & computing studies
East London P PhD/MPhil

Systems information
Lancaster U PhD/MPhil

Urban & regional development studies
Newcastle U PhD/MLitt/MPhil

Systems analysis

Higher degrees by instruction

Analysis, design & management of information systems
London U LSE MSc

Business systems analysis & design
City U MSc/dip

Computer aided engineering & automation technology
Leicester P dip

Computer based administration systems
Glasgow C MSc☆/dip☆

Computer science
Birmingham U MSc☆
East Anglia U MSc/dip
London U UC MSc☆   □

Computer studies
Glasgow C MSc

Computer systems
Glasgow C MSc☆/dip☆

Computing
Ulster U dip

Computing science
Newcastle U MSc☆/dip☆

Computing science (conversion)
Staffordshire P MSc☆/dip☆   □

Control systems
Sheffield U MEng/MScTech

Electrical power engineering
Aberdeen U MSc☆/dip☆

Gender analysis in development
East Anglia U MA☆

Geographical information systems
Leeds U MA
Leicester U MSc☆/dip☆

Human factors in manufacturing systems
Nottingham U MSc

Information systems
Leeds P MSc△

Information systems & technology
City U MSc△

Information technology
London U UC MSc☆/dip☆   □
Sheffield U MSc(Eng)/MSc(Tech)

Intelligent knowledge - based systems
Essex U MSc☆

Intelligent knowledge based systems in manufacturing
Cranfield IT MSc☆

Knowledge based systems
Sussex U MSc☆

Management of information systems
London U LSE dip☆

Microelectronic & information engineering
Liverpool P MSc☆/dip☆

Numerical methods & software systems
Royal Military C of Science
   MSc△

Operational research & computer techniques
Southampton IHE dip☆   *Bus*

Operations management & manufacturing systems
Nottingham U MSc

Optimisation & computing
Loughborough U MSc

Parallel computer systems
Bristol P MSc☆/dip☆

Software engineering with applications
Aston U MSc/dip   □

Software systems technology
Sheffield U MSc   □

Systems analysis & design
Aberdeen CC dip☆
Bell CT dip☆
Glasgow C dip (SCOTVEC)☆   □
Napier P dip☆

Higher degrees by research

Computer science
London U UC PhD☆/MPhil☆   □

Computing science
East Anglia U PhD☆/MPhil☆

Information systems
London U LSE PhD/MPhil
Middlesex P PhD/MPhil

Information systems analysis
Bradford U PhD/MPhil

Knowledge based systems
South Bank P PhD/MPhil

Systems information
Lancaster U PhD/MPhil

Systems science
City U PhD/MPhil

Artificial intelligence

PhD
MSc
1 year full time
20 places
MPhil
Diploma
9 months full time
Department of Computing
Science, University of
Aberdeen, The Meston
Building, Meston Walk, Old
Aberdeen AB9 2UE
Tel: 0224 272296

Present research areas in which opportunities for research leading to PhD and MPhil degrees may arise include Prolog and database technology; machine learning and intelligent tutoring systems; robotics; qualitative reasoning and applications to medicine; protein structure investigation; vision and protein structure investigation. Taught MSc and Diploma courses in Applied Artificial Intelligence provide a practical understanding of AI for industrial careerists. Modules covered include expert systems, intelligent tutoring systems, conceptual modelling, logic programming and databases, and cognitive science. **Entrance requirements** Honours degree or equivalent in computing science or related discipline.
Grants SERC studentships available.
Head of department Professor D H Sleeman.

Cognitive science

MSc
1 year full time
12 places
Cognitive Science
Programme, Department of
Psychology, University of
Manchester, Manchester
M13 9PL
Tel: 061 275 2586

The Cognitive Science MSc course is given jointly by the departments of Computer Science, Psychology, Linguistics, Medical Biophysics and Philosophy. Students will develop a working knowledge of artificial intelligence, expert systems, symbolic programming and human-computer interaction. Students will acquire a sound knowledge of the theoretical foundations of these techniques focussing on knowledge representation, language and vision. Students attend six months of lectures followed by six months of project work. Arrangements for attending the course for two years part time are possible.
Entrance requirements Good honours degree or equivalent in any relevant discipline.
Grants SERC studentships are available.
Head of department Professor J Gurd (Computer Science), Professor J Reason (Psychology).

Computation

MSc
1 year full time
30 places
Graduate Admissions,
Department of Mathematics,
University of Oxford, 11
Keble Road, Oxford OX1
3QD
Tel: 0865 273840

This course has been designed to teach the mathematical principles of specification, design and implementation of software and hardware. Students will obtain a theoretical and practical understanding of the entire development process, from abstract user-oriented specification, through concrete programming, down to final documentation and packaging of the delivered system.
Entrance requirements Good honours degree in scientific subject.
Grants SERC studentships available.

Computer aided engineering

MSc/PgD
(part time available)
1 year full time
Dr S Douglas, School of
Engineering and Technology
Management, The Liverpool
Polytechnic, Byrom Street,
Liverpool L3 3AF
Tel: 051 207 3581 ext
2033/2010

The CAE course is offered to provide a study in the application of computers in the areas of design and manufacture. The main themes are CAD and CAM, supporting studies include computation, microelectronics and computer technology. The MSc course is of one year duration or two years part-time. The mode of study is by examination and dissertation.
Entrance requirements Honours graduates or equivalent in engineering, mathematics or physics. A degree with compensating industrial experience will be considered.
Grants SERC and Training Agency Funding available.
Senior lecturer Dr S S Douglas.

Computer aided engineering (CAE)

MSc
1 year full time
The Admissions Tutor, Ref 2039, Department of Applied Computing & Mathematics, Cranfield Institute of Technology, Cranfield, Bedford MK43 0AL
Tel: 0234 752706
Fax: 0234 750728

The CAE course is concerned with the use of computers in all aspects of the design, analysis and manufacture of a product. Two terms of lectures on product modelling, computer science, manufacturing and computational geometry are followed by a substantial individual project of industrial relevance. Starting date for the course is October 1990.
Entrance requirements A good honours degree in engineering, physics, mathematics or computer science.
Grants SERC Advanced Course Studentships are available.

Computer science

MSc or dip
10 months full time (Diploma) plus project
Dr E M Stephens, Department of Computer Science, University College of Wales, Aberystwyth, Aberystwyth, Dyfed SY23 3BZ
Tel: 0970 622421

A full-time course for students *without* a background in Computing. This intensive course emphasises the design and engineering of software and is oriented to the needs of the computer industry and of computer users. Topics include: the design of programs, algorithms and data structures; programming; software engineering; operating systems; information systems; hardware; professional issues. Practical work is a major component throughout. The taught course begins early in September and is examined in April. Further practical work is carried out until June, when a diploma may be awarded. Students who achieve an appropriate level in April may proceed to a substantial project dissertation for MSc.
Entrance requirements A degree from a recognised University. Students with equivalent qualifications are considered, subject to testimonial and interview.
Grants European Commission funding may be available.

Computer science

Diploma
1 year full time
40 places
Admissions Secretary, University of Cambridge, Computer Laboratory, New Museums Site, Pembroke Street, Cambridge CB2 3QG
Tel: 0223 334603

A conversion course for those intending to enter the computing profession. It covers the basic aspects of computer hardware and software, with additional material on specialised topics. Applicants should normally have at least a second-class honours degree in mathematics, science or engineering. The course requires regular attendance at the Laboratory for one academical year from early October to the end of July. The examination is in two parts; four written papers and a dissertation on a practical project.
Grants SERC awards available for suitably qualified applicants.
Course organiser Dr N E Wiseman.

Computer science

PhD
3 years full time
MPhil
2 years full time
All MSc courses
1 year full time
The Friends Room,
University College London,
Gower Street, London WC1E
6BT
Tel: 071 380 7365

Active research groups at University College London include architectures for symbolic and numeric computing, artificial intelligence, expert systems , computer communications, distributed systems, network management, VLSI design, graphics and image processing, software engineering and human- computer interaction.

The MSc DCNDS is an advanced course for computer-science graduates who wish to learn about computer communication and distributed systems.

The MSc CS is a conversion course for non-computer-science graduates who wish to have a broad and thorough introduction to computer science. The MSc IT is a conversion course for science graduates who wish to have a good foundation in the hardware and software aspects of computer systems and information technology.

Grants SERC course studentships available for all courses.
Course directors *MSc DCNDS:* Professor S R Wilbur, *MSc CS:* Dr E T Keravnou, *MSc IT:* Dr R Offen
Head of department Professor P T Kirstein.

Computer science

PhD
3 years full time
4 years part time
MPhil
2 years full time
3 years part time
Dr D G Elliman,
Postgraduate Admissions
Tutor, Department of
Computer Science,
University of Nottingham,
Nottingham NG7 2RD
Tel: 0602 484848 ext 3451

Research opportunities exist in the following areas: electronic publishing and computerised typesetting, distributed messaging and documents systems, recognition of drawings, handwriting recognition, structured editors, parallel processing, logic programming, Modula-2.
Entrance requirements Good honours degree or MSc, with substantial computing content.
Grants SERC research studentships are available for suitably qualified candidates.
Head of department Professor P H Ford.

Computer science

PhD
3 years full time
MSc
2 years full time
Dr R G Wilson, Postgraduate
Tutor, Department of
Computer Science,
University of Warwick,
Coventry CV4 7AL
Tel: 0203 523195

Active research groups include: multilevel image analysis algorithms & architectures; software engineering - formal methods, real-time concurrency, distributed systems, error recovery in compilers; programming languages, semantics and their methodology - design principles; VLSI architectures - novel high speed processors for image & signal processing; AI - learning knowledge representation, inference and expert systems; mobile robots - protection, navigation and guidance.
Entrance requirements Good honours degree with a substantial computing content.
Grants SERC advanced course studentships.
Head of department Professor G R Nudd.

Computer science & software engineering

PhD
3 years full time
MSc
1 year full time
Diploma
1 year full time
Postgraduate Admissions Office, Department of Computer Science, Brunel University, Uxbridge, Middlesex UB8 3PH
Tel: 0895 74000 ext 2392

Research opportunities exist within the areas of knowledge based systems, natural language processing, software engineering, software re-use, and graphics.

The MSc in Software Engineering is a specialist course providing taught modules in software engineering, logic and automated reasoning, HMI and graphics, expert systems and formal software development.

The Postgraduate Diploma in Computer Studies is intended for non-computer graduates to gain expertise in modern computing concepts and techniques. Candidates who attain a satisfactory standard may be eligible for admission to the MSc in SE.

Entrance requirements For the MSc a good honours degree in computer science or related subject is required. A good degree in any subject is required for the Diploma.

Grants EC students may be eligible for funding for the MSc in SE, and for the Diploma.

Head of department Professor L Johnson.

Computer science research

PhD
3 years full time
5 years part time
MPhil
2 years full time
3 years part time
Dr E F Elsworth, Research Admissions Tutor, Computer Science, Aston University, Aston Triangle, Birmingham B4 7ET
Tel: 021 359 3611 ext 4264

Opportunities for research leading to PhD/MPhil. Active research areas include: information systems; artificial intelligence topics (eg expert systems, planning, natural language processing); software engineering; programming languages; geometric modelling; neural networks; transputer system; OSI networking.

Entrance requirements Good honours degree or MSc with a substantial computing content.

Grants SERC research studentships.

Head of department Dr B Gay.

Computer speech & language processing

MPhil
1 year full time
20 places
Secretary (MPhil Computer Speech & Language Processing), University Engineering Department, University of Cambridge, Trumpington Street, Cambridge CB2 1PZ
Tel: 0223 332752

For students with backgrounds in computing, electronic engineering, psychology, or linguistics. Interdisciplinary course organised by Computer laboratory and Engineering department and involving Faculties from all the above areas. Aims to provide practical and theoretical expertise in information technology computer systems for speech and language understanding. Lectures, practical work, 3 months supervised project. Industrial support and collaboration.

Entrance requirements Good honours degree or equivalent: computing experience preferred.

Grants SERC studentships available.

Course directors Professor F Fallside (Engineering Department), Dr K Sparck Jones (Computer laboratory).

Computer studies

MSc
1 year full time
2 years part time
50 places
PhD/MPhil
2-3 years full time
Graduate Secretary (PDG),
Department of Computer
Science, University of Essex,
Wivenhoe Park, Colchester,
Essex CO4 3SQ
Tel: 0206 872256

The wide choice of lecture and project courses comprising the first part of the MSc course make it equally suitable for graduates with a substantial background in computing, and those with little experience of the subject. Options are available in computer architecture, software engineering, artificial intelligence, cognitive science, theory of computation, and applications. All students complete a supervised research project during the second part of the year, and some go on to PhD or MPhil research in computer science.
Entrance requirements Good honours degree or equivalent.
Grants SERC studentships available.
Head of department I R MacCallum.

Computer studies

dip
1 year full time
60 places
Admissions Officer,
Department of Management
Studies, Glasgow College,
Cowcaddens Road, Glasgow
G4 0BA
Tel: 041 331 3000

This is an intensive one-year conversion course for graduates who wish to make a career as professionals in the computing market. Four streams of study are offered, equipping diplomates for careers as systems analysts/ programmers or systems programmers or specialists in business computing or specialists in user support. All four streams study fundamentals of software engineering, analysis and design, programming, and computer architecture. In addition each stream takes further specialised studies suitable to the intended career path. Finally, all students undertake a substantial project which integrates their studies. Successful diplomates may be eligible for exemption from BCS Part 1 examinations.
Entrance requirements Either a non-computing first degree or evidence of ability to sustain a course of study at postgraduate level together with either a non-computing HND or substantial experience in industry or commerce.
Senior lecturer Ms G Stewart BSc DipEd.

Computing science

12 month conversion course
45-50 places
MSc
1 year full time
Mr James Jacobson,
Admissions Tutor,
Department of Computing,
Imperial College of Science,
Technology & Medicine, 180
Queensgate, London SW7
2AZ
Tel: 071 589 5111

A full time 12 month conversion course starting in October, aimed at graduates of disciplines other than computing science. The course aims to give a comprehensive grounding in computing with a special emphasis on software engineering. The course is organised in three parts. The autumn term consists of compulsory lecture and laboratory courses covering fundamental concepts. During the spring term students participate in group projects and select courses from the following options: interactive graphics, human computer interaction, silicon compilation, data processing, management, functional programming, logic programming, artificial intelligence, operations research, numerical analysis, simulation, microprocessors, advanced systems architecture and distributed systems. A substantial individual project is undertaken during the summer months.
Entrance requirements Applicants should have a good honours degree. In addition, a mathematical background to A level standard is useful and some previous experience of computing is required.
Grants The course is recognised by the SERC for the tenure of its Advanced Course studentships.
Course director Mr Roger Bailey.

Computing science

MSc
13 months full time
70 places
dip
Admissions Officer,
Department of Computing,
Staffordshire Polytechnic,
Blackheath Lane, Stafford
ST18 0AD
Tel: 0785 53511

This is a conversion course accepting graduates in any discipline, and has been designed to prepare its students for a career involving computers and related areas of the latest technology. The course includes at least six months in an appropriate post in industry or commerce. The teaching syllabus comprises a foundation course in the fundamentals of computing science, which is compulsory for graduates in disciplines other than computing, plus a range of options covering the major aspects of current developments in the computer industry. There is considerable emphasis on practical work throughout the course.
Entrance requirements Good honours degree or equivalent, in any discipline.
Grants SERC advanced course studentships available.

Digital image processing (DIP)

MSc
1 year full time
The Admissions Tutor (Ref: 2154), Department of
Applied Computing &
Mathematics, Cranfield
Institute of Technology,
Cranfield, Bedford MK43
0AL
Tel: 0234 752706
Fax: 0234 750728

Digital image processing is a new and unique MSc course which has been established to help close the gap between industrial demand and UK university postgraduate output. The material covered includes computational methods, image formation and analysis, imaging systems and computer vision. A range of interest and research topics will be on offer; supplied in part by industry.
Entrance requirements A good honours degree in engineering, physics, mathematics or computer science.
Grants SERC Advanced Course Studentships are available.

Foundations of Advanced Information Technology (FAIT)

12 month advanced course
35-45 places
MSc and DIC
1 year full time
Admissions Officer,
Department of Computing,
Imperial College of Science,
Technology & Medicine,
London SW7 2BZ
Tel: 071 589 5111

A full time 12 month advanced course starting in October, aimed at graduates of IT related disciplines or other disciplines involving rigorous analytical thought. The course specialises in teaching the foundational material underpinning the more advanced topics in IT and provides the essential background for those interested in IT research and development, or in the application of state-of-the-art IT techniques. The course comprises two terms of taught material and a substantial individual project which is undertaken during the summer months. Given by leading researchers, the course allows specialisation in the general areas of Logic and Artifical Intelligence, Declarative Systems, Theory and Formal Methods, and Concurrency. The course comprises a small number of short foundational courses and a set of optional courses with a prerequisite structure. These are assessed by coursework and/or laboratory work and by written examination at the start of the summer term.
Entrance requirements Applicants should have a good honours degree in Computer Science, Information Technology, Mathematics or any other discipline involving rigorous analytical thought, eg; philosophy.
Grants The course is recognised by the SERC for the tenure of its Advanced Course studentships.
Course director Prof K L Clark.

Information technology

MSc
1 year full time
45 places
Dr L J Hazelwood,
Postgraduate Admissions
Tutor, Computer Science,
Aston University, Aston
Triangle, Birmingham B4
7ET
Tel: 021 359 3611

This conversion course consists of introductory material on programming techniques and computer systems, more advanced material on software engineering, artificial intelligence and information systems and a number of options in software and applications areas.
Entrance requirements Good honours degree in a discipline other than computer science.
Grants SERC advanced course studentships.
Head of department Dr B Gay.

Information technology

MSc or diploma
1 year full time
2 years part time
100 places
Department of Computing
Science, University of
Glasgow, Glasgow G12 8QQ
Tel: 041 339 8855

This multidisciplinary course offers core modules which include software engineering, computer systems and HCI and IKBS technologies, and a variety of optional modules including management and financial information systems, computer aided engineering, database management systems, computer graphics and health informatics.
Entrance requirements Good honours degree or equivalent qualification related to chosen application areas.
Grants SED awards and Training Agency support.
Director of IT studies Professor A C Allison.

Information technology

MSc
1 year full time
The Graduate and Associate
Student Officer, Queen Mary
& Westfield College, Mile
End Road, London E1 4NS
Tel: 071 975 5074

This conversion course in Information Technology aims to teach software information technology skills, including artificial intelligence and computer communication topics. It is available in two streams. One stream includes an introduction to the appropriate electronic hardware and requires mathematics to A level standard, whilst the other stream includes the human-computer interface and only requires O level mathematics. Both streams end with a three-month full-time project.
Entrance requirements A good honours degree that does not have a significant computing content, and mathematics to O level or A level standard (see above).
Course director Dr A J Pearmain.

Information technology (medical physics)

MSc and diploma
1 year full time
Admissions Secretary,
Department of Biomedical
Physics & Bioengineering,
University of Aberdeen,
Forester Hill, Aberdeen AB9
2ZD
Tel: 0224 681818 ext 53253

The conversion course has been designed to give a training in information technology using the discipline of medical physics as an application vehicle. The course covers computer languages, programming, numerical techniques, signal analysis, digital electronics and microprocessors. Experience on a wide range of computers is available and a theme of computer imaging and diagnostic instrumentation runs throughout the course.
Entrance requirements A good honours degree in a science based subject, or equivalent qualification.
Grants SERC advanced course studentships.
Head of department Professor J R Mallard.

Information technology for non electrical graduates

MSc
1 year full time
dip
1 year full time
Mr P H Etherington,
Department of Electrical &
Electronic Engineering,
Heriot-Watt University, 31-35
Grassmarket, Edinburgh EH1
2HT
Tel: 031 225 6465 ext 409

The conversion course is intended for graduates in the physical and mathematical sciences and for graduates of other disciplines who have the appropriate computing and mathematical ability. The major course units which are presented in the first two terms are basic digital techniques, computer hardware and software engineering, communications, systems engineering and information engineering.The formal lecture material is followed by a six months design project which provides an opportunity to apply the information technology techniques to a practical systems problem. The course provides a technical background for a future career in the wide field of information technology.

Entrance requirements First or second class honours degree in a science based subject or equivalent qualification.
Grants A number of SERC advanced course studentships are normally available.

Intelligent knowledge based systems

MSc
1 year full time
2 years part time
25 places
PhD/MPhil
2-3 years full time
Graduate Secretary (PDG),
Department of Computer
Science, University of Essex,
Wivenhoe Park, Colchester,
Essex C04 3SQ
Tel: 0206 872256

This area is a major branch of information technology, in which research has actively been pursued at Essex for many years. The MSc course enables graduates to move into this growth area. It covers practical expert systems work including the use of Prolog and other knowledge engineering tools, and basic AI research likely to bear practical fruit in the next decade. The course includes a major individual project. Research students are also welcomed.
Entrance requirements Good honours degree or equivalent. Computing experience an advantage but not essential.
Grants SERC studentships available.
Head of department I R MacCallum.

Microprocessor technology & applications

MSc
13 months full time
18 places
PgD (or diploma)
9 months full time
The Registry, Department of
Electrical & electronic
engineering, Brighton
Polytechnic, Mithras House,
Lewes Road, Brighton BN2
4AT
Tel: 0273 600900

An Information Technology Conversion Course designed for science and (non electronic) engineering graduates.
The course covers microprocessor systems, software engineering, computer-aided engineering, digital communications, real-time and embedded systems, project management and company management. A major element of the course is a six month full-time individual design project applied to a chosen area of information technology and linked with industry wherever possible.
Entrance requirements Good honours degree or equivalent in science or engineering. Mature applicants are welcome and relevant industrial experience will be taken into account.
Grants SERC advanced course studentships available.
Course Director Dr P N Mercer.

Software engineering with applications

MSc
1 year full time
27 months part time
dip
6 months full time
18 months part time
Dr L J Hazelwood,
Postgraduate Admissions
Tutor, Computer Science,
Aston University, Aston
Triangle, Birmingham B4
7ET
Tel: 021 359 3611

Software engineering with applications is a new specialist programme designed in response to the rapidly increasing demand of the IT industry for skilled software engineers. It includes modules in software engineering (including quality and project management), large-scale logic and functional programming, formal methods in software development and information systems. There is also a substantial practical element involving group and individual projects. The diploma and MSc programmes are the same except that the former does not include the individual project.
Entrance requirements A good honours degree with a substantial computing content, or equivalent qualifications and experience.
Grants SERC advanced course studentships.
Head of department Dr B Day.

Software systems technology

MSc
1 year full time
2-3 years part time
30 places
Mr Hugh Lafferty, Portobello
Centre, Department of
Computer Science,
University of Sheffield,
Sheffield S1 4DD
Tel: 0742 768555

This is a modular conversion MSc for graduates wishing to retrain in computer science. Five modules are taken over two terms, followed by a five month placement in industry for which a dissertation must be written. Industrial Fellows ensure the commercial relevance of the course. There are two mandatory modules viz. software engineering, computer systems. There are five optional modules: intelligent knowledge-based systems, database technology, graphics, commercial data processing, hardware systems.
Entrance requirements 2.2 in any logical/numerate discipline.
Grants Training agency.
Course director Mr H H Lafferty.

Software techniques for computer aided engineering

MSc
1 year full time
The Admissions Tutor (Ref
2155), Applied Computing
and Mathematics, Cranfield
Institute of Technology,
FREEPOST, Cranfield,
Bedford MK43 7BR
Tel: 0234 752703

This course offers opportunities for graduates and mature students in numerate disciplines to become skilled software professionals specialising in Computer Aided Engineering (CAE). Emphasis is on interactive graphical systems and the automation of interfaces between computer aided design and manufacturing, in particular by the use of parallel processing and artificial intelligence.
Entrance requirements Good honours degree in an appropriate subject.
Grants SERC.
Head of department Professor M J Pratt.

UNIVERSITY OF WALES COLLEGE OF CARDIFF

Postgraduate Courses
— One year full time

MSc/DIPLOMA IN ELECTRONIC ENGINEERING with specialisation in:
*Digital Systems *Control Engineering *Medical Electronics
*Communication, Radar & Navigational Aids

The course, which is aimed at scientists and engineers whose first degree may not be in Electrical Engineering, is broadly based initially with lectures in Analogue and Digital Circuits and Systems, Network and Field Theory, Microprocessors and Mathematics. The latter part of the course allows specialisation in a particular area of electronics. The last four months of the course are devoted to an experimental project.

Candidates should have a degree in Engineering, Physics or Mathematics. Suitable applicants holding qualifications deemed equivalent to graduation may be admitted under a two-year scheme of candidature.

MSc IN SYSTEMS ENGINEERING with specialisation in:
*Automation and Robotics *Information Systems
*Information Technology for Manufacture

Core Subjects: Computer and Software Engineering, Automatic Text Systems and Systems Behaviour. **Specialist Option Subjects** (1) Instrumentation & Measurement, Control Systems Synthesis, Robotics Technology. (2) Instrumentation & Measurement, Data System Technology, Information Systems. (3) Manufacturing Systems Design & Automation, Manufacturing Systems Modelling & Analysis, Behavioural Aspects of Management Information Systems. Candidates who are successful in the written examinations will pursue a four-month project.

Grants are available from the **SERC**, **Training Agency** and **European Social Fund**. Candidates should have a good honours degree in Engineering, Mathematics or Applied Science.

MSc IN ELECTRICAL AND ELECTROMAGNETIC ENGINEERING
with specialisation in:
*Electrical Materials *Measurements *Energy Conversion *Microwave Devices
*Magnetic Recording *Electromagnetic Communications Systems
*Permanent Magnets

MSc IN ARTIFICIAL INTELLIGENCE WITH ENGINEERING APPLICATIONS
with specialisation in:
*AI Languages *Knowledge Engineering *Development Tools/Techniques
*Robotics *Natural Language Processing *Expert Systems
*Vision and Image Processing Systems

Candidates who are successful in the written examinations will pursue a four-month project.

Grants are available from the **Employment Training Agency**. Candidates should have a good honours degree in Engineering, Computer Science, Mathematics, Applied or Physical Science.

For further details apply to:
The Academic Registrar, UWCC, PO Box 68, Cardiff CF1 3XA

Engineering and technology

What are the advantages of a higher degree in technology, be it a Master's, an MPhil or a PhD? The answer depends on your objectives. If you are expecting to graduate in 1991, it may be a stepping stone to a career in research, or a way of gaining specialist knowledge in part of your first degree subject. It can also be a way to change the direction of your career and gain knowledge and skills in another field.

Engineers or scientists already working in industry sometimes take a postgraduate course to gain new knowledge relevant to their employment, which might be an essential component in the climb up the career ladder. Most taught Master's courses take on students with several years' industrial experience as well as new graduates, creating a situation in which each can learn from the others. A few postgraduate courses in engineering and technology expect all their students to have work experience but most accept new graduates as well.

Specialised study
Most courses are highly specialised compared with undergraduate studies, and in some cases link a particular technology and the application of appropriate management techniques - an MSc in construction project management, for example. Some courses lead graduates into very new

fields, in particular conversion courses to information technology, computer science and electronics, areas in which many places are being offered at present. If you have little background in the course subject you'll inevitably need to do some intensive studying in the early stages to assimilate the content, so that you can build on it later.

Taught courses
Taught Master's courses normally start in October and require in-depth and self-motivated study of both familiar and new topics. There are usually plenty of lecturers around with a real interest in the subject matter who can be consulted when you need guidance. A few taught courses in relevant areas such as systems engineering, industrial robotics or micro-electronics have places sponsored by industry, although most of these tend to be reserved for employees of companies who join the course after working for some time in the industry. Industrial interest of this kind can also lead to real industrial project work for course members, sometimes on industrial premises.

Taught courses often consist of two terms of study, culminating in an exam and followed by five or six months of project work which is written up as a thesis. Some taught courses are offered on a part-time basis, taking two or three

years instead of the one calendar year taken to complete an MSc by full-time study. Part-time study has the advantage of allowing you to continue your employment and gain valuable experience in an engineering environment. It is, however, much more arduous than full-time study, your choice is limited to educational institutions close to your home, and study will gobble up most of your spare time.

Research degrees

Master's and other higher degrees can also be obtained by research. Research requires a different approach to studying, and a research degree is an excellent precursor to a career in research. Career opportunities in the academic world are few and exceedingly competitive these days. Good applied research, especially if it is conducted in conjunction with industry, can often lead to offers of employment from companies to whom it is relevant.

What about funding?

Financial support for MSc degree courses comes chiefly from the research councils, and in particular from the Science and Engineering Research Council (SERC) which offers awards each year for scientists and engineers on postgraduate courses. Details of the finance available for specific courses can best be obtained from course admission tutors. Universities and polytechnics sometimes have their own bursaries to offer, though these are few and competition for them is high. If you already work in industry, an approach to your employer may result in your being seconded onto a relevant course.

SERC is also the major source of finance for research degrees, most of which is channelled into studentships,

but some takes the form of research assistantships. Research assistants are, in effect, employees of an institution of higher education on a fixed-term contract. Their task is to complete a specific piece of research in a set time. A PhD tends to be awarded for three years of research which reaches the required standard, an MPhil for two years and an MSc for one year of study.

Two other SERC schemes are instant awards and teaching fellowships. Instant awards are grants for those already in employment who decide that they wish to study for an MSc. Teaching fellowships finance graduates to work on real industrial problems for two years, often on an industrial site rather than at a university or polytechnic. They do not necessarily lead to a higher degree but can be a promising start to an industrial career. The *Times Higher Educational Supplement*, *New Scientist* and the *Guardian* are good sources of information about such posts.

Things to look out for

A number of points should be borne in mind when selecting an appropriate route to a higher degree.
- The length of time allocated to the dissertation or project is a good indication of how much initiative and original work will be required.
- Check if there are optional modules on the course which fit in with your own requirements.
- Talk to the course director about what you hope to get from the course.
- If you are having difficulty in obtaining a grant, ask how previous students were financed.
- Check the employment prospects of graduates from the course with the institution's careers advisory service.
- Finally, find out what research is going on within the department, and

ENGINEERING FACULTY
University College London

The Faculty of Engineering offers opportunities for MᵖPhil/PhD research degrees and 1-year taught-course MSc and College Diplomas in the following departments:

Chemical and Biochemical Engineering
MSc and Diploma courses in Biochemical Engineering
MSc and Diploma courses in Chemical Engineering
Research opportunities in Biochemical Engineering, Combustion, Crystallisation, Fluidisation, Reaction Engineering, Particle Technology, Mixing and Two-phase Flow.

Photogrammetry and Surveying
MSc and Diploma courses in Geodesy, in Photogrammetry, in Surveying, and in Numerical Methods in Photogrammetry and Surveying. Research opportunities in Geodesy, Ground, Air and Space Surveying, Digital Image Processing and Artificial Vision.

Mechanical Engineering
MSc and Diploma courses in Marine Engineering, Ocean Engineering, Naval Architecture, and Non-destructive Evaluation.

Research opportunities in Automatic Control, Bioengineering, Fluid Mechanics, Thermodynamics, Materials, Naval Architecture and Offshore Structures.

Civil and Municipal Engineering
Intercollegiate MSc course in Transport. Research opportunities in Concrete, Fluids, Offshore Technology, Pollution, Public Health, Granular Materials, Geotechnics, Structural Mechanics, Dynamics, Structural Design, Computer Assisted Traffic Engineering, Transport Systems and Safety.

Electronic and Electrical Engineering
MSc and Diploma courses in Information Technology and in Microwaves and Modern Optics.
Research opportunities in Microwaves, Optoelectronics, VLSI Design, Neural Networks, Materials, Ultrasonics, Computing and Control.

For further details write to **The Tutor to Engineering Students, Engineering Faculty Office, University College, Torrington Place, London WC1E 7JE.**
Please specify the department and courses in which you are interested.

if possible, ask academics from another institution how it is regarded. Then you will be sure that your own study will be based on a firm foundation, in the company of those at the forefront of their field.

Neil Harris

This listing contains **taught courses** (under the heading 'Higher degrees by instruction') and **research opportunities** (under the heading 'Higher degrees by research'). All study exceeds two terms or six months and is offered on both a full-time and part-time basis unless otherwise indicated. Post-experience and in-service courses are only included when advertised.

☐   This symbol indicates that the **taught course(s)** or **research opportunities** are advertised at the end of this listing.

Biol   An italic abbreviation indicates that an advertisement has been placed at the end of another chapter.

✩   This symbol indicates full-time study only.

△   This symbol indicates part-time study only.

For quick reference to advertisements, please use the 'Advertiser's course entry index'. For further information regarding the listing, please refer to page 53.

General

Higher degrees by instruction

Advanced chemical engineering
London U Imperial C MSc✩/dip✩

Advanced manufacturing technology
Staffordshire P cert✩   ☐

Applied mathematics
Essex U MSc✩/dip✩

Applied optics
London U Imperial C MSc✩/ dip✩   *Phy*

Aviation electronics
Cranfield IT MSc✩   ☐

Bioengineering
Strathclyde U MSc/dip

Chemical engineering
Teesside P BEng✩

Communication systems
Cranfield IT MSc✩   ☐

Computational modelling & finite elements in engineering mechanics
Swansea UC MSc✩/cert✩

Computer aided engineering
Cranfield IT MSc✩   *Comp*
Staffordshire P MSc✩/dip✩   ☐

Teesside P MSc

Computing systems
Cranfield IT MSc✩   ☐

Control & information technology
Manchester UMIST MSc✩/dip✩ ☐

Control systems
Cranfield IT MSc✩   ☐
Sheffield U MEng/MScTech

Corrosion science & engineering
Manchester UMIST MSc✩/dip✩ ☐

Distribution technology & management
Cranfield IT MSc✩   *Bus*

Electrical power engineering
Strathclyde U MSc/dip   ☐

Electronic design
Cranfield IT MSc☆ □

Energy & development
Surrey U MSc/dip

Engineering
Sheffield City P MSc

Engineering ceramics
Leeds U MSc☆

Engineering computation
Belfast Queen's U MSc☆/dip☆ □

Engineering design
Loughborough U MSc△/
MTech☆ □

Engineering management
Glasgow U MSc

Engineering mathematics
Newcastle U MSc☆/cert☆

Engineering mechanics
Cranfield IT MSc☆

Engineering project management
Birmingham U MSc(Eng)☆

Engineering rock mechanics
London U Imperial C MSc☆/dip☆

Explosives ordnance technology
Royal Military C of Science dip☆

Flight dynamics
Cranfield IT MSc☆

Foundation engineering
Birmingham U MSc(Eng)

Geographical information systems
Nottingham U MSc☆

Geotechnical engineering
Cardiff U of Wales C MSc☆

Highway & traffic engineering
Birmingham U MSc(Eng)

History & philosophy of science
London U Imperial C MSc

History of science, medicine & technology
London U Imperial C MSc

History of technology
London U Imperial C MSc

Independent study
East London P MA/MSc/dip

Industrial design for engineers
Teesside P MA☆

Industrial mineralogy
Leicester U MSc☆/dip☆

Information technology
Glasgow U MSc/dip   *Comp*
Sheffield U MSc(Eng)/MSc(Tech)
Teesside P MSc☆

Information technology: design & manufacture of microelectronic systems
Edinburgh U MSc/dip

Instrumentation & analytical science
Manchester UMIST MSc☆

Intelligent knowledge based systems in manufacturing
Cranfield IT MSc☆

Machine design
Cranfield IT MSc☆ □

Management science & computer applications in management systems
Cranfield IT MSc☆   *Bus*

Manufacturing systems
Nottingham U MSc □

Mathematical techniques & their applications
Newcastle U MSc

Mechanical engineering
Strathclyde U MSc/dip □

Metrology & quality assurance
Cranfield IT MSc☆

Mineral production management
London U Imperial C MSc☆/dip☆

Mining engineering
Camborne S of Mines MSc/dip☆

Noise & vibration of rotating machines & gas turbines
Cranfield IT MSc☆ □

Nuclear reactor science & engineering
London U Queen Mary & Westfield C MSc/dip

Offshore engineering
Robert Gordon's IT MSc☆/dip☆

Petroleum engineering
London U Imperial C MSc☆/dip☆
Strathclyde U MSc/dip

Physics & electronics
Lancaster U dip☆

Process plant materials engineering
Cranfield IT MSc☆

Project engineering
Lancaster U MSc

Quality engineering
Paisley CT dip

Solar energy & energy conservation in buildings
Reading U MSc☆

Special engineering
Brunel U MEng△

Subsea engineering
Cranfield IT MSc☆

Systems engineering
Cardiff U of Wales C MSc □

Technology & information studies
Brunel U MA

Telecommunication & information systems
Essex U MSc

Thermal energy processes
Cranfield IT MSc □

Traffic engineering for developing countries
Birmingham U MSc(Eng)☆

Training & development
Sheffield U MEd△

Underwater technology
Cranfield IT MSc☆ □

Water resources technology
Birmingham U MSc(Eng)

Water supply & public health engineering
Middlesex P dip☆

Weapons' effects on structures
Royal Military C of Science MSc☆

Welding & adhesive bonding of materials
Brunel U MSc☆ □

Higher degrees by research

Bioengineering
Strathclyde U PhD/MPhil/MSc □

Biomedical engineering
Dundee U PhD/MSc

Biomedical physics & bioengineering
Aberdeen U PhD☆/MPhil☆/
MSc☆ □, Phy

Civil & structural engineering
Sussex U DPhil/MPhil □

Civil engineering
Birmingham U PhD/MPhil(Eng)

Civil engineering & building
Wales P PhD/MPhil □

Computational fluid dynamics
London U Imperial C PhD/MPhil/
dip

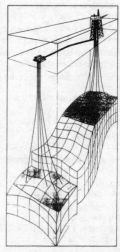

Computer applications in engineering
Cardiff U of Wales C PhD☆/ MPhil☆

Control engineering
Sheffield U PhD/MPhil

Control theory
Salford U PhD☆/MSc☆

Distribution studies
Cranfield IT PhD☆/MSc☆   *Bus*

Electrical, electronic & systems engineering
Cardiff U of Wales C PhD☆/ MPhil☆   □

Electronic & electrical engineering
Sheffield U PhD/MPhil   □

Electronic systems
Cranfield IT PhD☆/MSc☆

Energy engineering
Surrey U PhD/MPhil

Engineering
Aberdeen U PhD☆/MPhil☆/ MSc☆   □
Bristol P PhD/MPhil/dip
Exeter U PhD/MPhil   □
Humberside CHE PhD/MPhil
Lancaster U PhD/MPhil
Leicester U PhD/MPhil
Oxford P PhD/MPhil
Thames P PhD/MPhil
Warwick U PhD☆/MSc☆   □

Engineering & applied physics
North London P PhD/MPhil

Engineering design & manufacture
Hull U PhD/MSc

Engineering mathematics
Belfast Queen's U PhD/MSc
Newcastle U PhD/MPhil

Environmental physics
Nottingham U PhD☆/MPhil☆

Fluid processes
Cardiff U of Wales C PhD☆/ MPhil☆

Housing
Cardiff U of Wales C PhD☆/ MPhil☆

Independent study
East London P PhD/MPhil

Instrumentation & analytical science
Manchester UMIST PhD/MSc

Interdisciplinary studies
Aston U PhD/MPhil

Materials technology
Brunel U PhD/MPhil   □

Mechanical & structural engineering
Sussex U DPhil/MPhil   □

Metallurgy & engineering materials
Strathclyde U PhD☆/MPhil☆/ MSc☆

Mining
Wales P PhD☆/MPhil☆

Ports
Cardiff U of Wales C PhD/MPhil

Quality assurance
Cranfield IT PhD☆/MPhil☆/MSc☆

Robotics & automated systems
London U Imperial C PhD/MPhil

Ship science
Southampton U PhD/MPhil

Total technology
Manchester UMIST PhD/MSc

Transport
Cardiff U of Wales C PhD☆/ MPhil☆

Aeronautical, marine technology

Higher degrees by instruction

Advanced materials technology
Surrey U MSc/dip

Aerodynamics
Cranfield IT MSc☆

Aeronautical engineering
Glasgow U dip☆

Aerospace materials engineering
Cranfield IT MSc☆/dip☆   □

Aerospace propulsion
Cranfield IT MSc☆

Aerospace vehicle design
Cranfield IT MSc☆

Air transport engineering
Cranfield IT MSc☆

Airline transport pilot's licence
Air Service Training Ltd ATPL☆

Airport planning & management
Loughborough U MSc

Applied marine science
Swansea UC MSc☆/dip☆

Astronautics & space engineering
Cranfield IT MSc☆

Commercial pilot's licence & instrument rating
Air Service Training Ltd CPL☆/ IR☆

Composite materials
London U Imperial C MSc

Computational fluid dynamics & structural mechanics
London U Imperial C MSc/dip   □

Dynamics of engineering structures
Cranfield IT MSc☆

Electronics systems design (aviation electronics)
Cranfield IT MSc

Engineering design
Loughborough U MSc△/ MTech☆   □

Engineering solid mechanics
Manchester UMIST MSc☆/dip☆ □

Fighting experience
Royal Military C of Science dip☆

Flight dynamics
Cranfield IT MSc☆

Flight test engineering
Cranfield IT MSc☆

Hydrographic surveying
South West P dip☆   *Env*

Maintenance engineer's licence
Air Service Training Ltd CAA Lic A☆/CAA Lic C☆/CAA Lic X☆
Oxford Air Training S CAA Lic A/ CAA Lic C/CAA Lic X

Marine engineering
London U UC MSc☆/dip☆
Newcastle U MSc☆/cert☆/dip☆
Royal Naval Engineering C MSc☆

Marine resource development & protection
Heriot-Watt U MSc   *Env*

Marine technology
Newcastle U MSc☆/dip☆   □
Strathclyde U MSc/dip

Maritime civil engineering
Liverpool U MSc(Eng)☆/dip☆

Maritime defence technology
Royal Naval Engineering C MSc☆/dip☆

Modular studies
Heriot-Watt U MSc/dip

Naval architecture
London U UC MSc☆/dip☆
Newcastle U cert☆

Naval architecture & ocean engineering
Glasgow U dip☆

Non-destructive evaluation
London U UC MSc△

Ocean engineering
Glasgow U dip
London U UC MSc☆/dip☆

Offshore engineering
Cranfield IT MSc☆/dip☆   □
Newcastle U MSc☆

Offshore materials & corrosion engineering
Newcastle P MSc☆/dip☆
Robert Gordon's IT MSc☆/dip☆

Ship production technology
Strathclyde U MSc/dip

Shipping & maritime studies
Liverpool P MSc/dip△

Subsea engineering
Cranfield IT MSc☆
Heriot-Watt U MSc☆

Underwater technology
Cranfield IT MSc☆   □

Water resources engineering
City U MSc

Higher degrees by research

Aerodynamics & thermodynamics
Bath U PhD☆/MSc☆

Aerodynamics including computational fluid mechanics
Cranfield IT PhD☆/MSc☆

Aeronautical & mechanical engineering
Salford U PhD/MSc

Aeronautical engineering
Belfast Queen's U PhD/MSc
Bristol U PhD/MSc
Glasgow U PhD☆
Hatfield P PhD/MPhil
London U Queen Mary & Westfield C PhD☆/MPhil☆
Manchester U PhD/MSc

Aeronautics
City U PhD/MPhil
London U Imperial C PhD/MPhil/dip

Aeronautics & astronautics
Southampton U PhD/MPhil

Aerospace vehicle design
Cranfield IT PhD☆/MSc☆

Air engineering
Royal Naval Engineering C PhD☆/MSc☆

Air transport engineering, planning, maintenance & reliability
Cranfield IT PhD☆/MSc☆

Applied mathematics
East Anglia U PhD/MPhil

Aviation electronics
Cranfield IT PhD☆   □

Aviation safety & accident investigation
Cranfield IT PhD☆/MSc☆

Avionics, simulation & airborne computing
Cranfield IT PhD☆/MSc☆

Bioaeronautics
Cranfield IT PhD☆/MSc☆

Civil & structural engineering
Sussex U DPhil/MPhil   □

Civil aviation
City of London P PhD☆/MPhil☆

Computational fluid dynamics
London U Imperial C PhD/MPhil/dip

Electronics
East Anglia U PhD/MSc

Flight dynamics, stability, control & performance
Cranfield IT PhD☆/MSc☆

Marine engineering
Newcastle U PhD/MPhil
Royal Naval Engineering C PhD☆/MSc☆

Marine science & technology
South West P PhD/MPhil

Marine sciences
Liverpool U PhD/MSc

Marine simulation & systems
Cardiff U of Wales C PhD/MPhil

Marine studies
Swansea UC PhD/MPhil

Marine technology
Salford U PhD/MSc

Maritime civil engineering
Liverpool U PhD/MSc(Eng)

Maritime studies
Liverpool P PhD/MPhil

Mechanical & offshore engineering
Robert Gordon's IT PhD/MPhil

Mechanical & structural engineering
Sussex U DPhil/MPhil   □

Mechanical engineering
London U UC PhD☆/MPhil☆

Mechanical, aeronautical & production engineering
Kingston P PhD/MPhil

Naval architecture
Glasgow U PhD
Royal Naval Engineering C PhD☆/MSc☆

Ocean engineering
Glasgow U PhD

Offshore engineering
Heriot-Watt U PhD☆/MPhil☆

Petroleum engineering
Heriot-Watt U PhD☆/MPhil☆   □

Propulsion, power & automotive engineering (gas turbine, wind turbine, automobile)
Cranfield IT PhD☆/MPhil☆

Ship & marine technology
Strathclyde U PhD☆/MPhil☆

Ship science
Southampton U PhD/MPhil

Structures including computational analysis & impact design
Cranfield IT PhD☆/MSc☆

Transport studies
Ulster U DPhil/MPhil

Agricultural engineering and related studies

Higher degrees by instruction

Agrarian studies
Sussex U MA

Agricultural communications
Belfast Queen's U dip

Agricultural development
London U Wye C dip☆

Agricultural economics (agrarian development overseas)
London U Wye C MSc☆

Agricultural engineering
Newcastle U MSc☆/dip☆

Silsoe C MSc☆/Dip☆

Agricultural machinery mechanisation
Silsoe C MSc☆/dip☆

Agricultural science
Aberystwyth, UC of Wales MA☆/dip☆

Agrochemicals application technology
Silsoe C MSc☆

Crop protection
Bath U MSc☆

Drainage & land reclamation engineering
Silsoe C MSc☆/dip☆

Engineering for rural development
Silsoe C MSc☆

Engineering hydrology
London U Imperial C MSc/dip

Environmental acoustics
South Bank P MSc

Environmental engineering
Newcastle U MSc☆/cert☆/dip☆
South Bank P MSc/dip

Finite element method in stress and vibration analysis
Cranfield IT MSc☆   □

Food & agricultural biotechnology
Reading U MSc☆

Food technology
Reading U MSc☆

Irrigation
Newcastle U MSc☆/dip☆

Irrigation engineering
Silsoe C MSc☆
Southampton U MSc☆/dip☆

Manufacturing for agricultural & industrial development
Silsoe C MSc☆

Post harvest technology
Humberside CHE dip☆

Rural water supplies
Silsoe C MSc☆

Soil & water engineering
Silsoe C MSc☆/dip☆

Soil conservation
Silsoe C MSc☆

Soil conservation & land reclamation engineering
Southampton U MSc☆/dip☆

Tropical agricultural development
Reading U MAgrSc☆/MSc☆/dip☆

Higher degrees by research

Agrarian development overseas
London U Wye C PhD☆/MPhil☆

Agrarian studies
Sussex U DPhil/MPhil

Agricultural engineering
Aberdeen SAg PhD☆/MSc☆
Newcastle U PhD/MPhil

Agricultural engineering & buildings
Aberdeen U PhD☆/MPhil☆/MSc☆

Agricultural engineering & mechanisation
Silsoe C PhD/MPhil
West of Scotland C PhD☆/MSc☆

Agricultural production systems planning
Silsoe C PhD/MPhil

Agricultural science
Edinburgh U PhD/MPhil

Agriculture
Edinburgh U PhD/MPhil
Edinburgh U SAg PhD/MPhil
Glasgow U PhD/MSc
London U Wye C PhD☆/MPhil☆
Newcastle U PhD/MPhil
Reading U PhD/MPhil
West of Scotland C PhD☆/MSc☆

Biotechnology
Reading U PhD/MPhil

Dairy technology
West of Scotland C PhD☆/MSc☆

Engineering & technology
Wolverhampton P PhD☆/MPhil☆

Environmental engineering
South Bank P PhD/MPhil

European agricultural studies
London U Wye C PhD☆/MPhil☆

Irrigation engineering
Southampton U PhD/MPhil

Machinery design & manufacture
Silsoe C PhD/MPhil

Bioengineering

Higher degrees by instruction

Advanced engineering materials
Liverpool U MSc(Eng)☆   □

Biochemical & chemical engineering
Birmingham U MSc(Eng)☆

Biochemical engineering
London U UC MSc☆/dip☆
Swansea UC MSc☆

Biochemical engineering/biotechnology
Birmingham U MSc(Eng)

Bioengineering
Strathclyde U MSc/dip

Biomedical engineering
Aberdeen U MSc☆/dip☆   □
Surrey U MSc☆/dip☆   □

Biomedical engineering science
Dundee U MSc

Biophysics & engineering
London U Inst of Ophthalmology MSc☆

Biotechnology
Lancashire P MSc☆/cert△

Chemical engineering
Swansea UC MSc☆/dip☆

Crystallography
London U Birkbeck C MSc

Food & agricultural biotechnology
Reading U MSc☆

Telecommunications technology
Aston U MSc☆/dip☆   □

Higher degrees by research

Agriculture & horticulture
Bristol U PhD☆/MSc☆

Biochemical engineering
Swansea UC PhD/MPhil

Bioengineering
Bath U PhD☆/MSc☆
Birmingham U PhD/MSc
Strathclyde U PhD/MPhil/MSc   □
Ulster U DPhil/MPhil

UNIVERSITY OF BIRMINGHAM
School of Chemical Engineering

Opportunities exist for postgraduate studies leading to degrees of MSc(Eng) by course and project: 1 year full-time. MPhil(Eng)/PhD by research: 1-3 years full-time.

● **MSc(Eng) Biochemical Engineering** – a taught course to provide training in areas of process engineering related to the fermentation, pharmaceutical, food and water treatment industries. Structured to cater for graduates of chemical engineering or biological sciences. Taught course work and four-month research project.

● **MPhil/PhD** by research — 1-3 years full time. Research projects are available in the following areas:
(a) Biochemical engineering
(b) Chemical processes, chemical reaction engineering and catalysis
(c) Environmental engineering
(d) Heat transfer and fluid flow processes
(e) Minerals engineering and extractive metallurgy
(f) Mixing processes
(g) Solids processing

SERC Quota and CASE Awards will be available in all areas of research.

Head of School: Professor N A Warner
Further details from Dr J. M. Winterbottom,
School of Chemical Engineering,
University of Birmingham,
PO Box 363, Birmingham B15 2TT.
Tel: 021-414 5293 or 021-414 5331.

PORTSMOUTH POLYTECHNIC
School of Systems Engineering

MSc Signal Processing and Control.
One year full-time/three year part-time course (CNAA).
Lectures, tutorials, practical work and project. Commencing early October. *Analytical methods:* dynamic response, transform fundamentals, discrete systems, random signal analysis. *Engineering methods:* instrumentation, computer hardware/software/CADCAM, numerical methods, information processing. *Control systems:* modelling and identification, linear system theory, non-linear and stochastic systems, optimal control, robotics. *Signal processing:* filters, signal analysis, image and speech processing.

MSc/PgD Advanced Manufacturing Technology.
Modular 25/50 week full-time/two year part-time course (CNAA).
Lectures, coursework and project: advanced manufacturing processes and materials, automated control systems and robotics, CADCAM, management of AMT, manufacturing systems engineering, software engineering and data communications.

MPhil/PhD (CNAA) Research Supervision, Electrical, Electronic and Mechanical Engineering
A wide range of research activities are supported: microprocessor applications, robotics, wave techniques, terrestrial and satellite communications, signal processing, imaging, medical and environmental applications, ECAD, fatigue behaviour, energy technology, combustion, heat transfer and power systems, structural and control system computer modelling and automation.

Further information from: The Administrator, Engineering Faculty Registry, Burnaby Building, Burnaby Road, Portsmouth PO1 3QL. Tel: 0705 842525. Fax: 0705 842351.

Warwick U PhD/MSc

Biomedical engineering
Dundee U PhD/MSc
Kent U PhD☆/MPhil☆
Surrey U PhD/MPhil   □
Sussex U DPhil/MPhil   □

Biomedical physics & bioengineering
Aberdeen U PhD☆/MPhil☆/
  MSc☆   □, Phy

Biotechnology
Lancashire P PhD/MPhil
London U Imperial C PhD/MPhil/
  dip
Reading U PhD/MPhil

Chemical & biochemical engineering
London U UC PhD☆/MPhil☆

Chemical engineering
Loughborough U PhD☆/MPhil☆

Crystallography
London U Birkbeck C PhD/MPhil

Engineering
Leicester U PhD/MPhil

Materials science & engineering
Liverpool U PhD/MSc(Eng)   □

Mechanical engineering
Leeds U PhD/MPhil/MSc(Eng)   □

Medical biophysics
Manchester U PhD/MSc   Phy

Chemical engineering

Higher degrees by instruction

Advanced chemical technology
Manchester UMIST MSc☆   Chem

Biochemical & chemical engineering
Birmingham U MSc(Eng)☆

Biochemical engineering
London U UC MSc☆/dip☆
Swansea UC MSc☆

Biochemical engineering/ biotechnology
Birmingham U MSc(Eng)

Chemical engineering
Bradford U dip☆
Cambridge U cert☆
Leeds U dip☆

London U UC dip☆
Swansea UC MSc☆/dip☆
Teesside P BEng☆

Chemical engineering (separation processing)
Bradford U MSc☆

Chemical process engineering
London U UC MSc☆

Combustion science & pollution control
Sheffield U MSc(Eng)☆/
  MSc(Tech)☆

Desalination technology
Glasgow U MSc/dip

Engineering design
Loughborough U MSc△/
  MTech☆   □

Explosive ordnance engineering
Royal Military C of Science
  MSc☆

Integrated design of chemical plant
Leeds U MSc

Metallurgical engineering
Cranfield IT MSc☆/dip☆

Offshore materials & corrosion engineering
Newcastle P MSc☆/dip☆
Robert Gordon's IT MSc☆/dip☆

Petrochemical & hydrocarbon chemistry
Manchester UMIST MSc☆   Chem

Pollution & environmental control
Manchester U MSc☆/dip☆   Env
Manchester UMIST MSc☆

Polymer engineering
Manchester P dip△

Process integration
Manchester UMIST MSc☆

Process plant materials engineering
Cranfield IT MSc☆

Surface science & catalysis
Liverpool U MSc☆

Higher degrees by research

Architecture & building engineering
Bath U PhD☆/MSc☆

Biochemical & chemical engineering
Bath U PhD☆/MSc☆

Chemical & biochemical engineering
London U UC PhD☆/MPhil☆

Chemical & process engineering
Heriot-Watt U PhD☆/MPhil☆
Newcastle U PhD/MPhil☆/
  MSc△   □
Strathclyde U PhD☆/MPhil☆/
  MSc☆

Chemical engineering
Bath U PhD☆/MSc☆
Belfast Queen's U PhD/MSc
Birmingham U PhD/MPhil(Eng)
Bradford U PhD/MPhil
Cambridge U PhD☆/MSc☆
East London P PhD/MPhil
Edinburgh U PhD/MPhil
Exeter U PhD/MPhil
Leeds U PhD/MPhil/MSc(Eng)
Loughborough U PhD☆/MPhil☆
Manchester UMIST PhD/MSc
Nottingham U PhD/MPhil   Chem
South Bank P PhD/MPhil
Surrey U PhD/MPhil   □
Swansea UC PhD/MPhil
Teesside P PhD/MPhil
Wales P PhD/MPhil

Chemical engineering & applied chemistry
Aston U PhD/MPhil   □

Chemical engineering & chemical technology
London U Imperial C PhD/MPhil/
  dip   □

Chemical engineering & fuel technology
Sheffield U PhD/MPhil☆

Chemical with minerals engineering
Birmingham U PhD/MPhil(Eng)

Chemistry
Exeter U PhD/MPhil

Desalination technology
Glasgow U PhD/MEng

Fluid processes
Cardiff U of Wales C PhD☆/
  MPhil☆

Fuel & energy
Leeds U PhD/MPhil/MSc(Eng)/
  MSc   □

Mechanical, production & chemical engineering
Manchester P PhD/MPhil

Minerals engineering
Birmingham U PhD/MPhil(Eng)

Petroleum engineering
Heriot-Watt U PhD☆/MPhil☆   □

Pollution research
Manchester U PhD/MSc
Manchester UMIST PhD/MSc

Process engineering
Surrey U PhD/MPhil

Propulsion, power & automotive engineering (gas turbine, wind turbine, automobile)
Cranfield IT PhD☆/MPhil☆

Total technology
Manchester UMIST PhD/MSc

Transportation & highway engineering
Birmingham U PhD/MPhil(Eng)

Civil, structural engineering

Higher degrees by instruction

Advanced structural engineering
Southampton U MSc☆/dip☆

Airport planning & management
Loughborough U MSc

Applied structural geology & rock mechanics
London U Imperial C MSc☆/dip☆

Bridge engineering
Surrey U MSc/dip

Building services engineering
Glasgow U MSc/dip△

Civil & structural engineering
Sheffield U MScTech☆/ MSc(Eng)☆

Civil engineering
Aberdeen U MSc☆/dip☆
Belfast Queen's U MSc/cert/dip
Cardiff U of Wales C MSc
Dundee U MSc/dip
East London P MSc/dip
Glasgow U dip☆
Swansea UC MSc☆/cert☆
Wales P MSc△

Civil engineering (highways & transport)
City U MSc

Civil engineering (professional examination)
Coventry P cert△

Civil engineering (structures)
City U MSc

Computational fluid dynamics & structural mechanics
London U Imperial C MSc/dip   □

Computational modelling & finite elements in engineering mechanics
Swansea UC MSc☆/cert☆

Concrete structures
London U Imperial C MSc/dip

Construction
Loughborough U MSc☆

Construction engineering
Leeds U MSc(Eng)

Construction law & arbitration
London U King's C MSc△/dip△

Construction management
Bath U MSc   □
Birmingham U MSc(Eng)
Glasgow C of Building & Printing dip☆
Loughborough U MSc
Reading U MSc☆
Strathclyde U MSc/dip

Construction management (building maitainance)
Heriot-Watt U MSc/dip   □

Construction management (corporate strategy)
Heriot-Watt U MSc/dip   □

Construction management (production management)
Heriot-Watt U MSc/dip   □

Construction management (project management)
Heriot-Watt U MSc/dip   □

Desalination technology
Glasgow U MSc/dip

Dynamics & structural mechanics
London U Imperial C MSc☆/dip☆

Dynamics of engineering structures
Cranfield IT MSc☆

Earthquake engineering
London U Imperial C MSc/dip

Engineering
Cambridge U cert☆

Engineering computation
Belfast Queen's U MSc☆/dip☆   □

Engineering design of buildings
Paisley CT MSc/dip

Engineering geology
Durham U MSc☆   □
Leeds U MSc

Engineering hydrology
London U Imperial C MSc/dip
Newcastle U MSc☆/dip☆

Engineering rock mechanics
London U Imperial C MSc☆/dip☆

Engineering solid mechanics
Manchester UMIST MSc☆/dip☆ □

Engineering surveying & geodesy
Nottingham U MSc☆

Environmental civil engineering
Liverpool U MSc(Eng)☆

Environmental impact assessment
Brighton P MSc△

Foundation engineering
Birmingham U MSc(Eng)

Geotechnical engineering
Bolton IHE dip△
Newcastle U dip☆
Strathclyde U MSc/dip
Surrey U MSc△/dip△

Geotechnics
Middlesex P MSc△

Groundwater engineering
Newcastle U MSc☆

Highway & traffic engineering
Birmingham U MSc(Eng)

Highway engineering
Heriot-Watt U MSc/dip
Strathclyde U MSc/dip

Hydraulic engineering
Heriot-Watt U MSc/dip
Newcastle U MSc☆/dip☆

Hydraulics, hydrology & coastal dynamics
Strathclyde U MSc/dip

Irrigation
Newcastle U MSc☆/dip☆

Irrigation engineering
Southampton U MSc☆/dip☆

Management & implementation of development projects
Manchester UMIST MSc☆   *Bus*

Maritime civil engineering
Liverpool U MSc(Eng)☆/dip☆

Mining engineering
Camborne S of Mines MSc/dip☆
Nottingham U MSc☆

Modular studies
Heriot-Watt U MSc/dip

Petroleum engineering
Strathclyde U MSc/dip

Public health & environmental engineering
Strathclyde U MSc/dip

Public health engineering
London U Imperial C MSc/dip

River, estuary & coastal engineering
London U Imperial C MSc/dip

Road safety engineering
Middlesex P MSc△

Rock mechanics & excavation engineering
Newcastle U MSc☆

Soil & water management
Strathclyde U MSc/dip

Soil conservation & land reclamation engineering
Southampton U MSc☆/dip☆

Soil mechanics
Heriot-Watt U MSc/dip
London U Imperial C MSc/dip

Soil mechanics & engineering seismology
London U Imperial C MSc/dip

Soil mechanics & foundation engineering
Newcastle U MSc☆

Structural design
Cranfield IT MSc☆

Structural engineering
Bradford U MSc/dip
Cardiff U of Wales C MSc
Dundee U dip☆
Heriot-Watt U MSc/dip
Liverpool U MSc(Eng)☆
Manchester UMIST MSc ☐
Newcastle U MSc☆/cert☆/dip☆
Strathclyde U MSc/dip
Surrey U MSc/dip

Structural engineering & computational technology
Heriot-Watt U MSc☆/Dip☆

Structural engineering & foundations
Central London P MSc△/cert△/dip△

Structural geology & rock mechanics
London U Imperial C MSc/dip

Structural steel design
London U Imperial C MSc/dip

Surface mining & land reclamation
Strathclyde U MSc/dip

Traffic engineering for developing countries
Birmingham U MSc(Eng)☆

Transport
London U Imperial C MSc/dip

Transport engineering
Newcastle U Cert☆

Transport engineering & operations
Newcastle U MSc☆

Transport planning & engineering
Leeds U MSc(Eng)

Transportation planning & engineering
Southampton U MSc☆/dip☆

Tropical public health engineering
Leeds U MSc(Eng)☆

Urban engineering
South Bank P MSc☆/dip☆

Water engineering
Strathclyde U MSc/dip

Water resource systems engineering
Newcastle U MSc☆/dip☆

Water resources engineering
London U Queen Mary & Westfield C MSc☆

Water resources technology
Birmingham U MSc(Eng)

Higher degrees by research

Building & civil engineering
Liverpool P PhD/MPhil

Built environment studies
Anglia HEC PhD☆/MPhil☆

Civil & municipal engineering
London U UC PhD☆/MPhil☆

Civil & structural engineering
Bradford U PhD/MPhil
Bristol P PhD/MPhil/cert/dip
Manchester UMIST PhD/MSc
Nottingham P PhD☆/MPhil☆
Sheffield U PhD/MPhil
South Bank P PhD/MPhil
South West P PhD/MPhil
Sussex U DPhil/MPhil ☐

Civil & structural engineering & building
Teesside P PhD☆

Civil engineering
Aberdeen U PhD/MPhil☆/MSc
Belfast Queen's U PhD/MSc
Birmingham U PhD/MPhil(Eng)
Brighton P PhD/MPhil
Bristol U PhD/MSc
City U PhD/MPhil

Dundee IT PhD/MPhil
Dundee U PhD/MSc
East London P PhD/MPhil
Edinburgh U PhD/MPhil
Glasgow U PhD
Hatfield P PhD/MPhil
Heriot-Watt U PhD☆/MPhil☆
Kingston P PhD/MPhil
Leeds U PhD/MPhil/MSc(Eng)
Liverpool U PhD/MSc(Eng)
London U Imperial C PhD/MPhil
London U Queen Mary & Westfield C PhD☆/MPhil☆
Loughborough U PhD☆/MPhil☆
Manchester U PhD☆/MSc☆
Middlesex P PhD/MPhil
Napier P PhD/MPhil
Newcastle U PhD/MPhil
Nottingham U PhD/MPhil
Paisley CT PhD/MPhil
Portsmouth P PhD☆/MPhil☆
Salford U PhD/MSc
Southampton U PhD/MPhil
Strathclyde U PhD☆/MPhil☆/MSc☆
Sunderland P PhD/MPhil
Surrey U PhD/MPhil
Swansea UC PhD/MPhil
Thames P PhD/MPhil
Ulster U DPhil/MPhil
Warwick U PhD/MSc

Civil engineering & building
Coventry P PhD/MPhil
Wales P PhD/MPhil ☐

Civil engineering & construction
Aston U PhD/MPhil

Civil engineering, building & cartography
Oxford P PhD/MPhil

Combined engineering
Coventry P PhD/MPhil

Construction
Sheffield City P PhD/MPhil

Construction management
Reading U PhD/MPhil
South Bank P PhD/MPhil

Construction studies
Wolverhampton P PhD/MPhil

Corrosion engineering
Royal Naval Engineering C PhD☆/MSc☆

Desalination technology
Glasgow U PhD/MEng

Engineering
Aberdeen U PhD☆/MPhil☆/MSc☆ ☐
Cambridge U PhD☆/MSc☆
Lancaster U PhD/MPhil
Manchester U PhD/MSc

Reading U PhD/MPhil
Surrey U PhD/MPhil

Engineering science
Open U PhD/MPhil/BPhil

Engineering science & industrial management
Liverpool U PhD/MSc(Eng)

Estate management & quantity surveying
Wales P PhD/MPhil

Geotechnical engineering
City U PhD/MPhil
Newcastle U PhD/MPhil

Ground engineering
Cardiff U of Wales C PhD☆/ MPhil☆

Hydraulics
Liverpool U PhD/MSc(Eng)

Irrigation engineering
Southampton U PhD/MPhil

Maritime civil engineering
Liverpool U PhD/MSc(Eng)

Mechanical & offshore engineering
Robert Gordon's IT PhD/MPhil

Mechanics & power
Royal Naval Engineering C PhD☆/MSc☆

Ocean engineering
City U PhD/MPhil

Power engineering
Newcastle P PhD☆/MPhil☆

Rock engineering
Camborne S of Mines PhD/MPhil

Soil mechanics
Central London P PhD☆/MPhil☆

Strength of materials & stress analysis
Manchester U PhD/MSc

Structural engineering
Cardiff U of Wales C PhD☆/ MPhil☆

Structural mechanics
Royal Naval Engineering C PhD☆/MSc☆

Structures
Central London P PhD☆/MPhil☆

Communications, control, systems engineering

Higher degrees by instruction

Advanced manufacturing systems
Kingston P MSc△/dip△

Advanced manufacturing technology
Coventry P MSc/dip

Artificial intelligence
Kingston P MSc

Astronautics & space engineering
Cranfield IT MSc☆

Aviation electronics
Cranfield IT MSc☆ □

Building services engineering
Brunel U MSc

Communication engineering & digital electronics
Manchester UMIST MSc☆/dip☆

Communication studies
Belfast Queen's U DIPL

Communication systems
Cranfield IT MSc☆ □

Communications & signal processing
London U Imperial C MSc☆/dip☆

Communications engineering
Bradford U MSc☆/dip☆

Computer aided engineering
Coventry P MSc☆/dip☆

Computer based engineering systems
Dundee IT dip☆

Computing systems
Cranfield IT MSc☆ □

Control & information technology
Manchester UMIST MSc☆/dip☆ □

Control engineering
Bradford U MSc☆
Coventry P MSc△/dip△

Control systems
Cranfield IT MSc☆ □
London U Imperial C MSc/dip
Sheffield U MEng/MScTech

Control technology
Portsmouth P MSc△

Design of information systems
Royal Military C of Science MSc☆

Digital communication systems
Loughborough U MSc/dip □

Digital electronics (computers, communications & instrumentation)
London U King's C MSc☆

Digital systems
Brunel U MSc

Digital systems engineering
Manchester UMIST MSc☆

Digital techniques
Heriot-Watt U MSc/dip □

Digital techniques for information technology
Heriot-Watt U MSc☆/dip☆

Distributed & parallel systems
London U Queen Mary & Westfield C MSc

Electronic control engineering
Salford U MSc/dip△

Electronic design
Cranfield IT MSc☆ □

Electronic engineering
Cardiff U of Wales C MSc☆/ dip☆ □

Electronics
Southampton U MSc □

Electronics & communication engineering
Bradford U dip☆

Electronics & computer technology
Central London P dip△

Energy systems & environmental management
Glasgow C MSc☆/dip☆ *Env*

Engineering of dynamic systems
East London P MSc△

Fifth generation computing systems
St Andrews U MSc

Geographic information systems
Silsoe C dip☆

Geographical information systems
Leicester U MSc☆/dip☆

Guided weapon systems
Royal Military C of Science
MSc☆/dip☆

Gun systems design
Royal Military C of Science
MSc☆

Industrial measurement systems
Brunel U MSc

Industrial systems
Bath U MSc☆

Information & communication technologies
Sussex U MSc

Information engineering
City U MSc/dip

Information systems
Brighton P MSc☆/dip☆
East London P MSc
Portsmouth P MSc☆/dip☆

Information systems engineering
Manchester UMIST MSc☆
South Bank P MSc/dip

Information technology
Kingston P MSc☆
Sheffield U MSc(Eng)/MSc(Tech)

Information technology for non electrical graduates
Heriot-Watt U MSc☆/dip☆   *Comp*

Manufacturing systems (logistics in manufacturing)
Birmingham P MSc△   ☐

Manufacturing systems engineering
Bradford U MSc☆/dip☆
Dundee IT dip☆
Hatfield P MSc☆/dip☆
Wales P dip

Maritime defence technology
Royal Naval Engineering C
MSc☆/dip☆

Mathematics of modern control systems
Loughborough U MSc☆

Microelectronic & information engineering
Liverpool P MSc☆/dip☆

Microelectronic systems & telecommunications
Liverpool U MEng△/MSc(Eng)☆

Microelectronics system design
Southampton U MSc   ☐

Microwaves & optoelectronics
London U UC MSc/dip   ☐

Military electronic systems engineering
Royal Military C of Science
MSc☆

Optoelectronic & laser devices
Heriot-Watt U MSc

Optoelectronic devices & systems
Glasgow U MSc/dip

Power electronics engineering
Loughborough U MSc/dip   ☐

Public health & environmental engineering
Strathclyde U MSc/dip

Radio frequency & communications engineering
Bradford U MSc☆/dip☆

Radio frequency & microwave engineering
Bradford U MSc☆/dip☆

Reaction & separation systems
Manchester UMIST MSc☆

Real-time electronic systems
Bradford U MSc☆/dip☆

Robotics - systems & applications
Coventry P MSc/dip

Satellite communication engineering
Surrey U MSc/dip

Satellite communications
London U UC MSc☆

Signal processing
London U Imperial C MSc/dip☆
Portsmouth P MSc△

Spacecraft technology
London U UC MSc☆

Systems engineering
Cardiff U of Wales C MSc   ☐

Systems engineering (automatic control & computer engineering)
Surrey U MSc/dip

Telecommunication & information systems
Essex U MSc

Telecommunications technology
Aston U MSc☆/dip☆   ☐

Telematics
Surrey U MSc/dip

Theoretical foundations for software engineering
Central London P MSc△

Higher degrees by research

Applied computing & mathematics
Cranfield IT PhD☆/MPhil☆/MSc☆

Artificial intelligence & expert systems
Wessex IT PhD☆/MPhil☆

Chemical & process engineering
Newcastle U PhD/MPhil☆/
MSc△   ☐

Civil engineering
Leeds U MSc(Eng)☆

Communication engineering
South West P PhD/MPhil

Communication systems
Cranfield IT PhD☆   ☐

Computer & communication engineering
Teesside P PhD☆/MPhil☆

Computing
Brighton P PhD/MPhil

Control & system dynamics
Oxford U DPhil☆/MSc☆

Control engineering
Bradford U PhD/MPhil
City U PhD/MPhil
Royal Naval Engineering C
PhD☆/MSc☆
Sheffield U PhD/MPhil

Control systems
Manchester UMIST PhD/MSc
Warwick U PhD/MSc

Control theory
Warwick U PhD☆/MSc☆

Cryogenics
Southampton U PhD/MPhil

Cybernetics
Reading U PhD/MPhil   ☐

Digital systems engineering
Sunderland P PhD☆/MPhil☆

Dynamics
Sussex U DPhil/MPhil

Dynamics & control
Strathclyde U PhD☆/MPhil☆/
MSc☆

Electrical & electronic engineering
Bath U PhD/MSc   ☐
Swansea UC PhD/MPhil   ☐

Electrical engineering
London U Imperial C PhD/MPhil/
dip

UNIVERSITY OF WALES
CARDIFF

MECHANICAL ENGINEERING

MSc in Energy

Taught one year full time course, aimed at the graduate who wishes to know how industry can efficiently utilise energy. The course is based on teaching by internationally recognised experts. Funding available for selected EEC residents.

MPhil/PhD in Mechanical Engineering

Wide range of subjects available; funding can be arranged for some areas.

For further details contact:
Dr. J. Brandon, School of Engineering,
University of Wales, College of Cardiff,
PO Box 917, Cardiff CF2 1XH
(Tel: 0222 874824)

ADVANCED CIVIL ENGINEERING AT LEEDS UNIVERSITY

● **MSc (Eng) CONSTRUCTION ENGINEERING**
Course Director: Professor A.R. Cusens. A full-time one year course or a part-time course (one day and one evening) over two years. It is primarily intended for Civil Engineers with practical experience who wish to extend their studies beyond the scope of a first degree in civil engineering, and to bring themselves up to date with the latest techniques. Students choose either Concrete or Management as their main field of study together with a series of additional options.

● **MSc (Eng) TRANSPORT PLANNING AND ENGINEERING**
Course Director: Professor A.D. May. A full-time one year, or two year full- or part-time course for graduates in engineering, geography, economics and the sciences. Students are trained for careers in transport planning, analysis, design, management and operation. Four compulsory courses cover transport planning and policy, transport engineering, analytical methods, and computing. Students choose from fourteen options which cover all aspects of land-based transport.

● **MSc (Eng) TROPICAL PUBLIC HEALTH ENGINEERING**
Course Director: Professor D.D. Mara. A full-time course (one year for first and second class honours graduates, two years for others) suitable for engineers working, or intending to work, in tropical countries. It covers low-cost water supply and wastewater engineering, irrigation, sociocultural aspects, development planning, project appraisal and management.

FURTHER INFORMATION MAY BE OBTAINED FROM THE POSTGRADUATE TUTOR, DEPARTMENT OF CIVIL ENGINEERING, UNIVERSITY OF LEEDS LS2 9JT.
Telephone LEEDS (0532) 332269.

ASTON UNIVERSITY
Department of Civil Engineering

The Department of Civil Engineering has a large active post-graduate research school, working with the most up-to-date equipment. Much of the work is interdisciplinary, with graduates from a wide range of backgrounds. The research is supported by research councils, government departments and industry.

Opportunities exist for graduates with good honours degree qualifications in civil engineering and a number of other subjects such as: chemistry, computer science, geography, geology, materials, mathematics and physics to pursue research leading to a PhD or an MPhil.

There are two major research groups in the department.

Materials: Chemistry and technology of cements, Durability of reinforced concrete, Corrosion and protection of metals, Fire behaviour of structural materials, Exploitation of waste materials, Soil freezing phenomena, Computer simulation of the behaviour of particulate materials.

Systems and Remote Sensing: Water resources and hydrology, Applications of remote sensing to water resources, land resources and civil engineering; Development of software for image processing; Artificial intelligence and expert systems in engineering; the movement of soil moisture.

Individual research is also carried out in the fields of structural design, construction methods and management and transport planning.

SERC CASE awards are available in the department for suitably qualified candidates.

Further information may be obtained from the postgraduate admissions tutor:
Dr. C. Thornton, Department of Civil Engineering,
ASTON UNIVERSITY
Aston Triangle, Birmingham B4 7ET. (Phone: 021-359 3611 Ext. 4364) (Fax: 021 333 3389)

Electrical engineering & electronics
Manchester UMIST PhD/MSc

Electronic & communications engineering
Leeds P PhD/MPhil/dip
North London P PhD/MPhil

Electronic & electrical engineering
Sheffield U PhD/MPhil ☐

Electronic engineering
Hull U PhD/MSc
Kent U PhD/MPhil/MSc

Electronic engineering & computer science
Sussex U DPhil/MPhil ☐

Electronic systems
Cranfield IT PhD☆/MSc☆

Electronic systems engineering
Essex U PhD/MPhil/MSc
Kingston P PhD/MPhil

Electronics
East Anglia U PhD/MSc
Warwick U PhD☆/MPhil☆/MSc☆
York U DPhil/MPhil

Electronics & computer science
Southampton U PhD/MPhil ☐

Engineering
Bath U PhD/MSc
Lancaster U PhD/MPhil
Leicester U PhD/MPhil

Engineering & technology
Wolverhampton P PhD☆/MPhil☆

Engineering systems
Liverpool U PhD/MSc(Eng)

Fault detection & supervisory control
Manchester UMIST PhD/MSc

Industrial systems & control
Hatfield P PhD/MPhil

Information & communication technologies
Sussex U DPhil/MPhil

Information engineering
City U PhD/MPhil

Information systems
East Anglia U PhD☆/MPhil☆/ MSc☆
Leeds P PhD/MPhil/dip

Information systems analysis
Bradford U PhD/MPhil

Information systems design
Kingston P PhD/MPhil

Instrumentation & control engineering
Teesside P PhD☆/MPhil☆

Manufacturing systems
Central London P PhD☆/MSc☆
Coventry P PhD/MPhil

Maufacturing systems engineering
Hatfield P PhD/MPhil

Mechanical & manufacturing systems engineering
Cardiff U of Wales C PhD/MPhil

Mechanics & power
Royal Naval Engineering C
PhD☆/MSc☆

Microelectronic systems applications
Central London P PhD☆/MPhil☆

Optoelectronics
Newcastle P PhD☆/MSc☆

Parallel distributed processing
Manchester UMIST PhD/MSc

Process engineering
Surrey U PhD/MPhil

Robotics
Lancashire P PhD/MPhil

Systems
Central London P PhD☆/MPhil☆
Open U PhD/MPhil/BPhil

Systems & computing studies
East London P PhD/MPhil

Systems & control engineering
Coventry P PhD/MPhil

Systems control
Brunel U PhD/MSc/dip

Systems information
Lancaster U PhD/MPhil

Systems science
City U PhD/MPhil

Telecommunications systems
Anglia HEC PhD☆/MPhil☆

Weapon engineering
Royal Naval Engineering C
PhD☆/MSc☆

Construction, building services engineering

Higher degrees by instruction

Advanced building technology
Manchester UMIST MSc△

Advanced structural engineering
Southampton U MSc☆/dip☆

Building economics & management
London U UC MSc

Building engineering (structures)
Edinburgh U MSc/dip

Building management & economics
Lancashire P dip☆

Building services engineering
Brunel U MSc
Glasgow U MSc/dip△
Heriot-Watt U MSc/dip

Building technology & management
Newcastle P dip☆

Computer aided building design
Strathclyde U MSc/dip

Concrete structures
London U Imperial C MSc/dip

Concrete technology & construction
Dundee U MSc☆

Concrete technology, construction & management
Dundee U MSc☆

Construction
Loughborough U MSc☆

Construction engineering
Leeds U MSc(Eng)

Construction management
Bath U MSc ☐
Birmingham U MSc(Eng)
Dundee U MSc☆
Glasgow C of Building & Printing
dip☆
Loughborough U MSc
Reading U MSc☆
South Bank P MSc

Strathclyde U MSc/dip
Ulster U MSc☆/cert△/dip☆

**Construction management
(building maitainance)**
Heriot-Watt U MSc/dip ☐

**Construction management
(corporate strategy)**
Heriot-Watt U MSc/dip ☐

**Construction management
(production management)**
Heriot-Watt U MSc/dip ☐

**Construction management
(project management)**
Heriot-Watt U MSc/dip ☐

**Construction project
management**
Manchester UMIST MSc☆

Energy & buildings
Cranfield IT MSc☆ ☐

Energy efficient building design
Cranfield IT MSc☆/DipIng☆

Engineering
Cambridge U cert☆

Engineering design of buildings
Paisley CT MSc/dip

Environmental engineering
South Bank P MSc/dip

Fire engineering
Edinburgh U MSc/dip

**Management & economics for
construction & design**
Bristol P MSc

Mechanical engineering
Bristol U PhD☆/MSc☆

Modular studies
Heriot-Watt U MSc/dip

**Non destructive testing of
materials**
Brunel U MSc☆

**Production of the built
environment**
London U UC MSc

Road safety engineering
Middlesex P MSc△

Soil mechanics
London U Imperial C MSc/dip

**Soil mechanics & engineering
seismology**
London U Imperial C MSc/dip

Structural engineering
Liverpool U MSc(Eng)☆
Surrey U MSc/dip

Structural steel design
London U Imperial C MSc/dip

Technical science
Manchester UMIST dip☆

**Transport planning &
engineering**
Leeds U MSc(Eng)

**Tropical public health
engineering**
Leeds U MSc(Eng)☆

Urban engineering
South Bank P MSc☆/dip☆

Higher degrees by research

**Agricultural engineering &
buildings**
Aberdeen U PhD☆/MPhil☆/MSc☆

Architecture
Dundee U PhD/MSc   *Env*
Manchester U PhD/MPhil

Architecture & building science
Strathclyde U PhD☆/MArch☆/
MSc☆

**Architecture, design &
construction**
Huddersfield P PhD/MPhil

Building
Brighton P PhD/MPhil
Central London P PhD☆/MPhil☆
Heriot-Watt U PhD☆/MPhil☆
Ulster U DPhil/MPhil

Building & civil engineering
Liverpool P PhD/MPhil

Building & engineering
Manchester UMIST PhD/MSc

Building & environmental health
Nottingham P PhD☆/MPhil☆

Building & surveying
Napier P PhD/MPhil

Building economics
South Bank P PhD/MPhil

Building engineering
Liverpool U PhD/MSc(Eng)

Building science
Sheffield U PhD/MPhil

Building services engineering
Glasgow U PhD/MSc

**Building technology &
management**
Bristol P PhD/MPhil/cert/dip

Built environment studies
Anglia HEC PhD☆/MPhil☆
Central London P PhD☆/MPhil☆

Civil & municipal engineering
London U UC PhD☆/MPhil☆

Civil & structural engineering
Sussex U DPhil/MPhil ☐

**Civil & structural engineering &
building**
Teesside P PhD☆

Civil engineering
Leeds U PhD/MPhil/MSc(Eng)
Surrey U PhD/MPhil
Warwick U PhD/MSc

Civil engineering & building
Coventry P PhD/MPhil
Wales P PhD/MPhil ☐

Civil engineering & construction
Aston U PhD/MPhil

**Civil engineering, building &
cartography**
Oxford P PhD/MPhil

Combined engineering
Coventry P PhD/MPhil

Construction
Sheffield City P PhD/MPhil

Construction & building services
Newcastle P PhD☆/MPhil☆

**Construction & environmental
health**
Bristol P PhD/MPhil/cert/dip

Construction & surveying
Anglia HEC PhD☆/MPhil☆
Birmingham P PhD/MPhil
Lancashire P PhD/MPhil

**Construction law & project
management**
London U King's C PhD☆/MPhil☆

Construction management
Reading U PhD/MPhil

Construction practice
Anglia HEC PhD☆/MPhil☆

Construction studies
Wolverhampton P PhD/MPhil

Constructional studies
Leeds P PhD/MPhil/dip

**Design of energy efficient
buildings**
Cranfield IT PhD☆/MPhil☆

Engineering
Cambridge U PhD☆/MSc☆
Manchester U PhD/MSc
Reading U PhD/MPhil
Surrey U PhD/MPhil

Engineering science
Open U PhD/MPhil/BPhil

**Engineering science & industrial
management**
Liverpool U PhD/MSc(Eng)

Farm building
Aberdeen SAg PhD☆/MSc☆

Department of Electrical Engineering

ADVANCED COURSES
*Communications and Signal Processing (MSc/DIC; Full time, one year;
Part time, two years).
Further details: Dr AK Nandi.

* Control Systems (MSc/DIC; Full time, one year; Part-time, two years).
Further details: Professor MHA Davis

Electrical Power Systems (MSc; Part time, two to four years).
Further details: Dr BJ Cory.

*The SERC accepts this course for tenure of its Advanced Course
Studentships.

RESEARCH
We welcome enquiries from suitably qualified students wanting to pursue
research leading to the award of MPhil or PhD degrees in any of the
following areas:

Biomedical Systems
Computer Aided Design
Computer Vision Systems
Control Systems
Digital Communications
Electrical Machines
Electrical Power Systems
Electromagnetics CAD
Information Engineering
Microelectronics Applications
Neural System Engineering
Optimization and System Theory
Optical & Semiconductor Devices
Energy Economics and Power
   Systems
Signal Processing
Solid State Electronics
Thin Film Devices
VLSI Design and Architecture

Science and Engineering Research Council Studentships
are available to eligible applicants.

**Further details may be obtained from
Professor I Aleksander,
Head of Department of Electrical Engineering,
Imperial College of Science, Technology and Medicine,
London SW7 2BT.**

Farm buildings
West of Scotland C PhD☆/MSc☆

Farm mechanisation
Aberdeen SAg PhD☆/MSc☆

Fire safety engineering
Edinburgh U PhD/MPhil

Glasshouse investigation/soil science
West of Scotland C PhD☆/MSc☆

Land & building studies
Leicester P PhD/MPhil

Mechanical engineering
Bristol U PhD/MSc ☐

Power engineering
Newcastle P PhD☆/MPhil☆

Surveying & building
Dundee IT PhD/MPhil

Electrical engineering

Higher degrees by instruction

Advanced electronic control engineering studies
Salford U dip△

Building services engineering
Brunel U MSc

Communications & signal processing
London U Imperial C MSc☆/dip☆

Control & information technology
Manchester UMIST MSc☆/dip☆ ☐

Control systems
London U Imperial C MSc/dip

Design of energy efficient systems
Cranfield IT MSc☆/dip☆

Digital communication systems
Loughborough U MSc/dip ☐

Digital systems
Hatfield P MSc☆/dip

Digital techniques
Heriot-Watt U MSc/dip ☐

Digital techniques for information technology
Heriot-Watt U MSc☆/dip☆

Electrical & electromagnetic engineering
Cardiff U of Wales C MSc/dip ☐

Electrical & electronic engineering
Bell CT cert☆
Bradford U dip☆

Electrical engineering
Dundee U dip☆
Essex U MSc☆
London U Imperial C MSc△
London U King's C MSc△

Electrical power & control
Nottingham U MSc☆

Electrical power engineering
Aberdeen U MSc☆/dip☆
Heriot-Watt U MSc/dip
Leeds U MSc△
Manchester UMIST MSc☆
Newcastle U cert☆/dip☆
Strathclyde U MSc/dip ☐

Electrical power insulation engineering
Manchester UMIST MSc☆/dip☆

Electrical power system analysis
Manchester UMIST MSc☆/dip☆

Electrical power systems
London U Imperial C MSc△

Electrical power transmission & distribution
Manchester UMIST MSc☆/dip☆

Electronic engineering & microcomputer systems
Dundee U dip☆

Electronics & electrical engineering
Glasgow U dip☆

Engineering
Cambridge U cert☆

Engineering ceramics
Leeds U MSc☆

Engineering science (the science & applications of electric plasmas)
Oxford U MSc☆

Fire engineering
Edinburgh U MSc/dip

Information technology: design & manufacture of microelectronic systems
Edinburgh U MSc/dip

Integrated circuit system design
Manchester UMIST MSc☆/dip☆

Intelligent systems
South West P MSc

Laser engineering & pulsed power technology
St Andrews U MSc☆
Strathclyde U MSc☆

Microelectronic systems & telecommunications
Liverpool U MEng△/MSc(Eng)☆

Microelectronics systems design
Brunel U MSc

Microwave engineering
London U UC dip☆

Microwaves & optoelectronics
London U UC MSc/dip ☐

Modular studies
Heriot-Watt U MSc/dip

Optoelectronic devices & systems
Glasgow U MSc/dip

Physics & electronics
Lancaster U dip☆

Power electronics engineering
Loughborough U MSc/dip ☐

Radio frequency & microwave engineering
Bradford U MSc☆/dip☆

Robotics & computer integrated engineering
Middlesex P MSc☆/dip☆

Satellite communication engineering
Surrey U MSc/dip

Signal processing
Portsmouth P MSc△

Higher degrees by research

Applied electromagnetism
Liverpool U PhD/MSc(Eng)

Combined engineering
Coventry P PhD/MPhil

Control & electrical engineering
Sussex U DPhil/MPhil

Digital communication
Salford U PhD/MSc

Electrical & electronic engineering
Bath U PhD/MSc ☐
Belfast Queen's U PhD/MSc
Bradford U PhD/MPhil
Brighton P PhD/MPhil
Bristol U PhD☆/MSc☆
City U PhD/MPhil

Coventry P PhD/MPhil
Dundee IT PhD/MPhil
East London P PhD/MPhil
Glasgow U PhD/MEng
Hatfield P PhD/MPhil
Heriot-Watt U PhD☆/MPhil☆
Huddersfield P PhD/MPhil
Lancashire P PhD/MPhil
Leeds U PhD/MPhil/MSc(Eng)
Liverpool P PhD/MPhil
London U Queen Mary &
    Westfield C PhD☆/MPhil☆
Manchester P PhD/MPhil
Middlesex P PhD/MPhil
Napier P PhD/MPhil
Newcastle P PhD☆/MPhil☆
Newcastle U PhD/MPhil
Nottingham P PhD☆/MPhil☆
Nottingham U PhD/MPhil
Paisley CT PhD/MPhil
Portsmouth P PhD☆/MPhil☆
Robert Gordon's IT PhD/MPhil
Royal Naval Engineering C
    PhD☆/MSc☆
Sheffield City P PhD/MPhil
South Bank P PhD/MPhil
South West P PhD/MPhil☆/
    MPhil△
Staffordshire P PhD/MPhil
Swansea UC PhD/MPhil   □
Ulster U DPhil/MPhil
Wales P PhD☆/MPhil☆

**Electrical & electronic
engineering & applied physics**
Aston U PhD/MPhil

Electrical & electronic studies
Bolton IHE PhD/MSc

Electrical engineering
Aberdeen U PhD☆/MPhil☆/MSc☆
Liverpool U PhD/MSc(Eng)
London U Imperial C PhD/MPhil/
    dip
Manchester U PhD/MSc
Southampton U PhD/MPhil
Sunderland P PhD/MPhil
Warwick U PhD/MSc

**Electrical engineering &
electronics**
Brunel U PhD/MPhil
Dundee U PhD/MSc
Manchester UMIST PhD/MSc

**Electrical engineering &
microelectronics**
Edinburgh U PhD/MPhil

**Electrical engineering (total
technology)**
Bradford U PhD☆

Electrical engineering science
Essex U PhD/MPhil/MSc

**Electrical power & energy
systems**
City U PhD/MPhil

**Electronic & communications
engineering**
Leeds P PhD/MPhil/dip

**Electronic & electrical
engineering**
Birmingham P PhD/MPhil
Birmingham U PhD/MPhil(Eng)
Leicester P PhD/MPhil
London U King's C PhD☆/MPhil☆
London U UC PhD☆/MPhil☆
Loughborough U PhD☆/MPhil☆
Salford U PhD/MSc
Sheffield U PhD/MPhil   □
Strathclyde U PhD☆/MPhil☆/
    MSc☆
Surrey U PhD/MPhil

**Electronic engineering &
computer science**
Sussex U DPhil/MPhil   □

Electronic engineering science
Bangor, U of Wales PhD☆/
    MPhil☆

Electronic systems engineering
Essex U PhD/MPhil/MSc

Electronics
Kent U PhD☆/MPhil☆

Engineering
Aberdeen U PhD☆/MPhil☆/
    MSc☆   □
Bath U PhD/MSc
Cambridge U PhD☆/MSc☆
Durham U PhD/MSc
Manchester U PhD/MSc
Reading U PhD/MPhil
Surrey U PhD/MPhil
Thames P PhD/MPhil

Engineering & technology
Wolverhampton P PhD☆/MPhil☆

Engineering science
Open U PhD/MPhil/BPhil

**Engineering science & industrial
management**
Liverpool U PhD/MSc(Eng)

Fire safety engineering
Edinburgh U PhD/MPhil

High voltage engineering
City U PhD/MPhil

Instrumentation & automation
Salford U PhD/MSc

Marine engineering
Newcastle U PhD/MPhil

Measurement & instrumentation
City U PhD/MPhil

**Measurement & instrumentation
in medicine**
City U PhD/MPhil

Optical & nano-electronics
Glasgow U PhD☆   □

Power engineering
Newcastle P PhD☆/MPhil☆

Robotics & automated systems
London U Imperial C PhD/MPhil

Total technology
Manchester UMIST PhD/MSc

Electronic
engineering

Higher degrees by
instruction

**Advanced electronic control
engineering studies**
Salford U dip△

Advanced engineering materials
Liverpool U MSc(Eng)☆   □

**Advanced manufacturing
technology**
Liverpool P dip☆

Applied electronics
Newcastle U cert☆/dip☆

Applied optics
London U Imperial C MSc☆/
    dip☆   *Phy*

Aviation electronics
Cranfield IT MSc☆   □

Communication systems
Cranfield IT MSc☆   □

**Communications & signal
processing**
London U Imperial C MSc☆/dip☆

Computer aided engineering
Coventry P MSc☆/dip☆
Nottingham P MSc△/dip△

**Computer speech & language
processing**
Cambridge U MPhil☆   □ Lang,
                              Comp

Control systems
Cranfield IT MSc☆   □

Control technology
Portsmouth P MSc△

ASTON UNIVERSITY

Department of Electrical & Electronic Engineering & Applied Physics

PhD 3 years full time   MPhil 2 years full time

There are excellent facilities for research. Groups are:

INFORMATION TECHNOLOGY — Telecommunications, software engineering and programmable electronic systems. Special interests include digital communication with mobile terminals, systematic design of reliable fault tolerant distributed control systems, speech quality.

SOLID STATE ELECTRONICS — Electronic properties of surfaces; ion and fast atom spectroscopy; tribology; high voltage vacuum breakdown.

ELECTRIC POWER — power utilisation and supply; power electronics; systems; motor control; modelling.

Entrance requirements: Honours degree in engineering or relevant science.

Grants: SERC studentships and, for some projects, industrial and other support.

Research Admissions Tutor: Professor W.T. Norris.

**Department of Electrical & Electronic Engineering & Applied Physics,
Aston University, Aston Triangle, Birmingham B4 7ET.
Tel: 021 359 3611.**

LOUGHBOROUGH UNIVERSITY OF TECHNOLOGY

DEPARTMENT OF ELECTRONIC AND ELECTRICAL ENGINEERING — MSc COURSES

Each course consists of two terms devoted to lectures and tutorials and the third term and summer vacation to individual projects which may be carried out in industry subject to suitable arrangements. The lecture content consists of separate modules which may be taken on a Short Course basis. Both courses may also be taken part-time.

MSc IN DIGITAL COMMUNICATION SYSTEMS
Course content: Signal analysis; communication networks; communication theory; digital coding of speech and image signals; error-correcting codes; antennas and propagation; digital filters; digital modems; encryption and security; practical systems; satellite systems.

MSc IN POWER ELECTRONICS ENGINEERING (jointly with Bradford University)
Course content: Power device physics and characteristics; analogue and digital power circuitry; AC-DC conversion; AC load control and HVDC transmission; self-commutated converters; instrumentation, passive components, protection and cooling; control theory; power electronics control of electrical machines; microprocessor control in power electronics and drives. The first term is spent at Bradford University, the remainder at Loughborough. SERC studentships are available to qualified applicants.

Further details (please indicate course) from
Admissions Secretary, Department of Electronic and Electrical Engineering, University of Technology, Loughborough, Leics, LE11 3TU.

Design of energy efficient systems
Cranfield IT MSc☆/dip☆

Design of integrated systems
South Bank P MSc△

Digital communication systems
Loughborough U MSc/dip ☐

Digital electronics (computers, communications & instrumentation)
London U King's C MSc☆

Digital systems
Brunel U MSc
Hatfield P MSc☆/dip

Digital systems & instrumentation
Central London P MSc△

Digital techniques
Heriot-Watt U MSc/dip ☐

Digital techniques for information technology
Heriot-Watt U MSc☆/dip☆

Electrical & electronic engineering
Bell CT cert☆
Bradford U dip☆

Electrical engineering
Essex U MSc☆

Electrical power engineering
Heriot-Watt U MSc/dip

Electronic circuit design & manufacture
Dundee U MSc☆

Electronic control engineering
Salford U MSc/dip△

Electronic design
Cranfield IT MSc☆ ☐

Electronic engineering
Bangor, U of Wales MSc☆/dip☆
Cardiff U of Wales C MSc☆/ dip☆ ☐
Dundee U dip☆
Hull U MEng☆/dip☆

Electronic engineering & microcomputer systems
Dundee U dip☆

Electronic graphics
Coventry P MSc/dip

Electronic imaging
Duncan of Jordanstone CA dip☆

Electronic manufacture
Birmingham P dip☆

Electronics
Belfast Queen's U MSc
Durham U MSc☆

St Andrews U dip☆
Southampton U MSc ☐

Electronics & communication engineering
Bradford U dip☆

Electronics & computer technology
Central London P dip△

Electronics & electrical engineering
Glasgow U dip☆

Electronics systems design (aviation electronics)
Cranfield IT MSc

Electronics with computing applications
London U King's C dip☆

Engineering
Cambridge U cert☆

Engineering design for manufacture
Cranfield IT MSc☆

Fuel technology
Middlesex P dip

Information technology
London U Queen Mary & Westfield C MSc☆/dip☆ *Comp*

Information technology for non electrical graduates
Heriot-Watt U MSc☆/dip☆ *Comp*

Information technology: design & manufacture of microelectronic systems
Edinburgh U MSc/dip

Innovative design for manufacture of engineered products
Cranfield IT MSc☆

Intelligent systems
Brunel U MSc
South West P MSc

Medical electronics & physics
London U St Bartholomew's Hosp Med C MSc

Metallic & ceramic materials
Manchester UMIST MSc☆/dip☆

Microelectronic & information engineering
Liverpool P MSc☆/dip☆

Microelectronic materials & device technology
Manchester UMIST MSc☆

Microelectronic systems & telecommunications
Liverpool U MEng△/MSc(Eng)☆

Microelectronic technology & applications
Middlesex P MSc/dip

Microelectronics
Durham U MEng☆/MSc☆ ☐

Microelectronics & computer engineering
Surrey U MSc

Microelectronics & computer technology
Birmingham P dip☆

Microelectronics & microcomputer application
Ulster U dip△

Microelectronics system design
Southampton U MSc ☐

Microelectronics systems design
Brunel U MSc

Microprocessor engineering & digital electronics
Manchester UMIST MSc☆/dip☆

Microprocessor technology & applications
Brighton P MSc☆/dip☆ *Comp*

Microwave engineering
London U UC dip☆

Microwaves & optoelectronics
London U UC MSc/dip ☐

Military electronic systems engineering
Royal Military C of Science MSc☆

Modern electronics
Nottingham U MSc☆

Modular studies
Heriot-Watt U MSc/dip

Music information technology
City U dip

Music technology
York U MA☆/MSc☆/dip☆

Optical electronics
Strathclyde U MSc☆

Optoelectronic & laser devices
Heriot-Watt U MSc
St Andrews U MSc/dip☆ *Phy*

Optoelectronic devices & systems
Glasgow U MSc/dip

Optoelectronic technology
Kent U MSc

Optoelectronics
Heriot-Watt U dip☆
Newcastle P MSc☆/dip☆ ☐

Optoelectronics & optical information processing
Belfast Queen's U MSc/dip

Physics & technology of amorphous solids
Dundee U MSc☆

Power electronics engineering
Bradford U MSc☆/dip☆
Loughborough U MSc/dip ☐

Pulsed power technology
St Andrews U MSc/dip☆

Radio astronomy
Manchester U MSc☆/dip☆

Radio frequency & microwave engineering
Bradford U MSc☆/dip☆
Newcastle P MSc☆/dip☆

Real-time electronic systems
Bradford U MSc☆/dip☆

Robotics & computer integrated engineering
Middlesex P MSc☆/dip☆

Satellite communication engineering
Surrey U MSc/dip

Semiconductor science & technology
London U Imperial C MSc/
dip *Phy*

Signal processing
Portsmouth P MSc△

Surface science & technology
Loughborough U MSc

Systems engineering (automatic control & computer engineering)
Surrey U MSc/dip

Telecommunication & information systems
Essex U MSc

Telecommunications technology
Aston U MSc☆/dip☆ ☐

Telematics
Surrey U MSc/dip

Theoretical foundations for software engineering
Central London P MSc△

Tribology in machine design
Leeds U MSc(Eng)☆

Higher degrees by research

Applied physics & electronics
Durham U PhD/MSc

Applied physics & physical electronics
Portsmouth P PhD☆/MPhil☆

Aviation electronics
Cranfield IT PhD☆ ☐

Biomedical engineering
Sussex U DPhil/MPhil ☐

Combined engineering
Coventry P PhD/MPhil

Computing
Nottingham P PhD☆/MPhil☆

Control & electrical engineering
Sussex U DPhil/MPhil

Cybernetics
Reading U PhD/MPhil ☐

Digital communication
Salford U PhD/MSc

Electrical & electronic engineering
Bath U PhD/MSc ☐
Belfast Queen's U PhD/MSc
Bradford U PhD/MPhil
Brighton P PhD/MPhil
Bristol U PhD☆/MSc☆
City U PhD/MPhil
Coventry P PhD/MPhil
Dundee IT PhD/MPhil
East London P PhD/MPhil
Glasgow U PhD/MEng
Hatfield P PhD/MPhil
Heriot-Watt U PhD☆/MPhil☆
Huddersfield P PhD/MPhil
Lancashire P PhD/MPhil
Leeds U PhD/MPhil/MSc(Eng)
Liverpool P PhD/MPhil
London U Queen Mary &
Westfield C PhD☆/MPhil☆
Manchester P PhD/MPhil
Middlesex P PhD/MPhil
Napier P PhD/MPhil
Newcastle P PhD☆/MPhil☆
Newcastle U PhD/MPhil
Nottingham P PhD☆/MPhil☆
Nottingham U PhD/MPhil
Paisley CT PhD/MPhil
Portsmouth P PhD☆/MPhil☆
Robert Gordon's IT PhD/MPhil
Royal Naval Engineering C
PhD☆/MSC☆
Sheffield City P PhD/MPhil
South Bank P PhD/MPhil
South West P PhD/MPhil☆/
MPhil△
Staffordshire P PhD/MPhil
Swansea UC PhD/MPhil ☐
Ulster U DPhil/MPhil
Wales P PhD☆/MPhil☆

Electrical & electronic engineering & applied physics
Aston U PhD/MPhil

Electrical & electronic studies
Bolton IHE PhD/MSc

Electrical engineering
London U Imperial C PhD/MPhil/
dip
Manchester U PhD/MSc

Electrical engineering & electronics
Brunel U PhD/MPhil
Dundee U PhD/MSc
Manchester UMIST PhD/MSc

Electrical engineering & microelectronics
Edinburgh U PhD/MPhil

Electronic & communications engineering
North London P PhD/MPhil

Electronic & electrical engineering
Birmingham P PhD/MPhil
Birmingham U PhD/MPhil(Eng)
Leicester P PhD/MPhil
London U King's C PhD☆/MPhil☆
London U UC PhD☆/MPhil☆
Loughborough U PhD☆/MPhil☆
Salford U PhD/MSc
Sheffield U PhD/MPhil ☐
Strathclyde U PhD☆/MPhil☆/
MSc☆
Surrey U PhD/MPhil

Electronic engineering
Dorset Inst PhD/MPhil/dip
Hull U PhD/MSc
Kent U PhD/MPhil/MSc
Liverpool U PhD/MSc(Eng)
Oxford P PhD/MPhil
Sunderland P PhD/MPhil
West Glamorgan IHE PhD/MPhil

Electronic engineering & computer science
Sussex U DPhil/MPhil ☐

Electronic engineering science
Bangor, U of Wales PhD☆/
MPhil☆

Electronic instrumentation & on line computing
Newcastle U PhD/MSc

Electronic systems
Cranfield IT PhD☆/MSc☆

Electronic systems engineering
Essex U PhD/MPhil/MSc
Kingston P PhD/MPhil

Electronics
East Anglia U PhD/MSc
Keele U PhD/MSc

UNIVERSITY OF SURREY

DEPARTMENT OF ELECTRONIC & ELECTRICAL ENGINEERING

MSc Courses (Full-time or part-time)

Telematics
Satellite Communication Engineering
Signal Processing and Machine Intelligence

MSc by Advanced Course and Research

Microelectronics and Computer Engineering
Advanced Semiconductor Materials and
 Devices
Other areas related to courses shown

The courses benefit from the research strengths of the Department and involve a substantial element of project work. They are intended for new graduates wishing to specialise in one of the above areas and for older graduates in industry wishing to update their knowledge or convert to a new discipline. It is possible to attend selected parts of the courses as an occasional student. The duration of full-time courses is one academic year. Part-time courses require attendance on one day per week for two years. Financial support may be available for suitably qualified applicants.

For further information and application forms contact:

Postgraduate Admissions Secretary (MG1)
Department of Electronic & Electrical Engineering, University of Surrey,
GUILDFORD GU2 5XH. Telephone 0483 509272

*T*HE UNIVERSITY
OF BIRMINGHAM

SCHOOL of
ELECTRONIC and ELECTRICAL ENGINEERING

RESEARCH OPPORTUNITIES LEADING TO MPhil(Eng) and PhD degrees exist in:

- *Acoustics and Sonar*
- *Communications, Optics and Propagation*
- *Image Processing*
- *Information Technology*
- *Estimation and Control*

- *Drives, Power and Traction Systems*
- *Communication Systems*
- *Radar and Remote Sensing*
- *Solid State Devices*
- *Superconductivity*

FINANCIAL SUPPORT SERC CASE awards and other Studentships available for candidates possessing a class 1 or 2(i) Honours degree. Overseas Research Studentships may be available.

THE SCHOOL 33 academic staff. 25 research staff. 55 research students. 450 undergraduate students plus 50 technical and secretarial staff. Current research income exceeds £2,000,000, one third of which comes directly from industry. Three Wolfson Units interface research work into UK industry.

For further information please write to the School Postgraduate Admissions Tutor, Dr T S M Maclean, School of Electronic and Electrical Engineering, University of Birmingham, PO Box 363, Birmingham B15 2TT. Telephone: 021 414 4294/4300.

Kent U PhD☆/MPhil☆
Open U PhD/MPhil/BPhil
St Andrews U PhD☆/MSc☆
Warwick U PhD☆/MPhil☆/MSc☆
York U DPhil/MPhil

Electronics & computer science
Southampton U PhD/MPhil ☐

Engineering
Bath U PhD/MSc
Cambridge U PhD☆/MSc☆
Lancaster U PhD/MPhil
Manchester U PhD/MSc
Reading U PhD/MPhil
Surrey U PhD/MPhil
Thames P PhD/MPhil

Engineering & technology
Wolverhampton P PhD☆/MPhil☆

Engineering science
Open U PhD/MPhil/BPhil

Engineering science & industrial management
Liverpool U PhD/MSc(Eng)

Information systems
East Anglia U PhD☆/MPhil☆/MSc☆

Instrumentation & automation
Salford U PhD/MSc

Manufacturing systems
Central London P PhD☆/MSc☆

Materials engineering
Swansea UC PhD/MPhil ☐

Materials science & engineering
Liverpool U PhD/MSc(Eng) ☐

Medical electronics & physics
London U St Bartholomew's Hosp Med C PhD/MPhil

Metallurgy & materials science
Liverpool U PhD/MSc(Eng)

Microelectronic systems applications
Central London P PhD☆/MPhil☆

Microelectronics
Middlesex P PhD/MPhil

Microelectronics applications research
Newcastle U PhD/MSc

Optical & nano-electronics
Glasgow U PhD☆ ☐

Optoelectronics
Newcastle P PhD☆/MSc☆

Opto-electronics & optical information processing
Kent U PhD☆/MPhil☆

Physical electronics
Oxford U DPhil☆/MSc☆

Physics
Keele U PhD☆/MSc☆

Power engineering
Newcastle P PhD☆/MPhil☆

Signal processing
Central London P PhD☆/MPhil☆
Kent U PhD☆/MPhil☆

Signal processing & electronics
Royal Naval Engineering C PhD☆/MSc☆

Fuel science, energy studies, nuclear engineering

Higher degrees by instruction

Aerospace propulsion
Cranfield IT MSc☆

Alternative energy for developing countries
Reading U MSc☆/dip☆

Applied energy studies
Cranfield IT MSc☆/dip☆ ☐

Applied radiation physics
Birmingham U MSc☆ Phy

Chemical engineering
Teesside P BEng☆

Combustion & energy
Leeds U MSc☆

Combustion & fuels
Cranfield IT MSc☆

Design of energy efficient systems
Cranfield IT MSc☆/dip☆

Design of thermo-fluid systems
Swansea UC MSc☆

Economics of energy & development
Surrey U dip☆

Electrical power engineering
Strathclyde U MSc/dip ☐

Electrical power systems
London U Imperial C MSc△

Energy
Cardiff U of Wales C MSc☆

Energy & development
Surrey U MSc/dip

Energy conservation & the environment
Cranfield IT MSc☆ ☐

Energy economics
Surrey U MSc

Energy efficient building design
Cranfield IT MSc☆/DipIng☆

Energy engineering
Leeds U dip☆

Energy resources management
South Bank P MSc△/dip△

Environment & energy studies
Architectural Association S of Architecture dip☆

Energy studies
Sussex U MSc☆

Energy systems & environmental management
Glasgow C MSc☆/dip☆ Env

Energy technology for developing countries
Salford U MSc☆/dip☆

Environmental pollution control
Leeds U MSc☆

Environmental technology
London U Imperial C MSc☆/dip☆

Fire engineering
Edinburgh U MSc/dip

Fuel technology
Middlesex P dip

Nuclear reactor science & engineering
London U Queen Mary & Westfield C MSc/dip

Petroleum engineering
Heriot-Watt U MEng
London U Imperial C MSc☆/dip☆

Petroleum geology
Aberdeen U MSc☆
London U Imperial C MSc☆/dip☆

Petroleum technology & management systems
Brunel U MSc☆

Physics & technology of nuclear reactors
Birmingham U MSc Phy

Physics of energy resources
Salford U MSc△

Power generation
London U Queen Mary & Westfield C MSc☆

Power plants & energy related studies
Liverpool U MSc(Eng)☆

Propulsion & power
Cranfield IT MSc☆/dip☆

Renewable energy & the environment
Reading U MSc☆

Solar energy & energy conservation in buildings
Reading U MSc☆

Thermal energy engineering
Middlesex P MSc

Thermal energy processes
Cranfield IT MSc ☐

Thermal power & fluids engineering
Manchester UMIST MSc☆/dip☆

Higher degrees by research

Aerodynamics & thermodynamics
Bath U PhD☆/MSc☆

Chemical & process engineering
Newcastle U PhD/MPhil☆/
MSc△ ☐

Chemical engineering
Surrey U PhD/MPhil ☐

Chemical engineering & fuel technology
Sheffield U PhD/MPhil☆

Combustion & energy studies
Leeds U PhD/MPhil/MSc(Eng)

Cryogenic engineering
Oxford U DPhil☆/MSc☆

Design of energy efficient buildings
Cranfield IT PhD☆/MPhil☆

Energy & environment research
Open U PhD☆/MPhil☆/BPhil☆

Energy engineering
Surrey U PhD/MPhil

Energy management
Cranfield IT MPhil☆/MSc☆

Energy research
Ulster U DPhil/MPhil

Energy studies
Architectural Association S of
Architecture PhD☆/MPhil☆
Middlesex P PhD/MPhil
South Bank P PhD/MPhil
Strathclyde U PhD☆/MPhil☆/
MSc☆
Sussex U DPhil/MPhil

Engineering
Reading U PhD/MPhil

Fire safety engineering
Edinburgh U PhD/MPhil

Fuel & energy
Leeds U PhD/MPhil/MSc(Eng)/
MSc ☐

Fusion studies
London U Imperial C PhD/MPhil

Gas dynamics including combustion
Cranfield IT PhD☆/MSc☆

Heat transfer & thermodynamics
Oxford U DPhil☆/MSc☆

Industrial technology
Bradford U PhD/MPhil

Materials & energy science
Coventry P PhD/MPhil

Mechanical engineering
Leeds U PhD☆/MSc(Eng)☆ ☐
London U Imperial C PhD/MPhil/
dip
Newcastle U PhD/MPhil

Mechanical engineering & energy studies
Cardiff U of Wales C PhD☆/
MPhil☆

Mining
Wales P PhD☆/MPhil☆

Mining & minerals engineering
Cardiff U of Wales C PhD☆/
MPhil☆

Nuclear engineering
London U Queen Mary &
Westfield C PhD☆/MPhil☆
Manchester U PhD/MSc

Petroleum & mineral law studies
Dundee U PhD/LLM

Petroleum engineering
Heriot-Watt U PhD☆/MPhil☆ ☐

Reactor research
London U Imperial C PhD/MPhil

Science & technology studies
Manchester U PhD/MSc

Thermo fluids engineering
City U PhD/MPhil

Thermodynamics
Glasgow U PhD/MSc

Industrial, engineering design

Higher degrees by instruction

Advanced engineering design
Huddersfield P MSc☆/dip☆

Advanced manufacturing systems
Brunel U MSc ☐

Advanced robotics
Salford U MSc☆

Aerospace vehicle design
Cranfield IT MSc☆

Automotive engine & vehicle design technology
Southampton U MSc☆/cert☆/
dip☆

Bridge engineering
Surrey U MSc/dip

Computer aided design & manufacture of production machines & systems
Cranfield IT MSc☆

Computer aided engineering
Coventry P MSc☆/dip☆
Paisley CT dip☆

Computer based engineering systems
Dundee IT dip☆

Computer related industrial design
Royal CA MDes☆

Computer-aided engineering design
Strathclyde U MSc

Design
Liverpool U MDes☆

Design & economic manufacture
Swansea UC MSc☆

Design manufacture & management
Lancaster U MA

Design of energy efficient systems
Cranfield IT MSc☆/dip☆

Design of equipment for disability
London C of Furniture dip☆

Design of information systems
Royal Military C of Science
MSc☆

Design of integrated systems
South Bank P MSc△

Design research for disability
London C of Furniture MA

Design systems in production
Warwick U MSc

Digital systems
Hatfield P MSc☆/dip

Digital systems & instrumentation
Central London P MSc△

Engineering design for manufacture
Cranfield IT MSc☆

Ergonomics
Loughborough U MSc

Finite element method in stress and vibration analysis
Cranfield IT MSc☆   □

Fluid power technology
Bath U MSc☆/dip☆

Gun systems design
Royal Military C of Science
MSc☆

Industrial design
Birmingham P MA/dip
Glasgow SA dip☆
Manchester P MA☆
Royal CA MDes☆

Industrial design engineering
Central St Martins CAD MA☆
Leicester P MA☆
London U Imperial C MDes☆/
dip☆
Royal CA MDes☆

Industrial design for engineers
Teesside P MA☆

Industrial robotics & manufacturing automation
London U Imperial C MSc☆/
dip☆   □

Information technology
Ulster U MSc

Innovative design for manufacture of engineered products
Cranfield IT MSc☆

Instrument design
Aberdeen U MSc☆

Instrument design & application
Manchester U MSc☆/dip☆
Manchester UMIST MSc☆/dip☆

Instrumental methods of analysis
Strathclyde U MSc/dip☆

Integrated design of chemical plant
Leeds U MSc

Intelligent knowledge based systems in manufacturing
Cranfield IT MSc☆

Machine condition monitoring
Swansea UC MSc☆

Machine design
Cranfield IT MSc☆   □

Manufacturing systems engineering
Cranfield IT MSc☆   □
Warwick U MSc

Mechanical engineering
Strathclyde U MSc/dip   □

Metal manufacturing technology
Swansea UC MSc☆

Music information technology
City U dip

Noise & vibration of rotating machines & gas turbines
Cranfield IT MSc☆   □

Process plant materials engineering
Cranfield IT MSc☆

Software techniques for computer aided engineering
Cranfield IT MSc   Comp

Structural design
Cranfield IT MSc☆

System design
Manchester U MSc☆/dip☆

Three dimensional computer aided graphical technology applications
Teesside P MSc☆

Urban engineering
South Bank P MSc☆/dip☆

Vehicle design
Royal CA MDes☆

Higher degrees by research

CAD for VLSI
Kent U PhD☆/MPhil☆

Ceramic technology
Staffordshire P PhD/MPhil

Computer aided design
Ulster U DPhil/MPhil

Computing & information technology
Wolverhampton P PhD/MPhil

Design
Napier P PhD/MPhil
Open U PhD/MPhil/BPhil
Ulster U DPhil/MPhil

Design & technology
Brunel U PhD/MPhil

Electronic systems
Cranfield IT PhD☆/MSc☆

Engineering
Durham U PhD/MSc
Lancaster U PhD/MPhil

Engineering design
Loughborough U PhD/MPhil

Engineering design & drawing
Strathclyde U PhD☆/MPhil☆/
MSc☆

Engineering design & manufacture
Hull U PhD/MSc

Engineering design & production
Liverpool U PhD/MSc(Eng)

Engineering design for manufacture
Cranfield IT PhD☆

Fluid engineering & instrumentation
Cranfield IT PhD☆/MPhil☆/MSc☆

Industrial & geophysical fluid dynamics
Exeter U PhD/MPhil

Industrial design
Coventry P PhD/MPhil
Leicester P PhD/MPhil
Newcastle P PhD☆/MPhil☆
Royal CA PhD☆

Industrial design engineering
Central St Martins CAD PhD△/
MPhil△

Machinery design & manufacture
Silsoe C PhD/MPhil

Manufacturing engineering
Warwick U PhD

Mathematics & physics
Manchester P PhD/MPhil   Math

Mechanical & industrial engineering
Napier P PhD/MPhil

Mechanical engineering
Leeds U PhD△/MPhil/
MSc(Eng)△   □
London U Imperial C PhD/MPhil/
dip

School of
Mechanical Engineering

Cranfield
BRITAIN'S UNIQUE UNIVERSITY

MSc Courses

The School of Mechanical Engineering is one of the largest Departments of the Cranfield Institute of Technology, a unique university offering postgraduate degrees in advanced technology, applied science and management.

MSc Courses offered of 1 or 2 years study include :

- Energy Conservation and the Environment
- Energy and Buildings
- Thermal-Energy Processes
- Automotive Product Engineering
- Thermal Power with options in Aerospace Propulsion

  Combustion and Fuels

  Gas Turbine Technology

- Rotating Machinery Engineering and Management
- Noise and Vibration in Rotating Machines
- Machine Design
- Engineering Mechanics
- Finite-element Stress and Vibration Analysis
- Software Techniques for Computer-Aided Engineering
- Digital Image Processing

Excellent facilities are also available for those wishing to study for an MPhil/PhD degree by research in ENERGY, POWER, PROPULSION, MECHANICAL INTEGRITY, TURBOMACHINERY, INDUSTRIAL FLUID MECHANICS, COMPUTER AIDED ENGINEERING and OPTICAL SENSOR TECHNOLOGY.

●　　　　●　　　　●　　　　●

An Engineering Career in Europe

The School of Mechanical Engineering offers two-year DOUBLE DEGREE COURSES leading to the coveted DIPLÔME d'INGÉNIEUR in addition to MASTER OF SCIENCE degrees at the following Universities:

Université de Technologie de Compiègne, France: **Energy Studies**

Ecole Supérieure d'Ingénieurs de Marseille: **Design of Energy Efficient Systems** or **Thermal Energy Processes**

Ecole Supérieure d'Ingénieurs de Constructions Aéronautiques, Toulouse:

Propulsion and Power

Université de Liège, Belgium: **Propulsion and Power** or **Engineering Mechanics**

The first year of these Double Degree Courses is spent at one of the Continental universities and the second at Cranfield, England.

Double-degree holders can practice throughout Western Europe: they are truly **EUROPEAN ENGINEERS**, ready to take their full part in the integrated Europe of 1992.

Entry qualifications: A British university first or second class honours degree in an engineering/science subject, with some relevant experience in industry. Language tuition will be provided at the start of the course, but a knowledge of French is desirable.

Final selection will take place in May, for courses starting in Autumn 1991.

Financial assistance may be available within the framework of the EEC's ERASMUS Programme, or via the Science and Engineering Research Council, or by means of an industrial bursary.

Further particulars may be obtained from Mr J. R. Jammes (Ref 2143) for the 'Double-Degree' course or The Administrator (Ref 2142) for the MSc Course in the School of Mechanical Engineering, Cranfield Institute of Technology, Cranfield, Bedford MK43 0AL. Tel: 0234 750111 ext 2716.

Warwick U PhD/MSc

Mechanical, marine & production engineering
Liverpool P PhD☆/MPhil☆

Metallurgy & materials engineering
Swansea UC PhD/MPhil

Physics
Aberdeen U PhD☆/MPhil☆/MSc☆

Production engineering & design
Oxford U DPhil☆/MSc☆

Vehicle design
Royal CA PhD☆

Mechanical engineering

Higher degrees by instruction

Advanced chemical engineering
London U Imperial C MSc☆/dip☆

Advanced engineering materials
Liverpool U MSc(Eng)☆   ☐

Advanced manufacturing systems & technology
Liverpool U MSc(Eng)   ☐

Advanced manufacturing technology
Liverpool P dip☆
Manchester UMIST MSc☆/dip☆
Portsmouth P MSc/dip
Staffordshire P cert☆   ☐

Advanced mechanical engineering
London U Imperial C MSc/dip

Aerospace propulsion
Cranfield IT MSc☆

Aerospace vehicle design
Cranfield IT MSc☆

Applied energy studies
Cranfield IT MSc☆/dip☆   ☐

Applied mathematics & fluid mechanics
Manchester U MSc☆

Automotive product engineering
Cranfield IT MSc☆

Building services engineering
Brunel U MSc

Combustion & fuels
Cranfield IT MSc☆

Computational fluid dynamics & structural mechanics
London U Imperial C MSc/dip   ☐

Computer aided engineering
Liverpool P MSc☆/dip☆   *Comp*
Paisley CT dip☆
Staffordshire P MSc☆/dip☆   ☐
Teesside P MSc

Computer applications in mechanical engineering
Birmingham U MSc(Eng)☆

Desalination technology
Glasgow U MSc/dip

Design & economic manufacture
Swansea UC MSc☆

Design of energy efficient systems
Cranfield IT MSc☆/dip☆

Design of thermo-fluid systems
Swansea UC MSc☆

Devices, measurement & instrumentation
South Bank P MSc☆/dip☆

Dynamics & control
Bath U MSc☆

Energy & development
Surrey U MSc/dip

Energy efficient building design
Cranfield IT MSc☆/DipIng☆

Engineering
Cambridge U cert☆

Engineering ceramics
Leeds U MSc☆

Engineering computation
Belfast Queen's U MSc☆/dip☆   ☐

Engineering design
Loughborough U MSc△/ MTech☆   ☐

Engineering design for manufacture
Cranfield IT MSc☆

Engineering mechanics
Cranfield IT MSc☆

Engineering solid mechanics
Manchester UMIST MSc☆/dip☆☐

Engineering surveying & geodesy
Nottingham U MSc☆

Exchange & membrane technology
Cranfield IT MSc☆

Finite element method in stress and vibration analysis
Cranfield IT MSc☆   ☐

First class legislation
Nottingham P MQB△

Flexible manufacturing systems
Birmingham U MSc(Eng)☆

Flight test engineering
Cranfield IT MSc☆

Fluid mechanics
Cranfield IT MSc☆   ☐

Fluid power technology
Bath U MSc☆/dip☆

Gas turbine technology
Cranfield IT MSc☆

Hydraulic engineering
Heriot-Watt U MSc/dip
Newcastle U MSc☆/dip☆

Industrial robotics
Silsoe C MSc☆

Innovative design for manufacture of engineered products
Cranfield IT MSc☆

Machine condition monitoring
Swansea UC MSc☆

Machine design
Cranfield IT MSc☆   ☐

Mechanical & manufacture engineering
Birmingham P dip☆

Mechanical & manufacturing engineering
Liverpool P MEng☆

Mechanical engineering
Birmingham P B.Eng△   ☐
Bristol U PhD☆/MSc☆
Dundee U dip☆
Glasgow U PhD☆
Strathclyde U MSc/dip   ☐

Mechanical properties of solids
Newcastle U MSc☆

Mechatronics
Lancaster U MSc☆

Membrane technology
Glasgow U MSc☆/dip☆   *Phy*

Metal manufacturing technology
Swansea UC MSc☆

Metallic & ceramic materials
Manchester UMIST MSc☆/dip☆

Metallurgical engineering
Cranfield IT MSc☆/dip☆

Mineral technology
Camborne S of Mines dip☆

Mining engineering
Nottingham U MSc☆

Noise & vibration of rotating machines & gas turbines
Cranfield IT MSc☆   ☐

Non destructive testing of materials
Brunel U MSc☆

Non-destructive evaluation
London U UC MSc△

Nuclear reactor science & engineering
London U Queen Mary & Westfield C MSc/dip

Offshore engineering □
Cranfield IT MSc☆/dip☆
Robert Gordon's IT MSc☆/dip☆

Offshore materials & corrosion engineering
Newcastle P MSc☆/dip☆

Polymer engineering
Cranfield IT MSc☆   *Chem*
Manchester UMIST MSc☆/dip☆

Power & process engineering
Brunel U MSc△

Power generation
London U Queen Mary & Westfield C MSc☆

Process engineering
Strathclyde U MSc/dip☆

Process plant materials engineering
Cranfield IT MSc☆

Propulsion & power
Cranfield IT MSc☆/dip☆

Refrigeration & air conditioning
London U King's C MSc/dip☆

Robotics & computer integrated engineering
Middlesex P MSc☆/dip☆

Rotating machinery engineering & management
Cranfield IT MSc☆

Soil mechanics & engineering seismology
London U Imperial C MSc/dip

Soil mechanics & foundation engineering
Newcastle U MSc☆

Sound & vibration studies
Southampton U MSc☆/cert☆/dip☆

Structural steel design
London U Imperial C MSc/dip

Thermal energy processes
Cranfield IT MSc   □

Thermal power & fluids engineering
Manchester UMIST MSc☆/dip☆

Tribology in machine design
Leeds U MSc(Eng)☆

Water resources engineering
City U MSc

Welding & adhesive bonding of materials
Brunel U MSc☆   □

Welding technology
Cranfield IT MSc☆   □

Higher degrees by research

Aerodynamics & thermodynamics
Bath U PhD☆/MSc☆

Aeronautical & mechanical engineering
Salford U PhD/MSc

Agricultural engineering & mechanisation
West of Scotland C PhD☆/MSc☆

Applied mechanics
Liverpool U PhD/MSc(Eng)

Artificial intelligence & expert systems
Wessex IT PhD☆/MPhil☆

Boundary elements & numerical methods
Wessex IT PhD☆/MPhil☆

Combined engineering
Coventry P PhD/MPhil

Computational engineering mechanics
Cranfield IT PhD☆/MPhil☆

Computational fluid dynamics
London U Imperial C PhD/MPhil/dip

Corrosion engineering
Royal Naval Engineering C PhD☆/MSc☆

Dental materials science
London U London Hosp Med C PhD☆/MPhil☆

Desalination technology
Glasgow U PhD/MEng

Design of energy efficient buildings
Cranfield IT PhD☆/MPhil☆

Energy engineering
Surrey U PhD/MPhil

Energy utilisation in the catering & food industries
Cranfield IT MPhil☆/MSc☆

Engineering
Aberdeen U PhD☆/MPhil☆/MSc☆   □
Cambridge U PhD☆/MSc☆
Durham U PhD/MSc
Lancaster U PhD/MPhil
Leicester U PhD/MPhil
Manchester U PhD/MSc
Reading U PhD/MPhil
Surrey U PhD/MPhil
Thames P PhD/MPhil

Engineering & technology
London U King's C PhD☆/MPhil☆
Wolverhampton P PhD☆/MPhil☆

Engineering design & manufacture
Hull U PhD/MSc

Engineering mechanics
Open U PhD/MPhil/BPhil

Engineering science
Open U PhD/MPhil/BPhil

Engineering science & industrial management
Liverpool U PhD/MSc(Eng)

Ergonomics & operational research
Birmingham U PhD☆/MPhil☆   □

Farm mechanisation
Aberdeen SAg PhD☆/MSc☆

Fatigue & fracture mechanics
Wessex IT PhD☆/MPhil☆

Fluid engineering & instrumentation
Cranfield IT PhD☆/MPhil☆/MSc☆

Fluid flows in buildings
Cranfield IT PhD☆/MPhil☆

Fluid mechanics
Liverpool U PhD/MSc(Eng)
Oxford U DPhil☆/MSc☆

Hydraulics
Liverpool U PhD/MSc(Eng)

Industrial & geophysical fluid dynamics
Exeter U PhD/MPhil

Machine dynamics
Cranfield IT PhD☆/MPhil☆

Machinery design & manufacture
Silsoe C PhD/MPhil

Manufacturing & mechanical engineering
Birmingham U PhD/MPhil(Eng) □

Manufacturing systems
Central London P PhD☆/MSc☆
East London P PhD/MPhil

Manufacturing systems engineering
Leeds P PhD/MPhil/dip

Marine engineering
Newcastle U PhD/MPhil

Materials engineering
Swansea UC PhD/MPhil □

Materials science & condensed matter research
Keele U PhD/MSc

Materials science & engineering
Liverpool U PhD/MSc(Eng) □

Materials technology
Brunel U PhD/MPhil □

Mechanical & computer aided engineering
Staffordshire P PhD/MPhil

Mechanical & industrial engineering
Dundee IT PhD/MPhil
Napier P PhD/MPhil
Ulster U DPhil/MPhil

Mechanical & manufacturing engineering
Belfast Queen's U PhD/MSc

Mechanical & manufacturing systems engineering
Bradford U PhD/MPhil
Cardiff U of Wales C PhD/MPhil

Mechanical & offshore engineering
Robert Gordon's IT PhD/MPhil

Mechanical & process engineering
Sheffield U PhD/MPhil
Strathclyde U PhD☆/MPhil☆/ MSc☆ □

Mechanical & production engineering
Aston U PhD/MPhil
Birmingham P PhD/MPhil
Brighton P PhD/MPhil
Huddersfield P PhD/MPhil
Lancashire P PhD/MPhil
Leicester P PhD/MPhil
Middlesex P PhD/MPhil
Paisley CT PhD/MPhil
Sheffield City P PhD/MPhil
Sunderland P PhD/MPhil
Wales P PhD☆/MPhil☆

Mechanical & structural engineering
Sussex U DPhil/MPhil □

Mechanical engineering
Aberdeen U PhD☆/MPhil☆/MSc☆
Bath U PhD☆/MSc☆
Bristol U PhD/MSc □
Brunel U PhD/MPhil

City U PhD/MPhil
Coventry P PhD/MPhil
Dundee U PhD/MSc
Edinburgh U PhD/MPhil
Glasgow U PhD
Hatfield P PhD/MPhil
Heriot-Watt U PhD☆/MPhil☆
Leeds U PhD/MPhil/MSc(Eng) □
Liverpool U PhD/MSc(Eng)
London U Imperial C PhD/MPhil/ dip
London U King's C PhD☆/ MPhil☆ □
London U Queen Mary & Westfield C PhD☆/MPhil☆
London U UC PhD☆/MPhil☆
Loughborough U PhD☆/MPhil☆
Manchester U PhD/MSc
Manchester UMIST PhD/MSc
Newcastle U PhD/MPhil
Nottingham P PhD☆/MPhil☆
Nottingham U PhD/MPhil □
Oxford P PhD/MPhil
Portsmouth P PhD☆/MPhil☆
Salford U PhD/MPhil/MSc
South West P PhD/MPhil
Southampton U PhD/MPhil
Surrey U PhD/MPhil
Swansea UC PhD/MSc
Warwick U PhD/MSc

Mechanical engineering & energy studies
Cardiff U of Wales C PhD☆/ MPhil☆

Mechanical engineering & metallurgy
Teesside P PhD/MPhil

Mechanical engineering, design & manufacture
South Bank P PhD/MPhil

Mechanical properties of materials
Oxford U DPhil☆/MSc☆

Mechanical, aeronautical & production engineering
Kingston P PhD/MPhil

Mechanical, marine & production engineering
Liverpool P PhD☆/MPhil☆

Mechanical, production & chemical engineering
Manchester P PhD/MPhil

Mechanics & power
Royal Naval Engineering C PhD☆/MSc☆

Metallurgy & engineering materials
Newcastle U PhD/MPhil

Metallurgy & materials science
Liverpool U PhD/MSc(Eng)

Mine planning
Camborne S of Mines PhD/MPhil

Mineral resources engineering
London U Imperial C PhD/MPhil/ dip
Strathclyde U PhD☆/MPhil☆/ MSc☆

Mining
Nottingham P PhD☆/MPhil☆

Mining & mineral engineering
Leeds U PhD/MPhil/MSc(Eng)

Mining engineering
Newcastle U PhD/MPhil

Offshore engineering
Heriot-Watt U PhD☆/MPhil☆

Optical sensors
Cranfield IT PhD☆/MPhil☆

Propulsion, power & automotive engineering (gas turbine, wind turbine, automobile)
Cranfield IT PhD☆/MPhil☆

Rankine cycles & heat pumps
Cranfield IT PhD☆/MPhil☆

Robotics & automated systems
London U Imperial C PhD/MPhil

Soil mechanics
Central London P PhD☆/MPhil☆

Solid mechanics
Oxford U DPhil☆/MSc☆

Structural mechanics
Royal Naval Engineering C PhD☆/MSc☆

Surface analysis, real area of contact & thermal contact resistance
Cranfield IT PhD☆/MPhil☆

Textile industries
Leeds U PhD/MPhil/MSc(Eng)

Theoretical mechanics
Nottingham U PhD/MPhil

Thermal analyses & cooling
Cranfield IT PhD☆/MPhil☆

Thermal energy storage
Cranfield IT PhD☆/MPhil☆

Thermo fluids engineering
City U PhD/MPhil

Thermodynamic systems
London U King's C PhD☆/MPhil☆

Thermodynamics
Glasgow U PhD/MSc

Thermodynamics & mechanics of fluids
Strathclyde U PhD☆/MPhil☆/ MSc☆

Tribology & lubrication
Cranfield IT PhD☆/MPhil☆

Turbomachinery & fluids
Cranfield IT PhD☆/MPhil☆

Use of solar energy
Cranfield IT PhD☆/MPhil☆

Vehicle engineering
Hatfield P PhD/MPhil

Metallurgy, materials science

Higher degrees by instruction

Advanced materials technology
Surrey U MSc/dip

Advanced metallurgy
Sheffield U MMet

Aerospace materials engineering
Cranfield IT MSc☆/dip☆ ☐

Archaeometallurgy
London U UC MSc☆

Biodeterioration of materials
Portsmouth P MSc☆/dip☆

Ceramics & glass
Royal CA MA☆/MDes☆

Composite materials
London U Imperial C MSc

Concrete technology & construction
Dundee U MSc☆

Concrete technology, construction & management
Dundee U MSc☆

Corrosion science & engineering
Manchester UMIST MSc☆/dip☆ ☐

Electrical & electromagnetic engineering
Cardiff U of Wales C MSc/dip ☐

Engineering ceramics
Leeds U MSc☆

First class legislation
Nottingham P MQB△

Geomaterials
London U Queen Mary & Westfield C MSc☆

Instrumental methods of analysis
Strathclyde U MSc/dip☆

Materials
Cranfield IT MSc☆/dip☆

Materials engineering
Loughborough U MSc ☐

Materials process engineering
Sheffield City P MSc☆

Materials protection
Loughborough U MSc☆

Materials research
London U Imperial C MSc☆/dip☆

Materials science (synchrotron radiation & neutron scattering applied to materials)
Keele U MSc

Mechanical engineering
Bristol U PhD☆/MSc☆

Mechanical properties of solids
Newcastle U MSc☆

Metal manufacturing technology
Swansea UC MSc☆

Metallic & ceramic materials
Manchester U MSc☆
Manchester UMIST MSc☆/dip☆

Metallurgical engineering
Cranfield IT MSc☆/dip☆

Metallurgical manufacturing processes & management
Birmingham U MSc(Eng)☆

Metallurgy
Leeds U dip☆

Mineral technology
Camborne S of Mines dip☆

Mining engineering
Nottingham U MSc☆

Molecular electronics
Cranfield IT MSc☆ ☐

Molecular science of materials
Thames P MSc

Non destructive testing of materials
Brunel U MSc☆

Offshore engineering
Cranfield IT MSc☆/dip☆ ☐

Offshore materials & corrosion engineering
Newcastle P MSc☆/dip☆
Robert Gordon's IT MSc☆/dip☆

Physics of materials
Reading U MSc

Polymer engineering
Cranfield IT MSc☆ *Chem*

Polymer science & technology
Manchester UMIST MSc☆/dip☆
North London P MSc

Polymer technology
Loughborough U MSc/dip△ *Chem*

Process plant materials engineering
Cranfield IT MSc☆

Production, processing & fabrication of materials
Strathclyde U MSc/dip

Properties & applications of engineering materials
Strathclyde U MSc/dip

Robotics & computer integrated engineering
Middlesex P MSc☆/dip☆

Science & technology of ceramics/glasses/materials/polymers
Sheffield U dip

Semiconductor science & technology
London U Imperial C MSc/dip *Phy*

Solid state physics
Sheffield U MSc☆/dip

Structural steel design
London U Imperial C MSc/dip

Superconductivity & cryogenics
Southampton U MSc/dip

Surface science & technology
Loughborough U MSc

Welding & adhesive bonding of materials
Brunel U MSc☆ ☐

Welding technology
Cranfield IT MSc☆ ☐

Higher degrees by research

Aeronautical & mechanical engineering
Salford U PhD/MSc△

Archaeological conservation & materials science
London U UC PhD☆/MPhil☆

Ceramic technology
Staffordshire P PhD/MPhil

Ceramics & glass
Royal CA PhD☆

Ceramics, glasses & polymers
Sheffield U PhD/MPhil

Chemical crystallography
Oxford U DPhil☆/MSc☆

Chemical engineering
Surrey U PhD/MPhil ☐

Chemical with minerals engineering
Birmingham U PhD/MPhil(Eng)

Chemistry
Liverpool U PhD/MSc
Southampton U PhD/
MPhil☆ *Chem*

Composite materials
London U Imperial C PhD/MPhil

Corrosion & protection
Manchester UMIST PhD/MSc

Earth sciences
Oxford U DPhil☆/MSc☆

Engineering & technology
Wolverhampton P PhD☆/MPhil☆

Engineering materials
Southampton U PhD/MPhil

Extractive metallurgy
Camborne S of Mines PhD/MPhil

Fluid mechanics
Glasgow U PhD/MSc

Grinding
Bristol U PhD☆/MSc☆

Heat transfer & thermodynamics
Oxford U DPhil☆/MSc☆

Marine engineering
Newcastle U PhD/MPhil

Materials
Cardiff U of Wales C PhD☆/
MPhil☆
London U Queen Mary &
Westfield C PhD☆/MPhil☆

Materials & energy science
Coventry P PhD/MPhil

Materials analysis & molecular medicine
City U PhD/MPhil

Materials engineering
Loughborough U PhD/MPhil/
MTech
Newcastle P PhD☆/MPhil☆
Swansea UC PhD/MPhil ☐

Materials science
Bath U PhD☆/MPhil☆ ☐
Leeds U PhD/MPhil/MSc
Manchester U PhD/MPhil
Open U PhD/MPhil/BPhil
Sunderland P PhD/MPhil

Materials science & engineering
London U Imperial C PhD/MPhil/
dip ☐
Surrey U PhD/MPhil

Materials science & metallurgy
Cambridge U PhD☆

Materials science & physics
Thames P PhD/MPhil

Materials science & research
Warwick U PhD/MSc

Materials technology
Brunel U PhD/MPhil ☐
Royal Naval Engineering C
PhD☆/MSc☆

Mechanical & production engineering
Aston U PhD/MPhil

Mechanical engineering
Bristol U PhD/MSc ☐

Mechanical engineering & manufacturing systems
Newcastle P PhD☆/MPhil☆

Mechanical engineering & metallurgy
Teesside P PhD/MPhil

Mechanical properties of materials
Oxford U DPhil☆/MSc☆

Mechanics of materials
Strathclyde U PhD/MPhil

Metallurgy
Leeds U PhD/MPhil/MSc(Eng)

Metallurgy & engineering materials
Newcastle U PhD/MPhil
Strathclyde U PhD☆/MPhil☆/
MSc☆

Metallurgy & materials
Birmingham U PhD/MPhil(Eng)

Metallurgy & materials engineering
City of London P PhD☆/MPhil☆
Swansea UC PhD/MPhil

Metallurgy & materials science
Liverpool U PhD/MSc(Eng)
Manchester U PhD/MSc
Manchester UMIST PhD/MSc
Nottingham U PhD/MPhil ☐
Oxford U DPhil☆/MSc☆
Sheffield U PhD/MPhil

Metals & materials engineering
Sheffield City P PhD/MPhil

Mineral physics
London U UC PhD☆/MPhil☆

Mineral processing
Camborne S of Mines PhD/MPhil

Mineral resources engineering
London U Imperial C PhD/MPhil/
dip
Strathclyde U PhD☆/MPhil☆/
MSc☆

Minerals engineering
Birmingham U PhD/MPhil(Eng)

Mining
Nottingham P PhD☆/MPhil☆

Mining & mineral engineering
Leeds U PhD/MPhil/MSc(Eng)

Mining engineering
Newcastle U PhD/MPhil
Nottingham U PhD/MPhil

Novel materials & processing
Open U PhD/MPhil/BPhil

Offshore engineering
Heriot-Watt U PhD☆/MPhil☆

Ore genesis
Camborne S of Mines PhD/MPhil

Physical metallurgy
Liverpool U PhD/MSc(Eng)

Physics
Bristol U PhD☆/MSc☆
Kent U PhD/MPhil/MSc

Polymer science & technology
Manchester UMIST PhD/MSc

Polymer technology
Loughborough U PhD☆/MPhil☆

Polymer, metals & dental technology
Manchester P PhD/MPhil

Rock mechanics
London U UC PhD☆/MPhil☆

Science
Wales P PhD/MPhil

Strength of materials & stress analysis
Manchester U PhD/MSc

Thin film & surface research
Salford U PhD/MPhil/MSc

Welding
Cranfield IT PhD☆/MPhil☆/MSc☆

Production engineering, technology

Higher degrees by instruction

Advanced manufacturing systems
Brunel U MSc ☐
Kingston P MSc△/dip△

Cranfield

ADVANCED MANUFACTURING TECHNOLOGY (with an option in INTEGRATED FACTORY AUTOMATION)

MSc by course: 1 year
(2 years with lower qualifications)
PhD by research: 3 years
MSc by research: 1 year

Course Description There is an urgent need to provide industry with high-calibre, multi-disciplinary engineers able to make an immediate contribution to manufacturing technology. This course aims to provide such engineers by means of "hands on" projects and a broad-based **Lecture Programme** covering not only technical subjects such as CAD, CAM, CIM, Advanced Manufacturing and Machining Processes, Robotics and Automation but also "Management" topics. The importance of teamwork is learned during the **Group Project** whilst individual skills are developed by **Thesis** work.
Entrance Requirements 1st or 2nd Class Honours Degree, preferably with industrial experience.
Grants SERC or Industrial Sponsorship.

COMPUTER AIDED DESIGN & MANUFACTURE OF PRODUCTION MACHINES & SYSTEMS

PhD 3 years MSc
1 year full time

This course is aimed at the working interface between innovative design engineering and efficient manufacture of high technology products. Students will receive intensive training and teaching to ensure that industry is supplied with well educated computer literate engineers with knowledge and competence in the latest computer technology and who can respond rapidly to advances in it.
Entrance requirements First or second class honours degree in a relevant engineerring subject or applied physics or equivalent.
Grant Students may be industrially sponsored or receive a grant from SERC or other funding bodies.

DESIGN FOR MANUFACTURE

PhD
3 years
MSc
1 year full time

This unique master's degree offers a challenging industrially sponsored project with training in appropriate engineering science disciplines, advanced mechanics, modern microelectronics, microprocessor technology, hands-on experience with an advanced CAD system, and management skills. It leads to excellent career prospects. We also offer a combined course with UTC Compiegne leading to a double degree. Options in machine or product design available.
Entrance requirements Minimum 2nd class honours degree in a relevant engineering or design discipline or equivalent.

INDUSTRIAL ROBOTICS

PhD
3 years
MSc
1 Year Full Time

This unique course offers an excellent springboard for those seeking a career in Industrial Automation. Currently our graduates are commanding high salaries and securing excellent positions in this fast moving industry. There is an acute shortage of well qualified and experienced automation specialists. Through our very practical courses offering "hands on" experience on "Real Projects" for "Real Companies", we offer a route into this exciting and dynamic field.
If you have a first degree in science or technology then contact us without delay for your information pack.

METROLOGY & QUALITY ASSURANCE

MSc · 2 years full time · 10 places
PhD 3 years
For details of all these courses contact:
Mrs. S. Hyde,
College of Manufacturing,
Cranfield Institute of Technology,
Cranfield, Bedford, MK43 0AL
Tel: 0234 752771

Good metrology and quality assurance are vital requirements for developments in precision engineering and nanotechnology.

Coursework at Cranfield will be combined with two extended placement periods, either in industry, or at a National Physical Laboratory, which will provide exceptional opportunities for state-of-the-art project experience in measurement science.

This important course is sponsored by the Department of Trade and Industry and is receiving considerable support from industry. Scholarships are available for graduates holding or expecting to gain a good honours degree in engineering, the physical sciences or mathematics.

Advanced manufacturing systems & technology
Liverpool U MSc(Eng)   □

Advanced manufacturing technology
Cranfield IT MSc☆
Hatfield P MSc△/dip△
Liverpool P dip☆
Manchester UMIST MSc☆/dip☆
Portsmouth P MSc/dip
Silsoe C MSc☆
Staffordshire P cert☆   □
Sunderland P dip☆

Automotive engine & vehicle design technology
Southampton U MSc☆/cert☆/ dip☆

Clothing technology
Manchester P dip☆

Computer aided design & manufacture of production machines & systems
Cranfield IT MSc☆

Computer aided engineering
Liverpool P MSc☆/dip☆   *Comp*
Paisley CT dip☆
Staffordshire P MSc☆/dip☆   □

Computer based engineering systems
Dundee IT dip☆

Computer integrated manufacturing
Leeds P dip☆

Computer technology in manufacture
Sussex U MSc☆

Engineering
Cambridge U cert☆

Engineering design for manufacture
Cranfield IT MSc☆

Engineering production & management
Birmingham U MSc(Eng)☆

Flexible manufacturing systems
Birmingham U MSc(Eng)☆

Fluid power technology
Bath U MSc☆/dip☆

Fuel technology
Middlesex P dip

Industrial robotics & manufacturing automation
London U Imperial C MSc☆/ dip☆   □

Information technology for manufacture
Warwick U MSc

Innovative design for manufacture of engineered products
Cranfield IT MSc☆

Machine design
Cranfield IT MSc☆   □

Management with manufacturing
Glasgow C MA☆   *Bus*

Manufacturing engineering
Belfast Queen's U MSc

Manufacturing systems
Nottingham U MSc   □

Manufacturing systems (logistics in manufacturing)
Birmingham P MSc△   □

Manufacturing systems engineering
Cranfield IT MSc☆   □
Leeds P MSc△
Sheffield City P MEng
Wales P dip
Warwick U MSc

Materials engineering
Loughborough U MSc   □

Materials process engineering
Sheffield City P MSc☆

Mechanical & manufacture engineering
Birmingham P dip☆

Mechanical & manufacturing engineering
Liverpool P MEng☆

Mechanical engineering
Bristol U PhD☆/MSc☆

Metal manufacturing technology
Swansea UC MSc☆

Metrology & quality assurance
Cranfield IT MSc☆

Microelectronic materials & device technology
Manchester UMIST MSc☆

Mineral production management
London U Imperial C MSc☆/dip☆

Petroleum engineering
London U Imperial C MSc☆/dip☆

Plastics & rubber technology
North London P ALSPT/PRI

Polymer technology
Loughborough U MSc/dip△ *Chem*

Pressure vessel design
Paisley CT MSc△

Production engineering
Newcastle U cert☆/dip☆

Production engineering & management
Strathclyde U dip☆

Production management
Dundee U MSc☆

Production management & manufacturing technology
Strathclyde U MSc☆

Production methods & management
Cambridge U dip☆

Project engineering
Lancaster U MSc

Quality & reliability engineering
Birmingham U MSc(Eng)☆

Robotics & computer integrated engineering
Middlesex P MSc☆/dip☆

Systems engineering
Cardiff U of Wales C MSc   □

Technology
Lancashire P MSc☆/dip☆

Technology in education
Salford U MSc△

Welding technology
Cranfield IT MSc☆   □

Higher degrees by research

Appropriate technology
Open U PhD☆/MPhil☆/BPhil☆

Combined engineering
Coventry P PhD/MPhil-

Computer integrated manufacture
Cranfield IT PhD☆

Engineering
Cambridge U PhD☆/MSc☆
Durham U PhD/MSc
Manchester U PhD/MSc
Reading U PhD/MPhil
Surrey U PhD/MPhil
Thames P PhD/MPhil

Engineering & technology
Wolverhampton P PhD☆/MPhil☆

Engineering design & manufacture
Hull U PhD/MSc

Engineering design & production
Liverpool U PhD/MSc(Eng)

Engineering production
Birmingham U PhD/MPhil(Eng)

Engineering science
Open U PhD/MPhil/BPhil

Engineering science & industrial management
Liverpool U PhD/MSc(Eng)

Ergonomics & operational research
Birmingham U PhD☆/MPhil☆ ☐

Fibre science
Leeds U PhD/MPhil/MSc

Fluid engineering & instrumentation
Cranfield IT PhD☆/MPhil☆/MSc☆

Graphics technology
Manchester P PhD/MPhil

Industrial & geophysical fluid dynamics
Exeter U PhD/MPhil

Industrial & production engineering
Nottingham P PhD☆/MPhil☆

Industrial engineering
Belfast Queen's U PhD/MSc

Industrial systems & control
Hatfield P PhD/MPhil

Management sciences
Strathclyde U PhD☆/MPhil☆/ MSc☆

Manufacturing
Cranfield IT PhD☆/MSc☆
Dorset Inst PhD/MPhil/dip

Manufacturing & engineering systems
Brunel U PhD/MPhil

Manufacturing & mechanical engineering
Birmingham U PhD/MPhil(Eng) ☐

Manufacturing engineering
Dundee U PhD/MSc
Loughborough U PhD/MPhil
Oxford P PhD/MPhil
Warwick U PhD

Manufacturing systems
Coventry P PhD/MPhil

Manufacturing systems engineering
Leeds P PhD/MPhil/dip

Materials engineering
Swansea UC PhD/MPhil ☐

Mechanical & manufacturing systems engineering
Bradford U PhD/MPhil
Cardiff U of Wales C PhD/MPhil

Mechanical & production engineering
Aston U PhD/MPhil

Birmingham P PhD/MPhil
Brighton P PhD/MPhil
Huddersfield P PhD/MPhil
Lancashire P PhD/MPhil
Leicester P PhD/MPhil
Middlesex P PhD/MPhil
Paisley CT PhD/MPhil
Sheffield City P PhD/MPhil
Sunderland P PhD/MPhil
Wales P PhD☆/MPhil☆

Mechanical & structural engineering
Sussex U DPhil/MPhil ☐

Mechanical engineering
Bristol U PhD/MSc ☐
Hatfield P PhD/MPhil
Leeds U PhD/MPhil/MSc(Eng) ☐
London U UC PhD☆/MPhil☆
Newcastle U PhD/MPhil

Mechanical engineering & manufacturing systems
Newcastle P PhD☆/MPhil☆

Mechanical engineering, design & manufacture
South Bank P PhD/MPhil

Mechanical, aeronautical & production engineering
Kingston P PhD/MPhil

Mechanical, marine & production engineering
Liverpool P PhD☆/MPhil☆

Mechanical, production & chemical engineering
Manchester P PhD/MPhil

Metallurgy & materials engineering
Swansea UC PhD/MPhil

Metallurgy & materials science
Nottingham U PhD/MPhil ☐

Operations management
Cranfield IT PhD☆/MPhil☆

Polymer technology
Loughborough U PhD☆/MPhil☆

Post harvest technology
Silsoe C PhD/MPhil

Production engineering
Coventry P PhD/MPhil

Production engineering & design
Oxford U DPhil☆/MSc☆

Production engineering & production management
Nottingham U PhD/MPhil

Ship science
Southampton U PhD/MPhil

Textile & knitwear technology
Leicester P PhD/MPhil

Textile industries
Huddersfield P PhD/MPhil

Technology, industrial studies

Higher degrees by instruction

Acoustics
Salford U MSc△

Advanced building technology
Manchester UMIST MSc△

Advanced manufacturing systems
Brunel U MSc ☐

Advanced manufacturing technology
Coventry P MSc/dip
Hatfield P MSc△/dip△
Liverpool P dip☆
Manchester UMIST MSc☆/dip☆
Sunderland P dip☆

Bulk solids handling technology
Thames P MSc

Carpet technology & design
Kidderminster C dip☆

Clothing technology
Leeds U dip☆

Combustion & pollution technology
Sheffield U dip☆

Computer integrated manufacturing
Cranfield IT MSc☆

Design of equipment for disability
London C of Furniture dip☆

Devices, measurement & instrumentation
South Bank P MSc☆/dip☆

Educational technology
Bath U MEd

Energy & development
Surrey U MSc/dip

Explosive ordnance engineering
Royal Military C of Science MSc☆

Fire engineering
Edinburgh U MSc/dip

ENGINEERING/TECHNOLOGY/ENVIRONMENT 2

Fisheries (fishing gear technology)
Humberside CHE dip☆

Fluid power technology
Bath U MSc☆/dip☆

Forest industries technology
Bangor, U of Wales MSc☆/dip☆

Forestry & paper technology
Manchester UMIST MSc☆

History of science, medicine & technology
London U Imperial C MSc

History of technology
London U Imperial C MSc

Industrial development
East Anglia U MA☆

Information technology
Kingston P MSc☆

Information technology for manufacture
Warwick U MSc

Instrument design & application
Manchester U MSc☆/dip☆

Instrumental methods of analysis
Strathclyde U MSc/dip☆

Instrumentation & analytical science
Manchester UMIST dip☆

International business & industrial development
Ulster U MBA☆

Management of technological change
Salford U MSc△

Management of technology & operational research
Sussex U MSc☆

Manufacturing systems engineering
Cranfield IT MSc☆   □
Leeds P MSc△
Warwick U MSc

Metrology & quality assurance
Cranfield IT MSc☆

Military vehicle technology
Royal Military C of Science MSc☆

Mineral engineering
Leeds U dip☆

Mining engineering
Leeds U dip☆

Petroleum technology & management systems
Brunel U MSc☆

Robotics - systems & applications
Coventry P MSc/dip

Safety & reliability
Bradford U MSc△

Science & technology studies
Brunel U MA   *Soc*

Science, technology & industrialisation
Sussex U MSc☆

Science, technology & international affairs
Lancaster U MA☆

Ship production technology
Strathclyde U MSc/dip

Sound & vibration studies
Southampton U MSc☆/cert☆/dip☆

Structure & organisation of science & technology
Manchester U MSc☆/dip☆

Subsea engineering
Heriot-Watt U MSc☆

Technical change & industrial strategy
Manchester U MSc☆/dip☆

Technical science
Manchester UMIST dip☆

Technology & society
Salford U MSc△

Textile industries
Leeds U dip☆

Textile science & engineering
Leeds U MSc☆

Textile technology
Manchester UMIST MSc/dip

Transport engineering & planning
Salford U MSc

Tribology in machine design
Leeds U MSc(Eng)☆

Higher degrees by research

Applied acoustics
Salford U PhD/MSc

Appropriate technology
Open U PhD☆/MPhil☆/BPhil☆

Arts & technology in education
Thames P PhD/MPhil

Ceramic technology
Staffordshire P PhD/MPhil

Chemistry & chemical technology
Bradford U PhD/MPhil

Corrosion
Cranfield IT PhD☆/MPhil☆/MSc☆

Design & technology
Brunel U PhD/MPhil
Loughborough U PhD/MPhil

Economics & industrial studies
Leeds U PhD/MA/MPhil

Energy engineering
Surrey U PhD/MPhil

Energy management
Cranfield IT MPhil☆/MSc☆

Engineering & technology
Wolverhampton P PhD☆/MPhil☆

Engineering mathematics
Belfast Queen's U PhD/MSc

Environmental technology
London U Imperial C PhD/MPhil/dip

Fibre science
Leeds U PhD/MPhil/MSc

Fire safety engineering
Edinburgh U PhD/MPhil

Fluid engineering & instrumentation
Cranfield IT PhD☆/MPhil☆/MSc☆

Food technology
Reading U PhD/MPhil

Fracture & fatigue
Cranfield IT PhD☆/MPhil☆/MSc☆

High temperature & coatings technology
Cranfield IT PhD☆/MPhil☆/MSc☆

History of science & technology
Keele U PhD/MA/MSc☆

History of technology
Bath U PhD☆/MPhil☆

Industrial & business studies
Warwick U PhD/MA/MPhil/MSc

Industrial & defence studies
Royal Naval Engineering C PhD☆/MSc☆

Industrial & geophysical fluid dynamics
Exeter U PhD/MPhil

Industrial engineering
Belfast Queen's U PhD/MSc

Industrial physics
Cranfield IT PhD☆/MPhil☆/MSc☆

Industrial studies
Liverpool U PhD/MSc(Eng)

Industrial technology
Bradford U PhD/MPhil

315

Instrumentation & automation
Salford U PhD/MSc

Manufacturing engineering
Loughborough U PhD/MPhil
Warwick U PhD

Materials technology
Royal Naval Engineering C
PhD☆/MSc☆

Mechanical & industrial engineering
Ulster U DPhil/MPhil

Mechanical engineering
London U Imperial C PhD/MPhil/dip
Portsmouth P PhD☆/MPhil☆

Military & defence science & technology
Royal Military C of Science
PhD☆/MPhil☆

Molecular electronics
Cranfield IT PhD☆/MPhil☆/MSc☆

Non destructive testing
Paisley CT PhD/MPhil

Operations management
Cranfield S of Management PhD/MPhil

Quality assurance
Cranfield IT PhD☆/MPhil☆/MSc☆

Science & technology
Thames Valley C MPhil

Science & technology studies
Manchester U PhD/MSc

Science policy research unit
Sussex U DPhil/MPhil

Shipbuilding technology
Sunderland P PhD/MPhil

Social & economic aspects of information & communication technologies
Newcastle U PhD☆

Social implications of technical change
Sussex U DPhil/MPhil

Sound & vibration research
Southampton U PhD/MPhil

Systems science
City U PhD/MPhil

Technological management
Bradford U PhD/MPhil

Technology
Anglia HEC PhD☆/MPhil☆
Cardiff IHE PhD/MPhil/dip△

Technology policy
Aston U PhD/MPhil
Open U PhD/MPhil/BPhil

Telecommunications systems
Anglia HEC PhD☆/MPhil☆

Textile industries
Huddersfield P PhD/MPhil

Textile studies
Bolton IHE PhD/MPhil

Textile technology
Scottish C of Textiles PhD/MPhil

Textiles
Manchester UMIST PhD/MSc

Total technology
Manchester UMIST PhD/MSc

Underwater technology
Cranfield IT PhD☆/MPhil☆/MSc☆

Urban & regional development studies
Newcastle U PhD/MLitt/MPhil

Water science
Cranfield IT PhD☆/MPhil☆/MSc☆

Welding
Cranfield IT PhD☆/MPhil☆/MSc☆

Transport studies, port management

Higher degrees by instruction

Air transport engineering
Cranfield IT MSc☆

Air transport management
Cranfield IT MSc☆

Airline transport pilot's licence
Oxford Air Training S ATPL

Airport planning & management
Loughborough U MSc

Automotive engine & vehicle design technology
Southampton U MSc☆/cert☆/dip☆

Civil engineering (highways & transport)
City U MSc

Commercial pilot's licence & instrument rating
Oxford Air Training S ATPL/CPL

Commercial pilot's licence (helicopter)
Oxford Air Training S CPL(H)

Construction engineering
Leeds U MSc(Eng)

Distribution technology & management
Cranfield IT MSc☆   Bus

Engineering mechanics
Cranfield IT MSc☆

Highway & traffic engineering
Birmingham U MSc(Eng)
Middlesex P dip△

Highway engineering
Strathclyde U MSc/dip

Highway engineering for developing countries
Birmingham U MSc(Eng)

Highway planning, design & construction
Bradford U MSc/dip

International shipping
South West P MSc   □

Marine law & policy
Cardiff U of Wales C MSc☆

Marine resource management
Heriot-Watt U MSc☆

Maritime civil engineering
Liverpool U MSc(Eng)☆/dip☆

Maritime defence technology
Royal Naval Engineering C
MSc☆/dip☆

Maritime studies
Cardiff U of Wales C MSc☆
St Andrews U MLitt/MPhil☆/dip☆

Military vehicle technology
Royal Military C of Science
MSc☆

Port management/shipping management
Humberside CHE MSc☆

River, estuary & coastal engineering
London U Imperial C MSc/dip

Shipping & maritime studies
Liverpool P MSc/dip△

Shipping, trade & finance
City U MSc

Storage, handling & transportation of dangerous substances
Southampton IHE MSc☆/dip☆

Traffic engineering for developing countries
Birmingham U MSc(Eng)☆

Transport
Cardiff U of Wales C MSc
London U Imperial C MSc/dip
London U UC MSc

Transport & development
Salford U MSc☆/cert☆/dip☆

Transport & distribution
Birmingham P MSc△

Transport & distribution management
Salford U MSc△

Transport & distribution planning & management
Cranfield IT dip☆

Transport economics
Leeds U MA

Transport engineering
Newcastle U Cert☆

Transport engineering & operations
Newcastle U MSc☆

Transport engineering & planning
Salford U MSc

Transport for rural development
Silsoe C MSc☆

Transport in developing countries
Central London P MSc☆/dip☆

Transport management
City U MSc

Transport planning & engineering
Leeds U MSc(Eng)

Transport planning & management
Central London P MSc

Transport studies
Cranfield IT MSc   ☐

Transportation planning & engineering
Southampton U MSc☆/dip☆

Transportation planning in developing countries
Napier P dip☆

Tropical public health engineering
Leeds U MSc(Eng)☆

Vehicle design
Royal CA MDes☆

Higher degrees by research

Business studies
North London P PhD/MPhil

Civil & municipal engineering
London U UC PhD☆/MPhil☆

Civil engineering
Leeds U PhD/MPhil/MSc(Eng)△

Distribution studies
Cranfield IT PhD☆/MSc☆   *Bus*

Fisheries studies
Humberside CHE PhD/MPhil

Food manufacture & distribution
Manchester P PhD/MPhil

Information technology in transport
Cardiff U of Wales C PhD/MPhil

Marine resource management
Cardiff U of Wales C PhD/MPhil

Maritime studies
Cardiff U of Wales C PhD☆/MPhil☆
Liverpool P PhD/MPhil

Mechanical, marine & production engineering
Liverpool P PhD☆/MPhil☆

Shipbuilding technology
Sunderland P PhD/MPhil

Shipping & transport
South West P PhD/MPhil

Shipping operations
South West P PhD/MPhil

Transport economics
Leeds U PhD/MA/MPhil

Transport economics & policy
Cardiff U of Wales C PhD/MPhil

Transport operations research
Newcastle U PhD/MPhil

Transport research
Cranfield IT PhD/MPhil

Transport studies
Central London P PhD☆/MPhil☆
City of London P PhD☆/MPhil☆/dip☆
Leeds U PhD/MA/MPhil/MSc(Eng)/MSc
Oxford U DPhil☆/MLitt☆
Salford U PhD/MSc
Ulster U DPhil/MPhil

Transport technology
Loughborough U PhD☆/MPhil☆

Transportation
Bradford U PhD/MPhil
Cardiff U of Wales C PhD☆/MPhil☆

Transportation & highway engineering
Birmingham U PhD/MPhil(Eng)

Vehicle design
Royal CA PhD☆

Vehicle engineering
Hatfield P PhD/MPhil

Advanced manufacturing systems MSc 1 year full time 2 years part time 2 years (min) distance learning Course Director, Department of Manufacturing & Engineering Systems, Brunel University, Uxbridge, Middlesex UB8 3PH Tel: 0895 74000 Fax: 0895 32806	Modern manufacturing is changing faster than ever before. This course deals with the changing technologies, methodologies, and strategies of manufacturing as well as providing a firm grounding in the basic principles of manufacturing. Subjects covered include; robotics, computer integrated manufacturing, metrology, production management, manufacturing system design, computer aided design, quality, and manufacturing strategy. **Entrance requirements** Honours degree in appropriate subject. Other qualifications with experience may be considered.

Advanced manufacturing systems & technology

MSc(Eng)
1 year full time
24 places
AMST Course Director (Ref AMSTO2), Department of Mechanical Engineering, University of Liverpool, PO Box 147, Liverpool L69 3BX

Modern manufacturing practice is being significantly affected by the application of computers to design, organisation, financial management, machine control and robotics, as well as the introduction of new materials and processing methods such as the use of lasers, water jets and plasmas. This twelve month course is intended for persons wishing to take up a career in this challenging field. Taught courses are supported by a substantial six month industrially relevant project.

Entrance requirements A good honours degree or equivalent.

Grants SERC Advanced Course Studentships and industrial places.

Course Director Mr P Martin.

Aerospace materials engineering

MSc
1 year full time
15 places
PhD 3 years
Dr J P Chubb, School of Industrial Science, Cranfield Institute of Technology, Cranfield, Bedford MK43 0AL
Tel: 0234 750111

The MSc course is designed for scientists and engineers who wish to enter the aerospace and associated industries. A group and personal research project forms a major part of the course which is supplemented by a lecture programme covering the structure and properties of aerospace materials including production and processing techniques. Visiting specialists from industry and a high level of contract research maintain industrial relevance.

Entrance requirements Good honours degree or equivalent.

Grants SERC advanced course studentships and other bursaries.

Professor of Engineering Metallurgy Professor P Hancock.

Artificial intelligence with engineering applications

MSc
1 year full time
20 places
The Academic Registrar, Department of Electrical, Electronic & Systems Engineering, University of Wales College of Cardiff, PO Box 68, Cardiff CF1 3XA
Tel: 0222 874000

This course is aimed at producing graduates conversant with AI techniques and capable of applying them to the solution of engineering problems. Subject modules available are concepts of knowledge engineering, AI languages, AI engineering aspects, development tools and techniques, engineering applications, neural networks, robotics, natural language processing, image processing, vision systems, databases. Candidates who are successful in the written examination will pursue a four month project and submit a dissertation, which, if satisfactory, completes the requirement for the MSc degree.

Entrance requirements Honours degree (or equivalent) in engineering, computer science, mathematics, or physical science, or equivalent.

Head of department Professor D R Towill.

Aviation electronics

MSc/PhD
MSc
1 year full time
2 years part time
Executive Assistant, Ref 101, Department of Electronic System Design, Cranfield Institute of Technology, Cranfield, Bedford MK43 0AL
Tel: 0234 752703

Civil and military relies heavily on advanced electronics for all aspects of aircraft operation. The aim of this specialisation is to give the specialist electronic background in navigational aids, radar and communications for a career in electronics in the aircraft industry.

Entrance requirements A good degree in appropriate subject. For those with a good HND or equivalent, a preliminary year of study may be offered.

Grants SERC.

Acting Head of department Mr R Andrew.

Bioengineering

PhD
3 years full time
MPhil/MSc
1 year full time
21 months part time
Diploma
9 months full time
18 months part time
Bioengineering Unit,
University of Strathclyde,
Wolfson Centre, 106
Rottenrow, Glasgow G4
0NW
Tel: 041 552 4400 ext
3780/3030/3029
Fax: 041 552 6098

All candidates take a conversion course in life or engineering science, followed by advanced courses in bioengineering topics. This is followed by a research project in the area of locomotion or tissue mechanics, rehabilitation, instrumentation, signal analysis, biomaterials, artificial organs, lasers in surgery or functional electrical stimulation. **Entrance requirements** First degree in science, technology, life science, medical or paramedical field; minimum upper second class honours degree for PhD, lower second class or professional qualification for 12 months' MSc. **Grants** Funding is available from the MRC, SERC, DENI and the European Community. **Head of Unit** Professor J P Paul.

Biomedical engineering

MSc
1 year full time
PhD
3 years full time
Admissions Secretary,
Department of Biomedical
Physics & Bioengineering,
University of Aberdeen,
Forester Hill, Aberdeen AB9
2ZD
Tel: 0224 681818 ext 53194

The course includes the following topics; Rehabilitation Engineering, Biomedical Electronics and engineering, Biomaterials, Biomechanics, Computing and Information technology, Radiation Protection, Medical use of Radioisotopes and non-ionising radiations. **Entrance requirements** A degree in Science or Engineering or equivalent qualification. **Head of department** Professor J R Mallard.

Biomedical engineering

MSc by instruction
1 year full time
2 years part time
PhD
3 years full time
5 years part time
MPhil
1-2 years full time
2-3 years part time
Diploma by instruction
up to 1 year full time
Postgraduate Admissions
Secretary, Bioengineering
Group, Department of
Mechanical Engineering,
University of Surrey,
Guildford, Surrey GU2 5XH
Tel: 0483 571281 ext 9214

The MSc course combines engineering and technology with state of the art medical applications. All candidates take the core modules in musculo-skeletal, fluids and soft tissue, neurological, and whole body systems. Parallel systems are selective and include signal analysis, FEA, and electronics. Update training in maths and engineering is given to life/medical science students. A research project is taken in eg. artificial limbs, movement analysis, pressure sores, respiration, biomaterials, medical automation, tissue mechanics, heart valves. **Entrance requirements** Degree in engineering, physical science, life science, medical or paramedical discipline for the MSc course. Upper second for MPhil/PhD. **Grants** SERC.MRC,Northern Ireland Dept of Education. **Director of Biomedical Engineering** S C Hughes.

Biomedical engineering

DPhil
3 years full time
5 years part time
MPhil
1 year full time
2 years part time
Graduate Division of
Biomedical Engineering,
School of Engineering &
Applied Sciences, University
of Sussex, Falmer, Brighton,
East Sussex BN1 9QT
Tel: 0273 678358

Opportunities exist for research in a variety of areas including cardiac instrumentation and signal processing, ophthalmological instrumentation (contrast sensitivity, perimetry etc.), synthesised speech aids, automatic biochemical analysis, detection and prediction of apnoea, NMR image processing, analysis of blood flow, aspects of human and animal hearing.

The division is expanding and applicants are encouraged to suggest projects outside the current range of work.
Entrance requirements Good honours degree in engineering or other relevant subject.
Grants SERC studentships and industrial support may be available to suitable candidates.
Chairman Dr L G Ripley.

Chemical & process engineering

PhD
3 years full time
4-5 years part time
MPhil
1-2 years full time
Prof A J Morris, Department
of Chemical & Process
Engineering, University of
Newcastle upon Tyne, Merz
Court, Newcastle upon Tyne
NE1 7RU
Tel: 091 222 7342

Excellent facilities exist for research in the following areas: process control and computor applicatons; electrolytic process engineering; energy engineering; heat and mass tranfer and fluid mechanics; reactor engineering; pollution control and effluent treatment; biotechnology; information technology and expert systems.
Entrance requirements Good honours degree in chemical, mechanical or electrical engineering, chemistry, physics or maths. Other qualifications considered individually.
Grants SERC postgraduate studentships, CASE awards.
Head of department Mr K E Peet JP.

Chemical engineering

PhD/MPhil
2-3 years full time
MSc in Advanced chemical
engineering
1 year full time
Dr P F Luckham,
Department of Chemical
Engineering, Imperial College
of Science, Technology &
Medicine, London SW7 2BY
Tel: 071 589 5111 ext 8302
Fax: 071 584 1170

Excellent laboratory and computer facilities exist for research in: systems engineering, computer-aided design, process control, applied catalysis, reaction engineering, separation processes, multiphase flow systems, biotechnology, thermophysics of fluids, thermodynamics, polymer science, interface science, particle technology, combustion and safety, nuclear technology, properties of matter. The MSc course is modular and contains a wide range of options and a research project. Students may devote part of their studies to management options. The DIC (Diploma of Imperial College) is awarded to all who qualify for MSc, MPhil and PhD degrees.
Entrance requirements PhD/MPhil degrees: good honours degree. MSc degree: good honours degree in chemical engineering. Students whose prior education has not been in English must obtain satisfactory results in either the Princeton Test of English as a Foreign Language (required score 580), or in the British Council English Testing Service (required score 7).

Chemical engineering

PhD
full time
part time
MPhil
full time
part time
Postgraduate Admissions
Tutor, Department of
Chemical and Process
Engineering, University of
Surrey, Guildford, Surrey
GU2 5XH

0pportunities are available to join vigorous and well-equipped research groups working in the following areas:
Particle technology: fluid bed processing; agglomeration, attrition and erosion; storage and handling of bulk solids; gas cleaning; instrumentation, electrical effects in particulate systems.
Separation technology: membrane processes; synthesis and use of adsorbents; pressure swing processes; phase equilibria at high pressures.
Biochemical engineering: mixing and mass transfer in gas/liquid systems; control of bioreactors; affinity separations.
Fuel technology: high-intensity combustion; control systems.
   Collaborative study: An established scheme exists for external students to submit for higher degrees based on research carried out at their place of work; details on request.
Entrance requirements First or second class honours degree in chemical engineering or other suitable discipline. Physicists and materials scientists are particularly welcome.
Grants SERC postgraduate studentships; university studentships; direct industrial support. Applications considered at any time, but preferably by early July for SERC studentships.

Chemical engineering & applied chemistry

PhD/MPhil by research
full time
and part time
Dr C J Mumford, Department
of Chemical Engineering &
Applied Chemistry, Aston
University, Aston Triangle,
Birmingham B4 7ET
Tel: 021 359 3611

The Department provides a spectrum of research activity in chemical engineering and chemistry. The Separation Processes Group study economically- viable separation processes eg. distillation, liquid extraction, gas absorption, drying and membrane applications. The Chemical & Biochemical Processes Group study the design, modelling and evaluation of (a) biochemical, thermochemical and waste treatment processes (b) the reaction and separation of biochemicals using production scale chromatography and ultrafiltration membranes (c) biomass conversion processes (d) energy saving and heat transfer operations. The Speciality Materials Group is concerned with the application of fundamental studies in polylmer science, organic and organometallic chemistry to the design of novel materials, eg. biomaterials, electro-active materials, sensors and membranes. The polymer Processing and Performance Group investigate the fundamental chemical and physical changes in polymers during processing and fabrication, and applications of polymer modification science.
Entrance requirements A good first degree or equivalent in chemical engineering, chemistry or an appropriate science based discipline eg. some topics suit mechanical engineers, physicists or biologists.
Grants SERC and Industrial research Studentships are available.
Head of department Dr E L Smith.

Civil engineering

PhD
full time (min 33 months)
part time (min 45 months)
MPhil
full time (min 18 months)
part time (min 30 months)
Dr P S Coupe, Department
of Civil Engineering &
Building, Polytechnic of
Wales, Llantwit Road,
Treforest, Pontypridd, Mid
Glamorgan CF37 1DL
Tel: 0443 480480

Research is actively pursued in most aspects of civil engineering and building. Current active projects include creep and fatigue of road bases, assessment of residual life of highway pavements, behaviour of expansive soils, load transfer in piles, soil structure interaction, stability of slopes and sea cliffs, lime stabilisation, fracture of concrete and cement stabilised soils, new cementitious materials with pfa and micro-silica, analysis of multi cell structures and elastic shells, numerical analysis of a piled raft foundation, development of single image photogrammetric techniques, beach erosion and coastal engineering, recycling of 'grey water', energy analysis and heat transfer in cavity walls, urban regeneration, professional development in the building industry, design/construction/performance of buildings, simulation methods in building education, time and cost factor analysis in factory unit construction, financial and project organisation, quality assurance.

Twenty postgraduate students are registered for higher degrees in the department.

Entrance requirements First class or second class (upper division) honours degree in civil engineering, building or equivalent.

Head of department Dr P S Coupe.

Civil/structural engineering

DPhil
1 year full time
3 years part time
MPhil
1 year full time
3 years part time
Chairman of Mechanical &
Structural Engineering,
University of Sussex, Sussex
House, Falmer, Brighton
BN1 9RH
Tel: 0273 606755

Research opportunities are available in: stable and unstable behaviour of thin-walled structures, collapse of rectangular hollow section beams, shear strength of masonry, composite behaviour of masonry, composite behaviour of masonry walls interacting with steel and concrete members, prediction of strenght in plates, end stiffening of RHS beams.

Entrance requirements Good honours degree in civil engineering or equivalent.

Grants SERC.

Chairman Professor J B Roberts.

Communication systems

MSc/PhD
MSc
1 year full time
2 years part time
Executive Assistant, Ref 101,
Department of Electronic
System Design, Cranfield
Institute of Technology,
Cranfield, Bedford MK43
0AL
Tel: 0234 752703

The aim of this specialisation is to provide a balanced programme which includes a good grounding in such fundamentals as network characterization, e.m. field theory, microwave techniques and measurements, communications, and signal processing with a strong emphasis on the engineering application of these topics.

Entrance requirements A good degree in appropriate subject. For those with a good HND or equivalent, a preliminary year of study may be offered.

Grants SERC.

Acting Head of department Mr R Andrew.

Computational fluid dynamics & structural mechanics

MSc
1 year full time
2 years part time
Prof J K Harvey, Department of Aeronautics, Imperial College of Science, Technology & Medicine, London SW7 2BY
Tel: 071 589 5111 ext 4015

An MSc course that is designed for students who wish to specialise in Computational Fluid Dynamics (CFD) or Computational Structural Mechanics. The course, which is run jointly by the Departments of Aeronautics and Mathematics, covers the fundamental aspects of Numerical Methods and the application of these to Fluids Dynamic and Structural problems. The Course is suitable for students who have graduated in Engineering, Mathematics or Physics. It provides training that is relevant to those who aim at a career in the aircraft, automobile, off-shore, process and power industries, in civil engineering consulting and in Government research laboratories.
Grants SERC Advanced Course Studentship.
Head of Department Professor P W Bearman.

Computer speech & language processing

MPhil
1 year full time
20 places
Secretary (MPhil Computer Speech & Language Processing), University Engineering Department, University of Cambridge, Trumpington Street, Cambridge CB2 1PZ
Tel: 0223 332752

For students with backgrounds in computing, electronic engineering, psychology, or linguistics. Interdisciplinary course organised by Computer laboratory and Engineering department and involving Faculties from all the above areas. Aims to provide practical and theoretical expertise in information technology computer systems for speech and language understanding. Lectures, practical work, 3 months supervised project. Industrial support and collaboration.
Entrance requirements Good honours degree or equivalent: computing experience preferred.
Grants SERC studentships available.
Course directors Professor F Fallside (Engineering Department), Dr K Sparck Jones (Computer laboratory).

Computing systems

MSc/PhD
MSc
1 year full time
2 years part time
Executive Assistant, Ref 101, Department of Electronic System Design, Cranfield Institute of Technology, Cranfield, Bedford MK43 0AL
Tel: 0234 752703

This course gives a sound basis in the theoretical and practical aspects of computer systems, including microprocessor technology, and software engineering applied to the specification and design of on-line and real-time embedded systems. It includes optional modules on digital design, communications and networks, software engineering and artificial intelligence. This specialisation leads to career opportunities in computer systems and can be taken as an IT conversion course.
Entrance requirements A good degree in appropriate subject. For those with a good HND or equivalent, a preliminary year of study may be offered.
Grants SERC.
Acting Head of department Mr R Andrew.

Construction management

MSc
1 year full time
20 places
MSc
2 years part time
10 places
Distance learning over
2-4 years.
50 places in Nov.
50 in May
D Langford, The Director of
Postgraduate Studies,
School of Architecture and
Building Engineering,
University of Bath, Claverton
Down, Bath BA2 7AY
Tel: 0225 826826

The course comprises five modules, namely: management science, management principles, management practice, economics and case studies. The case studies seek to integrate academic work carried out in the course and course members' industrial experience. Following completion of the five modules, students write a dissertation in the field of construction management.
Entrance requirements Degree or professional qualification in any construction discipline.
Director of Postgraduate Studies D Langford.

Construction management

MSc/Diploma
12 months full time
24 months part time
24 months distance learning
Director of Studies,
Department of Building
Engineering & Surveying,
Heriot-Watt University,
Riccarton, Edinburgh EH14
4AS
Tel: 031 449 5111

Specialist streams in;
  Project Management
  Production Management
  Corporate Strategy
  Building Maintenance
Supported by funds from SERC and British Council.
Entrance requirements MSc - mininmum 2II Honours degree or Chartered Status. PhD study available.

Control & information technology

MSc
1 year full time
dip
9 months full time
35 places
Dr Peter Cook, Admissions
Officer, The Control Systems
Centre, UMIST - The
University of Manchester
Institute of Science and
Technology, The Control
Systems Centre, PO Box 88,
Manchester M60 1QD
Tel: 061 200 4658/4664

This course opens up career opportunities both in PhD research, and in industry in the fields of engineering systems analysis, control system design, control electronics, and specialist computer and engineering consultancy. The course includes control theory, simulation, engineering systems modelling, signal procesing, real-time control, and intelligent instrumentation. Its flexible structure provides options in neural networks, multivariable control, optimization, self-tuning control, nonlinear systems, expert systems, software engineering, fault detection, robotics and process control. The dissertation project enables students to sample academic research and/or collaborate with industry.
Entrance requirements Good honours degree in engineering/mathematics/physical science/computer science.
Grants SERC awards for EEC residents.

Control systems

MSc/PhD
MSc
1 year full time
2 years part time
Executive Assistant, Ref 101,
Department of Electronic
System Design, Cranfield
Institute of Technology,
Cranfield, Bedford MK43
0AL
Tel: 0234 752703

The engineering of control systems is a high technology discipline with application to aircraft, ships, mechanisms and industrial plants. The course gives the student a good grounding in basic and advanced control techniques and places strong emphasis on modern practice including computer aids and on-line microprocessor control.
Entrance requirements A good degree in appropriate subject. For those with a good HND or equivalent, a preliminary year of study may be offered.
Grants SERC.
Acting Head of department Mr R Andrew.

Corrosion science & engineering

MSc
1 year full time
25 places
dip
1 year full time
25 places
Postgraduate Admissions
Tutor, Corrosion and
Protection Centre, UMIST -
The University of
Manchester Institute of
Science and Technology, PO
Box 88, Manchester M60
1QD
Tel: 061 200 4848

The MSc course is designed for scientists and engineers intending to specialise in corrosion and protection, and for specialists in other disciplines, such as chemical engineering, where a sound knowledge of corrosion is required. Both principles and practical aspects of corrosion and corrosion control are covered by lectures, practical studies, analysis of industrial problems and a five month research project. An options scheme in the second term enables students to tailor their studies to particular interests such as advanced materials, conservation of materials, or industrial corrosion control.
Entrance requirements Honours degree or equivalent professional qualifications.
Grants SERC advanced course studentships.
Head of department Prof B E Thompson.

Cybernetics and information systems engineering

PhD/MPhil/MSc
full time
or part time
Department of Cybernetics,
University of Reading, 3
Earley Gate, Whiteknights,
PO Box 238, Reading,
Berkshire RG6 2AL

Cybernetics is concerned with systems and their control. Research topics may include intelligent sensors, multi sensor integration, FMS, signal processing, computer-graphics, CAD, adaptive control systems, neural networks,vision and speech processing, machine intelligence, robotics, multi-layer optical filters, solar energy conversion and microprocessor-controlled systems. Starting date can be at any time but is normally October. Apply to Dr M J Usher by early July for SERC studentships; otherwise at any time.
Grants SERC and university research studentships possible.
Head of department Professor K Warwick.

Digital communication systems

MSc
1 year full time
4 years maximum part time
dip
1 year full time
Department of Electronic &
Electrical Engineering,
Loughborough University of
Technology, Loughborough,
Leicestershire LE11 3TU
Tel: 0509 223330

The course consists of two terms of formal work and a project, and aims to give students a good grasp of the theories and techniques involved in the transmission of digital data over channels introducing noise and distortion, digital coding of speech and television signals and the switching of telecommunication networks.
Entrance requirements First or second class honours degree in electrical/electronic engineering, physics or equivalent qualification.
Course tutor Dr M J J Holt.

Digital techniques

MSc
1 year full time
2 years part time
dip
1 year full time
2 years part time
Mr P H Etherington,
Department of Electrical &
Electronic Engineering,
Heriot-Watt University, 31-35
Grassmarket, Edinburgh EH1
2HT
Tel: 031 225 6465 ext 409

The course is intended for electrical engineering graduates who wish to update their knowledge or to continue their studies to a higher level. The major course units which are presented in the first two terms are basic digital techniques, computer hardware and software engineering, control and communication systems, systems engineering. The formal lecture material is followed by a six month design projectwhich provides an opportunity to apply digital techniques to a practical system problem. Course provides up to date techniques useful for a future career in the rapidly changing industry of today.
Entrance requirements First or second class honours degree in electrical/electronic engineering, computer science, physics or equivalent qualification.
Grants A number of SERC advanced course studentships are normally available.

Electrical & electromagnetic engineering

MSc
1 year full time
2 years part time
The Postgraduate Section,
The Academic Registry,
University of Wales College
of Cardiff, PO Box 68,
Cardiff CF1 3XA
Tel: 0222 874000

The course consists of seven months formal work (lectures, laboratory classes, continuous assessment work), followed by a project and provides an opportunity for advanced study in the area of magnetic materials, measurements, computer eng., power electronics, electrical machines, magnetic storage and recording, variable speed drives, HV technology and power systems, CAD of electromagnetic devices. The course is industrially orientated.
Entrance requirements Degree in engineering or science.
Head of department Professor D R Towill.

Electrical & electronic engineering

PhD
MSc
Mr J K M MacCormac,
Director of Postgraduate
Studies, School of Electrical
Engineering, University of
Bath, Claverton Down, Bath
BA2 7AY
Tel: 0225 826826

Excellent facilities are available for research in the following areas: electrical machines, microwaves and optical electronics, power generation and transmission systems, digital electronics, power electronics and control, custom designed electronic circuits, ground transport systems, radio communications, optimal and adaptive control, parallel processing applications, system modelling and image processing.
Entrance requirements MSc, BSc Honours or equivalent.
Grants A number of SERC, university or industry sponsored studentships are normally available.
Head of Department Professor J F Eastham.

Electrical power engineering

MSc
1 year full time
2 years part time
dip
1 year full time
2 years part time
Professor K L Lo,
Department of Electronic &
Electrical Engineering,
University of Strathclyde,
204 George Street, Glasgow
G1 1XW
Tel: 041 552 4400 ext 2169

There is advanced instruction in the operation, design and analysis of electrical machines and electrical power systems; high voltage phenomena; applied control theory; plant design; CAD and laboratory work. A wide selection of project topics are also available as part of the course. The starting dates are September, February and July 1990/91.
There are approximately 20 places available.
Entrance requirements Good honours degree or equivalent.
Grants SERC.
Chairman of department Professor O Farish.

Electrical/electronic engineering

PhD
3 years full time
5 years part time
MPhil
1 year full time
2 years part time
Postgraduate Admissions Adviser, Electrical Engineering Department, University College of Swansea, Singleton Park, Swansea, West Glamorgan SA2 8PP
Tel: 0792 295415 Fax: 0792 295686

Exceptional research opportunities.Beautiful campus.
* Communications
* Computer integrated manufacture
* Control and computer-aided engineering
* Instrumentation and power electronics
* Microelectronics and device modelling
* Transducers and sensors
* Speech, signal and image processing.
Entrance requirements Good honours degree.
Grants SERC quota places and industrial support available.
Postgraduate Admissions Professor K Board.

Electronic & electrical engineering

PhD
full time
part time
MPhil
full time
part time
Dr R C Woods (ref: DOG 90), Department of Electronic & Electrical Engineering, University of Sheffield, Mappin Street, Sheffield S1 3JD
Tel: 0742 768555 ext 5144 or 5355

This prestigious Department invites applications from graduates, or students expecting to graduate, with a good honours degree in electronic or electrical engineering, or a related discipline, to undertake research in any of the following areas:- solid state devices and materials; medical applications of electronics and microwaves; electrical machines and controlled drive systems; microelectronic and microprocessor systems; microwave metrology, image diagnostics and antennas; molecular electronics; computer aided design and computer modelling; image processing; VLSI design. Further details and application forms may be obtained from the address given.
Grants SERC Quota and CASE studentships or other financial assistance may be available.

Electronic design

MSc/PhD
MSc
1 year full time
2 years part time
Executive Assistant, Ref 101, Department of Electronic System Design, Cranfield Institute of Technology, Cranfield, Bedford MK43 0AL
Tel: 0234 752703

Attention is focussed on the detailed design of both hardware and software of microprocessor based electronic systems. Topics include: electronic engineering, microprocessor engineering, logic design, signal processing and opto-electronics.
Entrance requirements A good degree in appropriate subject. For those with a good HND or equivalent, a preliminary year of study may be offered.
Grants SERC.
Acting Head of department Mr R Andrew.

Electronic engineering

MSc
1 year full time
2 years part time
dip
9 months full time
34 places
Mr G Pearce, ELSYM,
University of Wales College
of Cardiff, PO Box 904,
Cardiff CF1 3YH
Tel: 0222 874421

Schemes of study allow choice of topics from: electronic circuits, computer engineering, software engineering and Real Time systems, digital/ASIC design, advanced computer architectures, communication theory, data communications, signal processing, diagnostic imaging, physiological measurement and therapeutic techniques (in collaboration with the University Hospital of Wales). MSc candidates, successful in the written examinations pursue a four month project and submit a dissertation for MSc. Successful diploma candidates reaching commendation level, are eligible for entry into the MSc scheme.
Entrance requirements (For MSc) Honours degree in engineering, mathematics or science, or equivalent.
Head of department Professor D R Towill.

Electronic, electrical, control engineering & computer science

DPhil
3 years full time
5 years part time
MPhil
1 year full time
2 years part time
EEC/CS Subject Group
Office, School of Engineering
and Applied Sciences,
University of Sussex,
Falmer, Brighton, East
Sussex BN1 9QT
Tel: 0273 606755

Opportunities exist for research in the following areas: computer-aided design and simulation of multivariable and nonlinear systems, identification and adaptive control, electromechanical systems and robotics, power electronics, microprocessor control of electrical machines, magnetic suspension systems, artificial intelligence, computer communication protocols and networks, VLSI systems, VLSI design methodologies, advanced graphics systems, VLSI for graphics, signal analysis, neural networks, RISC systems, computer architecture, parallel processing systems, medical and space applications of microelectronics, signal processing, filter design, sonar, process control, factory automation.
Entrance requirements Good honours degree in engineering, computer science, mathematics or physics.
Grants SERC studentships, also some industrial support may be available.
Chairman Professor D P Atherton.

Electronics & computer science

PhD
3 years full time
MPhil
2 years full time
MSc
1 year full time
40 places
Postgraduate Admissions
Tutor, Department of
Electronics and Computing
Science (Ref DOG),
University of Southampton,
Highfield, Southampton SO9
5NH
Tel: 0703 592882

Excellent research facilities are available in integrated processing systems and design automation, computer architecture and computer generated graphics, digital mobile radio communications, programmable instrumentation and transducers, computer aided design, control and robotics, speech and image processing, software verification, VLSI technology, design and architectures, microwaves, optical inspection, optical fibre communications, man machine interfaces, testing and reliability, highly parallel computing, computer based training and electronic publishing. The MSc course in electronics is designed as an updating and conversion course for graduates with emphasis on digital and microprocessor based systems. The MSc course in microelectronics systems design is aimed at covering all aspects of the production of systems on silicon. It is a very design oriented and has backing from industry.
Entrance requirements Good honours degree in science, computer systems, mathematics or engineering.
Grants SERC studentship.
Head of department Professor D W Barron.

Energy & buildings

MSc
1 year full time
Course Director (Ref: 2145),
School of Mechanical
Engineering, Cranfield
Institute of Technology,
FREEPOST, Cranfield,
Bedford MK43 7BR
Tel: 0234 750111

Since its inception in 1985 this MSc course has successfully attracted graduates from the full spectrum of buildings related disciplines, including architecture and planning, as well as from the more traditional engineering and scientific backgrounds. The aim of the course is to produce graduates possessing an in-depth knowledge of the rational use of energy and trains personnel who need an exact understanding of the energy implications of their decisions. The course helps meet the growing demand for energy-conscious building and building-systems design professionals.

Entrance requirements Good honours degree in engineering, science, architecture or building related disciplines.

Grants Industrial bursaries or SERC advanced course studentships are available.

Course director Dr W J Batty.

Energy conservation & the environment

MSc
1 year full time
Dr Paul W O'Callaghan (Ref: 2146), Dept of Applied
Energy, Cranfield Institute of
Technology, School of
Mechanical Engineering,
FREEPOST , Cranfield,
Bedford MK43 7BR
Tel: 0234 750111

The rational use of energy, mineral and organic resources are vital to the future welfare of our planet. This course is suitable for engineers from all disciplines; pure and applied scientists, mathematicians and computer software engineers. It produces scientists, engineers and managers, who have an in-depth understanding of energy conservation and flow processes, the effective management of resources to promote conservation and the means to minimise pollution and so prevent environmental destruction. It satisfies the needs for energy managers and environmental engineers in industries, consultancies, the public sector and government agencies.

Entrance requirements A good honours degree in an appropriate discipline.

Grants SERC advanced course studentships and other bursaries.

Energy studies (double degree)

MSc/Dip Ing
2 years full time
Dr Paul W O'Callaghan (Ref: 2147), Dept of Applied
Energy, Cranfield Institute of
Technology, School of
Mechanical Engineering,
FREEPOST , Cranfield,
Bedford MK43 7BR
Tel: 0234 750111

The first year is spent in attending the final year of the five year Dipl.Ing course at the Université de Technologie at Compiègne near Paris in France. The second year comprises the MSc course: "Energy Conservation and the Environment" at Cranfield. It produces the European Specialists urgently needed to manage the use of depleting energy, mineral and organic resources, whilst simultaneously ensuring environmental and ecological protection. This course is suitable for engineers from all disciplines, pure and applied scientists, mathematicians and computer software engineers. It satisfies the needs for energy managers and environmental engineers in industries, consultancies, the public sector and governmental agencies throughout Europe.

Entrance requirements A good honours degree in an appropriate discipline.

Grants SERC advanced course studentships and other bursaries.

Engineering

PhD
3 years full time
4 years part time
MSc
1 year full time
2 years part time
Dr A A Rodger,
Postgraduate Adviser,
Department of Engineering,
University of Aberdeen,
Aberdeen AB9 2UE
Tel: 0224 272984

Opportunities exist for research in the following areas: river engineering; sediment transport; hydro-station surge prediction; fibre reinforced concrete; frost action in soils; geotechnical dynamics; power systems analysis; automatic monitoring systems; high voltage DC transmission; digital communication systems; VSLI design; optoelectronics; holography; dynamics and mechanical vibration; structural dynamics; fracture mechanics; fatigue; tribology; polymer engineering; wire rope behaviour; gas turbine performance.
Entrance requirements Good first degree or equivalent.
Head of department Professor A D S Barr.

Engineering

PhD
3 years full time
part time
MPhil
1 year full time
part time
The Director, School of
Engineering, University of
Exeter, Exeter EX4 4QF
Tel: 0392 263627

Supervised research in most engineering fields inc. aerodynamics and acoustics, instrumentation and control, reliability and maintenance, engines, electronic systems, microprocessors, CAD, materials science and corrosion, biomechanics, geotechnics, hydraulics and flow networks, structures, fluid mechanics, heat/mass transfer, separation processes, membrane science.
Entrance requirements Good honours or Master's degree in science or technology.
Grants SERC, SERC CASE and Industrial Studentships available.
Dean of Faculty of Engineering Dr A A Wragg.

Engineering

PhD
3 years full time
MPhil
2 years full time
MSc
1 year full time
all available part time
Dr C Thomas, Department of
Engineering, University of
Warwick, Coventry CV4 7AL
Tel: 0203 523139

Opportunities exist in this large unified engineering department for research in a wide range of subjects within the general areas of bioengineering, civil engineering, CAD, control engineering, development studies and appropriate technology, electronics, electrical machines and power electronics, fluid dynamics and thermodynamics, information technology, manufacturing engineering, materials science and engineering, microengineering and metrology. Further details on each of these areas is available on request.
Entrance requirements Good honours degree, Master's degree or an equivalent qualification in an appropriate discipline.
Grants SERC and SERC CASE studentships are available.
Head of department Professor J O Flower.

Engineering computation

MSc/dip
MSc
1 year full time
dip
8 months full time
Faculty of Engineering, The
Queen's University of
Belfast, Belfast BT7 1NN

The course provides an opportunity for graduates in any branch of engineering or science to obtain an advanced knowledge of the application of computers in engineering. Lecture topics are computer software, software engineering, computer systems and microprocessors, computer-aided design, numerical methods (MSc only), matrix computation (MSc only) and a choice from: finite element methods, computational fluid dynamics, mathematics of control, operational research, optimisation and data base technology. There are keynote lectures on areas of topical interest. For the MSc there is an individual computing project lasting five months and for the diploma a study report is to be written.
Entrance requirements MSc: First or second class honours degree in engineering or science. Diploma: Degree in engineering or science.
Grants MSc: SERC or DENI advanced course studentships. Diploma: LEA discretionary grants.
Course co-ordinator Professor A Jennings, Faculty of Engineering.

Engineering design

MSc
1 year full time
up to 5 years part time
Mr I Wright, Engineering
Design Institute,
Loughborough University of
Technology, Loughborough,
Leicestershire LE11 3TU
Tel: 0509 223176

Are you interested in total design with the ability to take a project through from market need to product in use? By taking a comprehensive and thoroughly professional approach to design the course prepares engineers for positions of responsibilty in industry, equipped to meet the challenge of product, process, and system design in today's highly competitive product environment. The major element of the course is a project of current commercial significance resulting in products being placed on the market and installed process equipment.
Entrance requirements A degree in engineering or science or equivalent professional qualification.
Course director Mr I Wright.

Engineering geology

MSc
1 year full time
2 years part time
20 places
The Secretary - Engineering
Geology, School of
Engineering & Applied
Science, University of
Durham, South road,
Durham DH1 3LE

The course, designed for a mixed entry of new and industrially experienced graduates, comprises six months of lectures, laboratory classes and field studies in rock and soil engineering, engineering geology, mining geotechnics, and engineering hydrology, followed by six months of project research, usually in close association with industry.
Entrance requirements Good honours degree in geology, civil engineering, applied/combined sciences or equivalent.
Grants SERC advanced course awards.
Course director Dr A R Selby.

Engineering solid mechanics

MSc
1 year full time
Dr J N Ashton, Department
of Mechanical Engineering,
UMIST - The University of
Manchester Institute of
Science and Technology, PO
Box 88, Manchester M60
1QD
Tel: 061 200 3741

Examined taught course for two terms, followed by dissertation project. The first term courses are on elasticity, plasticity, dynamics of solids and structures, materials, and numerical analysis. In the second term optional courses are taken from pressure vessels, impact mechanics, metal forming, plant design, composites, and finite element theory. Course booklet available.
Entrance requirements Good honours degree or equivalent, in science, mathematics or engineering.

Finite element method in stress and vibration analysis

MSc
1 year full time
Course Director (Ref: 2150),
School of Mechanical
Engineering, Cranfield
Institute of Technology,
FREEPOST, Cranfield,
Bedford MK43 7BR
Tel: 0234 750111

This course is designed to provide candidates with an engineering, mathematical or scientific degree with the basic knowledge about finite element and boundary-element techniques and their engineering applications to stress and vibration analysis. Thermal fluid flow problems may also be considered. The research project is aiming at allowing students to gain working experience with many commercial finite-element packages available at Cranfield such as PAFEC, I-DEAS and ABAQUS. Students are also encouraged to write their own programs or modify some of the extensive finite boundary element software already developed.
Entrance requirements Good honours degree in Engineering, Mathematics or any relevant topic.
Grants Industrially supported bursaries, SERC.
Course director Dr A El-Zafrany.

Fluid mechanics

PhD
3 years full time
MSc
1 year full time
The Admissions Tutor,
Department of Fluid
Engineering &
Instrumentation (Ref: 2153),
School of Mechanical
Engineering, Cranfield
Institute of Technology,
FREEPOST, Cranfield,
Bedford MK43 7BR
Tel: 0234 750111

The department offers unique opportunities for industrially linked research in areas which include flowmeter design and development, fluid instrumentation and associated signal processing, multiphase and two component flows, computational fluid mechanics, analysis of flow in pipes and rotating machinery etc. In addition to campus-based courses there are industrial programmes which allow engineers in employment to gain additional qualifications without disrupting their careers. Industrial students undertake research at their place of employment and attend supporting technical and interdisciplinary short courses at Cranfield.
Entrance requirements Good first degree or equivalent.
Grants Industrial sponsorship/SERC support.
Admissions tutor Professor M Sanderson.

Fuel & energy

PhD/MPhil
2-3 years full time
30 places
MSc
12 months full time
Professor A Williams,
Department of Fuel &
Energy, University of Leeds,
Leeds LS2 9JT
Tel: 0532 332508

Facilities are available for experimental or theoretical research into a wide range of subjects concerned with fuels, combustion, explosion and fire research, pollution control technology, and alternative sources of energy.
Entrance requirements Good honours degree or equivalent in pure or applied sciences.
Grants SERC research studentships, industrial grants and contracts.
Head of Department Professor A Williams.

Industrial robotics & manufacturing automation

MSc
1 year full time
dip
1 year full time
Dr R D Hibberd, Centre for
Robotics, Imperial College of
Science, Technology &
Medicine, Exhibition Road,
London SW7 2BX
Tel: 071 589 5111

An intensive conversion course for new and experienced honours graduates in science and technology leading to the MSc degree of the University of London and the Diploma of Imperial College. The course offers a thorough grounding in production processes, the theory, the crucial allied social, economic and managerial issues, in technology and the latest ideas in robotics and work in automated systems and carries this into practical work in laboratories and workshops.
Entrance requirements First or good second class honours degree preferably with industrial experience.
Grants SERC.
Course director Dr R D Hibberd.

International shipping/ international distribution

MSc
1 year full time
3 years part time
15 places
Faculty Adminstrator, Institute of Marine Studies, Plymouth: Polytechnic South West, Drake Circus, Plymouth PL4 8AA
Tel: 0752 232405 Fax: 0752 232293

A one year postgraduate course for graduates or managers in the shipping and transport sector with options in International Shipping or International Distribution. The course focusses on the strategic and policy issues relating to the operation of international transport.
Entrance requirements Appropriate first degree or equivalent plus relevant experience.
Head of department Professor D H Moreby ExC PhD FNI.

Logistics in manufacturing systems

MSc
1 year full time
2 years part time
George Smith, Faculty of Engineering and Computer Technology, Birmingham Polytechnic, Perry Barr, Birmingham B42 2SU
Tel: 021 331 6247 and 021 331 6242

Applications are invited from graduates in Engineering Science and Business disciplines. Other qualifications eg: HND and HNC plus experience will also be considered. Three months of the course are spent in industry on significant projects. The academic part of the part-time course takes the form of one week learning workshops. Both courses look deeply into modern manufacturing practices. Starting date 1st of October.
Grants Some grants are available.

Machine design

MSc
1 year full time
Course Director (Ref 2151), School of Mechanical Engineering, Cranfield Institute of Technology, FREEPOST, Cranfield, Bedford MK43 7BR
Tel: 0234 750111

The course offers instruction on the application of advanced techniques such as CAD-CAM and manufacture through the use of NC utilities, together with the extensive use of finite elements. Training is also provided in the more conventional hand tabulation techniques used in machine design in order to validate computer modelling and also to provide alternative procedures where computer facilities are not available. A major feature of the course is that it offers a unique opportunity for the candidate to undertake a complete design and manufacture exercise of a machine component, using computer-aided draughting followed by an extensive stress, vibration and thermal analysis using a comprehensive range of finite element software. Instruction is also given on the methods for down-loading information from the CAD workstation for NC machining. Finally, in order to promote confidence in the FE analysis and for product improvement, the machined component is experimentally tested to obtain the stress distribution and vibration characteristics.
Entrance requirements Good honours degree in engineering, science, physics or mathematics.
Grants Financial support is available from a number of sources.
Course director Dr R H Bannister.

Manufacturing & mechanical engineering

MPhil/PhD
2 or 3 years full time
Dr P Hartley, School of
Manufacturing & Mechanical
Engineering, University of
Birmingham, Birmingham
B15 2TT
Tel: 021 414 4145

Ergonomics and Operational Research: Management and workforce behaviour, decision support systems, work related musculo-skeletal disorders, dynamic anthropometry and machinery guarding, ergonomics and safety in developing countries, ergonomics in manufacturing industry.
Manufacturing Engineering: Management systems, manufacturing systems, risk analysis, cell control, three dimensional surface topography, CAD/CAM and CAQC integration, machining of hard materials, finite element plasticity, metalforming processes, CAD/CAM of forming tools, material failure in forming and fatigue, moulding processes.
Mechanical Engineering: Dynamics and control of machine systems, power transmission in machine systems, steam turbines, heat and fluid flow, solar energy, nuclear engineering, elastohydrodynamics, IC engines, automotive engineering, CAD/CAM, intelligent database systems.
Entrance requirements Good honours degree in engineering, science, mathematics or equivalent.
Head of school Professor K J Stout.

Manufacturing systems

MSc
1 year full time
Admissions Tutor MSc,
Department of Production
Engineering and Production
Management, University of
Nottingham, University Park,
Nottingham NG7 2RD
Tel: 0602 484848 ext 2987

This is a modular course to satisfy the demands of modern industry for people able to design, implement and manage advanced manufacturing systems. It is suitable both for new graduates wishing to specialise in manufacturing systems and experienced engineers wishing to update their skills or convert to a new discipline. A programme of lectures, seminars, industrial visits, individual and group exercises cover areas of computer aided design and manufacture, modelling and simulation, automation and systems integration, manufacturing management and human resource planning.
Entrance requirements Normally a good honours degree or equivalent in engineering or science. Other qualifications, with experience, may be considered.
Grants SERC advanced course studentships.
Admissons tutor Dr M D Byrne.

Manufacturing systems engineering

MSc
1 year full time
PhD 3 years
Mrs S Hyde, College of
Manufacturing, Cranfield
Institute of Technology,
Cranfield, Bedford MK43
0AL
Tel: 0234 752771

The course provides practical and professional training in Manufacturing Systems Engineering and has been devised to meet the urgent national need for manufacturing engineers who can plan, create and run modern manufacturing plants. It integrates those aspects relating to the specification, controls, and management of manufacturing systems, ranging from flexible automated batch manufacturing to adaptable high volume production, with special emphasis on computer based aids.
Entrance requirements 1st or 2nd Class Honours Degree preferably with industrial experience.
Grants Industrial Sponsorship/SERC Support.

Marine technology

PhD
full time
or part time
MPhil
full time
or part time
MSc
1 year full time
cert/dip
9 months full time
The Secretary, Department
of Marine Technology,
University of Newcastle upon
Tyne, Armstrong Building,
Newcastle upon Tyne NE1
7RU
Tel: 091 222 6000 ext 6171

Teaching and research in the Department concern marine engineering, marine transport, naval architecture, offshore engineering and shipbuilding. Research, leading to PhD or MPhil, can be undertaken in any of these areas.

Three full-time MSc courses include a programme in offshore engineering; a specialised course in marine engineering; and a more general course, with a wide variety of options, in marine technology. All courses include a substantial research project.

The Department has excellent experimental and computing facilities and participates in a major national programme of research sponsored by government and industry, with whom links are particularly good.

The diploma and certificate courses can also provide 'conversion'programmes towards higher postgraduate study.

Entrance requirements Good honours degree in engineering, naval architecture or an allied subject, or an equivalent qualification.

Grants SERC studentships available, and occasionally other possibilities.

Lloyds Professor of Offshore Engineering Professor P Bettess.

Materials engineering

MSc
1 year full time
2 years part time
24 places
Dr P J James, Course Tutor,
IPTME, Loughborough
University of Technology,
Loughborough,
Leicestershire LE11 3TU
Tel: 0509 223330

The course is designed for graduates in science, engineering and technology disciplines in preparation for a career in the materials manufacturing and user industries. Foundation subjects are taken by all students, together with a choice of two specialist subjects on an industrially orientated research project.

Entrance requirements Applicants should possess or expect to obtain an Honours Degree or equivalent professional qualification. Those persons with lower academic qualifications but having appropriate industrial experience may be eligible for MSc registration.

Grants A number of Higher Technology National Training Awards are available for unemployed graduates or equivalent.

Head of department Dr D R Gabe.

Materials engineering

PhD
3 years full time
5 years part time
MPhil
1 year full time
Department of Materials
engineering, University
College of Swansea,
Singleton Park, Swansea,
West Glamorgan SA2 8PP
Tel: 0792 205678

Opportunities exist within the following research centres: IRC in Materials for High Performance Applications; Electronic materials; Steel products; Polymers and composites.

Project areas include: computer aided manufacture; computer aided materials engineering; life prediction of components; materials testing with emphasis on creep, fatigue and stress corrosion; effect of environment on materials performance; iron and steel technology; relationship between structure and properties of materials; fabrication; characterization and computer modelling of electronic materials; joining.

Entrance requirements Good honours degree or equivalent.

Grants SERC studentships, industrial sponsorship, others.

Head of department Professor B Wilshire.

Materials engineering & materials design

PhD
2 years full time
4 years part time
MPhil
1 year full time
2 years part time
Postgraduate Admissions Tutor, Department of Materials Engineering and Materials Design, University of Nottingham, University Park, Nottingham NG7 2RD
Tel: 0602 484848 ext 2118

The Department's research activities emphasise an integrated approach to the application and design of material for specific situations. The current topics include: a) Production of novel materials (intermetallics, composites, diamond-like films, fibre-reinforced ceramics and coatings) for applications in aerospace, automobile, electronic, optical, biomedical and primary supply industries. b) The development of processing technologies and modelling (microwave heating, vapour phase deposition, spray deposition, powders, paints and other surface treatments). c) The evaluation of surface and bulk properties for the above applications. d) Recycling of materials. e) Modifications and applications of natural materials (wood and biological materials).

Entrance requirements First or second class honours degree.

Head of department Professor J V Wood.

Materials science & engineering

PhD
3 years full time
MSc(Eng)
1 year full time
Dr R C Pond, Department of Materials Science & Engineering, University of Liverpool,

The MSc(Eng) course, *Advanced Engineering Materials*, comprises coursework and research. Opportunities leading to PhD in the following areas: polymeric and composite materials, solidification and properties of metals and alloys, oxidation, radiation damage, electronic and superconducting materials.

Entrance requirements PhD, good honours degree; MSc(Eng) honours degree or equivalent.

Grants Training Agency, and European Social Fund.

Head of department Professor P J Goodhew.

Materials science & engineering

PhD
3 years full time
MPhil
2 years full time
20 places
MSc
1 year full time
Professor D W Pashley, Department of Materials, Imperial College of Science, Technology & Medicine, London SW7 2BZ
Tel: 071 589 5111

Opportunities for research leading to MPhil/PhD. A wide range of research activities offered including the following topics:- structure and properties of metals, ceramics, polymers and electrical materials; development of new alloys, energy devices, ceramic- and metal-matrix composites and glass-ceramics; processing of metals and ceramics by high-temperature and electrochemical techniques; powder processing; surface properties and corrosion; biomaterials.

A one year MSc course, Materials Research, consists of lectures and a long project selected from one of the research fields.

Entrance requirements Good honours degree in materials or a related subject.

Grants SERC, industrial and others.

Head of department Professor D W Pashley FRS.

Materials science and technology

PhD and MPhil
full time
and part time
Director of Postgraduate
Studies, School of Materials
Science, University of Bath,
Bath BA2 7AY
Tel: 0225 826196

Research: *biomedical materials;* cement/bone interface in implants, prosthetic ligaments, friction and wear of articular cartilage; *carbons and graphites;* fracture, oxidation, strength and structure; *ceramics and glasses;* solid electrolytes, high T_c superconductors, sprayed coatings; *composites;* fatigue and fracture of reinforced plastics and ceramic matrix composites (CMCs), fibre surface treatments, joining of metal matrix composites (MMCs), corrosion of MMCs, carbon-carbon composites; *electron optical studies;* quantitative methods in electron probe microanalysis (EPM), EPM using soft x-rays, light element analysis; *polymeric materials;* rubbers, adhesives, membranes, thermoplastic coatings; *surface engineering;* mould release problems, plasma-sprayed coatings and non-desructive evaluation, wear of surface- treated metals; *wood and natural fibres;* wood composites for wind energy generation, cellulose fibres for composite reinforcement.

Entrance requirements Good honours degree or equivalent in materials science, physics, chemistry, engineering.

Grants SERC quota and case awards usually available, together with sponsored studentships from other sources from time to time.

Head of school Professor V D Scott.

Mechanical & computer aided engineering

PgD/MSc
PgC
Department of Mechanical &
Computer-Aided
Engineering, Staffordshire
Polytechnic, Department of
Mechanical &
Computer Aided
Engineering, Staffordshire
Polytechnic, Beaconside,
Stafford ST18 0AD
Tel: 0785 52331 ext 5266

Up to 30 places for Honours Graduates or equivalent in Engineering, appropriate Scientific or Mathematical discipline (including Degree and compensating industrial experience) as follows:
Postgraduate taught courses
(i) PgD/MSc in Computer-Aided Engineering
(ii) PgC in Advanced Manufacturing Technology.

Grants Training agency and other grants may be available.

Contact Barrie Delves (Course Tutor).

Mechanical engineering

B.Eng
4 years part time
George Smith, Faculty of
Engineering and Computer
Technology, Birmingham
Polytechnic, Perry Barr,
Birmingham B42 2SU
Tel: 021 331 5422

Applications are invited from HNC holders or equivalent and applicants are welcome without normal entry qualifications but with industrial experience. Good HND or HNC enter directly on to the second year. The degree is accredited for C.Eng status by both the I.Mech.E. and I.Prod.E. The course is ideal for those living within 50 miles radius of the Polytechnic, situated near junction 7 of the M6, and attendance is one day per week only. The course commences 24 September.

Mechanical engineering

MSc/PhD by research
MSc
1 year full time
2 years part time
PhD
2 years full time
4 years part time
Professor E G Ellison,
Department of Mechanical
Engineering, University of
Bristol, Queen's Building,
University Walk, Bristol BS8
1TR
Tel: 0272 303243

Excellent laboratory and computing facilities are available for research in a wide range of topics:

Materials: High temperature fatigue-creep and crack growth; composites and bonded structures and associated non-destructive tests. Advanced production techniques for rubber components.

Manufacturing: Grinding of metals, polymers and ceramics. Control of industrial systems. Intelligent, vision-guided robots and associated sensors. CAD applications. Analysis of metal forming. Linear friction welding.

Process and Energy Management: Heat and mass transfer in condensation and moisture diffusion. Management, hardware and computer prediction of building energy consumption.

Bio-Engineering: Fixators and prostheses. Computed Tomography Scanning. Stress analysis of bones.

Entrance requirements Good honours degree or equivalent.
Grants SERC and industrial contracts.
Head of department Professor E G Ellison.

Mechanical engineering

PhD
3 years full time
part time
MSc(Eng)
1 year full time
part time
MPhil
2 years full time
part time
Mechanical Engineering
Department, University of
Leeds, Leeds LS2 9JT
Tel: 0532 332115

Excellent laboratory and computational facilities exist for research and advanced courses. Much of the research is industrially and internationally linked. An MSc course is available in combustion and energy (in collaboration with the departments of fuel and energy, and chemistry) and an MSc(Eng) course in tribology and machine design. Research is pursued over a broad spectrum and covers: bioengineering, combustion, computer aided design and manufacture, control, fluid mechanics, heat transfer, metals and polymer forming, stress analysis, tribology, and vibrations.

Entrance requirements Good honours degree or equivalent.
Grants SERC and some others.
Postgraduate tutor Professor Derek Bradley FRS.

Mechanical engineering

PhD
3 years full time
MPhil
2 years full time
MSc
1 or 2 years full time
Anne Robinson, Department
of Mechanical Engineering,
King's College, London,
Strand, London WC2R 2LS
Tel: 071 873 2696

The MSc course is structured for those seeking higher technical or managerial posts in the refrigeration and air conditioning industry.

Research facilities exist for PhD/MPhil studies in areas including machines, mechanisms and manipulators, manufacturing systems, internal combustion engineering, fluid flow measurement (bulk and local velocities and turbulence) using laser-Doppler and hot wire anemometry and other techniques, flow visualisation, refrigeration & air conditioning, fracture mechanics, materials and metallurgy.

Entrance requirements Good honours degree in engineering or related subjects.
Grants SERC and other sources.
Head of department Professor S W E Earles.

Mechanical engineering

PhD
2 years full time
MPhil
1 year full time
Postgraduate Admissions
Tutor, Department of
Mechanical Engineering,
University of Nottingham,
Nottingham NG7 2RD

Research opportunities, most in collaboration with industry, are available in: experimental and theoretical stress analysis, finite element methods, creep and fatigue of cracked components, composite materials and filament winding, polymer applications, vibration, heat transfer, turbine blade cooling, machinery noise, combustion, wind energy, internal combustion engines, fluid mechanics, cavitation, jet cutting, computer aided design, and robotics.
Entrance requirements Good honours degree in engineering or related sciences or professional equivalent.
Grants SERC and others.
Head of Department Professor B R Clayton.

Mechanical engineering

MPhil/PhD
1 or 3 years full time
MSc
1 or 2 years full time
2 years part time
dip
9 months full time
Chairman, Mechanical
Engineering, University of
Strathclyde, 75 Montrose
Street, Glasgow G1 1XJ
Tel: 041 552 4400

MPhil/PhD available in many areas. An MSc or Diploma Course incorporating lectures, seminars and research project can be taken in one of four options, viz
Mechanics of materials concentrates on stress analysis and structural mechanics with applications in power, offshore and structural fields.
Thermodynamics and fluid mechanics concentrates on rotodynamic machinery, two-phase flow and nuclear power with applications in nuclear and pump industries.
Computer-aided mechanical engineering combines aspects of the first two options. It is particularly computer oriented, leading to an up to date mechanics and CAE background in both structural and thermo/fluid environments.
All the above options make use of commercial packages, such as PATRAN, ANSYS and ABACUS, mainly for stress analysis, and PHOENICS, for heat transfer and fluid flow problems
Materials engineering concentrates on advanced materials, indicating potential, limitations, design capabilities and applications.
Entrance requirements Degree in engineering or related discipline, with minimum of second class honours for one year MSc course and research courses.
Grants Some scholarships may be available.
Head of department Professor J Spence.

Mechanical engineering

MPhil
1 year full time
3 years part time
DPhil
1 year full time
3 years part time
Chairman of Mechanical &
Structural Engineering,
University of Sussex,
Falmer, Brighton, Sussex
BN1 9QF
Tel: 0273 606755

Two MSc courses are available. One, in energy studies, based on lectures and practical work, is linked with scientific and engineering research in the science area at Sussex. The other, entitled Computer Technology in Manufacture, is run jointly with Brighton Polytechnic. In addition, research opportunites, many in collaboration with industry, are available in: heat transfer to turbine blading, heat transfer in rotating flows with special reference to cooling of gas turbine discs and blading, general studies in thermo-fluid mechanics, vibration control of flexible shafts, performance of squeeze film bearings used in aircraft gas turbine engines, random vibration dynamics of ships and offshore structures, computer-aided design and manufacture.
Entrance requirements Good honours degree in mechanical engineering, mathematics or equivalent.
Grants SERC and others.
Chairman Professor J B Roberts.

Microelectronics

MSc
1 year full time
15 places
Dr D W Wellby, School of
Engineering & Applied
Science, University of
Durham, South road,
Durham DH1 3LE

This is a specialist/conversion course covering the whole subject of chip-level microelectronics and with emphasis on integrated circuit design. It is intended for physical science, mathematics, or computing graduates wanting to convert to electronics and electronics graduates wanting further specialisation. The course includes introductory and advanced lectures, electronics and clean-room lab work, a semi-custom integrated circuit design, a major full-custom LSI chip design exercise using state-of-the-art CAD tools and a project that may be done in industry or in the University. **Entrance requirements** Good honours degree in an appropriate science or engineering subject.
Grants SERC advanced course studentships.
Course director Dr M J Morant.

Microwaves & optoelectronics

MSc and diploma
1 year full time
2 years part time
Mrs M D Small, Department
of Electronic & Electrical
Engineering, University
College London, Torrington
Place, London WC1E 7JE
Tel: 01 387 7050 ext 7306

The course provides an understanding of microwave and optical devices and systems, enabling students to undertake individual research or development work. The course is assessed by examinations and by a project. For part-time students, the project may be conducted at their place of employment. Optional lectures include microwave semiconductor devices, satellite and terrestrial communications, antennas and radar, computer modelling of fields, remote sensing of the earth, microwave circuits, systems and techniques, semiconductor optoelectronic devices, optical and electro-optic components, optical communication systems, lasers, coherent optical systems.
Entrance requirements Good honours degree or approved equivalent.
Grants SERC.
Reader Dr R S Cole.

Molecular electronics

PhD
3 years full time
MSc
1 year full time
15 places
Dr J P Chubb, School of
Industrial Science, Cranfield
Institute of Technology,
Cranfield, Bedford MK43
0AL
Tel: 0234 750111

The MSc course is designed to provide graduates with a qualification in the newly developing, interdisciplinary field of molecular electronics. The course has a modular structure incorporating a foundation module in selected aspects of physics or chemistry, modules in molecular electronics and a module in management. Visiting specialists lecture extensively to the course providing the latest and most relevant coverage of the subject. In the second half of the year students undertake an industrially relevant research project.
Entrance requirements Good honours degree or equivalent in an appropriate scientific or engineering discipline.
Grants Industrial and other bursaries.
Professor of Molecular Electronics Professor H Block.

Noise & vibration

MSc
1 year full time
Course Director (Ref: 2152),
School of Mechanical
Engineering, Cranfield
Institute of Technology,
FREEPOST, Cranfield,
Bedford MK43 7BR
Tel: 0234 750111

European harmonisation in 1992 will call for designers and manufacturers of machinery to comply with new regulations. This course will train engineers, physicists and mathematicians for the required specialisation in the field of noise and vibration. Lectures extend from the fundamental principles of noise and vibration theory to advanced problem solving techniques using computer-aided design, signal processing and finite element methods. The research project forms a major part of the assessment for this course. Recent projects have included machine condition monitoring, vehicle noise dynamics and signal diagnostics.
Entrance requirements Good honours degree in engineering, science, physics or mathematics.
Grants Financial support is available from a number of sources.
Course director Dr R H Bannister.

Offshore engineering

MSc
1 year full time
15 places
PhD
3 years full time
Dr J P Chubb, School of
Industrial Science, Cranfield
Institute of Technology,
Cranfield, Bedford MK43
0AL
Tel: 0234 750111

The MSc course is a specialisation in materials and welding technology related to the offshore engineering industry. Main emphasis is placed on material considerations for both constructional and operational phases including materials selection, welding, fracture, corrosion, inspection. Close liaison with industry is maintained in both course work and research programmes.
Entrance requirements Good honours degree or equivalent.
Grants SERC advanced course studentships and other bursaries.
Professor of Marine Technology Professor J Billingham.

Optical & nano-electronics

PhD
3 years full time
MSc by course
1 year full time
2 years part time
Professor P J R Laybourn,
Dr J M Arnold, Department
of Electronics & Electrical
Engineering, University of
Glasgow, Glasgow G12 8QQ
Tel: 041 339 8855

Research Optical electronics: guided wave and integrated optics, coherent systems, semiconductor quantum-well lasers and other devices. Nano-electronics: electron beam lithography, quantum dots and wires, transport theory in low-dimensional structures. Extensive fabrication and assessment facilities.
  MSc course in Optoelectronic Devices and Systems: physical and optical electronics, communication theory, optical transmission systems, integrated optics, optical signal processing, industrially-orientated research project.
Entrance requirements Good honours degree in science or engineering.

Optoelectronics

MSc/PgD
1 year full time
Dr M N Rudden, Faculty of
Engineering Science and
Technology, Newcastle upon
Tyne Polytechnic, Ellison
Place, Newcastle upon Tyne
NE1 8ST
Tel: 091 232 6002

The aim of this course is to train graduates of physics or engineering in optoelectronics and so equip them for an industrial career in the field. Topics covered in the course include optoelectronic devices, lasers, fibre optics, Fourier optics, computing, image and signal processing. The lectures are backed up by extensive well- equipped laboratories and a four month industrial project is carried out at the end of the course.
Entrance requirements For the MSc course - a good honours degree in physics or engineering, and for the PgD - a good pass degree or relvant HND is required.
Grants SERC and Training Agency support available.
Course leader Dr M N Rudden.

Petroleum engineering

MPhil/PhD
1-3 years full time
MEng
1 year full time
Mr J A Tweedie, Department
of Petroleum Engineering,
Heriot-Watt University,
Riccarton, Edinburgh EH14
4AS
Tel: 031 449 5111

The MEng is a conversion course including six months of lectures, a group design project and individual thesis.

Subjects include: geology, drilling, reservoir engineering, petrophysics, production technology and project economics.

Strong industrial links are maintained through seminars and visits.

Entrance requirements Good honours degree in engineering or science, or suitable industrial experience.
Grants SERC and industrial studentships.
Head of department Professor J M Peden.

Power electronics engineering

MSc
1 year full time
4 years part time
dip
1 year full time
Department of Electronic &
Electrical Engineering,
Loughborough University of
Technology, Loughborough,
Leicestershire LE11 3TU
Tel: 0509 223330

The course, run jointly with Bradford University, consists of two terms of formal work, one at Bradford, one at Loughborough, and a project. It aims to give students an understanding of semiconductor devices and their practical applications.

Entrance requirements First or second class honours degree in electrical engineering/electronics or an equivalent.
Grants SERC studentships are available to qualified applicants.
Course tutor Dr C D Manning.

Structural engineering

MSc
1 year full time
15 places
The Postgraduate
Admissions Officer,
Department of Civil &
Structural Engineering,
UMIST - The University of
Manchester Institute of
Science and Technology, PO
Box 88, Manchester M60
1QD

Examined taught course followed by dissertation projects. Taught course comprises - three core modules, General Theory, Steel Structures and Concrete Structures plus two electives from Finite elements, Properties of Materials and Project Management.
Entrance requirements Good honours degree or equivalent.

Surface engineering

MSc
1 year full time
15 places
Mr S Walton, Department of
Materials Technology, Brunel
University, Uxbridge,
Middlesex UB8 3PH
Tel: 0895 74000 ext 2970
Fax: 0895 32808

Surface processing produces composite materials with novel combinations of bulk and surface properties that cannot be achieved in a single material. This course, the only one of its kind in the UK, integrates surface processing, performance and characterisation of engineering surfaces into a single discipline. It consists of a two term lecture course with associated laboratory work, and a project in surface engineering is undertaken from June to September.
Entrance requirements Normally an honours degree in one of the following engineering, physics, chemistry, metallurgy, materials science or polymer science. Other qualifications will be considered.

Systems engineering

MSc
1 year full time
50 places
The Academic Registrar,
University of Wales College
of Cardiff, PO Box 68,
Cardiff CF1 3XA
Tel: 0222 874000

This course presents the material necessary to analyse, design and test systems for automatic production in the automotive, process and manufacturing industries. The course contains a significant amount of material devoted to microelectronic techniques and includes modules on: computers and programming, automation and robotics, control system synthesis, automatic test, information technology for manufacture, computer aided engineering and instrumentation and measurement.

Candidates who are successful in the written examinations will pursue a four-month project and submit a dissertation which, if satisfactory, completes the requirements for the MSc degree.

Entrance requirements Degree in engineering, mathematics, or applied science.

Head of department Professor D R Towill.

Telecommunications technology

MSc
1 year full time
dip
6 months full time
PhD
3 years full time
MPhil
2 years full time
Department of Electrical &
Electronic Engineering &
Applied Physics, Aston
University, Aston Triangle,
Birmingham B4 7ET
Tel: 021 359 3611

One year MSc course or six month postgraduate diploma course in Telecommunications technology. Topics include: communications principles, communications systems, switching systems engineering and software engineering and computing. MSc course includes six months full time project.

Entrance requirements Honours degree, preferably in engineering or associated discipline or equivalent.

Grants Some SERC postgraduate studentships are available for suitably qualified students.

Course tutor Dr R L Brewster.

Thermal energy processes

PhD
3 years full time
MSc
1 year full time
or part time
Course Tutor (Ref: 2148),
Dept of Applied Energy,
Cranfield Institute of
Technology, School of
Mechanical Engineering,
FREEPOST , Cranfield,
Bedford MK43 7BR
Tel: 0234 750111

This multidisciplinary MSc course has been devised, with British Industry, to equip engineering and science graduates with a much needed blend of design skills. Taught topics range from industrial fluidised-bed systems to domestic appliances, and from marketing to environmental protection. A variety of relevant research activities is encouraged and students may suggest suitable research projects of their own.

Entrance requirements Good honours degree or equivalent, *or* pass degree/HND plus for Preliminary Year course.

Grants Bursaries and Industrially-funded scholarships.

Course tutor Dr Marcus Newborough.

Transport studies

MSc
1 year full time
and part time
MPhil/PhD
2-3 years full time
and part time
Dr D S Wright, Centre for Transport Studies, Cranfield Institute of Technology, Cranfield, Bedford MK43 0AL
Tel: 0234 752770

The Master's programme provides students with the skills for management and planning in both freight and passenger transport. The programme comprises a four term equivalent with the first term providing intensive modules on transport systems analysis and specification. In the second of the two taught terms students specialise in particular fields:- transport management, international logistics, public transport management, transport policy and developing countries. Further specialism by air, sea, road and rail is also permitted. In the final two terms each student follows an individual project in their field of interest such as information systems, freight and distribution, passenger transport, transport in developing countries and policy issues. Research course opportunities in these and other areas are available.
Entrance requirements Good honours degree or recognised professional qualificaition with relevant experience.
Grants SERC advanced course and research studentships.
Course tutor I G Black.

Underwater technology

PhD 3 years
MSc
1 year full time
15 places
Dr J P Chubb, School of Industrial Science, Cranfield Institute of Technology, Cranfield, Bedford MK43 0AL
Tel: 0234 750111

This MSc course deals with the technology required for the planning of underwater tasks and procedures for inspection, monitoring, maintenance and repair of offshore structures and pipelines. The syllabus covers project planning and management, underwater tasks and delivery systems, underwater instrumentation, offshore structures and material performance, safety, risk and reliability. Close liaison with industry is maintained in both course work and project work. An option is available in Subsea Engineering.
Entrance requirements Good honours degree in a scientific discipline.
Grants SERC advanced course studentships and other bursaries.
Senior Lecturer Dr J Strutt.

Welding & adhesive bonding of materials

MSc
1 year full time
15 places
Mr S Walton, Department of Materials Technology, Brunel University, Uxbridge, Middlesex UB8 3PH
Tel: 0895 74000 Fax: 0895 32806

The study and application of all types of welding and bonding, particularly of high integrity structures utilising different materials in combination, is a rapidly expanding area of science and technology of engineering materials.
The advanced course in welding and adhesive bonding of engineering materials is intended to produce high quality graduates with specialised knowledge in the joining of both similar and dissimilar materials. The course is aimed primarily at the needs of industry but it will also satisfy the requirements for the training of potential research students.
Entrance requirements Candidates will normally be expected to hold an honours degree in one of the following: engineering, physics, chemistry, metallurgy/materials science or polymer science and technology.
Grants The Training Agency.

Welding technology

PhD 3 years
MSc
1 year full time
15 places
Dr J P Chubb, School of
Industrial Science, Cranfield
Institute of Technology,
Cranfield, Bedford MK43
0AL
Tel: 0234 750111

The MSc course is a specialisation for engineers, metallurgists and physicists who wish to start their career as welding engineers. Studies cover theoretical and practical aspects of welding processes, metallurgy, design and quality control. Close liaison with industry is maintained in course work and research.

Entrance requirements Good honours degree or equivalent.
Grants SERC advanced course studentships, bursaries.
Professor of Fabrication and Quality Systems Professor J M Rogerson.

Environmental studies

Environmental studies is a term covering a wide range of specialised disciplines all connected in some way with aspects of the natural environment. The specific career area you wish to enter will determine which type of qualification you pursue.

Many of the courses in this chapter are concerned with the study of the natural environment - its design, management and conservation. Some focus on the built environment. Some are explicitly concerned with ecological issues, in particular the environmental effects of different kinds of man-made developments. Others deal with the productive use of the landscape and in some instances its exploitation, notably for its mineral wealth. Whichever subject interests you most there are some basic observations one can make about further study in this field.

Course alternatives

It is important to distinguish between taught courses - MScs and MAs -and opportunities for further independent study which lead to higher degrees by research - PhD and MPhil. Both provide opportunities for different kinds of learning: on the one hand, a programme of study, lecture-based, usually lasting one year and on the other, three years or more of supervised research.

Which are you looking for? In terms of the taught courses featured here it is possible to distinguish four types of programme. Some are explicitly vocational. Those in town planning and landscape architecture, for example, act as essential qualification routes for graduates from other subject areas who want to qualify professionally. Other courses, such as animal nutrition, plant breeding or grassland science are employment-focussed, providing a basis for a research career in government institutes or private companies.

Vocational training

Other courses provide access to clearly defined skills and technical expertise. Courses in cartography and photogrammetry fall into this category. Yet again some courses are very much linked to a specific industry. The MSc in crop protection, run jointly by Bath and Bristol universities, is clearly designed to meet the needs of the agrochemical industry. Finally there are courses at postgraduate level which represent an extension of degree level academic work - an MA in human geography provides an obvious example.

In conclusion most courses will be specialised in nature, providing a vocational emphasis, and be concerned with the development of skills and techniques.

Securing funding

Having decided on the kind of course you want, what about applications and finance? In nearly every case applications should be made direct to the course centre; there are no central admissions systems. Grants are usually allocated to departments by the research councils and other funding bodies.

For courses in aquatic and terrestrial life sciences and geology the main funding body is the Natural Environment Research Council (NERC). The Agriculture and Food Research Council (AFRC) finances food-related research. Awards to students come in the form of advanced course studentships and research studentships. Generally there are too few studentships for the number of successful applicants, so a department may decide to split a grant between two students or offer a place in the hope that students can finance themselves.

Given the increased awareness of environmental issues, it is doubtful whether there will be sufficient studentships for all those wanting to undertake postgraduate study in this area. It may be easier, for example, to gain an award for a course in geology or oceanography than for environmental conservation or pollution control.

Award bodies

Many courses will have a range of sponsoring agencies, so it is always good practise to consult individual departments. On a course in agricultural economics, for example, students may be funded by awards from the Ministry of Agriculture, Fisheries and Food (MAFF) or organisations such as the Milk Marketing Board or the Overseas Development Administration, which gives awards to British students wishing to work abroad.

Students interested in research should be aware that in addition to studentships awarded by bodies like MAFF and NERC, there are the Co-operative Awards in Sciences of the Environment (CASE), which result from collaborative projects between industry and higher education, which offer practical, industry-based experience. In addition, posts as research assistants in universities and polytechnics offer the opportunity for generally low-paid work in assisting members of academic staff with particular research projects.

Entry qualifications

For most Master's courses a good honours degree is required, usually a 2ii at least. Research students will invariably need a first or 2i degree. However, with a buoyant job market, it is possible that there could be less competition for places than you might imagine and you may get the offer of a place with a lower class of degree. If you have a pass degree, you may well find a place on a postgraduate diploma level course, which can then lead to the related Master's programme. If lack of finance is a real problem you could consider the possibility of taking out a loan. Alternatively, you could opt for a full-time job which would give the opportunity of studying for a second degree on a part-time basis.

What of the returns?

It is clear that a postgraduate qualification in itself may not be a guarantee of a job, but it will help. And the skills and specialist knowledge it provides will probably open more doors for you than a first degree. The increasing demand for technologists and the professionally qualified in agricultural research, conservation,

landscape and recreation management, and the productive use and development of the environment, mean that the employment prospects are encouraging.

Those interested in environmental conservation and protection may, however, face a very competitive labour market because of the large number of graduates and postgraduates interested in 'green' issues.

Ben Ball

This listing contains **taught courses** (under the heading 'Higher degrees by instruction') and **research opportunities** (under the heading 'Higher degrees by research'). All study exceeds two terms or six months and is offered on both a full-time and part-time basis unless otherwise indicated. Post-experience and in-service courses are only included when advertised.

☐   This symbol indicates that the **taught course(s)** or **research opportunities** are advertised at the end of this listing.

Biol   An italic abbreviation indicates that an advertisement has been placed at the end of another chapter.

✩   This symbol indicates full-time study only.

△   This symbol indicates part-time study only.

For quick reference to advertisements, please use the 'Advertiser's course entry index'. For further information regarding the listing, please refer to page 53.

General

Higher degrees by instruction

Analytical chemistry & instrumentation
Loughborough U MSc   *Chem*

Applied policy analysis for developing countries
Nottingham U MA✩/dip✩

Atmospheric sciences
East Anglia U MSc✩

Crop protection
Harper Adams AgC dip✩

Energy & buildings
Cranfield IT MSc✩   *Eng*

Energy conservation & the environment
Cranfield IT MSc✩   *Eng*

Environmental & ecological sciences
Lancaster U MSc✩/dip✩

Environmental engineering
Newcastle U MSc✩/cert✩/dip✩

☐ **Environmental impact assessment**
Brighton P MSc△

Environmental psychology
Surrey U MSc✩

Environmental science
Aberdeen U MSc✩/dip✩

L|M|D

Department of Land Management
and Development
University of Reading

POSTGRADUATE EDUCATION IN LAND, PROPERTY AND PLANNING

The faculty draws upon the services of some 40 staff in the departments of Land Management, Economics, Law and Geography to mount professionally recognised courses and advanced tuition/research in the field of urban and regional studies. There is a particular emphasis upon urban and rural planning, property valuation and development, and investment appraisal in Britain and Europe.

COURSES

MPhil ENVIRONMENTAL PLANNING
RTPI recognised, two year full-time course *recognised by ESRC as AP priority.*

MPhil LAND MANAGEMENT
RICS recognised, two year full-time course *recognised by ESRC as AP priority. Commercially sponsored studentships may also be available.*

MSc LAND MANAGEMENT
RICS recognised, one year full-time course. *Commercially sponsored studentships may be available.*

MSc TOWN AND COUNTRY PLANNING
RTPI recognised, three year, one day a week course for planners already in practice.

MSc URBAN LAND APPRAISAL
A one year full time course dealing with problems of modern real estate appraisal from a quantitative point of view.

DOCTORAL PROGRAMME IN URBAN AND REGIONAL STUDIES
An ESRC recognised programme with supporting tuition in research methods for study on any topic within the general field of urban and regional studies, planning or property.

Write for further information and courses handbooks for any of these courses/programmes to:

The Administrative Assistant
Faculty of Urban and Regional Studies
University of Reading
Whiteknights
PO Box 219
Reading, RG6 2BU
Telephone 0734 318182

Environmental science: measurement, analysis & modelling
Nottingham U MSc☆/dip☆

Environmental sciences
East Anglia U dip☆

Environmental technology
London U Imperial C MSc☆/dip☆

Fighting experience
Royal Military C of Science dip☆

Forest industries technology
Bangor, U of Wales MSc☆/dip☆

Geographical information systems
Nottingham U MSc☆

Independent study
East London P MA/MSc/dip

International studies
Newcastle U MA☆

Land administration
East London P cert△/dip△

Management & scientific aspects of water surveillance & water quality
Surrey U dip☆

Marine & fisheries science
Aberdeen U MSc☆/dip☆   *Biol*

Marine geotechnics
Bangor, U of Wales MSc☆/dip☆

Marine resource development & protection
Heriot-Watt U MSc   □

Physical oceanography
Bangor, U of Wales MSc☆/dip☆

Politics of international resources & development
Leeds U MA

Pollution control engineering
Teesside P BEng☆

Regional development
Strathclyde U MSc/dip

Rural & regional resources planning
Robert Gordon's IT MSc☆

Soil science
Aberdeen U MSc☆/dip☆   □

Tropical coastal management
Newcastle U MSc☆/dip☆

Urban & regional planning
Strathclyde U MSc/dip

Urban & regional studies
Birmingham U PhD/MPhil/ MSocSc/dip   □

Urban development
Strathclyde U MSc/dip

Urban history
Leicester U MA

Water resources technology
Birmingham U MSc(Eng)

Higher degrees by research

Advanced studies
Manchester P PhD/MPhil

Architecture
Newcastle U PhD/MLitt/MSc

Control theory
Salford U PhD☆/MSc☆

Environmental sciences
East Anglia U PhD/MPhil
Lancaster U PhD/MPhil

Geography
Sheffield U PhD/MPhil   □

Geological sciences
London U UC PhD☆/MPhil☆

Humanities
Middlesex P PhD/MPhil/dip△

Independent study
East London P PhD/MPhil

Invertebrate biology & pest control
Cardiff U of Wales C PhD☆/ MPhil☆

Landscape architecture
Sheffield U PhD/MPhil

Mechanical engineering
London U King's C PhD☆/ MPhil☆   *Eng*

Pure & applied biology
London U Imperial C PhD/MPhil

Radiation chemistry research
Leeds U PhD/MPhil   *Chem*

Soil science
Aberdeen U PhD☆/MPhil☆/ MSc☆   □

Transport
Cardiff U of Wales C PhD☆/ MPhil☆

Urban & regional studies
Birmingham U PhD/MPhil/ MSocSc   □ *Soc*

Agriculture

Higher degrees by instruction

Agrarian studies
Sussex U MA

Agricultural & amenity grassland
Aberystwyth, UC of Wales MSc☆

Agricultural communications
Belfast Queen's U dip
Loughry CAg & Food Technology dip☆

Agricultural development
London U Wye C dip☆

Agricultural development economics
East Anglia U dip☆

Agricultural economics
Aberdeen SAg MSc/dip
Aberystwyth, UC of Wales MSc☆/dip☆   *Soc*
East Anglia U MSc☆
London U Wye C dip☆
Oxford U MSc☆
Reading U MSc☆/dip☆

Agricultural economics (agrarian development overseas)
London U Wye C MSc☆

Agricultural economics (agricultural marketing)
London U Wye C MSc☆

Agricultural economics (agricultural policy)
London U Wye C MSc☆

Agricultural economics (farm business management)
London U Wye C MSc☆

Agricultural education
Reading U MSc☆/dip☆

Agricultural extension
Reading U MSc☆/dip☆

Agricultural machinery mechanisation
Silsoe C MSc☆/dip☆

Agricultural policy analysis
Glasgow U MPhil

Agricultural research & development
East Anglia U MSc☆

Agricultural science
Bangor, U of Wales dip☆

Belfast Queen's U dip☆

Applied entomology
London U Imperial C MSc/dip

Applied insect taxonomy
Cardiff U of Wales C dip☆   *Biol*

Applied nematology
London U Imperial C MSc/dip

Beef, sheep production & marketing
Welsh AgC cert☆

Cell & molecular genetics of crop plants
Aberystwyth, UC of Wales MSc☆

Cellular & molecular plant science
Bangor, U of Wales MSc☆/dip☆

Conservation of soil fertility
Kent U MSc

Crop physiology
Reading U MSc☆

Crop production
Bath U MSc☆/dip☆

Crop protection
Harper Adams AgC dip☆   □

Drainage & land reclamation engineering
Silsoe C MSc☆/dip☆

Dryland farming
Silsoe C MSc☆

Engineering for rural development
Silsoe C MSc☆

Engineering hydrology
London U Imperial C MSc/dip

Farm business organisation & management
Aberdeen SAg dip☆

Farm management
South West P dip☆

Forestry
Bangor, U of Wales dip☆

Grassland science
Reading U MSc☆

History of the English landscape
Reading U MA

Integrated pest & disease management
London U Wye C MSc☆

International agricultural marketing
Newcastle U MSc☆/dip☆   *Bus*

Irrigation engineering
Silsoe C MSc☆
Southampton U MSc☆/dip☆

Management for agricultural development
Silsoe C MSc☆

Manufacturing for agricultural & industrial development
Silsoe C MSc☆

Marketing
Newcastle U MSc☆

Marketing & product management
Silsoe C MSc☆/dip☆

Pedology & soil survey
Reading U MSc☆

Plant pathology
London U Imperial C MSc/dip

Resource assessment for development planning
East Anglia U MSc☆

Rural & regional resources planning
Aberdeen U MSc☆/dip☆

Rural development
East Anglia U MA☆/MSc☆
Manchester U MA(Econ)☆

Rural resource management
Bangor, U of Wales MSc☆/dip☆

Rural social development
Reading U MA☆/dip☆

Soil & water engineering
Silsoe C MSc☆/dip☆

Soil chemistry & fertility
Reading U MSc

Soil conservation
Silsoe C MSc☆

Soil conservation & land reclamation engineering
Southampton U MSc☆/dip☆

Soil science
Newcastle U MSc☆/dip☆
Reading U MAgrSci☆/MSc☆

Soil water management
Reading U MSc

Symbiotic nitrogen fixation
Aberystwyth, UC of Wales MSc☆

Tropical agricultural & environmental science
Newcastle U MSc☆/dip☆

Tropical agricultural development
Reading U MAgrSc☆/MSc☆/dip☆

Tropical agriculture
London U Wye C MSc☆

Weed science
London U Imperial C MSc/dip☆

World animal production
Bangor, U of Wales MSc☆/dip☆

Higher degrees by research

Agrarian studies
Sussex U DPhil/MPhil

Agricultural & food chemistry
Edinburgh U PhD/MPhil

Agricultural & food marketing
Edinburgh U PhD/MPhil

Agricultural biochemistry
Edinburgh U PhD/MPhil

Agricultural biochemistry & nutrition
Edinburgh U PhD/MPhil
Newcastle U PhD/MPhil

Agricultural biology
Edinburgh U PhD/MPhil

Agricultural biology & environmental science
Newcastle U PhD/MPhil

Agricultural biometrics
Belfast Queen's U PhD/MAgr/MSc

Agricultural botany
Belfast Queen's U PhD/MAgr
Edinburgh U PhD/MPhil
Glasgow U PhD/MSc

Agricultural chemistry
Edinburgh U PhD/MPhil
Glasgow U PhD/MSc

Agricultural economics
Bangor, U of Wales PhD☆/MPhil☆
Edinburgh U PhD/MPhil
Glasgow U PhD/MSc
Manchester U PhD/MA(Econ)
Newcastle U PhD/MPhil
Oxford U DPhil☆/MLitt☆/MSc☆
West of Scotland C PhD☆/MSc☆

Agricultural economics & food marketing
Newcastle U PhD/MPhil

Agricultural economics & management
Edinburgh U PhD/MPhil
Reading U PhD/MPhil/MSc

Agricultural extension & rural development
Edinburgh U PhD/MPhil
Reading U PhD/MPhil

Agricultural history
Reading U PhD/MPhil

Agricultural microbiology
Edinburgh U PhD/MPhil

University of Strathclyde

Faculty of Engineering
Postgraduate studies

POSTGRADUATE INSTRUCTIONAL COURSES
One-year MSc (depending on entry qualifications) and nine-month Diploma in:

Hydraulics, Hydrology and Coastal Dynamics
Public Health and Environmental Control
   Engineering
Structural Engineering
Highway Engineering
Water Engineering
Soil and Water Management
Construction Management
Geotechnical Engineering
Petroleum Engineering
Surface Mining and Land Reclamation
Electrical Power Engineering
Information Technology Systems
Optical Electronics
Laser Engineering and Pulsed Power Technology
Energy Systems and the Environment

Information Technology
Process Engineering
Mechanical Engineering
Ship Production Technology
Marine Technology
Production, Processing and Fabrication of Materials
Properties and Applications of Engineering
   Materials
Computer-Integrated Manufacture
Production Engineering and Management
Bioengineering
Facilities Management
Computer-Aided Building Design
Urban Design
Computer-Aided Engineering Design

RESEARCH PROGRAMME
MPhil, PhD and Industrial Research are available in:

ABACUS (Architecture and Building Aids
Computer Unit, Strathclyde)
BPSU (Building Performance Studies Unit)
UDSU (Urban Design Studies Unit)
HRRU (Housing Research and Rehabilitation Unit)
ESRU (The Energy Simulation Research Unit)
Information Management
Bioengineering
Structural Engineering and Materials
Geotechnical Engineering
Hydraulics and Coastal Engineering
Surveying
Transportation
Construction Management
Environmental Health
Public Health Engineering
Water and Environmental Management

Energy Studies Unit
Mineral Resourses Engineering
Manufacture and Engineering Management
CAD Centre
Engineering Applications Centre
Communications
Industrial Control Unit
Optoelectronics
Power Engineering
Signal Processing
Chemical Engineering
Dynamics and Control
Mechanics of Materials
Metallurgy and Engineering Materials
Ship and Marine Technology
Thermo Fluid and Environmental Engineering

(Most of the Instructional Courses and Research Programmes can be undertaken on a full- and part-time basis).

Further information from: **The Faculty Officer (Engineering),
University of Strathclyde, Glasgow G1 1XO, Scotland, UK.
Telephone: 041-552 4400. Telex: 77472 UNSLIB-G.
Telefax: Int Code plus 41 552 0775**

Agricultural production systems planning
Silsoe C PhD/MPhil

Agricultural science
Edinburgh U PhD/MPhil

Agricultural zoology
Aberdeen SAg PhD☆/MSc☆
Belfast Queen's U PhD/MSc
Edinburgh U PhD/MPhil
Glasgow U PhD/MSc

Agriculture
Bangor, U of Wales PhD☆/
  MPhil☆
Edinburgh U PhD/MPhil
Edinburgh U SAg PhD/MPhil
Glasgow U PhD/MSc
London U Wye C PhD☆/MPhil☆
Newcastle U PhD/MPhil
West of Scotland C PhD☆/MSc☆

Agriculture & food economics
Belfast Queen's U PhD/MAgr/
  MSc

Agriculture, food & land use
South West P PhD/MPhil

Agronomy
Edinburgh U PhD/MPhil

Animal production & health
Aberdeen SAg PhD☆/MSc☆

Applied sciences
Wolverhampton P PhD/MPhil

Crop science
Reading U PhD☆/MPhil☆

Development studies
East Anglia U PhD☆
Manchester U PhD/MA(Econ)

Drainage, irrigation & water management
Silsoe C PhD/MPhil

European agricultural studies
London U Wye C PhD☆/MPhil☆

Food & agricultural chemistry
Belfast Queen's U PhD/MSc

Food science & agricultural microbiology
Belfast Queen's U PhD/MSc

Marketing & management
Silsoe C PhD/MPhil

Plant biology
Bath U PhD☆/MPhil☆

Post harvest technology
Silsoe C PhD/MPhil

Rural land use
Silsoe C PhD/MPhil

Zoology
West of Scotland C PhD☆/MSc☆

Animal science, husbandry

Higher degrees by instruction

Advanced agricultural business management
Royal AgC dip☆

Agricultural extension
Reading U MSc☆/dip☆

Agricultural science
Aberystwyth, UC of Wales MA☆/
dip☆

Animal breeding
Edinburgh U MSc☆/dip☆
Edinburgh U SAg MSc☆/dip☆

Animal health
London U Royal Veterinary C
MSc☆

Animal nutrition
Aberdeen SAg MSc/dip
Aberdeen U MSc☆/dip☆
Newcastle U MSc☆/dip☆

Animal parasitology
Bangor, U of Wales MSc☆/dip☆

Animal production
Aberdeen SAg MSc☆
Aberdeen U MSc☆
Reading U MSc☆/dip☆

Apiculture
Cardiff U of Wales C dip☆

Aquaculture
Stirling U MSc/dip   *Biol*

Beef, sheep production & marketing
Welsh AgC cert☆

Farm management
South West P dip☆

Fish marketing/fishery harbour management/fisheries policy & planning
Humberside CHE MSc☆

Fisheries & maritime studies
Humberside CHE MSc☆

Fisheries biology
Buckingham U MSc☆

Fisheries economics
Portsmouth P cert☆

Fisheries master fisherman/ fishing skipper
Humberside CHE Dip☆

Food & agricultural biotechnology
Reading U MSc☆

Insect pest management
Southampton U MSc/cert☆/dip

Pig production
Aberdeen SAg MSc☆
Aberdeen U MSc☆

Poultry science
Glasgow U MSc☆/dip☆
West of Scotland C MSc☆/dip☆

Ruminant science
Glasgow U MSc/dip
West of Scotland C MSc/dip

Rural land studies
Reading U dip☆

Rural science
Edinburgh U dip☆
Edinburgh U SAg dip☆

Shellfish biology, fisheries & culture
Bangor, U of Wales MSc/dip

Tropical animal production & health
Edinburgh U MSc☆/dip☆
Edinburgh U SAg MSc☆/dip☆

World animal production
Bangor, U of Wales MSc☆/dip☆

Higher degrees by research

Agricultural biochemistry & nutrition
Edinburgh U PhD/MPhil
Newcastle U PhD/MPhil

Agricultural extension & rural development
Edinburgh U PhD/MPhil
Reading U MPhil△

Agricultural science
Edinburgh U PhD/MPhil

Agricultural zoology
Edinburgh U PhD/MPhil
Glasgow U PhD/MSc

Agriculture
London U Wye C PhD☆/MPhil☆

Animal & microbial sciences
Reading U PhD/MPhil

Animal behaviour
Edinburgh U PhD/MPhil

Oxford U DPhil☆/MLitt☆

Animal biology
Bangor, U of Wales PhD☆/
MPhil☆
Edinburgh U PhD/MPhil
Sheffield U PhD/MPhil

Animal developmental biology
Glasgow U PhD/MSc

Animal health
Edinburgh U PhD/MPhil

Animal husbandry
Bristol U PhD☆/MSc☆
Edinburgh U PhD/MPhil
Glasgow U PhD/MSc
Liverpool U PhD/MVSc
London U Royal Veterinary C
PhD☆/MPhil☆

Animal nutrition
Aberdeen U PhD☆/MPhil☆/MSc☆
Edinburgh U PhD/MPhil

Animal nutriton
Belfast Queen's U PhD/MSc

Animal physiology
Edinburgh U PhD/MPhil
Nottingham U PhD/MPhil
Oxford U DPhil☆/MSc☆

Animal physiology & ecology
Bath U PhD☆/MPhil☆

Animal physiology & nutrition
Leeds U PhD/MPhil/MSc

Animal production & health
Aberdeen U PhD☆/MPhil☆/MSc☆
Edinburgh U PhD/MPhil

Animal sciences
Aberystwyth, UC of Wales
PhD☆/MPhil☆

Aquaculture
Stirling U PhD/MSc

Crop & animal production
Belfast Queen's U PhD/MSc
Edinburgh U PhD/MPhil

Crop & animal protection
Edinburgh U PhD/MPhil

Dairy science
Glasgow U PhD/MSc

Farm animals
London U Royal Veterinary C
PhD☆/MPhil☆

Fishery management
Stirling U PhD/MPhil

Human environmental sciences
London U King's C PhD☆/MPhil☆

Insect chemistry & physiology
Sussex U DPhil/MPhil

Invertebrate biology & pest control
Cardiff U of Wales C PhD☆/
MPhil☆

Invertebrate chemistry & comparative physiology
Portsmouth P PhD☆/MPhil☆

Laboratory animal science
London U Royal Veterinary C
PhD☆/MPhil☆

Morphology & development
Oxford U DPhil☆/MSc☆

Physiology
London U Wye C PhD☆/MPhil☆

Pig production
Aberdeen SAg PhD☆/MSc☆

Poultry science
Glasgow U PhD/MSc
West of Scotland C PhD☆/MSc☆

Ruminant science
West of Scotland C PhD☆/MSc☆

Tropical animal health
Edinburgh U PhD/MPhil

Wildlife & fisheries management
Edinburgh U PhD/MPhil

Architecture, design

Higher degrees by instruction

Advanced architectual studies
Architectural Association S of
Architecture dip☆/RIBA☆

Advanced architectural studies
Belfast Queen's U dip☆
London U UC MSc
Robert Gordon's IT dip☆

Advanced design research
London C of Furniture dip△

Archaeological practice
York U MA

Architectural conservation
Edinburgh CA MSc☆/dip☆
Heriot-Watt U MSc☆/dip☆

Architectural heritage management
York U MA

Architectural history
Keele U MA△

Architectural management
Nottingham U MA☆

Architectural practice
Humberside CHE cert☆/RIBA☆
York U MA

Architectural science
Sheffield U MArch☆

Architecture
Architectural Association S of
Architecture dip☆/RIBA☆
Belfast Queen's U MArch☆/
MSc☆
Birmingham P MA/RIBA
Cambridge U MPhil☆
Central London P dip☆/RIBA☆
Duncan of Jordanstone CA
BArch☆/RIBA☆
Edinburgh CA MArch☆/dip☆
Glasgow U MArch/dip
Heriot-Watt U MArch☆/dip☆
Humberside CHE dip☆/RIBA☆
Kingston P MArch△/dip☆/RIBA△
Leeds P dip
Leicester P dip☆
Liverpool P dip/RIBA
London U UC dip☆/RIBA☆
Manchester P dip
Nottingham P MA☆
Oxford P dip☆
Portsmouth P dip☆/RIBA☆
Royal CA MA☆
Sheffield U MArch/MA/dip☆/
RIBA☆
South Bank P dip/RIBA
South West P dip☆/RIBA☆
York U MA☆

Architecture & building
Liverpool U MArch/MDes

Architecture: housing studies
Newcastle U MPhil☆/dip☆

Art & architecture
Kent IAD MA

Building conservation
Architectural Association S of
Architecture dip△

Building design for developing countries
London U UC MSc

Building economics & management
London U UC MSc

Building rehabilitation studies
Nottingham P dip△
Thames P MA△

Computer aided building design
Strathclyde U MSc/dip

Conservation of architectural stonework
Weymouth C dip☆

Construction management
Bath U MSc   *Eng*

Construction management (building maitainance)
Heriot-Watt U MSc/dip   *Eng*

Construction management (corporate strategy)
Heriot-Watt U MSc/dip   *Eng*

Construction management (production management)
Heriot-Watt U MSc/dip   *Eng*

Construction management (project management)
Heriot-Watt U MSc/dip   *Eng*

Design
Glasgow SA MA☆

Energy & buildings
Cranfield IT MSc☆   *Eng*

Environment & energy studies
Architectural Association S of Architecture dip☆

Environmental art
Glasgow SA dip☆

Environmental design & engineering
London U UC MSc

Garden & landscape conservation
Architectural Association S of Architecture dip△

Graduate design
Architectural Association S of Architecture dip☆

History & theory of architecture
Architectural Association S of Architecture dip☆
Essex U MA☆

History of modern architecture
London U UC MSc

Housing
Heriot-Watt U dip☆

Housing studies
Architectural Association S of Architecture dip☆

Industrial design
Glasgow SA dip☆

Interior design
Leicester P MA☆

Landscape
Sheffield U MArch

Landscape architecture
Birmingham P MA△/dip△

Cheltenham & Gloucester CHE dip☆
Leeds P dip
Manchester P dip☆
Thames P dip

Landscape design
Manchester U MA(LD)☆/MLD☆/ BLD☆
Newcastle U MPhil☆/dip
Sheffield U MArch☆/MA☆/cert△/ dip☆

Landscape ecology, design & management
London U Wye C MSc☆

Landscape studies
Edinburgh U dip☆

Light & lighting
London U UC MSc

Liturgy & architecture
Birmingham U dip

Oriental studies (Islamic art & architecture)
Oxford U MPhil☆/MSt☆

Production of the built environment
London U UC MSc

Public art & design
Duncan of Jordanstone CA MPhil☆

Sculpture studies
Leeds U MA☆

Solar energy & energy conservation in buildings
Reading U MSc☆

Town & country planning
Newcastle U MPhil☆/dip☆

Town planning
London U UC MPhil

Urban design
Edinburgh CA MSc☆/dip☆/ RIBA☆
Glasgow U MArch
Heriot-Watt U MSc☆/dip☆
Nottingham U MA/dip
Sheffield U MArch☆

Valuation & auctioneering (fine arts & chattels)
Southampton IHE ISVA☆

Higher degrees by research

Architecture
Birmingham P PhD/MPhil

Cambridge U PhD☆/MLitt☆/ MSc☆
Cardiff U of Wales C PhD☆/ MPhil☆
Central London P PhD☆/MPhil☆
Dundee U PhD/MSc   □
East London P PhD/MPhil
Edinburgh CA PhD/MArch/MSc
Edinburgh U PhD/MPhil
Glasgow U PhD/MArch
Heriot-Watt U PhD☆/MPhil☆
Kingston P PhD/MPhil
Leicester P PhD/MPhil
Liverpool P PhD/MPhil
Liverpool U PhD/MPhil
Manchester U PhD/MPhil
Newcastle U PhD/MLitt/MSc
North London P PhD/MPhil
Nottingham U PhD/MPhil
Oxford P PhD/MPhil
Portsmouth P PhD☆/MPhil☆
Robert Gordon's IT PhD/MPhil
Royal CA PhD☆
Sheffield U PhD/MPhil
South Bank P PhD/MPhil
South West P PhD/MPhil
York U DPhil/MPhil

Architecture & building science
Strathclyde U PhD☆/MArch☆/ MSc☆

Architecture & interior design
Brighton P PhD/MPhil

Architecture & landscape
Leeds P PhD/MPhil/dip
Manchester P PhD/MPhil
Thames P PhD/MPhil

Architecture & planning
Belfast Queen's U PhD/MSc
London U UC PhD☆/MPhil☆

Architecture, art & design
Humberside CHE PhD/MPhil

Architecture, design & construction
Huddersfield P PhD/MPhil

Building science
Sheffield U PhD/MPhil

Core & theoretical studies
Ulster U DPhil/MPhil

Design
Napier P PhD/MPhil
Open U PhD/MPhil/BPhil
Teesside P PhD☆/MPhil☆
Ulster U DPhil/MPhil

Design & technology
Loughborough U PhD/MPhil

Energy studies
Architectural Association S of Architecture PhD☆/MPhil☆

Historical studies
Robert Gordon's IT MLitt

History & theory of architecture
Architectural Association S of
Architecture PhD☆/MPhil☆

Housing studies
Architectural Association S of
Architecture PhD☆/MPhil☆

Industrial design
Leicester P PhD/MPhil

Interior design
North London P PhD/MPhil

Land & building studies
Leicester P PhD/MPhil

Landscape architecture
Edinburgh CA PhD/MArch/MSc
Heriot-Watt U PhD☆/MPhil☆
Sheffield U PhD/MPhil

Naval architecture
Royal Naval Engineering C
PhD☆/MSc☆

Urban design
Central London P PhD☆/MPhil☆

Ecology, soil science, conservation

Higher degrees by instruction

Advanced environmental practice
Farnborough CT dip

Agricultural science
Bangor, U of Wales dip☆

Agronomy
Nottingham U MSc☆

Air & water pollution control
Central London P dip△
Middlesex P dip☆

Aquatic resource management
London U King's C MSc☆

Atmospheric pollution control
Nottingham P dip△

Behavioural ecology
Manchester P MSc△/dip△   *Biol*

Biology of water management
Napier P MSc☆

Biotechnology
Kent U MSc☆/dip☆

Building conservation
Architectural Association S of
Architecture dip△

Cellular & molecular plant science
Bangor, U of Wales MSc☆/dip☆

Computing in earth sciences
Keele U MSc☆

Conservation
London U UC MSc☆/dip☆

Conservation & utilisation of plant genetic resources
Birmingham U MSc

Conservation of architectural stonework
Weymouth C dip☆

Conservation of soil fertility
London U Wye C MSc☆

Conservation policy
Middlesex P MA△/dip△

Conservation studies
York U MA☆

Countryside management
Bangor Normal C cert☆

Crop protection
Aberdeen U MSc☆/dip☆

Cultural resource management
Edinburgh U MSc☆

Earth science & the environment
Kingston P MSc△

Earth surface & environmental science
London U Birkbeck C cert△

Ecology
Bangor, U of Wales MSc☆/dip☆
Durham U MSc☆/dip☆
East Anglia U MSc☆/dip☆
Kent U dip☆
Sunderland P MSc△/dip△

Energy conservation & the environment
Cranfield IT MSc☆   *Eng*

Environmental & ecological sciences
Lancaster U MSc☆/dip☆

Environmental biology
Swansea UC MSc☆

Environmental forestry
Bangor, U of Wales MSc☆/dip☆

Environmental health
Middlesex P dip△

Environmental management
Stirling U MSc☆/dip☆

Environmental resources
Salford U MSc/dip

Environmental sciences
East Anglia U dip☆

Environmental technology
London U Imperial C MSc☆/dip☆

Fisheries biology & management
Bangor, U of Wales MSc☆/dip☆

Forest business management
Aberdeen U MSc☆/dip☆

Forest industries technology
Bangor, U of Wales MSc☆/dip☆

Forest inventory & soil science
Aberdeen U MSc☆/dip☆

Forest mensuration & inventory
Aberdeen U MSc☆/dip☆

Forest resource studies
Aberdeen U MSc☆/dip☆

Forestry & its relation to land use
Oxford U MSc☆

Foundation engineering
Birmingham U MSc(Eng)

Garden & landscape conservation
Architectural Association S of
Architecture dip△

Hydraulics, hydrology & coastal dynamics
Strathclyde U MSc/dip

Hydrogeology
London U UC MSc☆/dip☆

Improvement & renovation of grassland
Aberystwyth, UC of Wales MSc☆

Irrigation
Newcastle U MSc☆/dip☆

Irrigation water management
Silsoe C MSc☆/dip☆

Land administration
East London P cert△/dip△

Land management
Reading U MPhil☆/dip☆

Land resource management & planning
Silsoe C MSc☆/dip☆

Land resources & land utilisation
St Andrews U MPhil☆

Landscape ecology, design & management
London U Wye C MSc☆

Landscape management
Manchester U MA(LM)☆/dip☆

Man, environment & resource development
Salford U MSc☆/dip☆

Man, environment & resources
Salford U MSc☆/dip☆

Marginal land development
Swansea UC MA☆

Marine environmental protection
Bangor, U of Wales MSc/dip☆

Marine pollution chemistry
Liverpool U dip☆

Microbial ecology
Aberdeen U MSc☆

Natural environments & plant growth
London U Birkbeck C MSc△

Natural resource management
Leicester U MSc☆/dip☆

Pedology & soil survey
Reading U MSc☆

Plant biotechnology
London U Wye C MSc☆

Plant ecology & environmental science
London U Birkbeck C cert△

Plant toxins in nutrition
London U Wye C MSc☆

Plantation management
Silsoe C MSc☆

Pollution & environmental control
Manchester UMIST MSc☆

Range management
Silsoe C MSc☆

Resource assessment for development planning
East Anglia U MSc☆

Resource management
Edinburgh U MSc☆/dip☆
Edinburgh U SAg MSc☆

Rural development
Sussex U MSc☆

Rural resource management
Bangor, U of Wales MSc☆/dip☆

Rural resources & environmental policy
London U Wye C MSc☆

Scientific methods in archaeology
Bradford U MA☆/dip☆

Soil & water engineering
Silsoe C MSc☆/dip☆

Soil & water management
Strathclyde U MSc/dip

Soil chemistry & fertility
Reading U MSc

Soil conservation
Silsoe C MSc☆

Soil mechanics
London U Imperial C MSc/dip

Soil mechanics & engineering seismology
London U Imperial C MSc/dip

Soil mechanics & foundation engineering
Newcastle U MSc☆

Soil science
Aberdeen U MSc☆/dip☆   □
Newcastle U MSc☆/dip☆
Reading U MAgrSci☆/MSc☆

Soil science & plant performance
Aberystwyth, UC of Wales MSc☆

Soil water management
Reading U MSc

Tropical & sub tropical horticulture & crop science
London U Wye C MSc☆

Tropical agricultural & environmental science
Newcastle U MSc☆/dip☆

Tropical coastal management
Newcastle U MSc☆/dip☆

Tropical public health engineering
Leeds U MSc(Eng)☆

Urban land studies
Reading U dip☆

Values & the environment
Lancaster U MA

Water pollution control
Middlesex P MSc

Water resources engineering
London U Queen Mary & Westfield C MSc☆

Water resources technology
Birmingham U MSc(Eng)

Water supply & public health engineering
Middlesex P dip☆

Wood preservation research
London U Imperial C MSc/dip☆

Higher degrees by research

Agronomy
Aberdeen SAg PhD☆/MSc☆

Edinburgh U PhD/MPhil
West of Scotland C PhD☆/MSc☆

Animal physiology & ecology
Bath U PhD☆/MPhil☆

Applied ecology
Central London P PhD☆/MPhil☆

Biochemistry, physiology & soil science
Edinburgh U PhD/MPhil

Biological sciences
Bath U PhD☆/MPhil☆

Biological sciences & environmental health
Thames P PhD/MPhil

Biotechnology
Kent U PhD/MPhil/MSc

Botany
Liverpool U PhD/MSc

Conservation
London U UC PhD☆/MPhil☆

Crop production & protection
Aberdeen U PhD☆/MPhil☆/MSc☆

Development studies
East Anglia U PhD☆/MPhil☆

Drainage, irrigation & water management
Silsoe C PhD/MPhil

Earth science
Swansea UC PhD/MPhil

Earth sciences
Cambridge U PhD☆/MSc☆
Leeds U PhD/MPhil/MSc
Liverpool U PhD/MPhil
Open U PhD/MPhil/BPhil
Thames P PhD☆/MPhil☆

Ecological science
Edinburgh U PhD/MPhil

Ecology
Aberdeen U PhD☆/MPhil☆/MSc☆
Kent U PhD/MPhil
London U UC PhD☆/MPhil☆
Middlesex P PhD/MPhil
Newcastle U PhD/MPhil

Ecology & environmental biology
Durham U PhD/MPhil

Ecology & environmental management
Cardiff U of Wales C PhD☆/ MPhil☆

Energy & environment research
Open U PhD☆/MPhil☆/BPhil☆

Environmental & earth studies
Hatfield P PhD/MPhil

Environmental & evolutionary biology
Liverpool U PhD/MPhil

Environmental & geographical studies
Manchester P PhD/MPhil/dip

Environmental biology
Manchester U PhD/MSc
Swansea UC PhD/MPhil

Environmental design
North London P PhD/MPhil

Environmental engineering
South Bank P PhD/MPhil

Environmental science
Aberdeen U PhD☆/MPhil☆/MSc☆
Bradford U PhD/MPhil
Southampton U PhD/MPhil
Stirling U PhD/MSc
Sussex U DPhil/MPhil

Environmental sciences
East Anglia U PhD/MPhil
Lancaster U PhD/MPhil
South West P PhD/MPhil

Environmental studies
Salford U PhD/MSc

Environmental studies & countryside planning
London U Wye C PhD☆/MPhil☆

Environmental technology
London U Imperial C PhD/MPhil/dip

Geography
Liverpool U PhD/MPhil/MSc ☐
London U Queen Mary &
  Westfield C PhD☆/MPhil☆ ☐
London U UC PhD☆/MPhil☆

Geography & environmental studies
Newcastle P PhD☆/MPhil☆
Sheffield City P PhD/MPhil

Geological sciences
South West P PhD/MPhil

Glasshouse investigation/soil science
West of Scotland C PhD☆/MSc☆

Human environment studies
London U UC PhD☆/MPhil☆

Human environmental sciences
London U King's C PhD☆/MPhil☆

Irrigation engineering
Southampton U PhD/MPhil

Irrigation studies
Edinburgh U PhD/MPhil

Land & building studies
Leicester P PhD/MPhil

Land management & development
Reading U PhD/MPhil

Landscape design
Manchester U PhD/MPhil

Landscape management
Manchester U PhD/MPhil

Palaeoecology centre
Belfast Queen's U PhD/MSc

Physiology & environmental science
Nottingham U PhD☆/MPhil☆

Plant ecology
Edinburgh U PhD/MPhil

Plant pathology
London U UC PhD☆/MPhil☆

Plant science
Aberdeen U PhD☆/MPhil☆/MSc☆
Edinburgh U PhD/MPhil

Pure & applied biology
London U Imperial C PhD/MPhil/
  dip

Recreation & environmental studies
Sheffield City P PhD/MPhil

Rural land use
Silsoe C PhD/MPhil

Science
Wales P PhD/MPhil

Seed & grain technology
Silsoe C PhD/MPhil

Social & environmental education
Thames P PhD/MPhil

Soil erosion & conservation
Silsoe C PhD/MPhil

Soil mechanics
Central London P PhD☆/MPhil☆
London U Queen Mary &
  Westfield C PhD☆/MPhil☆

Soil science
Aberdeen U PhD☆/MPhil☆/
  MSc☆ ☐
Edinburgh U PhD/MPhil
London U Wye C PhD☆/MPhil☆
Newcastle U PhD/MPhil
Nottingham U PhD☆/MPhil☆
Oxford U DPhil☆/MSc☆
Reading U PhD/MPhil ☐

Soils & plant nutrition
Belfast Queen's U PhD/MSc

Taxonomy & ecology
Oxford U DPhil☆/MSc☆

Tillage soil management
Silsoe C PhD/MPhil

Zoology
Durham U PhD/MSc
Liverpool U PhD/MSc

Environmental control

Higher degrees by instruction

Advanced environmental practice
Farnborough CT dip

Air & water pollution control
Middlesex P dip☆

Applied insect taxonomy
Cardiff U of Wales C dip☆   Biol

Architectural conservation
Edinburgh CA MSc☆/dip☆

Atmospheric pollution control
Nottingham P dip△

Atmospheric sciences
East Anglia U MSc☆

Biochemical engineering/ biotechnology
Birmingham U MSc(Eng)

Biology of water management
Napier P MSc☆

Combustion & pollution technology
Sheffield U dip☆

Combustion science & pollution control
Sheffield U MSc(Eng)☆/
  MSc(Tech)☆

Conservation of soil fertility
London U Wye C MSc☆

Construction engineering
Leeds U MSc(Eng)

Desalination technology
Glasgow U MSc/dip

Economic geography
London U LSE dip

Energy conservation & the environment
Cranfield IT MSc☆   Eng

Energy systems & environmental management
Glasgow C MSc☆/dip☆ ☐

Engineering hydrology
London U Imperial C MSc/dip

Environmental & ecological sciences
Lancaster U MSc☆/dip☆

Environmental acoustics
South Bank P MSc

Environmental change
Portsmouth P MSc△

Environmental civil engineering
Liverpool U MSc(Eng)☆

Environmental design & engineering
London U UC MSc

Environmental engineering
South Bank P MSc/dip

Environmental forestry
Bangor, U of Wales MSc☆/dip☆

Environmental health
Dundee U MSc
Nottingham P dip☆

Environmental impact assessment
Aberystwyth, UC of Wales dip☆

Environmental law
Aberdeen U LLM☆

Environmental management
Birmingham P MA△/dip△
Stirling U MSc☆/dip☆
Ulster U MSc△/dip△

Environmental planning
Anglia HEC dip△
Nottingham U MA/dip
Reading U MPhil/dip

Environmental planning for developing countries
Nottingham U MA/dip

Environmental pollution control
Leeds U MSc☆

Environmental pollution science
Brunel U MSc

Environmental resources
Salford U MSc/dip

Environmental science
Aberdeen U MSc☆/dip☆

Environmental technology
London U Imperial C MSc☆/dip☆

Heritage management
Birmingham U dip

Housing
Salford U dip☆

Housing studies
Anglia HEC dip△
Glasgow U MPhil△/dip△

Hydrogeology
London U UC MSc☆/dip☆

Insect pest management
Southampton U MSc/cert☆/dip

Integrated pest & disease management
London U Wye C MSc☆

Land administration
East London P cert△/dip△

Land economy
Cambridge U MPhil☆

Land resources & land utilisation
St Andrews U MPhil☆

Marine environmental protection
Bangor, U of Wales MSc/dip☆

National Trust for Scotland studies
St Andrews U MLitt

Natural resource management
Leicester U MSc☆/dip☆

Pollution & environmental control
Manchester U MSc☆/dip☆   □
Manchester UMIST MSc☆

Pollution control engineering
Teesside P BEng☆

Production of the built environment
London U UC MSc

Public health & environmental engineering
Strathclyde U MSc/dip

Public health engineering
London U Imperial C MSc/dip

Quaternary environmental change
North London P MSc△/dip△

Radiation & environmental protection
Surrey U MSc/dip

Remote sensing
London U Imperial C MSc☆

Renewable energy & the environment
Reading U MSc☆

Resource assessment for development planning
East Anglia U MSc☆

River, estuary & coastal engineering
London U Imperial C MSc/dip

Rural & regional resources planning
Aberdeen U MSc☆/dip☆

Rural resources & environmental policy
London U Wye C MSc☆

Shellfish biology, fisheries & culture
Bangor, U of Wales MSc/dip

Social anthropology
Durham U MA☆/dip☆

Soil science
Reading U MAgrSci☆/MSc☆

Toxicology
Birmingham U MSc/dip☆   *Biol*

Transport planning & engineering
Leeds U MSc(Eng)

Tropical public health engineering
Leeds U MSc(Eng)☆

Urban land appraisal
Reading U MSc☆/dip☆

Water pollution control
Central London P MSc△
Middlesex P MSc

Water supply & public health engineering
Middlesex P dip☆

Wildlife management & control
Reading U MSc☆

Higher degrees by research

Botany
Liverpool U PhD/MSc

Built environment studies
Central London P PhD☆/MPhil☆

Chemical engineering
Nottingham U PhD/MPhil   *Chem*

Civil & municipal engineering
London U UC PhD☆/MPhil☆

Civil engineering
Leeds U PhD/MPhil/MSc(Eng)

Countryside management
Newcastle U PhD/MPhil

Desalination technology
Glasgow U PhD/MEng

Development policy & practice
Open U PhD/MPhil/BPhil

Ecological science
Edinburgh U PhD/MPhil

Ecology
Aberdeen U PhD☆/MPhil☆/MSc☆

Ecology & environmental biology
Durham U PhD/MPhil

Ecology & environmental management
Cardiff U of Wales C PhD☆/MPhil☆

Energy & environment research
Open U PhD☆/MPhil☆/BPhil☆

Environmental & earth studies
Hatfield P PhD/MPhil

Environmental & geographical studies
Manchester P PhD/MPhil/dip

Environmental biology
Swansea UC PhD/MPhil

Environmental biotechnology & biodeterioration
Cranfield IT MPhil☆/MSc☆

Environmental design
North London P PhD/MPhil

Environmental engineering
Camborne S of Mines PhD/MPhil
South Bank P PhD/MPhil

Environmental physics
Nottingham U PhD☆/MPhil☆

Environmental planning & management
Manchester U PhD/MPhil

Environmental science
Bradford U PhD/MPhil
Southampton U PhD/MPhil
Stirling U PhD/MSc
Sussex U DPhil/MPhil
Ulster U DPhil/MPhil

Environmental sciences
Lancaster U PhD/MPhil
South West P PhD/MPhil

Environmental studies
Salford U PhD/MSc

Environmental studies & countryside planning
London U Wye C PhD☆/MPhil☆

Environmental technology
London U Imperial C PhD/MPhil/dip

Fuel & energy
Leeds U PhD/MPhil/MSc(Eng)/MSc   *Eng*

Geography
Aberdeen U PhD☆/MPhil☆/MSc☆

Geography & environmental studies
Newcastle P PhD☆/MPhil☆
Sheffield City P PhD/MPhil

Human environment studies
London U UC PhD☆/MPhil☆

Human environmental sciences
London U King's C PhD☆/MPhil☆

Human geography
Aberystwyth, UC of Wales PhD☆/MPhil☆

Industrial & environmental health & safety
Surrey U PhD/MPhil

Land economy
Aberdeen U PhD☆/MPhil☆/MSc☆
Cambridge U PhD☆/MLitt☆/MSc☆

Physiology & environmental science
Nottingham U PhD☆/MPhil☆

Plant science
Aberdeen U PhD☆/MPhil☆/MSc☆
Edinburgh U PhD/MPhil

Pollution research
Manchester U PhD/MSc
Manchester UMIST PhD/MSc

Recreation & environmental studies
Sheffield City P PhD/MPhil

Remote sensing
London U Imperial C PhD/MPhil/dip

Science
Wales P PhD/MPhil

Social, economic & environmental studies
Middlesex P PhD/MPhil

Toxicology
Birmingham U PhD☆/MSc☆

Urban & regional studies
Sheffield City P PhD/MPhil

Geography

Higher degrees by instruction

Applied geography
Salford U MSc△

Applied geography & policy
St David's UC MA☆

Cartography
Glasgow U dip

Comparative regional analysis
Glasgow U MPhil

Conservation
London U UC MSc☆/dip☆

Development economics
East Anglia U MA☆

Digital mapping & automated cartography
Glasgow U dip

Digital mapping & remote sensing
Dundee U dip☆

Earth science & the environment
Kingston P MSc△

Economic geography
London U LSE dip

Energy technology for developing countries
Salford U MSc☆/dip☆

Environmental change
Portsmouth P MSc△

Environmental sciences
East Anglia U dip☆

Geographic information systems
Silsoe C dip☆

Geographical information systems
Edinburgh U MSc☆/dip☆   □
Leeds U MA
Leicester U MSc☆/dip☆
Nottingham U MSc☆

Geography
Durham U MA☆/MSc☆
Edinburgh U dip☆
Glasgow U dip
London U LSE MSc
London U Royal Holloway & Bedford New C MA/MSc
Salford U MA/MSc/cert☆/dip
Sheffield U dip☆
Strathclyde U MSc☆/dip☆
Sussex U MA

Geography in education
London U Inst of Education MA

Geography of Africa & the Middle East
London U SOAS MSc

Human geography
Leeds U MA

Hydrogeology
London U UC MSc☆/dip☆

International studies
Salford U MA☆/cert☆

Land administration
East London P cert△/dip△

London studies
London U Birkbeck C MA△

Meteorology & climatology
Birmingham U MA☆/MSc☆

North American geographical studies
London U Birkbeck C MA△

Pedology & soil survey
Reading U MSc☆

Photogrammetery & remote sensing
Glasgow U dip

Physical geography
Aberystwyth, UC of Wales MSc☆
Manchester U MSc☆

Physical geography updated
London U Birkbeck C cert△

Polar studies
Cambridge U MPhil☆

Population policies & programmes
Cardiff U of Wales C MSc(Econ)☆

Quaternary studies
City of London P MSc△

Remote sensing
London U Imperial C MSc☆
London U UC MSc☆

Sedimentology & its applications
Reading U MSc☆

Social & population geography
St Andrews U MLitt/MPhil☆/dip☆

Soil chemistry & fertility
Reading U MSc

Soil science
Newcastle U MSc☆/dip☆
Reading U MAgrSci☆/MSc☆

Soil water management
Reading U MSc

Soviet & East European studies
Glasgow U MPhil/dip

Spatial information technology
Reading U MSc☆/dip☆

Topographic science
Swansea UC dip☆

Topographical science
Glasgow U MAppSci

Urban & social geography
London U LSE dip

Urban policy
Glasgow U MPhil/dip☆   □

Higher degrees by research

Anthropology
Durham U PhD/MA/MPhil/MSc

Applied sciences
Wolverhampton P PhD/MPhil

British policy studies
Sheffield U PhD

Conservation
London U UC PhD☆/MPhil☆

Continental tectonics & sedimentation
Cardiff U of Wales C PhD☆

East Anglian studies
East Anglia U PhD/MPhil

English studies
Worcester CHE PhD/MPhil

Environmental & evolutionary biology
Liverpool U PhD/MPhil

Environmental & geographical studies
Manchester P PhD/MPhil/dip

Environmental sciences
East Anglia U PhD/MPhil

European population studies
Liverpool U PhD/MPhil

Geographical information systems
Edinburgh U PhD☆

Geographical sciences
South West P PhD/MPhil

Geography
Belfast Queen's U PhD/MSc
Birmingham U PhD/MLitt/MPhil/MSc
Bristol U PhD/MPhil/MSc
Cambridge U PhD☆/MLitt☆/MSc☆
Canterbury Christ Church C PhD/MPhil
Central London P PhD☆/MPhil☆
Cheltenham & Gloucester CHE PhD/MPhil
City of London P PhD☆/MPhil☆
Coventry P PhD/MPhil
Dundee U PhD/MPhil
Durham U PhD/MA/MPhil/MSc
Edinburgh U PhD/MPhil
Exeter U PhD/MPhil
Glasgow U PhD/MSc
Hull U PhD/MPhil/MSc
Keele U PhD/MA
Kingston P PhD/MPhil
Lancaster U PhD/MPhil
Leeds U PhD/MA/MPhil
Leicester U PhD/MPhil
Liverpool P PhD/MPhil/MSc
Liverpool U PhD/MPhil/MSc   □
London U Birkbeck C PhD/MPhil
London U King's C PhD☆/MPhil☆
London U LSE PhD/MPhil

London U Royal Holloway & Bedford New C PhD/MA/MPhil/MSc
London U SOAS PhD/MPhil
London U UC PhD☆/MPhil☆
Loughborough U PhD/MPhil
Luton CHE PhD☆/MPhil☆
Manchester U PhD/MA/MPhil/MSc
Newcastle U PhD/MPhil
North London P PhD/MPhil
Nottingham U PhD/MPhil   □
Open U PhD/MPhil/BPhil
Oxford U DPhil☆/MLitt☆/MSc☆
Portsmouth P PhD/MPhil
Reading U PhD/MPhil
St Andrews U PhD/MPhil/MSc
St David's UC PhD☆/MA☆
Salford U PhD/MPhil
Sheffield U PhD/MPhil   □
Southampton U PhD/MPhil
Strathclyde U PhD☆/MPhil☆/MSc☆
Sunderland P PhD/MPhil
Sussex U DPhil/MPhil
Swansea UC PhD/MPhil
Ulster U DPhil/MPhil
Worcester CHE PhD/MPhil

Geography & environmental studies
Newcastle P PhD☆/MPhil☆
Sheffield City P PhD/MPhil

Geography & planning
Middlesex P PhD/MPhil

Geography & recreation studies
Staffordshire P PhD/MPhil

Geomorphology
London U King's C PhD☆/MPhil☆

Geophysics & planetary physics
London U UC PhD☆/MPhil☆

History & geography
Nottingham P PhD☆/MPhil☆

Humanities
Brighton P PhD/MPhil
Bristol P PhD/MPhil/dip
Thames P PhD/MPhil

Palaeoecology centre
Belfast Queen's U PhD/MSc

Photogrammetry & surveying
London U UC PhD☆/MPhil☆

Physical geography
Aberystwyth, UC of Wales PhD☆/MPhil☆

Polar studies
Cambridge U PhD☆/MSc☆

Remote sensing
London U UC PhD☆/MPhil☆

Social & population geography
St Andrews U MPhil

Soviet & East European studies
Glasgow U PhD/MLitt   Soc

Urban & regional development studies
Newcastle U PhD/MLitt/MPhil

Geology, geophysics, surveying

Higher degrees by instruction

Agricultural & amenity grassland
Aberystwyth, UC of Wales MSc☆

Analysis of geological data
Kingston P dip△

Applied geophysics
Birmingham U MSc☆
Leeds U dip☆

Applied remote sensing
Silsoe C MSc☆

Applied structural geology & rock mechanics
London U Imperial C MSc☆/dip☆

Basin evolution & dynamics
London U Royal Holloway & Bedford New C MSc☆

Cartography
Glasgow U dip

Chartered surveying (general practice - chattels option)
Southampton IHE RICS

Computing in earth sciences
Keele U MSc☆

Digital mapping & automated cartography
Glasgow U dip

Earth surface & environmental science
London U Birkbeck C cert△

Earthquake engineering
London U Imperial C MSc/dip

Engineering geology
Durham U MSc☆   Eng
Leeds U MSc
London U Imperial C MSc☆/dip☆
Newcastle U MSc☆

Engineering rock mechanics
London U Imperial C MSc☆/dip☆

Engineering surveying & geodesy
Nottingham U MSc☆

Environmental sciences
East Anglia U dip☆

Exploration geophysics
Leeds U MSc☆
London U Imperial C MSc☆/dip☆

First class legislation
Nottingham P MQB△

Geochemistry
Leeds U MSc

Geodesy
London U UC MSc☆/dip☆

Geological exploration methods
Nottingham U MSc

Geological studies
Leicester U dip☆

Geology
St Andrews U dip☆

Geomaterials
London U Queen Mary & Westfield C MSc☆

Geophysics
Durham U MSc☆

Geophysics & planetary physics
Newcastle U MSc☆/dip☆

Geotechnical engineering
Bolton IHE dip△
Newcastle U dip☆
Strathclyde U MSc/dip
Surrey U MSc△/dip△

Geotechnics
Hatfield P MSc△
Middlesex P MSc△

Groundwater engineering
Newcastle U MSc☆

Hydraulics, hydrology & coastal dynamics
Strathclyde U MSc/dip

Hydrogeology
Birmingham U MSc
London U UC MSc☆/dip☆

Hydrographic surveying
South West P dip☆   □

Industrial mineralogy
Leicester U MSc☆/dip☆

Land resources & land utilisation
St Andrews U MPhil☆

Marine archaeology
Bangor, U of Wales MSc☆/dip☆

Marine geology & geophysics
London U UC MSc☆

Micropalaeontology
Aberystwyth, UC of Wales MSc☆
London U UC MSc☆/dip☆
Southampton U MSc☆   □

Mineral engineering
Leeds U dip☆

Mineral exploration
London U Imperial C MSc☆/dip☆

Mineral exploration & mining geology
Leicester U MSc/dip☆

Mineral technology
Camborne S of Mines dip☆

Mining engineering
Camborne S of Mines MSc/dip☆
Leeds U dip☆

Mining geology
Camborne S of Mines MSc☆

Mining geostatistics
Leeds U MSc

Numerical methods in photogrammetry & surveying
London U UC MSc☆/dip☆

Ore petrology & process mineralogy
Cardiff U of Wales C MSc☆

Organic petrology & organic geochemistry
Newcastle U MSc☆

Petroleum engineering
Strathclyde U MSc/dip

Petroleum exploration geology
Oxford P dip☆

Petroleum geology
Aberdeen U MSc☆
London U Imperial C MSc☆/dip☆

Photogrammetery & remote sensing
Glasgow U dip

Photogrammetry
London U UC MSc☆/dip☆

Physical oceanography
Bangor, U of Wales MSc☆/dip☆

Quaternary environmental change
North London P MSc△/dip△

Quaternary studies
City of London P MSc△

Remote sensing
London U Imperial C MSc☆
London U UC MSc☆

Remote sensing & image processing
Edinburgh U MSc☆/dip☆

Remote sensing, image processing & applications
Dundee U MSc☆

Rock mechanics & excavation engineering
Newcastle U MSc☆

Sedimentology & its applications
Reading U MSc☆

Stratigraphy
London U Birkbeck C MSc△

Structural geology & rock mechanics
London U Imperial C MSc/dip

Surface mining & land reclamation
Strathclyde U MSc/dip

Surveying
Glasgow U dip
London U UC MSc☆/dip☆

Topographic science
Swansea UC dip☆

Topographical science
Glasgow U MAppSci

Vertebrate palaeontology
London U UC MSc

Higher degrees by research

Applied geology
Sunderland P PhD/MPhil

Applied sciences
Staffordshire P PhD/MPhil

Building & surveying
Napier P PhD/MPhil

Civil engineering, building & cartography
Oxford P PhD/MPhil

Construction & surveying
Anglia HEC PhD☆/MPhil☆
Lancashire P PhD/MPhil

Continental tectonics & sedimentation
Cardiff U of Wales C PhD☆

Earth science
Swansea UC PhD/MPhil
Ulster U DPhil/MPhil

Earth sciences
Cambridge U PhD☆/MSc☆
Liverpool U PhD/MPhil
Oxford U DPhil☆/MSc☆
Thames P PhD☆/MPhil☆

Economic geology
Camborne S of Mines PhD/MPhil☆

Environmental engineering
Camborne S of Mines PhD/MPhil

Environmental sciences
East Anglia U PhD/MPhil

Estate management & quantity surveying
Wales P PhD/MPhil

Evolution
Oxford U DPhil☆/MSc☆

Exploration geochemistry & geophysics
Camborne S of Mines PhD/MPhil

Geochemistry & geophysics
Oxford U DPhil☆/MSc☆

Geographical information systems
Edinburgh U PhD☆

Geological sciences
Aston U PhD/MPhil
Birmingham U PhD/MSc
Durham U PhD/MSc
Liverpool U PhD/MSc
London U UC PhD☆/MPhil☆
South West P PhD/MPhil
Staffordshire P PhD/MPhil

Geology
Aberystwyth, UC of Wales PhD☆/MPhil☆
Belfast Queen's U PhD/MSc
Bristol U PhD☆/MSc☆
Cardiff U of Wales C PhD/MPhil☆
Cheltenham & Gloucester CHE PhD/MPhil
City of London P PhD☆/MPhil☆
Dundee U PhD/MSc
Edinburgh U PhD/MPhil
Exeter U PhD/MPhil
Glasgow U PhD/MSc
Hatfield P PhD/MPhil
Keele U PhD/MSc
Kingston P PhD/MPhil
Leicester U PhD/MPhil
London U Birkbeck C PhD/MPhil
London U Imperial C PhD/MPhil
London U Royal Holloway & Bedford New C PhD/MPhil
Luton CHE PhD☆/MPhil☆
Manchester U PhD/MSc
Newcastle U PhD/MPhil
Nottingham U PhD/MPhil
Oxford P PhD/MPhil
Portsmouth P PhD☆/MPhil☆
Reading U PhD/MPhil
St Andrews U PhD/MSc
Sheffield U PhD/MPhil

Southampton U PhD/MPhil
Swansea UC PhD/MPhil
West London IHE MPhil☆

Geology & petroleum geology
Aberdeen U PhD☆/MPhil☆

Geomaterials
London U Queen Mary & Westfield C PhD☆/MPhil☆

Geomorphology
London U King's C PhD☆/MPhil☆

Geophysics
Edinburgh U PhD/MPhil
Liverpool U PhD/MSc

Geophysics & planetary physics
London U UC PhD☆/MPhil☆
Newcastle U PhD/MPhil

Geotechnical engineering
City U PhD/MPhil

Grinding
Bristol U PhD☆/MSc☆

Human environmental sciences
London U King's C PhD☆/MPhil☆

Land & building studies
Leicester P PhD/MPhil

Land surveying
East London P PhD/MPhil
Newcastle U PhD/MPhil

Micropalaeontology
London U UC PhD☆/MPhil☆

Mine planning
Camborne S of Mines PhD/MPhil

Mineral physics
London U UC PhD☆/MPhil☆

Mineral processing
Camborne S of Mines PhD/MPhil

Mineral resources engineering
London U Imperial C PhD/MPhil/dip
Strathclyde U PhD☆/MPhil☆/MSc☆

Minerals engineering
Birmingham U PhD/MPhil(Eng)

Mining
Nottingham P PhD☆/MPhil☆

Mining & mineral engineering
Leeds U PhD/MPhil/MSc(Eng)

Mining economics & management
Camborne S of Mines PhD/MPhil

Mining engineering
Newcastle U PhD/MPhil
Nottingham U PhD/MPhil

Mining geology
Camborne S of Mines PhD/MPhil

Ore genesis
Camborne S of Mines PhD/MPhil

Ore geology
Cardiff U of Wales C PhD☆

Paleontology & stratigraphy
Cardiff U of Wales C PhD☆

Petroleum engineering
Heriot-Watt U PhD☆/MPhil☆ *Eng*

Photogrammetry & surveying
London U UC PhD☆/MPhil☆

Quaternary geology & processes
Cardiff U of Wales C PhD☆

Remote sensing
London U Imperial C PhD/MPhil/dip
London U UC PhD☆/MPhil☆
Silsoe C PhD/MPhil

Rock engineering
Camborne S of Mines PhD/MPhil

Rock mechanics
London U UC PhD☆/MPhil☆

Sedimentology
Reading U PhD☆/MPhil☆

Surveying
Bristol P PhD/MPhil/cert/dip
Kingston P PhD/MPhil
Liverpool P PhD/MPhil
Newcastle P PhD☆/MPhil☆
Nottingham P PhD☆/MPhil☆
Portsmouth P PhD☆/MPhil☆
Robert Gordon's IT PhD/MPhil
Thames P PhD/MPhil
Ulster U DPhil/MPhil

Surveying & building
Dundee IT PhD/MPhil

Surveying & geodesy
Oxford U DPhil☆/MSc☆

Topographical science
Glasgow U PhD/MSc

Vertebrate palaeontology
Oxford U DPhil☆/MSc☆

Horticulture, forestry, crop production

Higher degrees by instruction

Agrarian studies
Sussex U MA

Agricultural & food marketing marketing
Aberystwyth, UC of Wales MSc☆

Agricultural development
London U Wye C dip☆

Agricultural economics
Aberdeen SAg MSc/dip
Aberdeen U MSc☆/dip☆
Manchester U MA(Econ)☆/dip☆
Reading U MSc☆/dip☆

Agricultural economics (agrarian development overseas)
London U Wye C MSc☆

Agricultural education
Reading U MSc☆/dip☆

Agricultural extension
Reading U MSc☆/dip☆

Agricultural management
Reading U MSc☆

Agricultural research & development
East Anglia U MSc☆

Agricultural science
Aberystwyth, UC of Wales MA☆/dip☆
Bangor, U of Wales dip☆

Agronomy
Nottingham U MSc☆

Applied genetics
Birmingham U MSc☆

Applied insect taxonomy
Cardiff U of Wales C dip☆ *Biol*

Applied plant sciences
London U Wye C MSc☆

Cadastre & land information management
East London P MSc☆/dip☆

Conservation of soil fertility
London U Wye C MSc☆

Crop market technology
Silsoe C MSc☆

Crop physiology
Reading U MSc☆

Crop production
Bath U MSc☆/dip☆

Crop protection
Aberdeen U MSc☆/dip☆
Bristol U MSc☆

Crop science
Aberdeen SAg MSc☆
Aberdeen U MSc☆

Dryland farming
Silsoe C MSc☆

Environmental forestry
Bangor, U of Wales MSc☆/dip☆

Forest business management
Aberdeen U MSc☆/dip☆

Forest industries technology
Bangor, U of Wales MSc☆/dip☆

Forest inventory & soil science
Aberdeen U MSc☆/dip☆

Forest mensuration & inventory
Aberdeen U MSc☆/dip☆

Forest resource studies
Aberdeen U MSc☆/dip☆

Forestry
Bangor, U of Wales dip☆

Forestry & its relation to land use
Oxford U MSc☆

Forestry & paper technology
Manchester UMIST MSc☆

Fungal technology
Kent U MSc☆

Grassland science
Reading U MSc☆

Improvement & renovation of grassland
Aberystwyth, UC of Wales MSc☆

Insect science
London U Birkbeck C MSc△

Integrated pest & disease management
London U Wye C MSc☆

Irrigation engineering
Southampton U MSc☆/dip☆

Landscape ecology, design & management
London U Wye C MSc☆

Pedology & soil survey
Reading U MSc☆

Pest & disease management
London U Imperial C MSc/dip☆

Plant biochemistry & bioenergetics
Sussex U MSc☆

Plant breeding
Cambridge U MPhil☆

Plant pathology
London U Imperial C MSc/dip

Plant productivity & photosynthesis
London U King's C dip☆

Plant taxonomy
Reading U MSc☆

Plant toxins in nutrition
London U Wye C MSc☆

Post harvest technology
Silsoe C MSc☆/dip☆

Resource assessment for development planning
East Anglia U MSc☆

Rural development
Manchester U MA(Econ)☆

Rural land studies
Reading U dip☆

Rural resources & environmental policy
London U Wye C MSc☆

Rural social development
Reading U MA☆/dip☆

Seed technology
Edinburgh U MSc☆/dip☆
Edinburgh U SAg MSc☆/dip☆

Soil chemistry & fertility
Reading U MSc

Soil conservation
Silsoe C MSc☆

Soil conservation & land reclamation engineering
Southampton U MSc☆/dip☆

Soil science
Aberdeen U MSc☆/dip☆   ☐
Newcastle U MSc☆/dip☆

Soil water management
Reading U MSc

Technology of crop protection
Reading U MSc☆

Timber engineering
Bangor, U of Wales MSc☆/dip☆

Timber studies
Buckinghamshire CHE dip☆

Tropical & sub tropical horticulture & crop science
London U Wye C MSc☆

Tropical agricultural & environmental science
Newcastle U MSc☆/dip☆

Tropical agricultural development
Reading U MAgrSc☆/MSc☆/dip☆

Tropical crop storage & processing
Silsoe C MSc☆/dip☆

Weed science
London U Imperial C MSc/dip☆

Wood preservation research
London U Imperial C MSc/dip☆

Wood science
Bangor, U of Wales dip☆

Higher degrees by research

Agrarian development overseas
London U Wye C PhD☆/MPhil☆

Agrarian studies
Sussex U DPhil/MPhil

Agricultural & food chemistry
Edinburgh U PhD/MPhil

Agricultural & food marketing
Edinburgh U PhD/MPhil

Agricultural biochemistry
Aberdeen SAg PhD☆/MSc☆
Aberdeen U PhD☆/MPhil☆/MSc☆
Edinburgh U PhD/MPhil

Agricultural biochemistry & soil sciences
Aberystwyth, UC of Wales PhD☆/MPhil☆

Agricultural botany
Aberdeen SAg PhD☆/MSc☆
Glasgow U PhD/MSc

Agricultural chemistry
Aberdeen U PhD☆/MPhil☆/MSc☆
Glasgow U PhD/MSc
West of Scotland C PhD☆/MSc☆

Agricultural economics
Aberdeen SAg PhD☆/MSc☆
Aberdeen U PhD☆/MPhil☆/MSc☆
Bangor, U of Wales PhD☆/MPhil☆
Edinburgh U PhD/MPhil
Glasgow U PhD/MSc
London U Wye C PhD☆/MPhil☆
Manchester U PhD/MA(Econ)

Agricultural economics & management
Edinburgh U PhD/MPhil
Reading U PhD/MPhil/MSc

Agricultural economics & marketing
Aberystwyth, UC of Wales PhD☆/MPhil☆

Agricultural extension & rural development
Edinburgh U PhD/MPhil
Reading U PhD/MPhil☆

Agricultural microbiology
Aberdeen SAg PhD☆/MSc☆
Aberdeen U PhD☆/MPhil☆/MSc☆
Edinburgh U PhD/MPhil

Agricultural science
Aberystwyth, UC of Wales PhD☆/MPhil☆
Edinburgh U PhD/MPhil

Agricultural zoology
Aberdeen SAg PhD☆/MSc☆
Glasgow U PhD/MSc

Agriculture
Aberdeen U PhD☆/MPhil☆/MSc☆
Bangor, U of Wales PhD☆/MPhil☆
Edinburgh U PhD/MPhil
Glasgow U PhD/MSc
London U Wye C PhD☆/MPhil☆
Reading U PhD/MPhil
West of Scotland C PhD☆/MSc☆

Agriculture & food economics
Belfast Queen's U PhD/MAgr/MSc

Agriculture & horticulture
Bristol U PhD☆/MSc☆
Nottingham U PhD/MPhil

Agriculture, food & land use
South West P PhD/MPhil

Agronomy
Aberdeen SAg PhD☆/MSc☆
West of Scotland C PhD☆/MSc☆

Animal nutrition
Aberdeen SAg PhD☆/MSc☆
Edinburgh U PhD/MPhil

Applied sciences
Wolverhampton P PhD/MPhil

Biological sciences
Bath U PhD☆/MPhil☆
London U Wye C PhD☆/MPhil☆

Biophysics
London U UC PhD☆/MPhil☆

Botany
West of Scotland C PhD☆/MSc☆

Crop & animal production
Belfast Queen's U PhD/MSc
Edinburgh U PhD/MPhil

Crop & animal protection
Edinburgh U PhD/MPhil

Crop drying
Silsoe C PhD/MPhil

Crop market technology
Silsoe C PhD/MPhil

Crop production & protection
Aberdeen U PhD☆/MPhil☆/MSc☆

Crop science
Aberdeen SAg PhD☆/MSc☆
Edinburgh U PhD/MPhil

European agricultural studies
London U Wye C PhD☆/MPhil☆

Food marketing
Newcastle U PhD☆/MPhil☆

Forestry
Aberdeen U PhD☆/MPhil☆/MSc☆
Oxford U DPhil☆/MSc☆

Forestry & agroforestry
Bangor, U of Wales PhD☆/
MPhil☆

Forestry & natural resources
Edinburgh U PhD/MPhil

Hop research
London U Wye C PhD☆/MPhil☆

Horticulture
London U Wye C PhD☆/MPhil☆
Reading U PhD/MPhil

Horticulture & beekeeping
West of Scotland C PhD☆/MSc☆

Human environmental sciences
London U King's C PhD☆/MPhil☆

Mycology & plant pathology
Belfast Queen's U PhD/MAgr/
MSc

Plant biology
Bangor, U of Wales PhD☆/
MPhil☆
Bath U PhD☆/MPhil☆
Birmingham U PhD/MSc
Edinburgh U PhD/MPhil
Newcastle U PhD/MPhil

Plant breeding
Nottingham U PhD☆/MPhil☆

Plant molecular biology
Nottingham U PhD☆/MPhil☆

Plant pathology
Glasgow U PhD/MSc
London U UC PhD☆/MPhil☆
Nottingham U PhD☆/MPhil☆
West of Scotland C PhD☆/MSc☆

Plant physiology
Nottingham U PhD☆/MPhil☆

Plant science
Aberdeen U PhD☆/MPhil☆/MSc☆
Cardiff U of Wales C PhD☆/
MPhil☆
Edinburgh U PhD/MPhil

Seed & grain technology
Silsoe C PhD/MPhil

Soil science
Aberdeen U PhD☆/MPhil☆/
MSc☆   ☐

Wood science
Bangor, U of Wales PhD☆/
MPhil☆

Zoology
West of Scotland C PhD☆/MSc☆

Meteorology, oceanography

Higher degrees by instruction

Agricultural meteorology
Reading U MSc

Applied marine science
Swansea UC MSc☆/dip☆

Applied oceanography
Bangor, U of Wales MSc☆

Atmospheric sciences
East Anglia U MSc☆

Combustion science & pollution control
Sheffield U MSc(Eng)☆/
MSc(Tech)☆

Marine archaeology
Bangor, U of Wales MSc☆/dip☆

Marine environmental protection
Bangor, U of Wales MSc/dip☆

Marine geotechnics
Bangor, U of Wales MSc☆/dip☆

Marine science
Glasgow U MAppSci/dip

Maritime civil engineering
Liverpool U MSc(Eng)☆/dip☆

Meteorolgy
Reading U MSc

Meteorology & climatology
Birmingham U MA☆/MSc☆

Micropalaeontology
Southampton U MSc☆   ☐

Oceanography
Southampton U MSc☆/dip☆

Physical oceanography
Bangor, U of Wales MSc☆/dip☆

Pollution & environmental control
Manchester U MSc☆/dip☆   ☐

Soil & water management
Strathclyde U MSc/dip

Synoptic & statistical climatology
Birmingham U MA☆

Higher degrees by research

Applied mathematics
Exeter U PhD☆

Climatic research
East Anglia U PhD/MPhil

Geography
Liverpool U PhD/MPhil/MSc   ☐
London U Queen Mary &
Westfield C PhD☆/MPhil☆   ☐

Grinding
Bristol U PhD☆/MSc☆

Human environmental sciences
London U King's C PhD☆/MPhil☆

Marine law & policy
Cardiff U of Wales C PhD☆/
MPhil☆/LLM☆

Marine science
Glasgow U PhD/MSc

Marine science & technology
South West P PhD/MPhil

Marine studies
Swansea UC PhD/MPhil

Maritime studies
Cardiff U of Wales C PhD☆/
MPhil☆

Mechanical engineering
London U UC PhD☆/MPhil☆

Meteorology
Edinburgh U PhD/MPhil
Reading U PhD/MPhil

Ocean engineering
City U PhD/MPhil

Oceanography
Liverpool U PhD/MSc
Southampton U PhD/MPhil

Physical oceanography
Bangor, U of Wales PhD☆/
MPhil☆

Pollution research
Manchester U PhD/MSc
Manchester UMIST PhD/MSc

Pure & applied mathematics
Exeter U PhD☆/MPhil☆

Tourism, recreation management

Higher degrees by instruction

Agricultural economics
Aberystwyth, UC of Wales
MSc☆/dip☆ _Soc_

Countryside management
Bangor Normal C cert☆

European tourism management
Dorset Inst dip☆

Hotel administration
Strathclyde U MSc☆/dip☆

International hotel management
Surrey U MSc☆/dip☆

Leisure & tourism studies
North London P MA△

Leisure management
Sheffield U MA/dip ☐

Leisure services & tourism
Birmingham U PhD/MPhil/
MSocSc/dip _Soc_

Physical education & exercise studies
Glasgow U MEd/MPhil

Physical education & sports science
Loughborough U MSc☆/dip☆

Recreation & leisure practice
Moray House CE dip☆

Recreation management
Loughborough U MSc☆

Sociology & anthropology of travel & tourism
Roehampton I MA☆

Sociology of sport
Leicester U MA

Tourism
Manchester P dip☆
Strathclyde U MSc☆/dip

Tourism & leisure management
Ealing C London dip☆

Tourism & leisure services
Birmingham U PhD/MPhil/
MSocSc/dip

Tourism management
Newcastle P dip☆

Tourism marketing
Surrey U MSc☆/dip☆

Tourism planning & development
Surrey U MSc☆/dip☆

Tourism studies
Surrey U MSc☆/dip☆

Tourism, food & hospitality management
Sheffield City P MSc☆

Transport planning & management
Central London P MSc

Higher degrees by research

Environmental planning & management
Manchester U PhD/MPhil

Food & tourism management
Sheffield City P PhD/MPhil

Geography & recreation studies
Staffordshire P PhD/MPhil

Home economics & institutional management
Cardiff U of Wales C PhD☆/
MPhil☆

Hotel & institution administration
Robert Gordon's IT PhD/MPhil

Language studies
Canterbury Christ Church C
PhD/MPhil

Leisure services & tourism
Birmingham U PhD/MPhil/
MSocSci

Marketing & tourism management
Newcastle P PhD☆/MPhil☆

Physical education & recreation
Glasgow U PhD/MSc

Physical education & sports science
Loughborough U PhD☆/MPhil☆

Recreation & environmental studies
Sheffield City P PhD/MPhil

Sport & recreation studies
Liverpool P PhD/MPhil

Sports & recreation studies
Birmingham U PhD/MSc

Sports science
Brighton P PhD/MPhil

Glasgow U PhD/MSc

Tourism
Dorset Inst PhD/MPhil/dip

Town planning, urban and regional planning

Higher degrees by instruction

Civic design
Liverpool U MA☆/MCD☆/DipCD☆

Construction management
Glasgow C of Building & Printing
dip☆
Loughborough U MSc
Reading U MSc☆

Development policy & planning
Swansea UC dip☆

Employment & planning
Middlesex P MA△/dip△

Environmental civil engineering
Liverpool U MSc(Eng)☆

Environmental design & engineering
London U UC MSc

Environmental planning
Anglia HEC dip△
Nottingham U MA/dip
Reading U MPhil/dip

Environmental planning for developing countries
Nottingham U MA/dip

Forestry & its relation to land use
Oxford U MSc☆

Highway engineering for developing countries
Birmingham U MSc(Eng)

Housing
Cardiff U of Wales C dip☆
Edinburgh CA dip☆
Heriot-Watt U dip☆
London U LSE dip☆
Middlesex P dip△
New C dip△
Salford U dip☆
Stirling U dip☆

Housing administration
Sheffield City P dip△

Housing management & administration
Humberside CHE dip△

Housing policy & practice
Birmingham U PhD/MPhil/
MSocSc/dip   Soc

Housing studies
Anglia HEC dip△
Architectural Association S of
Architecture dip☆
Bristol P dip
Glasgow U MPhil△/dip△
South Bank P dip△

Irrigation water management
Silsoe C MSc☆/dip☆

Land economy
Aberdeen U MLE☆/dipLE☆

Land management
Reading U MPhil☆/dip☆

Land resource management & planning
Silsoe C MSc☆/dip☆

Land resources & land utilisation
St Andrews U MPhil☆

Landscape architecture
Leeds P dip
Manchester P dip☆

Landscape design
Manchester U MA(LD)☆/MLD☆/
BLD☆
Newcastle U MPhil☆/dip
Sheffield U MArch☆/MA☆/cert△/
dip☆

Landscape ecology, design & management
London U Wye C MSc☆

Landscape management
Manchester U MA(LM)☆/dip☆

Landscape studies
Edinburgh U dip☆

Metropolitan planning
Liverpool U MA☆

National development & project planning
Bradford U MSc☆/dip☆

Planning
Oxford P dip

Planning studies
Newcastle U MA☆
Sheffield U dip☆

Planning studies (developing countries)
Edinburgh CA MSc☆/dip☆
Heriot-Watt U dip☆

Production of the built environment
London U UC MSc

Regional & urban planning studies
London U LSE MSc

Regional development
Strathclyde U MSc/dip

Regional development planning
Swansea UC MSc(Econ)☆

Regional planning
Coventry P MA/dip

Regional science
Liverpool U MA☆

Rural & regional resources planning
Robert Gordon's IT MSc☆

Rural development
East Anglia U MA☆/MSc☆

Rural resources & environmental policy
London U Wye C MSc☆

Rural social development
Reading U MA☆/dip☆

Town & country planning
Belfast Queen's U MSc☆/dip☆
Edinburgh CA dip
Heriot-Watt U dip
Manchester U MTPL☆/MTP☆
Newcastle U MPhil☆/dip☆

Town & regional planning
Leeds P dip△
Liverpool U MCD☆/dip☆
Sheffield U MA☆/dip☆

Town planning
Birmingham P MA△/dip△
Cardiff U of Wales C MSc☆/
RTPI☆
Central London P MA△
London U UC MPhil
Manchester U MTPL☆
South Bank P MA△/dip☆

Transport
London U Imperial C MSc/dip

Transport planning & management
Central London P MSc

Transportation planning & engineering
Southampton U MSc☆/dip☆

Urban & regional planning
Edinburgh CA MSc☆
Heriot-Watt U MSc☆
Strathclyde U MSc/dip

Urban & regional planning studies
London U Birkbeck C MSc△

Urban & regional studies
Birmingham U PhD/MPhil/
MSocSc/dip   □
Sussex U MA

Urban design
Central London P MA△
Glasgow U MArch
Heriot-Watt U MSc☆/dip☆
Nottingham U MA/dip
Oxford P MA/dip
Sheffield U MArch☆
Strathclyde U MSc/dip

Urban development
Strathclyde U MSc/dip

Urban engineering
South Bank P MSc☆/dip☆

Urban land appraisal
Reading U MSc☆/dip☆

Urban land studies
Reading U dip☆

Urban planning
Oxford P MSc/dip

Urban planning implementation
Central London P dip☆

Urban planning in developing countries
Cardiff U of Wales C MSc☆

Urban planning practice for developing countries
London U UC dip☆

Urban planning studies
Oxford P MSc
South Bank P MSc△/dip△

Urban policy
Glasgow U MPhil/dip☆   □

Higher degrees by research

Advanced urban studies
Bristol U PhD/MPhil

Agricultural extension & rural development
Reading U PhD/MPhil

Architecture
Dundee U PhD/MSc   □
Manchester U PhD/MPhil
Newcastle U PhD/MLitt/MSc

Architecture & landscape
Leeds P PhD/MPhil/dip
Manchester P PhD/MPhil
Thames P PhD/MPhil

Architecture & planning
London U UC PhD☆/MPhil☆

2 POSTGRADUATE OPPORTUNITIES

Building science
Sheffield U PhD/MPhil

Built environment studies
Central London P PhD☆/MPhil☆

Civic design
Liverpool U PhD/MPhil

Construction & surveying
Lancashire P PhD/MPhil

Construction management
Reading U PhD/MPhil

Construction studies
Wolverhampton P PhD/MPhil

Development & project planning
Bradford U PhD/MPhil

Development studies
East Anglia U PhD☆/MPhil☆
Salford U PhD/MSc

Environmental studies & countryside planning
London U Wye C PhD☆/MPhil☆

Geography
Liverpool U PhD/MPhil/MSc ☐
London U Queen Mary & Westfield C PhD☆/MPhil☆ ☐
Strathclyde U PhD☆/MPhil☆/ MSc☆

Geography & planning
Middlesex P PhD/MPhil

Horticulture
London U Wye C PhD☆/MPhil☆

Housing & housing policy
Birmingham U PhD/MPhil/ MSocSci

Housing studies
Architectural Association S of Architecture PhD☆/MPhil☆

Land economy
Aberdeen U PhD☆/MPhil☆/MSc☆

Land management & development
Reading U PhD/MPhil

Landscape architecture
Sheffield U PhD/MPhil

Landscape design
Manchester U PhD/MPhil

Landscape management
Manchester U PhD/MPhil

Planning
Central London P PhD☆/MPhil☆

Planning & landscape
Birmingham P PhD/MPhil

Planning studies
London U LSE PhD/MPhil
Nottingham U PhD/MPhil
Reading U PhD/MPhil

Planning, housing & development
South Bank P PhD/MPhil

Surveying
Ulster U DPhil/MPhil

Town & country planning
Bristol P PhD/MPhil/cert/dip
Heriot-Watt U PhD/MPhil
Liverpool P PhD/MPhil

Manchester U PhD/MPhil
Newcastle U PhD/MPhil
Nottingham P PhD☆/MPhil☆

Town & regional planning
Dundee U PhD/MSc
Sheffield U PhD/MPhil

Town planning
Cardiff U of Wales C PhD☆/ MPhil☆
Oxford P PhD/MPhil
South Bank P PhD/MPhil

Urban & regional planning
Coventry P PhD/MPhil
Strathclyde U PhD☆/MPhil☆/ MSc☆

Urban & regional research
Open U PhD/MPhil/BPhil

Urban & regional studies
Birmingham U PhD/MPhil/ MSocSc   Soc, @
Sheffield City P PhD/MPhil
Sussex U DPhil/MPhil

Urban design
Central London P PhD☆/MPhil☆
Oxford P PhD/MPhil

Urban design & regional planning
Edinburgh U PhD/MPhil

Urban studies
Kent U PhD/MPhil
Liverpool U PhD/MPhil

Architecture

PhD
3 years minimum full time
(part time available)
MSc
1 year full time
(part time available)
Department of Architecture,
University of Dundee,
Duncan of Jordanston
College of Art, Perth Road,
Dundee DD1 4HT
Tel: 0382 23181

MSc/PhD: supervision available. Current research interests are: Scottish vernacular building, housing in exposed environments, rehabilitation potential for tenements, housing in low let and demand estates, access for disabled, optimum ideology, theories in architectural education, architectural knowledge and discourse, building performance studies, C.A.A.D., and tropical architecture studies.
Entrance requirements Recognised degree.
Contact Professor J Paul.

Crop protection

dip
1 year full time
24 places
The Academic Registrar,
Department of Agriculture,
Harper Adams Agricultural
College, Newport,
Shropshire TF10 8NB
Tel: 0952 820280

The aim of the Crop protection course is to provide a vocational training for persons wishing to enter the crop production and agrochemical industries. It is a practically oriented course which, in addition to providing a training in crop protection technology, gives an understanding of agricultural systems.
Entrance requirements An appropriate degree.
Grants LEA discretionary.
Course tutor Dr C P Beckwith.

Ecology

MSc
1 year full time
15 places
dip
1 year full time
15 places
Dr M R Young, Department
of Zoology, University of
Aberdeen, Tillydrone
Avenue, Aberdeen AB9 2TN
Tel: 0224 272859

The course covers plant and animal ecology, aspects of forestry, soil science, computing etc; emphasis is placed on field work and there is a six week research project. The widely based training in ecology is relevant to employment in conservation, land management, teaching or research. Visits are made to ecological institutes in the Aberdeen area. The course is arranged on a modular basis and a variety of additional options in related environmental sciences are also available.
Entrance requirements Good honours degree or equivalent in biological or environmental science with at least one basic course in ecology.
Grants NERC.
Course organiser Dr M R Young.

Energy systems and environmental management

dip/MSc
1 year full time
The Admissions Officer,
Glasgow College,
Cowcaddens Road, Glasgow
G4 0BA
Tel: 041 331 3000

The course provides an insight into energy systems and the environment and is founded in the principles and methods of applied science, engineering and other areas such as social sciences. Course includes energy over-view, computer skills, waste and recycling, heat exchangers.
Entrance requirements Degree or equivalent.
Grants Training agency.

Geographical information systems (GIS)

PhD
3 years full time
MSc
1 year full time
dip
9 months full time
Mr B M Gittings, Department
of Geography, University of
Edinburgh, Drummond
Street, Edinburgh EH8 9XP

The core of the course concerns the theory and implementation of systems for the capture, storage, mapping and analysis of spatially referenced data using interactive graphics and relational database technology. Options cover computer programming, remote sensing, simulation modelling, digital mapping, advanced database techniques and the use of GIS for public policy formulation and development planning. Access to state-of-the-art techniques such as parallel processing and artificial intelligence. There are two terms of coursework followed by a 20,000 word (MSc) or 6000 word (diploma) dissertation. Emphasis is placed on practical work using an extensive range of hardware/software tools. MSc modules may be taken as part of a PhD in GIS.
Entrance requirements Good honours degree or equivalent.
Grants *MSc* NERC (Quota), ESRC (quota and competition). *Diploma* LEA discretionary. SED.

Geography

PhD
full time
part time
MPhil
full time
part time
MSc
full time
part time
MA
full time
Department of Geography,
University of Liverpool, PO
Box 147, Liverpool L69 3BX
Tel: 051 794 2838

MA Population Studies.
Research: 1. Human Geography.
a) *Urban and regional economic change*
Urban geography metropolitan areas; policy evaluation,
regional & industrial development, UK. EEC
b) *3rd World Studies;* migration, education & health industrial
development, conservation, land reform; esp in Africa, Latin
America, Carribean.
c) *Population Studies* population dynamics, third world UK
historical demography of Britain & Europe.
2. Physical Geography
a) *Mineral magnetism*applications of mineral magnetics to
environmental change.
b) *Geomorphology* fluvial; Quaternary; volcanic. range of
environments glacierised to temperate to semi arid.
c) *Man/environment relations* resource evaluation and
management; volcanic hazards, biogeog aspects of tourism &
conservation; ecological, pedological & socioecon change.
Contact Professor R I Woods.

Geography

PhD
3 years full time
MPhil
2 years by research
Head of Department,
Department of Geography,
Queen Mary & Westfield
College, Mile End Road,
London E1 4NS

Research degree programmes available in social, economic
and historical geography, population studies,
geomorphology, soils and meteorology. Regional interests in
UK (especially London), Western Europe, USA, the
Caribbean and South Africa. Facilities include extensive
computing and geomorphological laboratories. Department
hosts Centres for Health and Health Care Research, and for
East London Studies.
Entrance requirements Good honours degree in geography,
or related discipline.
Grants ESRC, MAFF, NERC studentships, University of
London and Queen Mary and Westfield studentships.
Head of department Dr G Rose.

Geography

PhD
3 years full time
4 years part time
MPhil
2 years full time
3 years part time
Department of Geography,
University of Nottingham,
University Park, Nottingham
NG7 2RD
Tel: 0602 484848

Research: PhD normally three years; MPhil two years. *Taught
course:* MSc Geographical Information Systems (1989) - one
calendar year. Supervision (possibly in collaboration with
another department) normally available in: *geomorphology*
(coastal, glacial, tectonic), *biogeography, applied physical
geography*(incl hazards), *meteorology, automated cartography,
remote sensing, GIS, economic geography* (industrial,
retailing), *urban geography, historical geography, history of
cartography, medical/health care geography, cultural
geography*. Regional interests include *EC, Mediterranean
Europe, Latin America, Soviet Union, Middle East.*
Entrance requirements First or upper second honours
degree in geography (or cognate subject) preferred.
Grants ESRC or NERC (UK students only), University of
Nottingham studentships. Overseas government
scholarships/sponsorships.
Contact Head of department.

Geography

PhD
3 years full time
MPhil
1-2 years full time
dip
1 year full time
Postgraduate Admissions
Secretary, Department of
Geography, University of
Sheffield, Sheffield S10 2TN
Tel: 0742 768555

Research: PhD 3 years; Masters 1-2 years. *Taught course:* Diploma in Geography, 1 year, tailored to meet individual needs, (lectures, practicals, quantitative methods and computing and a project). For both research and diploma, subjects include: biogeography, soils, hydrology, climatology, geomorphology, remote sensing; regional economic, industrial, population, urban, transport and political geography; resources.
Entrance requirements *PhD:* 1st or upper second honours degree in a relevant subject, or a diploma, as above. *Masters:* 1st or second class honours degree. *Diploma:* normally a first degree but equivalent relevant work experience considered.
Grants NERC and ESRC studentships as advertised (UK students only). Overseas students may also apply directly to the Commonwealth Scholarships scheme or to their own Institutes/Governments for support. Diploma students can also apply to local authorities/own institutes for support in some cases.
Chairman Professor Alan Hay.

Hydrographic surveying

dip
9 months (36 weeks) full
time
18 places
The Faculty Administrator
(Ref: DOG 4), Institute of
Marine Studies, Plymouth:
Polytechnic South West,
Drake Circus, Plymouth PL4
8AA
Tel: 0762 232405 Fax: 0762
232293

The Diploma is an intensive in-depth study of the science of hydrography. It emphasises the practical aspects of hydrography and provides a level of skill with an understanding of the concepts of measurement at sea. The main subject of hydrography is supported by the study of application of computers, oceanography, law, etc. Exemption from RICS Final Examinations. A FIG/IHO category A course.
Entrance requirements Appropriate first degree or professional qualification and experience.
Grants Discretionary fourth year award from some LEAs.
Admissions Tutor Mr G E Jones.

Leisure management

MA/Diploma
1 year full time
3 years part time
Miss T Starr, CCVE,
University of Sheffield, 65
Wilkinson Street, Sheffield
S10 2GJ
Tel: 0742 768653

This taught diploma/MA course is aimed at both recent graduates and those with experience in the field of leisure who are seeking to develop their careers in the leisure industries.
The course is centred around practical examples drawn from indoor and outdoor sports, arts management, countryside recreation, tourism and cultural events promoted by both the public and private sectors.
Entrance requirements A good honours degree or professional qualification with experience.
Course director Mr R Lewis.

Marine resource development & protection

MSc/diploma
1 year full time
Dr J Mair, The Institute of
Offshore Engineering, Heriot-
Watt University, Research
Park, Riccarton Campus,
Edinburgh EH14 4AS
Tel: 031 449 5111

This multidisciplinary MSc course is designed to meet the needs of industry and government agencies involved in marine resource exploitation. The course is modular in structure with optional taught subjects which include: environmental policy control and monitoring; waste processing procedures and technology; marine bioresource technology and management (fish, shellfish, and seaweed); coastal and estuarine development; diving science. Taught modules are followed by a research project, carried out where appropriate in association with industry.
Entrance requirements Good honours degree in engineering or science discipline.
Grants NERC and SERC.
Head of department Professor C S Johnston.

Micropalaeontology

MSc
1 year full time
10 places
R L Austin, Department of
Geology, University of
Southampton, Southampton
SO9 5NH
Tel: 0703 592031
Telex: 47661
Fax: 0703 593052

This course trains micropalaeontologists for the petroleum industry, geological surveys and research. It develops micropalaeontological expertise in the wider context of geology and oceanography including skills such as basin analysis, logging, palaeoceanography and hydrocarbon source rocks. A foundation course term is followed by an option for a term on calcareous microfossils or palynology. The final six months are devoted to a research dissertation. **Entrance requirements** BSc Honours degree (lower 2) in Geology, Geography, Biology, Environmental Sciences or Oceanography.
Grants At least six scholarships, some industrially sponsored will be available in 1990/91.

Pollution & environmental control

PhD 3 years
MSc 1 year
20 places
Secretary of Pollution
Studies, Department of
Environmental Biology,
University of Manchester,
Oxford Road, Manchester
M13 9PL
Tel: 061 275 3884

The course is jointly organised by UMIST and Manchester University and provides a multi-disciplinary exposure to the technical aspects of the subject coupled with elements of the legal, plannning and economic considerations affecting control. On completion of the examined course work each student undertakes a dissertation project. Research opportunities also exist for suitably qualified candidates to undertake studies leading to the award of PhD.
Entrance requirements Degree in science or engineering.
Grants SERC advanced course studentships.
Course organiser Dr E Bellinger.

Soil science

PhD
3 years full time
MSc
1-2 years full time
dip
9 months full time
10 places
MPhil
2 years full time
Professor M S Cresser,
Department of Plant & Soil
Science, University of
Aberdeen, Aberdeen AB9
2UE
Tel: 0224 272257

Aberdeen is an important centre for soil science research and teaching, with the university in close proximity to the Macaulay Land Use Research Institute. The department offers taught diploma and MSc courses and an MPhil and PhD by research. Successful candidates to taught courses will choose one of the following options: soil physics; soil chemistry, fertility and management; soil, plant and water analysis; pedology, land use and soil survey; soil microbiology.
Entrance requirements Diploma: pass degree or equivalent in relevant science. MSc, MPhil and PhD: honours degree or equivalent in relevant science at an appropriate level.
Head of department Professor M S Cresser.

Soil science

PhD
3 years full time
MPhil
2 years full time
Professor R S Swift,
Department of Soil Science,
University of Reading,
London Road, Reading RG1
5AQ

A taught MSc course is offered over one or two years in pedology, soil survey and land evaluation, soil chemistry and fertility, and soil water management, each with a dissertation. A two-year course (MAgrSc) in general soil science is also offered. There is opportunity for dissertation work to be done away from the department. Suitably qualified candidates are accepted for studies leading towards MPhil (2 years) or PhD (3 years).
Entrance requirements Honours degree in pure or applied science.
Grants Write to Head of department.
Head of department Professor R S Swift.

Urban & regional studies

PhD/MPhil (2 years)

MSocSc/dip (1 year)

(double/part-time)
20-25 places
Graduate Admissions Tutor,
Centre for Urban & Regional
Studies, J G Smith Building,
University of Birmingham,
Birmingham B15 2TT
Tel: 021 414 6372

The Centre offers a wide range of opportunities to study for postgraduate degrees by research, coursework or both. Specialisms include: housing; economic development; leisure and tourism, and policy in relation to these.
Entrance requirements Good honours degree in an appropriate subject, or professional qualification and experience.
Grants ESRC awards.
Head of centre C J Watson.

Urban policy

MPhil (Urban Policy)
1 year full time
2 years part time
MLitt/PhD
The Clerk, Faculty of Social
Sciences, University of
Glasgow, Adam Smith
Building, Glasgow G12 8RT
Tel: 041 339 8855

The MPhil course typically has around 30 students and caters for people interested in further academic work, careers in urban development bodies, housing agencies, voluntary and community organisations etc. The degree offers specialisation in either housing or local economic development. The teaching staff are heavily involved in research and advisory work in the urban policy field. MLitt and PhD supervision is also offered in these areas. Graduate work in housing and local economic development is ESRC accredited.
Entrance requirements Good honours degree or equivalent.
Course director Dr Andrew McArthur.

2

Mathematics/ sciences

Manchester Polytechnic
Faculty of Community Studies
and Education
Department of Nursing Studies

PRACTITIONER RESEARCH

A new two year Postgraduate Diploma/
MSc course is offered. The course is
designed to meet the needs of
practitioners who wish to research their
practice but lack the necessary skills.
The first year covers a wide range of
methods so that the course member
arrives at the start of Year II with the
ability to make an informed choice about
the best way to research his/her practice.

Assessment of the MSc is by dissertation
and the course is open to all practitioners
with or without a first degree.

Contact: Dr D. Skidmore.

DEPARTMENT OF BIOLOGY
IMPERIAL COLLEGE, LONDON UNIVERSITY

MSc Degrees (normally one year, with taught courses
and a research project) in: **Applied Entomology;
Applied Nematology; Plant Pathology; Weed Science**
(these four degrees have core subjects in common, in
pest and disease management, then specialist
sections); **Timber Technology : Wood Preservation
Research.**

PhD Degrees (normally three years) in **most areas of
pure and applied biology** including:- agriculture;
animal physiology; biotechnology; botany; cell
biology; ecology; entomology; environmental
management; epidemiology; genetics; immunology;
microbiology; molecular biology; neurobiology;
parasitology; pesticides; photosynthesis; plant
pathology, physiology and technology; pollution;
protozoa; timber technology; virology; zoology.

There are about 38 academic staff, 80 research staff and
125 postgraduates, so teaching and research
supervision are by real specialists. There are excellent
laboratory and computing facilities at the main
campus, South Kensington, London, and also at
Silwood Park, near Ascot, Berkshire, where there are
100 hectares for field experiments, and large, new
laboratories.

Details of courses and available studentships from:
**The Registrar, Imperial College,
London SW7 2AZ, UK.**

THE UNIVERSITY
OF BIRMINGHAM

FACULTY OF SCIENCE
Postgraduate Prospectus 1990

Copies of the above prospectus may be obtained from the Assistant
Registrar, Science Division, Academic Secretary's Office, University
of Birmingham, PO Box 363, Birmingham, B15 2TT.

The publication contains information about:

a) The **RESEARCH** facilities (full-time, part-time and part external)
offered in the Schools of Biochemistry, Biological Sciences,
Chemistry, Computing and Computer Science, Earth Sciences,
Geography, Mathematics and Statistics, Physics and Space
Research, Psychology, Sport and Exercise Sciences, and in non-
clinical Medical Science Departments.

b) Full-time one year **TAUGHT COURSES,** leading to the degree of
MSc in Applied Genetics, Applied Geophysics, Applied Radiation
Physics, Clinical Psychology, Cognitive Science, Computer
Science, Conservation and Utilisation of Plant Genetic Resoures,
Hydrogeology, Immunology, Meteorology and Climatology, the
Physics and Technology of Nuclear Reactors, Pest Management,
Toxicology.

The University
of Birmingham
Faculty of Science
PO Box 363
Birmingham
B15 2TT

The MSc courses in Applied Radiation Physics and the Physics and
Technology of Nuclear Reactors may be studied on a modular basis
over 2 years. In addition we offer a full-time two year MPhil course in
Plant Breeding and Crop Improvement, run jointly by the Universities
of Birmingham and Reading.

Biological sciences

For many people with first degrees in biological sciences the main aim is to work in a related area - somewhere where they can use their interest and ability in biology, preferably in research and/or development. In fact, the majority of people don't get the opportunity to do so because the supply of biological science graduates outstrips demand, and has done for several years.

About four fifths of those with a higher degree in a biological science go into employment related directly to their studies, compared with just under half of those with a first degree. So getting a higher degree certainly improves your chances of working in some area of biology. Research and development, teaching and medical services are the three careers which attract most postgraduate biologists. But a few do take employment in such occupations as computing; buying, selling and marketing; and administration and finance.

Research opportunities

A glance through the advertisements in any of the scientific magazines and journals shows that most of the research jobs are for those with higher degrees and usually relevant research experience as well. So, if you're aiming at a research post a higher degree is going to be almost essential. Research studentships are offered in universities and polytechnics as well as the research institutes of the Medical Research Council (MRC), the Natural

Environment Research Council (NERC) and the Agricultural and Food Research Council (AFRC) - refer to the information on applications and grants for further details. Teaching hospitals, cancer research institutes and the Scientific Civil Service all offer a few opportunities for their research staff to do further study, although they may want you to show how good you are before agreeing to your starting a higher degree course.

The competition for places and grants is fierce. There are, however, some indications that awards for research are more readily available in areas that can be applied to industry. The Science and Engineering Research Council (SERC) offers Co-operative Awards in Science and Engineering (CASE) studentships for projects developed jointly between higher education establishments and industry or public bodies. Areas of interest include the development of 'new' strains of micro-organisms and further research on the biochemistry and physiology of bacteria, which is related to the pharmaceutical or food and drink industries. Plant physiology is also important in developing the techniques of plant cell culture.

It is very useful to consider developments in the biological industries in this way and look for areas of research which are relevant to the development of new products, processes and techniques. Important areas include fermentation, separation techniques for downstream processing including chromatography, the biochemistry and physiology of micro-organisms, molecular biology, recombinant DNA techniques, and so on.

Ultimately, all research work is likely to have an application at some stage, but the applications of the more obscure branches of the biological sciences may not be readily appreciated by employers. If you are prepared to study a particular topic for its own sake, and then change direction at a later stage when or if you look for permanent employment, then this need not be a worry. You should, however, make sure that you can justify your change of direction to a potential employer, and that you won't want a postgraduate award at a later stage.

Changing direction

Many biological scientists use their biological knowledge by changing direction to an area which has greater employment opportunities. For example, a postgraduate course in biophysics could lead to hospital medical physics, with specialisation in such areas as radiotherapy or bioengineering.

Postgraduate courses in biochemical engineering for biologists concentrate on engineering aspects, for research and development as well as production work. Qualifications in this area could enable you to apply for posts in a wide range of biological industries, including pharmaceuticals, food and drink, waste treatment and utilisation. Courses in food science could lead to employment in the food industry, either on the research and development side or in production and quality control.

Other useful areas include the more numerate subjects, such as computing and statistics. All biological scientists have to be numerate but further study

in this area could enhance your opportunities.

Agriculture and horticulture are other areas which employ biological scientists who have changed direction. Usually you will require some practical experience on a farm or market garden before being accepted for these courses, but this requirement applies equally to all entrants, not just to biologists who are changing direction.

Vocational training

There is a wide range of potential courses which lead to vocational and professional qualifications - ranging from the totally non-biological, such as accountancy, to those which would build on your present knowledge. One obvious area is medicine and the related professions. For medicine, dentistry and veterinary science, the main problem is finance, as you will usually be required to study the full course (there may be some exemption for graduates in relevant disciplines such as physiology), and having had one grant there is little chance of getting another for the full period.

Several institutions offer postgraduate nurse training but many people still prefer to do the standard training. Finance is not usually a problem as student nurses receive a wage; recent recommendations to make them 'proper' students are unlikely to be implemented, at least in the short term.

Having already had a grant, it is more difficult for graduates to get finance for training in the paramedical professions such as occupational therapy and physiotherapy, and there are no courses specifically for graduates. It may, however, be possible to gain exemption from some areas of certain courses if you have a relevant degree.

Alternatively, an interest in the environment could lead you on to landscape architecture, planning or estate management. You will usually need some relevant experience for landscape architecture or estate management. Environmental health courses are mainly open to non-graduates, unless you can finance yourself, as it is very difficult for graduates to get grants. Trainee environmental health officers are often sent on block release courses by their employers.

There are many opportunities for graduates who want to pursue further studies in biological sciences and related areas, and who are willing to apply themselves and their knowledge to changing trends in industry as well as in academia.

Elizabeth Ingleton

This listing contains **taught courses** (under the heading 'Higher degrees by instruction') and **research opportunities** (under the heading 'Higher degrees by research'). All study exceeds two terms or six months and is offered on both a full-time and part-time basis unless otherwise indicated. Post-experience and in-service courses are only included when advertised.

☐   This symbol indicates that the **taught course(s)** or **research opportunities** are advertised at the end of this listing.

Biol   An italic abbreviation indicates that an advertisement has been placed at the end of another chapter.

☆   This symbol indicates full-time study only.

△   This symbol indicates part-time study only.

For quick reference to advertisements, please use the 'Advertiser's course entry index'. For further information regarding the listing, please refer to page 53.

General

Higher degrees by instruction

Animal parasitology
Bangor, U of Wales MSc☆/dip☆

Applied entomology
London U Imperial C MSc/dip☆

Applied genetics
Birmingham U MSc☆

Applied insect taxonomy
Cardiff U of Wales C dip☆   □

Applied nematology
London U Imperial C MSc/dip

Archaeological textile studies
Manchester U MA☆

Bioactive molecules: design, synthesis, action
North London P MSc△

Biological electron microscopy
Aberystwyth, UC of Wales
MSc☆/dip☆

Biomedical sciences
Nottingham P MSc△

Biotechnology
Lancashire P MSc☆/cert△
Teesside P BEng☆

Contemporary biological sciences
Ulster U MSc△

Crop protection
Harper Adams AgC dip☆   *Env*

Dental surgery
Belfast Queen's U MDS☆

Ecology
Aberdeen U MSc☆/dip☆   *Env*

Educational studies for nurses
Ulster U dip☆

Experimental psychology
Sussex U MSc☆

Fisheries biology & management
Bangor, U of Wales MSc☆/dip☆

Food biotechnology
Strathclyde U MSc☆

General & medical microbiology
London U UC MSc☆/dip☆   □

History & philosophy of science
Leeds U dip

Human biology
Loughborough U MSc☆

Independent study
East London P MA/MSc/dip

Law & science: intellectual property
London U Queen Mary & Westfield C MSc

Life sciences
London U King's C cert☆

Marine & fisheries science
Aberdeen U MSc☆/dip☆   □

Marine environmental protection
Bangor, U of Wales MSc/dip☆

Marine resource development & protection
Heriot-Watt U MSc   *Env*

Medical molecular biology
Central London P MSc△/dip△

Mental handicap studies
York U MA△

Molecular biology
East Anglia U MSc☆

Molecular genetics
Leicester U MSc☆   □

Natural science
Cambridge U cert☆

Physical education & sports science
Loughborough U MSc☆/dip☆

Physical habilitation
Liverpool U MSc☆

Plant pathology
London U Imperial C MSc/dip

Psychological research methods
Southampton U MSc☆/dip☆

Science & science education
Glasgow U MSc

Science, technology & international affairs
Lancaster U MA☆

Shellfish biology, fisheries & culture
Bangor, U of Wales MSc/dip

Tropical coastal management
Newcastle U MSc☆/dip☆

Weed science
London U Imperial C MSc/dip☆

Higher degrees by research

Anthropology
Durham U PhD/MA/MPhil/MSc

Applied science
Middlesex P PhD/MPhil

Applied sciences
Kingston P PhD/MPhil

Biochemistry
Aberdeen U PhD☆/MPhil☆/MSc☆
London U UC PhD☆/MPhil☆

Biological chemistry & molecular enzymology
Sussex U DPhil/MPhil

Biological sciences
Lancaster U PhD/MPhil
Swansea UC PhD/MPhil

Biophysics
London U UC PhD☆/MPhil☆

Bioscience & biotechnology
Strathclyde U PhD☆/MPhil☆/
MSc☆   □

Cell & tissue biology
Cardiff U of Wales C PhD☆/
MPhil☆

Cell biology
London U UC PhD☆/MPhil☆
St Andrews U PhD☆/MSc☆

Comparative physiology
Oxford U DPhil☆/MSc☆

Computers in medicine
Kent U PhD☆/MPhil☆

Cytology
London U UC PhD☆/MPhil☆

Developmental biology
London U UC PhD☆/MPhil☆
St Andrews U PhD☆/MSc☆

Developmental, cell, & reproductive biology
Oxford U DPhil☆/MSc☆

Experimental pathology
St Andrews U PhD☆/MSc☆

Genetics & biometry
London U UC PhD☆/MPhil☆

Independent study
East London P PhD/MPhil

Psychology
Southampton U PhD/MPhil

Pure & applied biology
London U Imperial C PhD/MPhil

Science
Canterbury Christ Church C
  PhD/MPhil
Cardiff IHE PhD/MPhil/dip△
Humberside CHE PhD/MPhil
Worcester CHE PhD/MPhil

Science & technology
Thames Valley C MPhil

Science studies
Bath U PhD☆/MPhil☆

Science, mathematics & computing
Cheltenham & Gloucester CHE
  PhD/MPhil

Anatomy, physiology, neurology

Higher degrees by instruction

Anatomical sciences
Glasgow U MSc(MedSci)

Anatomy & cell biology
Sheffield U MMedSci☆

Applied parasitology
Liverpool U MVSc

Applied parasitology & entomology
Liverpool U MSc☆

Biophysics & physiology
East Anglia U MSc☆/dip☆

Cardiology
London U Royal Postgraduate
  Med S dip☆

Cardiovascular studies
Leeds U MSc☆

Comparative physiology
London U Birkbeck C MSc△

Experimental parasitology
Glasgow U MAppSci/dip

Funerary archaeology & human skeletal studies
Sheffield U MSc

Health sciences
Leeds P MSc

Human & applied physiology
London U King's C MSc☆

Human biology
Loughborough U MSc☆

Human fertility & infertility
Bristol U MSc☆

Micropalaeontology
Southampton U MSc☆   Env

Neurochemistry
London U Inst of Ophthalmology
  MSc☆
London U Inst of Psychiatry
  MSc☆

Neuroendoctrine cell biology
London U Royal Postgraduate
  Med S MSc☆

Neurological science
London U UC MSc

Neurophysical basis of behaviour
City of London P MSc△

Neuroscience
Edinburgh U MSc☆/dip☆

Optometry
Bradford U MSc

Oral pathology
Manchester U MSc

Pathology
Belfast Queen's U MMedSc☆

Pharmacology
Strathclyde U MSc/dip☆

Physiological flow studies
London U Imperial C MSc☆/dip☆

Physiology
London U UC MSc

Ultrastructural anatomy & pathology
Belfast Queen's U MMedSc☆

Higher degrees by research

Anatomy
Aberdeen U PhD☆/MPhil☆/MSc☆
Belfast Queen's U PhD
Birmingham U PhD/MSc
Bristol U PhD☆/MSc☆
Cambridge U PhD☆/MSc☆
Cardiff U of Wales C PhD☆/
  MD☆/MPhil☆
Dundee U PhD/MSc
Edinburgh U PhD/MPhil
Glasgow U PhD/MSc(MedSci)
Leeds U PhD/MPhil
Leicester U PhD/MPhil
Liverpool U PhD/MSc
London U Royal Veterinary C
  PhD☆/MPhil☆
London U UC PhD☆/MPhil☆

London U Charing Cross &
  Westminster Med S PhD/MPhil
London U Royal Free Hosp S of
  Med PhD☆/MPhil☆
London U St Bartholomew's
  Hosp Med C PhD/MPhil
London U St George's Hosp
  Med S PhD☆/MPhil☆
London U United Med & Dent S,
  Guys's & St Thomas's PhD☆/
  MPhil☆
Manchester U PhD/MSc
Newcastle U MD/MPhil
Oxford U DPhil☆/MSc☆

Anatomy & cell biology
London U Imperial C PhD☆/
  MPhil☆

Anatomy & experimental pathology
St Andrews U PhD/MSc

Anatomy & human biology
London U King's C PhD☆/MPhil☆

Animal physiology
Nottingham U PhD/MPhil
Oxford U DPhil☆/MSc☆

Animal physiology & nutrition
Leeds U PhD/MPhil/MSc

Biological sciences
Bath U PhD☆/MPhil☆
Salford U PhD/MSc

Biomedical & physiological studies
Swansea UC PhD/MPhil

Cardiology
London U Imperial C PhD☆/
  MPhil☆
London U St Bartholomew's
  Hosp Med C PhD/MPhil
London U United Med & Dent S,
  Guys's & St Thomas's PhD☆/
  MPhil☆
Newcastle U MD/MPhil
Wales U C of Med PhD☆/MSc☆

Cardiovascular epidemiology
Dundee U PhD/MSc

Cardiovascular medicine
Birmingham U PhD/MSc

Cardiovascular studies
Leeds U PhD/MPhil/MSc☆

Chemical pathology & human metabolism
London U Royal Free Hosp S of
  Med PhD☆/MPhil☆

Clinical neurology
Oxford U DPhil☆/MSc☆

Communication & neuroscience
Keele U PhD/MSc

Comparative physiology
Oxford U DPhil☆/MSc☆

Cytology
London U UC PhD☆/MPhil☆

Developmental biology
London U UC PhD☆/MPhil☆

Diseases of the nervous system
London U United Med & Dent S,
Guys's & St Thomas's PhD☆/
MPhil☆

Embryology
London U UC PhD☆/MPhil☆

Experimental pathology
St Andrews U PhD☆/MSc☆

Histology
Liverpool U PhD/MSc

Histopathology
London U St George's Hosp
Med S PhD☆/MPhil☆
Manchester U PhD/MPhil

Histopathology & experimental pathology
London U Imperial C PhD☆/
MPhil☆

Human anatomy & cell biology
Liverpool U PhD/MSc

Human morphology (anatomy)
Southampton U PhD/MPhil

Human movement
Brighton P PhD/MPhil

Human sciences
Loughborough U PhD/MPhil

Insect chemistry & physiology
Sussex U DPhil/MPhil

Invertebrate chemistry & comparative physiology
Portsmouth P PhD☆/MPhil☆

Mineralised tissue biology
London U UC PhD☆/MPhil☆

Molecular sciences
Aston U PhD/MPhil

Morbid anatomy
London U King's C S of Med &
Dentistry PhD/MPhil
London U London Hosp Med C
PhD☆/MPhil☆

Neurobiology
Central London P PhD☆/MPhil☆
London U UC PhD☆/MPhil☆
St Andrews U PhD☆/MSc☆

Neurological science
Liverpool U PhD
London U Royal Free Hosp S of
Med PhD☆/MPhil☆

Neurological sciences
London U St Bartholomew's
Hosp Med C PhD/MPhil

Neurological studies
London U UC PhD☆/MPhil☆

Neurological surgery
London U St Bartholomew's
Hosp Med C PhD/MPhil

Neurology
London U Imperial C PhD☆/
MPhil☆
London U Inst of Psychiatry
PhD☆/MPhil☆
London U King's C S of Med &
Dentistry PhD☆/MPhil☆
Newcastle U MD/MPhil
Wales U C of Med PhD☆/MD☆/
MSc☆

Neuropathology
London U Inst of Psychiatry
PhD☆/MPhil☆

Neurophysiology
Southampton U PhD/MPhil

Neuroscience
Lancashire P PhD/MPhil
London U Royal Veterinary C
PhD☆/MPhil☆

Nitrogen fixation
Sussex U DPhil/MPhil

Ophthalmology (clinical & basic science)
London U Inst of Ophthalmology
PhD☆/MPhil☆

Ophthalmology
Aberdeen U PhD☆/MPhil☆/MSc☆
Dundee U PhD/MSc

Optometry & physiological optics
Bradford U PhD/MPhil

Optometry & visual science
City U PhD/MPhil

Oral pathology
London U King's C S of Med &
Dentistry PhD☆/MPhil☆

Parasitology
Liverpool U PhD/MSc
Portsmouth P PhD☆/MPhil☆

Pathology
Cambridge U PhD☆/MSc☆
Dundee U PhD/MSc
Edinburgh U PhD/MPhil
Leicester U PhD/MD/MPhil
Liverpool U PhD/MSc
London U King's C S of Med &
Dentistry PhD☆/MPhil☆
London U London Hosp Med C
PhD☆/MPhil☆

London U Royal Postgraduate
Med S PhD☆/MPhil☆
Manchester U PhD/MSc
Newcastle U PhD/MD/MPhil
Nottingham U PhD/MPhil
Oxford U DPhil☆/MSc☆
Sheffield U PhD/MMedSci
Southampton U PhD/MPhil
Wales U C of Med PhD☆/MSc☆

Physiological biochemistry
Buckingham U DPhil/MPhil

Physiological flow studies
London U Imperial C PhD/MD

Physiological sciences
Manchester U PhD/MSc
Newcastle U PhD/MPhil

Physiology
Aberdeen U PhD☆/MPhil☆/MSc☆
Belfast Queen's U PhD
Birmingham U PhD/MSc
Bristol U PhD☆/MSc☆
Cambridge U PhD☆/MSc☆
Cardiff U of Wales C PhD☆/
MPhil☆
Dundee U PhD/MSc
Edinburgh U PhD/MPhil
Glasgow U PhD/MSc(MedSci)
Lancashire P PhD/MPhil
Leeds U PhD/MPhil
Leicester U PhD/MPhil
Liverpool U PhD/MSc
London U Inst of Psychiatry
PhD☆/MPhil☆
London U King's C PhD☆/MPhil☆
London U Royal Holloway &
Bedford New C PhD/MPhil
London U Royal Veterinary C
PhD☆/MPhil☆
London U UC PhD☆/MPhil☆
London U Wye C PhD☆/MPhil☆
London U Charing Cross &
Westminster Med S PhD/MPhil
London U London Hosp Med C
PhD☆/MPhil☆
London U Royal Free Hosp S of
Med PhD☆/MPhil☆
London U St Bartholomew's
Hosp Med C PhD/MPhil
London U St George's Hosp
Med S PhD☆/MPhil☆
London U United Med & Dent S,
Guys's & St Thomas's PhD☆/
MPhil☆
Manchester U PhD/MSc
Oxford U DPhil☆/MSc☆
Sunderland P PhD/MPhil
Ulster U DPhil/MPhil

Physiology & biochemistry
Reading U PhD/MPhil

Physiology & biophysics
London U Imperial C PhD☆/ MPhil☆

Physiology & environmental science
Nottingham U PhD☆/MPhil☆

Physiology & pharmacology
Nottingham U PhD/MPhil
St Andrews U PhD/MSc
Southampton U PhD/MPhil
Strathclyde U PhD☆/MPhil☆/ MSc☆

Psychology & speech pathology
Manchester P PhD/MPhil

Pure & applied biology
London U Imperial C PhD/MPhil/ dip

Reproductive physiology
London U St Bartholomew's Hosp Med C PhD/MPhil

Science
Bristol P PhD/MPhil

Speech science
London U UC PhD☆/MPhil☆

Surgical neurology
Dundee U PhD/MSc

Veterinary anaesthesia
Liverpool U PhD/MVSc

Veterinary anatomy
Edinburgh U PhD/MPhil
Liverpool U PhD/MVSc

Veterinary physiology
Edinburgh U PhD/MPhil
Liverpool U PhD/MVSc

Vision sciences
Aston U PhD/MPhil

Zoology & comparative physiology
Birmingham U PhD/MSc

Biochemistry, endocrinology, toxicology

Higher degrees by instruction

Analytical biochemistry
Dundee U MSc☆

Applied parasitology
Liverpool U MVSc

Applied parasitology & entomology
Liverpool U MSc☆

Applied toxicology
Portsmouth P MSc☆

Bioanalytical chemistry
Dundee U dip☆

Biochemical endocrinology
Sussex U MSc☆

Biochemical immunology
East London P MSc△

Biochemical pharmacology
Southampton U MSc☆

Biochemistry
Cambridge U MPhil☆/cert☆
East Anglia U MSc☆/dip☆
Edinburgh U dip☆
London U UC MSc
Salford U MSc△
Sussex U MSc☆

Biochemistry & chemistry applied to medicine
London U London Hosp Med C MSc

Biochemistry & genetics
Newcastle U MSc☆

Biochemistry (conversion)
Newcastle U MSc☆

Biology of water management
Napier P MSc☆

Biopharmacy
London U King's C MSc

Biosensors
Newcastle U MSc☆

Biotechnology
Kent U MSc☆/dip☆
London U Imperial C MSc☆/ dip☆   □

Cellular & molecular plant science
Bangor, U of Wales MSc☆/dip☆

Chemistry & biological chemistry
Essex U dip☆

Clinical biochemistry
Leeds U MSc
London U UC MSc
London U King's C S of Med & Dentistry MSc△
London U United Med & Dent S, Guys's & St Thomas's MSc△
Newcastle U MSc☆
Surrey U MSc☆

Clinical immunology
Leeds U MSc☆

Clinical laboratory sciences
Leeds U dip☆

Ecology
Bangor, U of Wales MSc☆/dip☆

Endocrinology
Sheffield U MMedSci☆

Endocrinology (biochemistry or pathology)
London U Royal Postgraduate Med S dip☆

Experimental parasitology
Glasgow U MAppSci/dip

Experimental pathology (toxicology)
London U Royal Postgraduate Med S MSc☆

Food science
Leeds U MSc☆/dip☆   *Chem*

Forensic science
London U King's C MSc☆

Forensic toxicology
Glasgow U MSc/dip

General biochemistry
London U King's C MSc

Genetic toxicology
Swansea UC dip☆

Human nutrition
Aberdeen U MSc☆/dip☆

Insect science
London U Birkbeck C MSc△

Medical biochemistry
Belfast Queen's U dip☆
Brunel U MSc

Medical virology
Manchester U MSc☆

Medicinal chemistry
Loughborough U MSc☆   *Chem*

Molecular biochemistry
Essex U MSc☆

Neuroendoctrine cell biology
London U Royal Postgraduate Med S MSc☆

Nutritional biochemistry
Nottingham U MSc☆

Pest & disease management
London U Imperial C MSc/dip☆

Pharmacological biochemistry
Hatfield P MSc△

Pharmacology
Strathclyde U MSc/dip☆

Plant biochemistry
Aberystwyth, UC of Wales MSc☆

Plant biochemistry & bioenergetics
Sussex U MSc☆

Post harvest food technology
Humberside CHE MSc☆

Steroid endocrinology
Leeds U MSc☆

Synthesis & synthetic matters
Thames P MSc☆

Toxicology
Birmingham U MSc/dip☆ □
Surrey U MSc □

Higher degrees by research

Agricultural biochemistry
Aberdeen SAg PhD☆/MSc☆
Aberdeen U PhD☆/MPhil☆/MSc☆
Edinburgh U PhD/MPhil

Agricultural biochemistry & nutrition
Edinburgh U PhD/MPhil
Newcastle U PhD/MPhil

Agricultural biochemistry & soil sciences
Aberystwyth, UC of Wales PhD☆/MPhil☆

Agricultural botany
Aberdeen SAg PhD☆/MSc☆
Edinburgh U PhD/MPhil

Animal biochemistry & physiology
Edinburgh U PhD/MPhil

Applied biochemistry & food science
Nottingham U PhD/MPhil

Architecture & building engineering
Bath U PhD☆/MSc☆

Biochemical & chemical engineering
Bath U PhD☆/MSc☆

Biochemical engineering
Swansea UC PhD/MPhil

Biochemical medicine
Dundee U PhD/MSc

Biochemistry
Aberdeen U PhD☆/MPhil☆/MSc☆
Aberystwyth, UC of Wales PhD☆/MPhil☆
Bangor, U of Wales PhD☆/MPhil☆
Bath U PhD☆/MPhil☆
Belfast Queen's U PhD/MSc
Birmingham U PhD/MSc
Bristol P PhD△/MPhil△/dip△
Bristol U PhD☆/MSc☆
Brunel U PhD/MPhil
Cambridge U PhD☆/MSc☆

Cardiff U of Wales C PhD☆/MPhil☆
Dundee U PhD/MSc
Edinburgh U PhD/MPhil
Glasgow U PhD/MSc
Keele U PhD/MSc
Kent U PhD/MPhil/MSc
Leeds U PhD/MPhil/MSc
Leicester U PhD/MPhil
Liverpool U PhD/MSc
London U Imperial C PhD/MPhil/dip
London U Inst of Psychiatry PhD☆/MPhil☆
London U King's C PhD☆/MPhil☆
London U Royal Holloway & Bedford New C PhD/MPhil
London U Royal Veterinary C PhD☆/MPhil☆
London U UC PhD☆/MPhil☆
London U Wye C PhD☆/MPhil☆
London U Charing Cross & Westminster Med S PhD/MPhil
London U London Hosp Med C PhD☆/MPhil☆
London U St Bartholomew's Hosp Med C PhD/MPhil
London U St George's Hosp Med S PhD☆/MPhil☆
London U United Med & Dent S, Guys's & St Thomas's PhD☆/MPhil☆
Newcastle U PhD/MPhil
North East Wales IHE PhD☆/MSc☆
Oxford U DPhil☆/MSc☆
Sheffield U PhD/MPhil
Southampton U PhD/MPhil
Surrey U PhD/MPhil
Sussex U DPhil/MPhil
Swansea UC PhD/MPhil
Ulster U DPhil/MPhil

Biochemistry & applied molecular biology
Manchester UMIST PhD/MSc

Biochemistry & chemistry
London U Royal Free Hosp S of Med PhD☆/MPhil☆

Biochemistry & microbiology
St Andrews U PhD/MSc

Biochemistry & molecular biology
Manchester U PhD/MSc

Biochemistry & nutrition
Edinburgh U PhD/MPhil

Bioengineering
Birmingham U PhD/MSc

Biological sciences
Aston U PhD/MPhil

Bath U PhD☆/MPhil☆
Buckingham U DPhil/MPhil
Salford U PhD/MSc

Biology & biochemistry
East London P PhD/MPhil

Biology (including biochemistry)
York U DPhil/MPhil

Biomechanics
Central London P PhD☆/MSc☆

Biomedical sciences
Bradford U PhD/MPhil

Biotechnology
Belfast Queen's U PhD/MSc
Kent U PhD/MPhil/MSc
London U Imperial C PhD/MPhil/dip

Botany
Edinburgh U PhD/MPhil

Chemical endocrinology
London U St Bartholomew's Hosp Med C PhD/MPhil

Chemical pathology
Aberdeen U PhD☆/MPhil☆/MSc☆
London U St Bartholomew's Hosp Med C PhD/MPhil

Chemistry
Southampton U PhD/MPhil *Chem*

Chemistry & biochemistry
Liverpool P PhD/MPhil

Chemistry & biological chemistry
Essex U PhD/MPhil/MSc

Clinical biochemistry
Aberdeen U PhD☆/MPhil☆/MSc☆
Cambridge U PhD☆/MSc☆
Leeds U MMedSc
Liverpool U PhD
Manchester U PhD/MSc
Oxford U DPhil☆/MSc☆

Clinical biochemistry & metabolic medicine
Newcastle U PhD/MPhil

Endocrinology
London U St Bartholomew's Hosp Med C PhD/MPhil
London U United Med & Dent S, Guys's & St Thomas's PhD☆/MPhil☆
Wales U C of Med PhD☆/MSc☆

Food chemistry & biochemistry
Belfast Queen's U PhD/MSc

Food science
Leeds U PhD/MPhil/MSc *Chem*

Forensic medicine & toxicology
London U Charing Cross & Westminster Med S PhD/MPhil

Genetics
Swansea UC PhD/MPhil

Health sciences
Birmingham P PhD/MPhil

Human metabolism & clinical biochemistry
Sheffield U PhD/MMedSci

Human sciences
Loughborough U PhD/MPhil

Invertebrate chemistry & comparative physiology
Portsmouth P PhD☆/MPhil☆

Medical biochemistry
Wales U C of Med PhD☆/MSc☆

Microbiology
Kent U PhD/MPhil/MSc

Mineralised tissue biology
London U UC PhD☆/MPhil☆

Molecular endocrinology
London U UC PhD☆/MPhil☆

Molecular sciences
Aston U PhD/MPhil

Neurobiology
London U UC PhD☆/MPhil☆

Neuroendocrinology
Newcastle U MD/MPhil

Nitrogen fixation
Sussex U DPhil/MPhil

Parasitology
Liverpool U PhD/MSc
Portsmouth P PhD☆/MPhil☆

Pharmaceutical sciences
Aston U PhD/MPhil

Pharmacology
London U UC PhD☆/MPhil☆

Physiological biochemistry
Buckingham U DPhil/MPhil

Physiology & biochemistry
Reading U PhD/MPhil

Plant & microbial metabolism studies
Swansea UC PhD/MPhil

Science
Bristol P PhD/MPhil
Wales P PhD/MPhil

Steroid endocrinology
Leeds U MMedSc

Toxicology
Birmingham U PhD☆/MSc☆
Glasgow U PhD/MPhil
London U S of Pharmacy PhD☆/MPhil☆
London U St Bartholomew's Hosp Med C PhD/MPhil

Veterinary biochemistry
Liverpool U PhD/MVSc

Biology, botanical sciences

Higher degrees by instruction

Anatomy & cell biology
Sheffield U MMedSci☆

Applied biology
Salford U MSc△

Applied entomology
West of Scotland C MSc/dip

Applied entomology & crop protection
Newcastle U MSc☆/dip☆

Applied fish biology
South West P MSc☆/dip☆

Applied genetics
Birmingham U MSc☆

Applied hydrobiology
Cardiff U of Wales C MSc☆

Applied microbiology
Heriot-Watt U MSc☆
Strathclyde U dip☆

Applied molecular biology & biotechnology
London U UC MSc

Applied parasitology
Liverpool U MVSc

Applied parasitology & entomology
Liverpool U MSc☆

Applied parasitology & medical entomology
Incorporated Liverpool S of Tropical Med MSc☆

Applied plant sciences
London U Wye C MSc☆

Aquaculture
Stirling U MSc/dip   □

Aquatic pathobiology
Stirling U MSc/dip

Aquatic resource management
London U King's C MSc☆

Bacteriology & virology
Manchester U MSc☆

Behavioural biology & health care
Roehampton I MSc☆

Behavioural ecology
Manchester P MSc△/dip△   □

Bioactive molecules: design, synthesis, action
North London P MSc△

Biochemistry
Salford U MSc△

Biocolloid chemistry
East Anglia U MSc☆

Biodeterioration of materials
Portsmouth P MSc☆/dip☆

Biological anthropology
Cambridge U MPhil☆
Durham U MSc☆
London U UC MSc

Biological computation
York U MSc☆/dip☆

Biological electron microscopy
Aberystwyth, UC of Wales MSc☆/dip☆

Biology
East Anglia U MSc☆/dip☆
Essex U dip☆

Biology (botany, genetics, physiology, zoology & pharmacology)
Edinburgh U dip☆

Biology (ecology & behaviour)
Bolton IHE dip△

Biomedical methods
Wales U C of Med dip☆

Biomedical sciences
Glasgow C MSc☆/dip☆

Biometry
Reading U MSc

Bioreactor systems
Manchester UMIST MSc☆

Biotechnology
Central London P MSc△
London U Imperial C MSc☆/dip☆   □

Biotechnology & environmental biology
Dundee U MSc☆

Cell & molecular genetics of crop plants
Aberystwyth, UC of Wales MSc☆

Cell biology
East Anglia U MSc☆

Cellular & molecular plant science
Bangor, U of Wales MSc☆/dip☆

Clinical microbiology
London U London Hosp Med C MSc/dip

Combustion science & pollution control
Sheffield U MSc(Eng)☆/ MSc(Tech)☆

Conservation
London U UC MSc☆/dip☆

Conservation & utilisation of plant genetic resources
Birmingham U MSc

Contemporary biological sciences
Ulster U MSc△

Crop physiology
Reading U MSc☆

Crop production
Bath U MSc☆/dip☆

Crop science
Aberdeen SAg MSc☆
Aberdeen U MSc☆

Development of pest management systems
Birmingham U MSc☆

Ecology
Aberdeen U MSc☆/dip☆   *Env*
Bangor, U of Wales MSc☆/dip☆
Durham U MSc☆/dip☆

Environmental biology
Swansea UC MSc☆

Experimental parasitology
Glasgow U MAppSci/dip

Fisheries biology
Buckingham U MSc☆

Fisheries biology & management
Bangor, U of Wales MSc☆/dip☆

Food & agricultural biotechnology
Reading U MSc☆

Forensic science
Strathclyde U MSc☆/dip☆

Fungal technology
Kent U MSc☆

General & medical microbiology
London U S of Hygiene & Tropical Med MSc☆
London U UC MSc☆/dip☆   ☐

Genetic manipulation & molecular biology
Sussex U MSc☆

Grassland science
Reading U MSc☆

Human biology
Oxford U MSc☆/dip☆

Industrial microbiology
Heriot-Watt U dip☆

Laboratory aspects of medical microbiology
Wales U C of Med MSc☆

Marine science
Glasgow U MAppSci/dip

Mathematical biology
Dundee U MSc☆

Medical microbiology
East Anglia U MSc☆
London U S of Hygiene & Tropical Med MSc☆/dip☆
London U UC MSc
Surrey U MSc△/dip△

Medical molecular biology
Central London P MSc△/dip△

Microbial ecology
Aberdeen U MSc☆

Microbiology
City of London P dip
East Anglia U MSc☆/dip☆
London U Birkbeck C MSc△

Micropalaeontology
London U UC MSc☆/dip☆
Southampton U MSc☆   *Env*

Mineralised tissue biology
London U UC MSc

Modern botanical methods
Aberdeen U MSc/dip

Molecular biology
East Anglia U MSc☆
London U UC MSc☆
Swansea UC MSc☆

Palynology
Aberystwyth, UC of Wales MSc☆
Sheffield U MSc☆

Pest & disease management
London U Imperial C MSc/dip☆

Plant biochemistry
Aberystwyth, UC of Wales MSc☆

Plant biology
East Anglia U MSc☆/dip☆

Plant biotechnology
London U Wye C MSc☆

Plant breeding
Cambridge U MPhil☆

Plant disease management
Aberystwyth, UC of Wales MSc☆

Plant pathology
London U Imperial C MSc/dip

Plant physiology
Aberystwyth, UC of Wales dip☆

Plant productivity & photosynthesis
London U King's C dip☆

Plant taxonomy
Reading U MSc☆

Plant toxins in nutrition
London U Wye C MSc☆

Pollution & environmental control
Manchester U MSc☆/dip☆   *Env*

Post harvest food technology
Humberside CHE MSc☆

Radiation biology
London U UC MSc
London U St Bartholomew's Hosp Med C MSc

Rural resource management
Bangor, U of Wales MSc☆/dip☆

Science education
London U King's C MA/MEd△/ dip☆

Soil science & plant performance
Aberystwyth, UC of Wales MSc☆

Symbiotic nitrogen fixation
Aberystwyth, UC of Wales MSc☆

Vertebrate palaeontology
London U UC MSc

Weed science
London U Imperial C MSc/dip☆

Higher degrees by research

Agricultural biology
Edinburgh U PhD/MPhil

Agricultural biology & environmental science
Newcastle U PhD/MPhil

Agricultural botany
Belfast Queen's U PhD/MAgr
Edinburgh U PhD/MPhil
Glasgow U PhD/MSc

Agricultural microbiology
Aberdeen SAg PhD☆/MSc☆
Aberdeen U PhD☆/MPhil☆/MSc☆
Edinburgh U PhD/MPhil

Agriculture & horticulture
Nottingham U PhD/MPhil

Anatomy & cell biology
London U Imperial C PhD☆/ MPhil☆

Anatomy & experimental pathology
St Andrews U PhD/MSc

Anatomy & human biology
London U King's C PhD☆/MPhil☆

Animal & plant sciences
Bristol P PhD△/MPhil△/dip△

Animal biology
Bangor, U of Wales PhD☆/
MPhil☆
Sheffield U PhD/MPhil

Animal developmental biology
Glasgow U PhD/MSc

Animal physiology & ecology
Bath U PhD☆/MPhil☆

Applied biology
Brunel U PhD/MPhil
Cambridge U PhD☆/MSc☆
Hull U PhD/MSc
Lancashire P PhD/MPhil
Oxford U DPhil☆/MSc☆

Applied biology & food science
South Bank P PhD/MPhil

Applied chemistry & life sciences
North London P PhD/MPhil

Applied microbiology
Strathclyde U PhD☆/MPhil☆

Applied sciences
Staffordshire P PhD/MPhil
Wolverhampton P PhD/MPhil

Aquatic biology
Liverpool U PhD/MSc

Bacteriology
Edinburgh U PhD/MPhil
London U Royal Postgraduate
Med S PhD☆/MPhil☆

Bacteriology & virology
Manchester U PhD/MSc

Biochemistry
Bath U PhD☆/MPhil☆
Kent U PhD/MPhil/MSc

Biochemistry & applied molecular biology
Manchester UMIST PhD/MSc

Biochemistry & microbiology
St Andrews U PhD/MSc

Biological & molecular sciences
Oxford P PhD/MPhil

Biological anthropology
Cambridge U PhD☆/MSc☆
Oxford U DPhil☆/MSc☆

Biological sciences
Aston U PhD/MPhil
Bath U PhD☆/MPhil☆
Buckingham U DPhil/MPhil
City of London P PhD☆/MPhil☆
Coventry P PhD/MPhil
Dundee U PhD/MSc
East Anglia U PhD/MPhil
Exeter U PhD/MPhil
Hatfield P PhD/MPhil
Keele U PhD/MSc
Lancaster U PhD/MPhil

London U Queen Mary &
Westfield C PhD☆/MPhil☆
London U Wye C PhD☆/MPhil☆
Manchester P PhD/MPhil
Manchester U PhD/MSc
Napier P PhD/MPhil
North East Surrey CT PhD☆/
MPhil☆
Portsmouth P PhD☆/MPhil☆
Salford P PhD/MSc
Sheffield City P PhD/MPhil
South West P PhD/MPhil
Stirling U PhD/MSc
Warwick U PhD/MSc

Biological sciences & environmental health
Thames P PhD/MPhil

Biology
Belfast Queen's U PhD/MSc
Bolton IHE PhD△/MSc△
Bristol P PhD△/MPhil△/dip△
Edinburgh U PhD/MPhil
Essex U PhD/MPhil
Glasgow U PhD/MSc
Liverpool P PhD/MPhil
Liverpool U PhD/MSc
London U Birkbeck C PhD/MPhil
London U King's C PhD☆/MPhil☆
London U Royal Holloway &
Bedford New C PhD/MPhil
Luton CHE PhD☆/MPhil☆
Mid Kent CHFE PhD/MPhil
Newcastle U PhD/MPhil
North East Wales IHE PhD☆/
MSc☆
Open U PhD/MPhil/BPhil
Paisley CT DPhil/MPhil
Southampton U PhD/MPhil
Staffordshire P PhD/MPhil
Sunderland P PhD/MPhil
Sussex U DPhil/MPhil
Ulster U DPhil/MPhil

Biology & biochemistry
East London P PhD/MPhil

Biology (including biochemistry)
York U DPhil/MPhil

Biomedical sciences
Bradford U PhD/MPhil
Liverpool P PhD/MPhil
London U King's C PhD☆/MPhil☆
Sheffield City P PhD/MPhil
Sheffield U PhD/MMed/MPhil

Biometrics
London U Inst of Psychiatry
PhD☆/MPhil☆

Biophysics
London U UC PhD☆/MPhil☆

Biophysics, cell & molecular biology
London U King's C PhD☆/MPhil☆

Biotechnology
Cambridge U PhD☆
Central London P PhD☆/MPhil☆
Sheffield U PhD/MPhil

Botany
Aberdeen U PhD☆/MPhil☆/MSc☆
Bristol U PhD☆/MSc☆
Cambridge U PhD☆/MSc☆
Durham U PhD/MSc
Edinburgh U PhD/MPhil
Glasgow U PhD/MSc
Keele U PhD/MSc
Leicester U PhD/MPhil
Liverpool U PhD/MSc
London U UC PhD☆/MPhil☆
Manchester U PhD/MSc
Nottingham U PhD/MPhil
Reading U PhD/MPhil
West of Scotland C PhD☆/MSc☆

Botany & microbiology
Swansea UC PhD/MPhil

Brewing & biological sciences
Heriot-Watt U PhD☆/MPhil☆

Cell & molecular biology
Kent U PhD/MPhil/MSc

Cell & structural biology
Manchester U PhD/MSc

Cell & tissue biology
Cardiff U of Wales C PhD☆/
MPhil☆

Cell biology
Glasgow U PhD/MSc
Keele U PhD/MSc
London U Royal Holloway &
Bedford New C PhD/MPhil
London U UC PhD☆/MPhil☆
St Andrews U PhD☆/MSc☆

Cell mutation
Sussex U DPhil/MPhil

Chemical & life sciences
Newcastle P PhD☆/MPhil☆

Clinical bacteriology & virology
London U United Med & Dent S,
Guys's & St Thomas's PhD☆/
MPhil☆

Conservation
London U UC PhD☆/MPhil☆

Crop production & protection
Aberdeen U PhD☆/MPhil☆/MSc☆

Crop science
Aberdeen SAg PhD☆/MSc☆
Edinburgh U PhD/MPhil

Developmental biology
St Andrews U PhD☆/MSc☆

Developmental, cell, & reproductive biology
Oxford U DPhil☆/MSc☆

Ecology
Aberdeen U PhD☆/MPhil☆/MSc☆
London U UC PhD☆/MPhil☆

Environmental & evolutionary biology
Liverpool U PhD/MPhil

Environmental biology
Manchester U PhD/MSc
Swansea UC PhD/MPhil

Fermentation, process control & biocatalysis
Cranfield IT MPhil☆/MSc☆

Health sciences
Birmingham P PhD/MPhil

Histology
Liverpool U PhD/MSc

Histopathology
London U Charing Cross & Westminster Med S PhD/MPhil
London U St George's Hosp Med S PhD☆/MPhil☆
Manchester U PhD/MPhil

Histopathology & experimental pathology
London U Imperial C PhD☆/MPhil☆

Human anatomy & cell biology
Liverpool U PhD/MSc

Human biology
Aberdeen U PhD☆/MPhil☆/MSc☆
Oxford U DPhil☆/MSc☆/MSt☆

Human sciences
Loughborough U PhD/MPhil

Invertebrate biology & pest control
Cardiff U of Wales C PhD☆/MPhil☆

Life sciences
Buckingham U DPhil☆/MPhil☆
Huddersfield P PhD/MPhil
Leicester P PhD/MPhil
Nottingham P PhD☆/MPhil☆

Marine biology
Aberdeen U PhD☆/MPhil☆/MSc☆
Bangor, U of Wales PhD☆/MPhil☆
Liverpool U PhD/MSc
Portsmouth P PhD☆/MPhil☆
St Andrews U PhD/MSC☆/MSc△

Marine science
Glasgow U PhD/MSc

Marine science & technology
South West P PhD/MPhil

Medical microbiology
Aberdeen U PhD☆/MD☆/MPhil☆/MSc☆
Birmingham U PhD/MSc
Dundee U PhD/MSc
Liverpool U PhD/MSc
London U Imperial C PhD☆/MPhil☆
London U S of Hygiene & Tropical Med PhD/MPhil
London U UC PhD☆/MPhil☆
London U Charing Cross & Westminster Med S PhD/MPhil
London U King's C S of Med & Dentistry PhD/MPhil
London U Royal Free Hosp S of Med PhD☆/MPhil☆
London U St Bartholomew's Hosp Med C PhD/MPhil
London U St George's Hosp Med S PhD☆/MPhil☆
Manchester U PhD/MSc
Sheffield U PhD/MMedSci/MPhil
Wales U C of Med PhD☆/MSc☆

Microbal & molecular biology
Cardiff U of Wales C PhD☆/MPhil☆

Microbiology
Aberystwyth, UC of Wales PhD☆/MPhil☆
Bath U PhD☆/MPhil☆
Birmingham U PhD/MSc
Bristol U PhD☆/MSc☆
Glasgow U PhD/MSc
Kent U PhD/MPhil/MSc
Leeds U PhD/MPhil/MSc
Leicester U PhD/MPhil
Liverpool U PhD/MSc
London U King's C PhD☆/MPhil☆
London U S of Pharmacy PhD☆/MPhil☆
London U UC PhD☆/MPhil☆
London U United Med & Dent S, Guys's & St Thomas's PhD☆/MPhil☆
Newcastle U PhD/MPhil
Nottingham U PhD/MPhil
Portsmouth P PhD☆/MPhil☆
Reading U PhD/MPhil
Sheffield U PhD
Southampton U PhD/MPhil
Surrey U PhD/MPhil☆/Mphil△
West of Scotland C PhD☆/MSc☆

Microbiology & immunobiology
Belfast Queen's U PhD

Microbiology & parasitology
London U Royal Veterinary C PhD☆/MPhil☆

Microbiology, mycology & pathology
Oxford U MLitt☆/MSc☆

Molecular & cellular biology
London U Royal Veterinary C PhD☆/MPhil☆

Molecular & life sciences
Dundee IT PhD/MPhil

Molecular biology
Edinburgh U PhD/MPhil
Glasgow U PhD/MSc
Kent U PhD/MSc

Morphology & development
Oxford U DPhil☆/MSc☆

Mycology & plant pathology
Belfast Queen's U PhD/MAgr/MSc

Neurobiology
Central London P PhD☆/MPhil☆

Oral biology
Newcastle U PhD/MPhil
Wales U C of Med PhD☆/MScD☆/MSc☆

Oral immunology & microbiology
London U United Med & Dent S, Guys's & St Thomas's PhD☆/MPhil☆
Wales U C of Med PhD☆/MSc☆

Oral microbiology
London U London Hosp Med C PhD☆/MPhil☆

Oral pathology
London U King's C S of Med & Dentistry PhD☆/MPhil☆

Palaeoecology centre
Belfast Queen's U PhD/MSc

Parasitology
Liverpool U PhD/MSc
Portsmouth P PhD☆/MPhil☆

Pathology
Cambridge U PhD☆/MSc☆
Dundee U PhD/MSc
Edinburgh U PhD/MPhil
Leicester U PhD/MD/MPhil
Liverpool U PhD/MSc
London U King's C S of Med & Dentistry PhD☆/MPhil☆
London U London Hosp Med C PhD☆/MPhil☆
Manchester U PhD/MSc
Newcastle U PhD/MD/MPhil
Nottingham U PhD/MPhil
Sheffield U PhD/MMedSci
Southampton U PhD/MPhil
Wales U C of Med PhD☆/MSc☆

Pharmaceutical sciences
Aston U PhD/MPhil

Physiological sciences
Manchester U PhD/MSc

Physiology
Manchester U PhD/MSc

Plant & microbial metabolism studies
Swansea UC PhD/MPhil

Plant biology
Bangor, U of Wales PhD☆/MPhil☆
Bath U PhD☆/MPhil☆
Birmingham U PhD/MSc
Edinburgh U PhD/MPhil
Newcastle U PhD/MPhil

Plant biology & genetics
St Andrews U PhD/MSc

Plant breeding
Nottingham U PhD☆/MPhil☆

Plant molecular biology
Nottingham U PhD☆/MPhil☆

Plant molecular biology & biotechnology
Durham U PhD/MPhil

Plant pathology
Glasgow U PhD/MSc
London U UC PhD☆/MPhil☆
Nottingham U PhD☆/MPhil☆
West of Scotland C PhD☆/MSc☆

Plant Pathology & Biological Control
London U Wye C PhD☆/MPhil☆

Plant physiology
Nottingham U PhD☆/MPhil☆
Oxford U DPhil☆/MSc☆

Plant Physiology & Genetics
London U Wye C PhD☆/MPhil☆

Plant science
Aberdeen U PhD☆/MPhil☆/MSc☆
Cardiff U of Wales C PhD☆/MPhil☆

Plant sciences
Aberystwyth, UC of Wales PhD☆/MPhil☆
Oxford U DPhil☆/MSc☆
Sheffield U PhD/MPhil

Pollution research
Manchester U PhD/MSc
Manchester UMIST PhD/MSc

Pure & applied biology
Cardiff U of Wales C PhD☆/MPhil☆
Leeds U PhD/MPhil/MSc
London U Imperial C PhD/MPhil/dip
London U Imperial C PhD/MPhil

Radiation biology
London U St Bartholomew's Hosp Med C PhD/MPhil

Science
Bristol P PhD/MPhil
Wales P PhD/MPhil

Soil science
London U Wye C PhD☆/MPhil☆
Nottingham U PhD☆/MPhil☆

Sports science
Glasgow U PhD/MSc

Taxonomy & ecology
Oxford U DPhil☆/MSc☆

Veterinary microbiology
Edinburgh U PhD/MPhil

Zoology
Durham U PhD/MSc

Biotechnology

Higher degrees by instruction

Applied molecular biology & biotechnology
London U UC MSc

Biochemical engineering
Swansea UC MSc☆

Biochemical engineering/biotechnology
Birmingham U MSc(Eng)

Biochemistry
London U UC MSc

Biological electron microscopy
Aberystwyth, UC of Wales MSc☆/dip☆

Biomedical engineering science
Dundee U MSc

Biomedical methods
Wales U C of Med dip☆

Biomedical sciences
Bradford U MSc☆

Biomolecular organisation
London U Birkbeck C MSc△

Biophysics & bioengineering
London U Birkbeck C MSc△

Biophysics & physiology
East Anglia U MSc☆/dip☆

Bioreactor systems
Manchester UMIST MSc☆

Biosensors
Newcastle U MSc☆

Biotechnology
Bell CT dip☆
Central London P MSc△
Durham U MSc☆
Hatfield P MSc△/dip△
Heriot-Watt U MSc☆
Kent U MSc☆/dip☆
Lancashire P MSc☆/cert△
London U Imperial C MSc☆/dip☆ □
Manchester UMIST MSc☆
South Bank P MSc△
Teesside P BEng☆

Biotechnology & environmental biology
Dundee U MSc☆

Computer modelling of molecular & biological processes
London U Birkbeck C MSc△

Food & agricultural biotechnology
Reading U MSc☆

Food biotechnology
Strathclyde U MSc☆

Food technology
Reading U MSc☆

Molecular genetics
Leicester U MSc☆ □

Plant biotechnology
London U Wye C MSc☆

Process biotechnology
Birmingham U MSc(Eng)☆

Strategies in organic synthesis
Manchester P MSc△/dip△

Higher degrees by research

Biochemistry
Kent U PhD/MPhil/MSc
London U UC PhD☆/MPhil☆

Bioelectronics, bioelectrochemistry & biosensors
Cranfield IT MPhil☆/MSc☆

Bioengineering
Oxford U DPhil☆/MSc☆

Biological sciences
London U Wye C PhD☆/MPhil☆

Biomaterials science
Manchester U PhD/MSc

Biomathematics
Oxford U DPhil☆/MSc☆

Biomechanics
Central London P PhD✫/MSc✫

Biomedical research
Central London P PhD✫/MPhil✫

Biomolecular organisation
London U Birkbeck C PhD/MPhil

Biophysics
Leeds U PhD/MPhil/MSc
London U UC PhD✫/MPhil✫
Open U PhD/MPhil/BPhil
Oxford U DPhil✫/MSc✫
Portsmouth P PhD✫/MPhil✫

Biophysics, cell & molecular biology
London U King's C PhD✫/MPhil✫

Bioscience & biotechnology
Strathclyde U PhD✫/MPhil✫/
  MSc✫   □

Biotechnology
Belfast Queen's U PhD/MSc
Cambridge U PhD✫
Central London P PhD✫/MPhil✫
Cranfield IT PhD✫   □
Exeter U PhD/MPhil
Glasgow U PhD/MSc
Kent U PhD/MPhil/MSc
Leeds U PhD/MPhil
London U Imperial C PhD/MPhil/
  dip
London U King's C PhD✫/MPhil△
Reading U PhD/MPhil
Sheffield U PhD/MPhil
South Bank P PhD/MPhil

Botany
Edinburgh U PhD/MPhil
Liverpool U PhD/MSc

Chemical & biochemical engineering
London U UC PhD✫/MPhil✫

Chemical engineering
Loughborough U PhD✫/MPhil✫
Surrey U PhD/MPhil   *Eng*

Chemistry
Exeter U PhD/MPhil

Environmental biotechnology & biodeterioration
Cranfield IT MPhil✫/MSc✫

Human sciences
Loughborough U PhD/MPhil

Medical electronics
Bath U MSc✫

Medical engineering & physics
London U King's C S of Med & Dentistry PhD✫/MPhil✫
Wales U C of Med PhD✫/MSc✫

Microbiology
Kent U PhD/MPhil/MSc
Sheffield U PhD

Molecular biology, genetics & protein engineering
Cranfield IT MPhil✫/MSc✫

Molecular biophysics
Oxford U DPhil✫/MSc✫

Molecular sciences
Aston U PhD/MPhil

Nitrogen fixation
Sussex U DPhil/MPhil

Physiology & biophysics
London U Imperial C PhD✫/
  MPhil✫

Plant molecular biology & biotechnology
Durham U PhD/MPhil

Radiation & biophysical chemistry
Newcastle U PhD/MSc

Genetics, virology, immunology

Higher degrees by instruction

Animal parasitology
Bangor, U of Wales MSc✫/dip✫

Application of genetics in developing areas
Swansea UC MSc✫

Applied genetics
Birmingham U MSc✫

Applied immunology
Brunel U MSc
Portsmouth P MSc△

Applied parasitology
Liverpool U MVSc

Applied parasitology & entomology
Liverpool U MSc✫

Bacteriology & virology
Manchester U MSc✫

Biochemical immunology
East London P MSc△

Biochemistry & genetics
Newcastle U MSc✫

Biological anthropology
Durham U MSc✫

Biotechnology
Kent U MSc✫/dip✫

Clinical immunology
Leeds U MSc✫

Clinical laboratory sciences
Leeds U dip✫

Experimental parasitology
Glasgow U MAppSci/dip

Genetic manipulation & molecular biology
Sussex U MSc✫

Genetic toxicology
Swansea UC dip✫

Genetics
East Anglia U MSc✫/dip✫
Edinburgh U dip✫

Genetics & its applications
Swansea UC MSc✫

Health sciences
Leeds P MSc

Human & clinical genetics
London U S of Hygiene & Tropical Med dip

Immunology
Birmingham U MSc✫   □
London U King's C MSc△
London U Royal Postgraduate Med S dip✫
Surrey U MSc

Medical genetics
Glasgow U MSc(MedSci)✫
Newcastle U MSc✫

Medical immunology
London U UC MSc

Molecular genetics
Leicester U MSc✫   □

Psychopathology
Cambridge U MPhil✫

Theoretical & practical aspects of immunoassay
London U St Bartholomew's Hosp Med C dip✫

Tropical animal production & health
Edinburgh U MSc✫/dip✫
Edinburgh U SAg MSc✫/dip✫

Virology
London U S of Hygiene & Tropical Med MSc✫

Higher degrees by research

Agriculture
London U Wye C PhD☆/MPhil☆

Bacteriology
Aberdeen U PhD☆/MPhil☆/MSc☆
Edinburgh U PhD/MPhil
Glasgow U PhD/MSc(MedSci)
London U Royal Postgraduate
Med S PhD☆/MPhil☆

Bacteriology & virology
Manchester U PhD/MSc

Biochemistry
Kent U PhD/MPhil/MSc

Biological sciences
Salford U PhD/MSc

Bioscience & biotechnology
Strathclyde U PhD☆/MPhil☆/
MSc☆ □

Biotechnology
Kent U PhD/MPhil/MSc
London U Imperial C PhD/MPhil/
dip

Chemical immunology
London U Charing Cross &
Westminster Med S PhD/MPhil

Clinical bacteriology & virology
London U United Med & Dent S,
Guys's & St Thomas's PhD☆/
MPhil☆

Communicable diseases
London U St George's Hosp
Med S PhD☆/MPhil☆

Evolution
Oxford U DPhil☆/MSc☆

Experimental pathology
St Andrews U PhD☆/MSc☆

Genetics
Belfast Queen's U PhD/MSc
Birmingham U PhD/MSc
Bristol P PhD△/MPhil△/cert△
Cambridge U PhD☆/MSc☆
Edinburgh U PhD/MPhil
Glasgow U PhD/MSc
Leeds U PhD/MPhil/MSc☆
Leicester U PhD/MPhil
Liverpool U PhD/MSc
London U St George's Hosp
Med S PhD☆/MPhil☆
Newcastle U PhD/MSc
Nottingham U PhD/MPhil
Oxford U DPhil☆/MSc☆
Sheffield U PhD/MPhil
Swansea UC PhD/MPhil

Genetics & biometry
London U UC PhD☆/MPhil☆

Genetics & microbiology
Aberdeen U PhD☆/MPhil☆/MSc☆

Haematology
Birmingham U PhD/MSc
Edinburgh U PhD/MPhil
London U King's C S of Med &
Dentistry PhD☆/MPhil☆
Sheffield U PhD/MD

Histology
Liverpool U PhD/MSc

Horticulture
London U Wye C PhD☆/MPhil☆

Human genetics
Newcastle U MD/MPhil

Human sciences
Loughborough U PhD/MPhil

Immunochemistry
Southampton U PhD/MPhil

Immunology
Birmingham U PhD/MSc
Bristol P PhD/MPhil/dip
Glasgow U PhD/MSc(MedSci)
Liverpool U PhD
London U Imperial C PhD/MPhil/
dip
London U King's C PhD☆/MPhil☆
London U Royal Veterinary C
PhD☆/MPhil☆
London U UC PhD☆/MPhil☆
London U UC PhD☆/MPhil☆
London U London Hosp Med C
PhD☆/MPhil☆
London U Royal Free Hosp S of
Med PhD☆/MPhil☆
London U Royal Postgraduate
Med S PhD☆/MPhil☆
London U St George's Hosp
Med S PhD☆/MPhil☆
Nottingham U PhD☆/MPhil☆
Sheffield U PhD/MMedSci

**Immunology of rheumatic
diseases**
London U Charing Cross &
Westminster Med S PhD/MPhil

Infectious diseases
Glasgow U PhD/MSc(MedSci)

Medical genetics
Belfast Queen's U PhD
Manchester U PhD/MSc
Wales U C of Med PhD☆/MSc☆

Medical immunology
Sheffield U PhD/MMedSci/MPhil

Microbiology
Kent U PhD/MPhil/MSc

Nitrogen fixation
Sussex U DPhil/MPhil

Oral immunology & microbiology
London U United Med & Dent S,
Guys's & St Thomas's PhD☆/
MPhil☆

Parasitology
Glasgow U PhD/MSc
Liverpool U PhD/MSc
Portsmouth P PhD☆/MPhil☆

Plant Physiology & Genetics
London U Wye C PhD☆/MPhil☆

Preventive teratology
London U S of Hygiene &
Tropical Med PhD/MPhil

Pure & applied biology
London U Imperial C PhD/MPhil/
dip
London U Imperial C PhD/MPhil

Science
Bristol P PhD/MPhil

Tenovus research
Southampton U PhD/MPhil

Virology
Glasgow U PhD/MSc
London U Royal Free Hosp S of
Med PhD☆/MPhil☆
London U Royal Postgraduate
Med S PhD☆/MPhil☆
London U St Bartholomew's
Hosp Med C PhD/MPhil
Newcastle U PhD/MPhil
Oxford U DPhil☆/MSc☆
Sheffield U PhD/MMedSci

Nursing

Higher degrees by instruction

Dental surgery
Belfast Queen's U MDS☆

Educational studies for nurses
Ulster U dip☆

Immunology for disease control
North East Surrey CT MSc

Medical anthropology
Brunel U MSc   Soc

Mental handicap studies
York U MA△

Nursing
London U King's C MSc△
South Bank P dip△
Wales U C of Med MN☆

Nursing - state registration
South Glamorgan S of Nursing
RGN✮

Nursing - state registration for graduates
Parkside & Harrow C of nursing
& midwifery RGN✮
St George's District S of Nursing
RGN✮
South Lothian C of Nursing &
Midwifery RGN✮

Nursing studies
Hull U MSc✮/dip✮

Social research methods
Surrey U MSc✮

Higher degrees by research

Health sciences
Birmingham P PhD/MPhil

Midwifery & gynaecology
Belfast Queen's U PhD

Nursing
Brighton P PhD/MPhil
Glasgow U PhD/MSc(MedSci)
Manchester P PhD/MPhil
Manchester U PhD/MPhil

Nursing & community health studies
South Bank P PhD/MPhil

Nursing & health education
Liverpool P PhD/MPhil

Nursing & health visiting
Ulster U DPhil/MPhil

Nursing & social service
Dorset Inst PhD/MPhil/dip

Nursing health & applied social studies
Bristol P PhD△/MPhil△/dip△

Nursing studies
Birmingham U PhD/MSc
Edinburgh U PhD/MPhil
Hull U PhD/MPhil/MSc
Liverpool U PhD/MSc
London U King's C PhD✮/MPhil✮
Wales U C of Med PhD/MSc

Studies allied to dentistry

Higher degrees by instruction

Advanced dental surgery
Bristol U MSc✮

Applied prevention in the management of dental caries
Bristol U MSc✮

Basic dental science
Manchester U MSc

Biomaterials science
Manchester U MSc

Child dental health
Belfast Queen's U dip

Child dental heath
Bristol U MSc

Children's dentistry
Liverpool U MDS
London U London Hosp Med C
MSc/dip

Clinical psychology
Liverpool U MSc

Community dentistry
Manchester U MSc△

Conservative dentistry
Dundee U dip✮
Glasgow U MSc(MedSci)
Liverpool U MDS
London U United Med & Dent S,
Guys's & St Thomas's MSc

Dental care of the elderly
Bristol U MSc✮

Dental materials science
Dundee U dip✮
London U UC MSc
London U London Hosp Med C
MSc

Dental prosthetics
Dundee U dip✮

Dental public health
London U UC MSc
London U King's C S of Med &
Dentistry MSc/dip
London U London Hosp Med C
MSc✮

Dental radiology
London U King's C S of Med &
Dentistry MSc✮

Dental surgery
Belfast Queen's U MDS✮

Dentistry
Newcastle U MSc✮
Wales U C of Med MScD

Endodontics
London U United Med & Dent S,
Guys's & St Thomas's MSc

Experimental oral pathology
London U London Hosp Med C
MSc

Forensic odontology
London U London Hosp Med C
dip△

Gerodontics
London U London Hosp Med C
MSc

Odontology
Dundee U dip✮

Opthalmology
Bristol U MSc✮

Oral & maxillofacial surgery
London U UC MSc

Oral medicine
Glasgow U MSc(MedSci)
Liverpool U MDS

Oral medicine & oral surgery
Bristol U MSc

Oral medicine with pathology
Bristol U MSc✮

Oral medicine with periodontology
Bristol U MSc✮

Oral microbiology
Glasgow U MSc(MedSci)✮/
Msc(MedSci)△
Liverpool U MDS

Oral pathology
Bristol U MSc✮
Glasgow U MSc(MedSci)
Liverpool U MDS
Manchester U MSc
Sheffield U MMedSci✮

Oral surgery
Bristol U MSc✮
Dundee U PhD✮/MDSc✮/dip✮
Glasgow U Msc(MedSci)✮/
MSc(MedSci)△
Liverpool U MDS
London U King's C S of Med &
Dentistry MScA△
London U United Med & Dent S,
Guys's & St Thomas's MSc
Manchester U MSc
Sheffield U MMedSci✮

Orthodontics
Glasgow U MSc(MedSci)

Liverpool U MDS/dip
London U King's C S of Med & Dentistry MSc
London U London Hosp Med C MSc
London U United Med & Dent S, Guys's & St Thomas's MSc△
Manchester U MSc

Paediatric & preventative dentistry
Belfast Queen's U MMedSc

Paediatric dentistry
Dundee U dip☆
Leeds U MDSc△
Manchester U MSc

Paedodontics
London U United Med & Dent S, Guys's & St Thomas's MSc

Periodontology
Bristol U MSc☆
Dundee U dip☆
Liverpool U MDS
London U UC MSc☆
London U London Hosp Med C MSc☆
London U United Med & Dent S, Guys's & St Thomas's MSc
Wales U C of Med dip☆

Prosthetic dentistry
Bristol U MSc☆
Liverpool U MDS
London U United Med & Dent S, Guys's & St Thomas's MSc

Prosthodontics
Glasgow U MSc(MedSci)

Restorative dentistry
Manchester U MSc

Higher degrees by research

Biomaterials science
Manchester U PhD/MSc

Child dental health
Leeds U PhD/MDSc
London U London Hosp Med C PhD☆/MPhil☆
Manchester U PhD/MSc
Newcastle U MDSc/MD
Sheffield U PhD/MMedSci
Wales U C of Med PhD☆/MDSc☆

Children's dentistry
London U King's C S of Med & Dentistry PhD/MPhil

Community dental health
London U King's C S of Med & Dentistry PhD☆/MPhil☆

Conservative dental surgery
London U United Med & Dent S, Guys's & St Thomas's PhD☆/MPhil☆

Conservative dentistry
Bristol U PhD☆/MSc☆
Dundee U PhD/MDSc
Glasgow U PhD/MSc(MedSci)
London U King's C S of Med & Dentistry PhD☆/MPhil☆
London U London Hosp Med C PhD☆/MPhil☆
Manchester U PhD/MSc
Wales U C of Med PhD☆/MDSc☆

Dental community health
London U London Hosp Med C PhD☆/MPhil☆

Dental materials science
London U London Hosp Med C PhD☆/MPhil☆

Dental prosthetics
Dundee U PhD/MDSc

Dental prosthetics & materials science
Belfast Queen's U PhD

Dental radiology
London U King's C S of Med & Dentistry PhD☆/MPhil☆
London U United Med & Dent S, Guys's & St Thomas's PhD☆/MPhil☆

Dental services
Sheffield U PhD☆/MMedSci☆

Dental surgery
Belfast Queen's U PhD
Bristol U PhD/MSc
Dundee U PhD/MDSc
Glasgow U PhD/MSc(MedSci)
Leeds U PhD/MDSc/MSc
Liverpool U PhD/MDS
London U Imperial C PhD☆/MPhil☆
Sheffield U PhD/MMedSci

Dentistry
Birmingham U PhD/MDentSc/MSc
Edinburgh U PhD/MPhil
London U UC PhD☆/MPhil☆

Educational science
Manchester U PhD/MSc

Epidemiology & community studies
Manchester U PhD/MSc

Medical & dental education
Wales U C of Med PhD☆/MSc☆

Operative dentistry
Newcastle U PhD/MDSc/MPhil

Oral & maxillo facial surgery
London U King's C S of Med & Dentistry PhD☆/MPhil☆
London U London Hosp Med C PhD☆/MPhil☆
London U United Med & Dent S, Guys's & St Thomas's PhD☆/MPhil☆
Manchester U PhD/MSc
Wales U C of Med PhD☆/MScD☆

Oral biology
Leeds U PhD/MPhil/MSc
Newcastle U PhD/MPhil
Wales U C of Med PhD☆/MScD☆/MSc☆

Oral immunology & microbiology
London U United Med & Dent S, Guys's & St Thomas's PhD☆/MPhil☆

Oral medicine
Manchester U PhD/MSc

Oral medicine & oral surgery
Bristol U PhD☆/MSc☆

Oral medicine & pathology
Dundee U MDSc☆
Glasgow U PhD/MSc(MedSci)
London U United Med & Dent S, Guys's & St Thomas's PhD☆/MPhil☆

Oral medicine & periodontology
London U London Hosp Med C PhD☆/MPhil☆

Oral microbiology
London U King's C S of Med & Dentistry PhD☆/MPhil☆
London U London Hosp Med C PhD☆/MPhil☆

Oral pathology
London U King's C S of Med & Dentistry PhD☆/MPhil☆
London U London Hosp Med C PhD☆/MPhil☆
Manchester U PhD/MSc
Newcastle U PhD/MDSc/MPhil
Sheffield U PhD/MMedSci

Oral surgery
Glasgow U PhD/MSc(MedSci)
Newcastle U PhD/MDSc/MPhil

Oral surgery & orthodontics
London U St Bartholomew's Hosp Med C PhD/MPhil

Oral surgery medicine & pathology
Wales U C of Med PhD☆/MScD☆

Orthodontics
Belfast Queen's U PhD

Bristol U PhD☆/MSc☆
Glasgow U PhD/MSc(MedSci)
London U King's C S of Med &
 Dentistry PhD☆/MPhil☆
Manchester U PhD/MSc

**Orthodontics & child dental
health**
Dundee U PhD/MDSc/MSc

**Orthodontics & dentistry for
children**
London U United Med & Dent S,
 Guys's & St Thomas's PhD☆/
 MPhil☆

**Paediatric & preventive
dentistry**
Belfast Queen's U PhD

Paediatric dentistry
Bristol U PhD☆/MSc☆

Paedodontics
London U King's C S of Med &
 Dentistry PhD☆/MPhil☆

Periodontics
Belfast Queen's U PhD

Periodontology
London U King's C S of Med &
 Dentistry PhD☆/MPhil☆
Wales U C of Med PhD/MDSc

**Periodontology & community
dentistry**
Dundee U PhD/MSc

**Periodontology & preventive
dentistry**
London U United Med & Dent S,
 Guys's & St Thomas's PhD☆/
 MPhil☆

**Polymer, metals & dental
technology**
Manchester P PhD/MPhil

Prostheric dentistry
London U London Hosp Med C
 PhD☆/MPhil☆

Prosthetic dentistry
Bristol U PhD☆/MSc☆
London U United Med & Dent S,
 Guys's & St Thomas's PhD☆/
 MPhil☆
Manchester U PhD/MSc
Wales U C of Med PhD☆/MDSc☆

Prosthetics
Belfast Queen's U PhD/MSc
London U King's C S of Med &
 Dentistry PhD☆/MPhil☆

Prosthodontics
Glasgow U PhD/MSc(MedSci)
Newcastle U MDSc/MD/MPhil

Provision of dental care
London U London Hosp Med C
 PhD☆/MPhil☆

Restorative dentistry
Belfast Queen's U PhD☆
Leeds U PhD/MDSc
Sheffield U PhD/MMedSci
Wales U C of Med PhD☆/MScD☆

Studies allied to health and medicine

Higher degrees by instruction

Advanced training in art therapy
Hertfordshire CAD dip△

**Advanced training in
dramatherapy**
Hertfordshire CAD dip△

Anaesthesia
Glasgow U MSc(MedSci)
Leicester U dip△

Anaesthesia & intensive care
Wales U C of Med MSc☆

**Analytical chemistry &
instrumentation**
Loughborough U MSc   *Chem*

Applied entomology
London U Imperial C MSc/dip

**Applied parasitology & medical
entomology**
Incorporated Liverpool S of
 Tropical Med MSc☆

Applied psychology
Nottingham U dip☆

Art therapy
Hertfordshire CAD MA△/dip

Audiology
Manchester U MSc☆
Southampton U MSc☆/dip☆

Bacteriology & virology
Manchester U MSc☆

**Behavioural biology & health
care**
Roehampton I MSc☆

**Biochemistry & chemistry
applied to medicine**
London U London Hosp Med C
 MSc

Bioengineering
Strathclyde U MSc/dip

Biomedical engineering
Aberdeen U MSc☆/dip☆   *Eng*
Surrey U MSc☆/dip☆   *Eng*

Biomedical engineering science
Dundee U MSc

Biomedical methods
Wales U C of Med dip☆

Biomedical sciences
Bradford U MSc☆
Glasgow C MSc☆/dip☆
Nottingham P MSc△
Ulster U MSc/dip△

Biosensors
Newcastle U MSc☆

Cardiology
London U Royal Postgraduate
 Med S dip☆

Cardiovascular studies
Leeds U MSc☆

Child & adolescent psychiatry
London U Inst of Psychiatry dip☆

**Clinical & community
psychology**
Exeter U MSc☆

Clinical audiology
Manchester U MSc☆

Clinical biochemistry
Leeds U MSc
London U UC MSc
London U King's C S of Med &
 Dentistry MSc△
London U Royal Postgraduate
 Med S MSc☆
London U United Med & Dent S,
 Guys's & St Thomas's MSc△
Newcastle U MSc☆
Surrey U MSc☆

Clinical communication studies
City U dip☆

Clinical immunology
Leeds U MSc☆

Clinical laboratory sciences
Leeds U dip☆

Clinical microbiology
London U London Hosp Med C
 MSc/dip

Clinical pathology
London U Royal Postgraduate
 Med S dip☆

Clinical pharmacology
London U St Bartholomew's
 Hosp Med C dip☆

Clinical psychiatry
Leeds U MMedSc△

Clinical psychology
Belfast Queen's U MSc☆
East London P MSc△
Edinburgh U MPhil☆
Leicester U MSc☆
London U Inst of Psychiatry MSc☆
Manchester U MSc☆
Newcastle U MSc☆
South West P MSc
Surrey U MSc☆

Clinical tropical medicine
London U S of Hygiene & Tropical Med MSc☆

Community care (mental handicap)
Keele U MA/Dip

Community health
Incorporated Liverpool S of Tropical Med MCommH☆

Community health in developing countries
London U S of Hygiene & Tropical Med MSc☆/dip☆

Community medicine
Manchester U MSc
Newcastle U MSc△

Community paediatrics
Newcastle U MSc△
Warwick U MSc/cert/dip

Computational methods in medical science
Manchester U MSc△

Counselling in formal & informal settings
Roehampton I cert△

Dance movement therapy
Hertfordshire CAD dip△
Roehampton I dip△

Dental surgery
Belfast Queen's U MDS☆

Dermatological sciences
Wales U C of Med dip☆

Dermatology
Glasgow U MSc(MedSci)
London U United Med & Dent S, Guys's & St Thomas's dip☆

Dietetics
Queen's C Glasgow dip☆   *Chem*

Dramatherapy
Hertfordshire CAD MA△/dip

Education for primary health care
Manchester U MEd☆

Electronic engineering
Cardiff U of Wales C MSc☆/dip☆   *Eng*

Environmental health
Bristol P dip☆
Dundee U MSc
Middlesex P dip△

Epidemiology
London U S of Hygiene & Tropical Med MSc/dip

Epidemiology & health planning
Swansea UC MSc(Econ)☆
Wales U C of Med MSc☆

Epidemiology & medical statistics
London U S of Hygiene & Tropical Med dip△

Family medicine
Newcastle U MSc☆

Family therapy
Brunel U MSc△

Forensic medicine & science
Glasgow U MSc(MedSci)/dip☆

Forensic science
Strathclyde U MSc☆/dip☆

General & medical microbiology
London U S of Hygiene & Tropical Med MSc☆
London U UC MSc☆/dip☆   □

General practice
Glasgow U MSc(MedSci)
London U United Med & Dent S, Guys's & St Thomas's MSc△

Geriatric medicine
Glasgow U MSc(MedSci)

Gerontology
London U King's C MSc☆

Graduate nursing
Glasgow Northern C of Nursing RGN☆

Haematology
Glasgow U MSc(MedSc)☆
London U Royal Postgraduate Med S dip☆

Health care
Exeter U MSc△/cert△

Health care ethics
Manchester U MA☆

Health economics
York U MSc☆/dip☆

Health education
Bristol P dip☆
Edinburgh U MSc☆/dip☆
London U King's C MSc/dip△

Health education & health promotion
Leeds P MSc/dip

Health education & health promotion studies
Manchester U MSc/dip

Health facility planning
North London P MA/dip☆

Health management, planning & policy
Leeds U MA☆

Health planning & administration
Leeds U dip☆

Health planning & financing
London U LSE MSc

Health planning, finance & management
Cardiff U of Wales C MSc☆
Wales U C of Med MSc☆

Health promotion
Birmingham P MSc△/dip△

Health promotion & health education
Wales U C of Med MSc

Health psychology
London U United Med & Dent S, Guys's & St Thomas's MSc△
Surrey U MSc☆/dip☆

Health sciences
Leeds P MSc

Health services management
Manchester U MA(Econ)☆/dip☆

Health services studies
Leeds U MA   □

Health visiting
South Bank P dip☆
Wales U C of Med cert☆

History of medicine
Cambridge U MPhil☆

History of science, medicine & technology
London U Imperial C MSc

Human fertility & infertility
Bristol U MSc☆

Immunology
Aberdeen U MSc/dip
London U King's C MSc△

Internal medicine
London U Royal Postgraduate Med S dip☆

Laboratory aspects of medical microbiology
Wales U C of Med MSc☆

Local government & health service studies
Birmingham U MSocSc

Medical art
London U St Bartholomew's Hosp Med C dip☆

Medical biochemistry
Belfast Queen's U dip☆
Brunel U MSc

Medical cardiology
Glasgow U MSc(MedSci)

Medical computing
Wales U C of Med MSc☆/dip☆

Medical demography
London U S of Hygiene &
  Tropical Med MSc/dip

Medical education
Wales U C of Med MSc☆

Medical electronics & physics
London U St Bartholomew's
  Hosp Med C MSc

Medical ethics & law
London U King's C MA

Medical genetics
Glasgow U MSc(MedSci)☆
Newcastle U MSc☆

Medical immunology
London U UC MSc
London U King's C S of Med &
  Dentistry MSc△
London U United Med & Dent S,
  Guys's & St Thomas's MSc△

Medical laboratory management
City of Westminster C FIMLS
  dip△

Medical laboratory science
City of Westminster C FIMLS△

Medical microbiology
East Anglia U MSc☆
London U S of Hygiene &
  Tropical Med MSc☆/dip☆
London U UC MSc
Surrey U MSc△/dip△

Medical molecular biology
Central London P MSc△/dip△

Medical parasitology
London U S of Hygiene &
  Tropical Med MSc☆

Medical physics (lasers & optics)
Heriot-Watt U MSc☆/dip☆

Medical radiodiagnosis
Edinburgh U dip△

Medical social anthropology
Keele U MSc☆

Medical statistics
London U S of Hygiene &
  Tropical Med MSc
Newcastle U MSc☆

Medical statistics & information technology
Leicester P MSc☆/dip☆
Leicester U MSc☆/dip☆

Medical virology
Manchester U MSc☆

Medicinal chemistry
Loughborough U MSc☆   Chem

Medicine
Glasgow U MSc(MedSci)

Neuropsychology
St Andrews U dip☆

Nuclear medicine
London U UC MSc
London U King's C S of Med &
  Dentistry MSc
London U London Hosp Med C
  MSc
London U Royal Free Hosp S of
  Med MSc
London U Royal Postgraduate
  Med S MSc
London U United Med & Dent S,
  Guys's & St Thomas's MSc

Nursing - state registration
South Glamorgan S of Nursing
  RGN☆

Nutrition
London U King's C MSc☆/dip☆

Occupational health & hygiene
Dundee U MSc☆

Occupational hygiene
Manchester U MSc
Newcastle U MSc☆   Bus

Occupational therapy
Newcastle P dip☆

Oncology
Glasgow U MSc(MedSci)△

Opthalmology
Glasgow U MSc(MedSci)

Optometry
Bradford U MSc

Organisational health
Nottingham U MA☆

Orthopaedics
London U UC MSc

Pathology
Belfast Queen's U MMedSc☆
Glasgow U MSc(MedSci)

Pharmacology
Manchester U MSc/dip☆
Strathclyde U MSc/dip☆

Physiological flow studies
London U Imperial C MSc☆/dip☆

Physiotherapy
Teesside P dip☆

Preclinical science & education
Glasgow U MSc(MedSci)☆

Preventative health care administration for developing countries
Wales U C of Med MSc☆

Psychiatric social work
Manchester U MSc/dip

Psychiatry
Edinburgh U MPhil△
Liverpool U dip☆

Psychoanalytic studies
Kent U MA

Psychotherapy
Aberdeen U MMedSci☆/dip△
Belfast Queen's U MMedSc△
Liverpool U dip△

Public health
Dundee U MPH
Glasgow U MPH

Public health & environmental engineering
Strathclyde U MSc/dip

Radiodiagnosis
Liverpool U dip☆

Rehabilitation studies
Southampton U MSc/dip

Social gerontology
Aberdeen U MLitt△

Social research
Surrey U MSc/dip

Sociological research in health care
Warwick U MA/dip

Sociology as applied to medicine
London U Royal Holloway &
  Bedford New C MSc

Sport & exercise sciences
Birmingham U MA☆

Sports medicine
London U London Hosp Med C
  dip☆

Statistics with applications in medicine
Southampton U MSc☆

Steroid endocrinology
Leeds U MSc☆

Theoretical & practical aspects of immunoassay
London U St Bartholomew's
  Hosp Med C dip☆

Toxicology
Birmingham U MSc/dip☆   ☐
Surrey U MSc   ☐

Tropical child health
Incorporated Liverpool S of
  Tropical Med dip☆

Tropical medicine & hygiene
London U S of Hygiene &
Tropical Med dip☆

Tuberculosis & chest diseases
Wales U C of Med dip☆

Higher degrees by research

Accident & emergency
London U Imperial C PhD☆/
MPhil☆
London U St Bartholomew's
Hosp Med C PhD/MPhil

Anaesthesia
Bristol U PhD☆/MSc☆
Glasgow U PhD/MSc(MedSci)
Leeds U PhD/MPhil/MSc
Leicester U PhD/MPhil
Liverpool U PhD/MSc
London U Charing Cross &
Westminster Med S PhD☆/
MPhil☆
Manchester U PhD/MSc
Newcastle U MD/MPhil
Nottingham U PhD/MPhil
Sheffield U PhD/MMedSci

Anaesthetics
Belfast Queen's U PhD
London U Imperial C PhD☆/
MPhil☆
London U King's C S of Med &
Dentistry PhD☆/MPhil☆
London U London Hosp Med C
PhD☆/MPhil☆
London U Royal Postgraduate
Med S PhD☆/MPhil☆
London U St Bartholomew's
Hosp Med C PhD☆/MPhil☆
London U United Med & Dent S,
Guys's & St Thomas's PhD☆/
MPhil☆
Oxford U DPhil☆/MSc☆
Southampton U PhD/MPhil
Wales U C of Med PhD☆/MSc☆

Anatomy & experimental pathology
St Andrews U PhD/MSc

Applied health studies
Ulster U DPhil/MPhil

Art therapy
Goldsmiths' C London U PhD/
MPhil

Audiological medicine
Manchester U PhD/MPhil

Bacteriology & virology
Manchester U PhD/MSc

Behavioural science
Glasgow U PhD/MSc(MedSci)

Biochemical medicine
Dundee U PhD/MSc

Bioengineering
Strathclyde U PhD/MPhil/
MSc   *Eng*

Biological sciences
Aston U PhD/MPhil
Salford U PhD/MSc

Biological sciences & environmental health
Thames P PhD/MPhil

Biomedical engineering
Dundee U PhD/MSc
Surrey U PhD/MPhil   *Eng*

Biomedical research
Central London P PhD☆/MPhil☆

Biomedical sciences
Bradford U PhD/MPhil
Liverpool P PhD/MPhil
London U King's C PhD☆/MPhil☆
Sheffield City P PhD/MPhil
Sheffield U PhD/MMed/MPhil

Biometry & medical statistics
London U London Hosp Med C
PhD☆/MPhil☆

Bone & joint research
London U London Hosp Med C
PhD☆/MPhil☆

Building & environmental health
Nottingham P PhD☆/MPhil☆

Cancer epidemiology & clinical trials
Oxford U DPhil☆/MSc☆

Cancer research
Brunel U PhD/MPhil
Newcastle U MD/MSc
Nottingham U PhD☆/MPhil☆
Oxford U DPhil☆/MSc☆
Ulster U PhD/MPhil
Wales U C of Med PhD☆/MSc☆

Cancer studies
Birmingham U PhD/MSc

Cardiology
Belfast Queen's U PhD
London U Imperial C PhD☆/
MPhil☆
London U St Bartholomew's
Hosp Med C PhD/MPhil
London U United Med & Dent S,
Guys's & St Thomas's PhD☆/
MPhil☆
Newcastle U MD/MPhil
Wales U C of Med PhD☆/MSc☆

Cardiovascular epidemiology
Dundee U PhD/MSc

Cardiovascular medicine
Birmingham U PhD/MSc
Oxford U DPhil☆/MSc☆

Cardiovascular sciences
London U St George's Hosp
Med S PhD☆/MPhil☆

Cardiovascular studies
Leeds U PhD/MPhil/MSc☆

Chemical endocrinology
London U St Bartholomew's
Hosp Med C PhD/MPhil

Chemical pathology
Aberdeen U PhD☆/MPhil☆/MSc☆
London U Imperial C PhD☆/
MPhil☆
London U UC PhD☆/MPhil☆
London U Charing Cross &
Westminster Med S PhD/MPhil
London U London Hosp Med C
PhD☆/MPhil☆
London U Royal Postgraduate
Med S PhD☆/MPhil☆
London U St Bartholomew's
Hosp Med C PhD/MPhil
London U St George's Hosp
Med S PhD☆/MPhil☆
London U United Med & Dent S,
Guys's & St Thomas's PhD☆/
MPhil☆

Chemical pathology & human metabolism
Southampton U PhD/MPhil

Chemical pathology & immunology
Leeds U PhD/MPhil/MSc

Chest medicine
London U St Bartholomew's
Hosp Med C PhD/MPhil

Child & adolescent psychiatry
London U United Med & Dent S,
Guys's & St Thomas's PhD☆/
MPhil☆

Child & adolescent psychology
Glasgow U PhD/MSc(MedSci)

Child health
Aberdeen U PhD☆/MPhil☆
Belfast Queen's U PhD
Bristol U PhD☆/MSc☆
Dundee U PhD/MSc
Leicester U PhD/MPhil
Liverpool U PhD/MSc
London U Charing Cross &
Westminster Med S PhD/MPhil
London U King's C S of Med &
Dentistry PhD☆/MPhil☆

London U London Hosp Med C
PhD☆/MPhil☆
London U St Bartholomew's
Hosp Med C PhD/MPhil
London U St George's Hosp
Med S PhD☆/MPhil☆
Manchester U PhD/MSc
Newcastle U MD/MPhil
Nottingham U PhD/MPhil
Southampton U PhD/MPhil
Wales U C of Med PhD☆/MSc☆

Child life & health
Edinburgh U PhD/MPhil

Child psychiatry
London U Imperial C PhD☆/
MPhil☆

Childhood cancer research
Oxford U DPhil☆/MSc☆

Clinical bacteriology & virology
London U United Med & Dent S,
Guys's & St Thomas's PhD☆/
MPhil☆

Clinical biochemistry
Leeds U MMedSc
Liverpool U PhD
Manchester U PhD/MSc
Oxford U DPhil☆/MSc☆

Clinical biochemistry & metabolic medicine
Newcastle U PhD/MPhil

Clinical chemistry
Birmingham U PhD/MSc
London U United Med & Dent S,
Guys's & St Thomas's PhD☆/
MPhil☆

Clinical communication studies
City U PhD/MPhil

Clinical epidemiology
Oxford U DPhil☆/MSc☆

Clinical epidemiology & general practice
London U Royal Free Hosp S of
Med PhD☆/MPhil☆

Clinical epidemiology & social medicine
London U St George's Hosp
Med S PhD☆/MPhil☆

Clinical medicine
Leeds U PhD/MPhil
London U London Hosp Med C
PhD☆/MPhil☆
Oxford U DPhil☆/MSc☆

Clinical neurology
Oxford U DPhil☆/MSc☆

Clinical oncology
Bradford U PhD/MPhil
London U Royal Postgraduate
Med S PhD☆/MPhil☆

Clinical oncology & radiotherapeutics
Cambridge U PhD☆/MSc☆

Clinical pharmacology
London U UC PhD☆/MPhil☆
London U Royal Postgraduate
Med S PhD☆/MPhil☆
London U St Bartholomew's
Hosp Med C PhD/MPhil
London U United Med & Dent S,
Guys's & St Thomas's PhD☆/
MPhil☆
Oxford U DPhil☆/MSc☆

Clinical pharmacology & therapeutics
London U Imperial C PhD☆/
MPhil☆
London U Charing Cross &
Westminster Med S PhD/MPhil

Clinical physics
Glasgow U PhD/MSc

Clinical psychiatry
Leeds U PhD/MPhil

Clinical psychology
Leeds U PhD/MPhil
Liverpool U PhD
London U Inst of Psychiatry
PhD☆/MPhil☆

Clinical tropical medicine
London U S of Hygiene &
Tropical Med PhD/MPhil

Communicable diseases
London U St George's Hosp
Med S PhD☆/MPhil☆

Communication studies
Ulster U DPhil/MPhil

Community health
Bristol U PhD☆/MSc☆
Leicester U PhD/MPhil
Liverpool U PhD/MSc
London U S of Hygiene &
Tropical Med PhD/MPhil

Community health & epidemiology
London U St Bartholomew's
Hosp Med C PhD/MPhil

Community medicine
Aberdeen U PhD☆/MPhil☆/MSc☆
Cambridge U PhD☆/MSc☆
Dundee U PhD/MSc
Edinburgh U PhD/MPhil
Glasgow U PhD/MSc(MedSci)
Leeds U PhD/MPhil
London U Imperial C PhD☆/
MPhil☆
London U UC PhD☆/MPhil☆
London U Charing Cross &
Westminster Med S PhD/MPhil

London U United Med & Dent S,
Guys's & St Thomas's PhD☆/
MPhil☆
Manchester U PhD/MSc
Sheffield U PhD/MMedSci

Community medicine & epidemiology
Nottingham U PhD/MPhil

Community medicine & general practice
Oxford U DPhil☆/MSc☆

Community medicine & medical statistics
Belfast Queen's U PhD
Southampton U PhD/MPhil

Computation in medicine
Manchester U PhD/MPhil

Computerised tomography
London U UC PhD☆/MPhil☆

Computers in medicine
Kent U PhD☆/MPhil☆

Construction & environmental health
Bristol P PhD/MPhil/cert/dip

Cytology
London U UC PhD☆/MPhil☆

Dermatology
Dundee U PhD/MSc
Glasgow U PhD/MSc(MedSci)
Liverpool U PhD/MSc
London U Imperial C PhD☆/
MPhil☆
London U St Bartholomew's
Hosp Med C PhD/MPhil
London U United Med & Dent S,
Guys's & St Thomas's PhD☆/
MPhil☆
Newcastle U MD/MPhil
Wales U C of Med PhD☆/MSc☆

Developmental biology
London U UC PhD☆/MPhil☆

Diabetes
London U King's C S of Med &
Dentistry PhD/MPhil

Diagnostic radiology
Dundee U PhD/MSc
London U Royal Postgraduate
Med S PhD☆/MPhil☆
London U St Bartholomew's
Hosp Med C PhD/MPhil
London U St George's Hosp
Med S PhD☆/MPhil☆
London U United Med & Dent S,
Guys's & St Thomas's PhD☆/
MPhil☆
Manchester U PhD/MSc
Wales U C of Med PhD☆/MSc☆

Diseases of the ear
London U United Med & Dent S, Guys's & St Thomas's PhD☆/MPhil☆

Diseases of the ear, nose & throat
London U United Med & Dent S, Guys's & St Thomas's PhD☆/MPhil☆

Drug dependence
London U Imperial C PhD☆/MPhil☆

Drug surveillance research
Southampton U PhD/MPhil

Ear, nose & throat
London U St Bartholomew's Hosp Med C PhD/MPhil

Electron microscopy
London U S of Hygiene & Tropical Med PhD/MPhil

Embryology
London U UC PhD☆/MPhil☆

Entomology
London U S of Hygiene & Tropical Med PhD/MPhil

Environmental & occupational medicine
Aberdeen U PhD☆/MPhil☆/MSc☆

Environmental & preventative medicine
London U St Bartholomew's Hosp Med C PhD/MPhil

Environmental epidemiology
Southampton U PhD/MPhil

Environmental health
Bristol P PhD/MPhil/dip△
Strathclyde U PhD☆/MPhil☆/MSc☆

Epidemiology
London U S of Hygiene & Tropical Med PhD☆/MPhil☆
London U London Hosp Med C PhD/MPhil

Epidemiology & community medicine
Wales U C of Med PhD☆/MSc☆

Epidemiology & community studies
Manchester U PhD/MSc

Evaluation & planning for health care
London U S of Hygiene & Tropical Med PhD/MPhil

Exercise sciences
Birmingham U PhD/MSc

Experimental pathology
London U UC PhD☆/MPhil☆

Family & community medicine
Newcastle U MD/MPhil

Forensic medicine
Dundee U PhD/MPhil
Edinburgh U PhD/MPhil
Leeds U PhD/MPhil
London U London Hosp Med C PhD☆/MPhil☆
London U United Med & Dent S, Guys's & St Thomas's PhD☆/MPhil☆

Forensic medicine & science
Glasgow U PhD/MSc(MedSci)

Forensic medicine & toxicology
London U Charing Cross & Westminster Med S PhD/MPhil

Forensic science
Strathclyde U PhD☆/MPhil☆/MSc☆

Free radicals & disease
Brunel U PhD/MPhil

Gastroenterology
London U London Hosp Med C PhD☆/MPhil☆
London U St Bartholomew's Hosp Med C PhD/MPhil

Gastrointestinal science
London U London Hosp Med C PhD☆/MPhil☆

General practice
Aberdeen U PhD☆/MPhil☆
Belfast Queen's U PhD
Dundee U PhD/MSc
Glasgow U PhD/MSc(MedSci)
Leeds U PhD/MPhil
Liverpool U PhD/MSc
London U Imperial C PhD☆/MPhil☆
London U King's C S of Med & Dentistry PhD/MPhil
London U London Hosp Med C PhD☆/MPhil☆
London U St Bartholomew's Hosp Med C PhD/MPhil
London U St George's Hosp Med S PhD☆/MPhil☆
London U United Med & Dent S, Guys's & St Thomas's PhD☆/MPhil☆
Manchester U PhD/MSc
Nottingham U PhD/MPhil
Wales U C of Med PhD☆/MD☆/MSc☆

Genital medicine
London U St Bartholomew's Hosp Med C PhD/MPhil

Genito urinary medicine
Edinburgh U PhD/MPhil
Liverpool U PhD/MSc

London U UC PhD☆/MPhil☆
London U United Med & Dent S, Guys's & St Thomas's PhD☆/Mphil☆

Geriatric medicine
Belfast Queen's U PhD
Birmingham U PhD/MSc
Glasgow U PhD/MSc(MedSci)
Liverpool U PhD/MSc
London U St Bartholomew's Hosp Med C PhD/MPhil
London U St George's Hosp Med S PhD☆/MPhil☆
Manchester U PhD/MSc
Southampton U PhD☆/MPhil☆
Wales U C of Med PhD☆/MD☆/MSc☆

Geriatrics
London U Imperial C PhD☆/MPhil☆

Haematological medicine
Cambridge U PhD☆/MSc☆

Haematology
Belfast Queen's U PhD
Birmingham U PhD/MSc
Edinburgh U PhD/MPhil
Liverpool U PhD/MSc
London U Imperial C PhD☆/MPhil☆
London U UC PhD☆/MPhil☆
London U Charing Cross & Westminster Med S PhD/MPhil
London U London Hosp Med C PhD☆/MPhil☆
London U Royal Free Hosp S of Med PhD☆/MPhil☆
London U Royal Postgraduate Med S PhD☆/MPhil☆
London U St Bartholomew's Hosp Med C PhD/MPhil
London U St George's Hosp Med S PhD☆/MPhil☆
London U United Med & Dent S, Guys's & St Thomas's PhD☆/MPhil☆
Sheffield U PhD/MD
Southampton U PhD☆/MPhil☆
Wales U C of Med PhD☆/MSc☆

Health & community studies
Leeds P PhD/MPhil/dip
Teesside P PhD☆/MPhil☆

Health & medicine studies
Queen's C Glasgow PhD/MPhil

Health & social welfare
Open U PhD/MPhil/BPhil

Health care of the elderly
London U King's C S of Med & Dentistry PhD/MPhil
Nottingham U PhD/MPhil

Health care studies
Swansea UC PhD/MPhil

Health economics
York U DPhil☆/MPhil☆

Health economics research
Brunel U PhD/MPhil

Health planning & management
Keele U PhD/MSc

Health promotion
Wales U C of Med PhD☆/MSc☆

Health sciences
Birmingham P PhD/MPhil
Wolverhampton P PhD/MPhil

Health services management
Birmingham U PhD☆/MPhil☆/
 MSocSc☆
Manchester U PhD/MA(Econ)

Health services studies
Leeds U PhD/MPhil

Health studies
Exeter U PhD/MPhil
Hatfield P PhD/MPhil
Lancashire P PhD/MPhil
Newcastle P PhD☆/MPhil☆
Sheffield City P PhD/MPhil
West London IHE MPhil☆

Hearing research
Nottingham U PhD/MPhil

Histology
Liverpool U PhD/MSc

Histopathology
London U UC PhD☆/MPhil☆
London U Charing Cross &
 Westminster Med S PhD/MPhil
London U Royal Free Hosp S of
 Med PhD☆/MPhil☆
London U Royal Postgraduate
 Med S PhD☆/MPhil☆
London U St Bartholomew's
 Hosp Med C PhD/MPhil
London U St George's Hosp
 Med S PhD☆/MPhil☆
London U United Med & Dent S,
 Guys's & St Thomas's PhD☆/
 MPhil☆
Manchester U PhD/MPhil

Histopathology & experimental pathology
London U Imperial C PhD☆/
 MPhil☆

History of medicine
London U UC PhD☆/MPhil☆

Human metabolism
London U Imperial C PhD☆/
 MPhil☆

Human metabolism & clinical biochemistry
Sheffield U PhD/MMedSci

Human morphology
Nottingham U PhD/MPhil

Human morphology (anatomy)
Southampton U PhD/MPhil

Human reproduction & obstetrics
Southampton U PhD/MPhil

Immunology
London U Royal Free Hosp S of
 Med PhD☆/MPhil☆
London U Royal Postgraduate
 Med S PhD☆/MPhil☆

Infectious diseases
Glasgow U PhD/MSc(MedSci)

International community health
Liverpool U PhD/MSc

Laryngology, rhinology & otology
Bristol U PhD☆/MSc☆

Larynology & otology
London U UC PhD☆/MPhil☆

Law & ethics in medicine
Glasgow U PhD/MSc(MedSci)

Liver studies
London U King's C S of Med &
 Dentistry PhD/MPhil

Materia medica
Glasgow U PhD/MSc(MedSci)

Materia medica & therapeutics
Manchester U PhD/MSc

Measurement & instrumentation in medicine
City U PhD/MPhil

Medical & dental education
Wales U C of Med PhD☆/MSc☆

Medical & surgical child health
Glasgow U PhD/MSc(MedSci)

Medical biochemistry
Wales U C of Med PhD☆/MSc☆

Medical biophysics
Manchester U PhD/MSc   Phy

Medical cardiology
Glasgow U PhD/MSc(MedSci)

Medical computing & statistics
Edinburgh U PhD/MPhil
Wales U C of Med PhD☆/MSc☆

Medical demography
London U S of Hygiene &
 Tropical Med PhD/MPhil

Medical education
Dundee U PhD/MSc
Glasgow U PhD/MSc(MedSci)
Warwick U PhD☆/MSc☆

Medical electronics
Bath U PhD☆/MSc☆

Medical electronics & physics
London U St Bartholomew's
 Hosp Med C PhD/MPhil

Medical engineering
Oxford U DPhil☆/MSc☆

Medical entomology
Liverpool U PhD/MSc

Medical genetics
Glasgow U PhD/MSc(MedSci)
Manchester U PhD/MSc

Medical helminthology
London U S of Hygiene &
 Tropical Med PhD/MPhil

Medical immunology
Sheffield U PhD/MMedSci/MPhil

Medical microbiology
Birmingham U PhD/MSc
Dundee U PhD/MSc
Liverpool U PhD/MSc
London U Imperial C PhD☆/
 MPhil☆
London U S of Hygiene &
 Tropical Med PhD/MPhil
London U UC PhD☆/MPhil☆
London U Charing Cross &
 Westminster Med S PhD/MPhil
London U King's C S of Med &
 Dentistry PhD/MPhil
London U London Hosp Med C
 PhD☆/MPhil☆
London U Royal Free Hosp S of
 Med PhD☆/MPhil☆
London U St Bartholomew's
 Hosp Med C PhD/MPhil
London U St George's Hosp
 Med S PhD☆/MPhil☆
Manchester U PhD/MSc
Sheffield U PhD/MMedSci/MPhil
Wales U C of Med PhD☆/MSc☆

Medical oncology
London U Charing Cross &
 Westminster Med S PhD/MPhil
London U St Bartholomew's
 Hosp Med C PhD/MPhil
Southampton U PhD/MPhil

Medical physics
London U UC PhD☆/MPhil☆
London U London Hosp Med C
 PhD☆/MPhil☆

Medical physics & bioengineering
Wales U C of Med PhD☆/MSc☆

Medical physics & clinical engineering
Sheffield U PhD/MMedSci

Medical physics & engineering
Southampton U PhD/MPhil

Medical physics & medical engineering
Edinburgh U PhD/MPhil

Medical protozoology
London U S of Hygiene & Tropical Med PhD/MPhil

Medical radiology
Edinburgh U PhD/MPhil

Medical sciences & health studies
East London P PhD/MPhil

Medical social anthropology
Keele U PhD/MA

Medical statistics
London U S of Hygiene & Tropical Med PhD/MPhil
Newcastle U MD/MPhil

Medical studies
Bath U PhD☆/MSc☆

Medicine & therapeutics
Aberdeen U PhD☆/MD☆/MPhil☆/ MSc☆

Medicine
Belfast Queen's U PhD
Bristol U PhD/MSc
Cambridge U PhD☆/MSc☆
Dundee U PhD/MSc
Edinburgh U PhD/MPhil
Glasgow U PhD/MSc(MedSci)
Keele U PhD/MSc
Leeds U PhD/MPhil
Leicester U PhD/MPhil
Liverpool U PhD/MSc
London U Imperial C PhD☆/ MPhil☆
London U UC PhD☆/MPhil☆
London U Charing Cross & Westminster Med S PhD/MPhil
London U King's C S of Med & Dentistry PhD☆/MPhil☆
London U London Hosp Med C PhD☆/MPhil☆
London U Royal Free Hosp S of Med PhD☆/MPhil☆
London U Royal Postgraduate Med S PhD☆/MPhil☆
London U St George's Hosp Med S PhD☆/MPhil☆
London U United Med & Dent S, Guys's & St Thomas's PhD☆/ MPhil☆
Manchester U PhD/MSc
Newcastle U MD/MPhil
Nottingham U PhD/MPhil
Sheffield U PhD/MMedSci
Southampton U PhD/MPhil

Wales U C of Med PhD☆/MSc☆

Mental handicap
Nottingham U PhD/MPhil

Mental health
Belfast Queen's U PhD
Bristol U PhD/MSc

Mental health & psychotherapy
Aberdeen U PhD☆/MPhil☆/MSc☆

Metabolic bone diseases
Oxford U DPhil☆/MSc☆

Microbiology
London U UC PhD☆/MPhil☆

Microbiology, mycology & pathology
Oxford U MLitt☆/MSc☆

Midwifery & gynaecology
Belfast Queen's U PhD

Mineralised tissue biology
London U UC PhD☆/MPhil☆

Molecular haematology
Oxford U DPhil☆/MSc☆

Molecular sciences
Aston U PhD/MPhil

Morbid anatomy
London U King's C S of Med & Dentistry PhD/MPhil

Muscular dystrophy research
Newcastle U MD/MPhil

Nephrology
London U Imperial C PhD☆/ MPhil☆
London U St Bartholomew's Hosp Med C PhD/MPhil

Neurobiology
Central London P PhD☆/MPhil☆
London U UC PhD☆/MPhil☆

Neurological science
London U Royal Free Hosp S of Med PhD☆/MPhil☆

Neurology
Glasgow U PhD/MSc(MedSci)

Neuropathology
Glasgow U PhD/MSc(MedSci)

Neurosurgery
London U London Hosp Med C PhD☆/MPhil☆

Nuclear medicine
London U King's C S of Med & Dentistry PhD☆/MPhil☆
London U St Bartholomew's Hosp Med C PhD/MPhil
London U United Med & Dent S, Guys's & St Thomas's PhD☆/ MPhil☆
PhD☆/MPhil☆

Obstetrics & gynaecology
Aberdeen U PhD☆/MPhil☆/MSc☆
Belfast Queen's U PhD☆
Birmingham U PhD/MSc
Bristol U PhD☆/MSc☆
Cambridge U PhD☆/MSc☆
Dundee U PhD/MSc
Edinburgh U PhD/MPhil
Glasgow U PhD/MSc(MedSci)
Leeds U PhD/MPhil
Leicester U PhD/MD/MPhil
Liverpool U PhD
London U Imperial C PhD☆/ MPhil☆
London U Charing Cross & Westminster Med S PhD/MPhil
London U King's C S of Med & Dentistry PhD☆/MPhil☆
London U Royal Free Hosp S of Med PhD☆/MPhil☆
London U Royal Postgraduate Med S PhD☆/MPhil☆
London U St Bartholomew's Hosp Med C PhD/MPhil
London U St George's Hosp Med S PhD☆/MPhil☆
London U United Med & Dent S, Guys's & St Thomas's PhD☆/ MPhil☆
PhD☆/MPhil☆
Manchester U PhD/MSc
Newcastle U MD/MPhil
Nottingham U PhD/MPhil
Oxford U DPhil☆/MSc☆
Sheffield U PhD/MMedSci
Wales U C of Med PhD☆/MSc☆

Occupational health
London U S of Hygiene & Tropical Med PhD/MPhil
Manchester U PhD/MSc

Occupational health & hygiene
Newcastle U PhD/MPhil

Occupational medicine
London U S of Hygiene & Tropical Med PhD/MPhil

Occupational therapy & physiotherapy
Ulster U DPhil/MPhil

Oncology
Belfast Queen's U PhD
Glasgow U PhD/MSc(MedSci)
London U London Hosp Med C PhD☆/MPhil☆
PhD☆/MPhil☆
Manchester U PhD/MSc
Southampton U PhD/MPhil

Ophtalmology
Leicester U PhD/MPhil

Ophtalmology (clinical & basic science)
London U Inst of Ophthalmology PhD☆/MPhil☆

Ophthalmic optics
Manchester UMIST PhD/MSc

Ophthalmology
Aberdeen U PhD☆/MPhil☆/MSc☆
Belfast Queen's U PhD
Bristol U PhD☆/MSc☆
Dundee U PhD/MSc
Glasgow U PhD/MSc(MedSci)
Liverpool U PhD/MSc
London U Imperial C PhD☆/ MPhil☆
London U St Bartholomew's Hosp Med C PhD/MPhil
Manchester U PhD/MSc
Newcastle U MD/MPhil
Oxford U DPhil☆/MSc☆
Sheffield U PhD/MMedSci

Optometry & physiological optics
Bradford U PhD/MPhil

Optometry & visual science
City U PhD/MPhil

Oral medicine & pathology
London U United Med & Dent S, Guys's & St Thomas's PhD☆/ MPhil☆

Oral pathology
London U King's C S of Med & Dentistry PhD☆/MPhil☆

Oral surgery medicine & pathology
Wales U C of Med PhD☆/MScD☆

Orthodontics
Manchester U PhD/MSc

Orthopaedic & accident surgery
Liverpool U PhD/MSc
Nottingham U PhD/MPhil

Orthopaedic & traumatic surgery
Dundee U PhD/MSc
Newcastle U MD/MPhil

Orthopaedic mechanics
Salford U PhD/MSc

Orthopaedic surgery
Southampton U PhD/MPhil

Orthopaedic surgery & traumatology
Oxford U DPhil☆/MSc☆

Orthopaedics
Glasgow U PhD/MSc(MedSci)
London U St Bartholomew's Hosp Med C PhD/MPhil
Sheffield U PhD/MMedSci

Otolaryngology
Glasgow U PhD/MSc(MedSci)

Otorhinolaryngology
Belfast Queen's U PhD
Liverpool U PhD/MSc

Paediatrics
Cambridge U PhD☆/MSc☆
London U Imperial C PhD☆/ MPhil☆
London U United Med & Dent S, Guys's & St Thomas's PhD☆/ MPhil☆
Oxford U DPhil☆/MSc☆
Sheffield U PhD/MMedSci

Paediatrics & child health
Birmingham U PhD/MSc
Leeds U PhD/MPhil/MSc

Paediatrics & neonatal medicine
London U Royal Postgraduate Med S PhD☆/MPhil☆

Parasitology
Liverpool U PhD/MSc

Pathology
Aberdeen U PhD☆/MPhil☆/ MSc(Med Sci)☆
Belfast Queen's U PhD/MSc
Bristol U PhD☆/MSc☆
Cambridge U PhD☆/MSc☆
Dundee U PhD/MSc
Edinburgh U PhD/MPhil
Glasgow U PhD/MSc(MedSci)
Leeds U PhD/MPhil
Leicester U PhD/MD/MPhil
Liverpool U PhD/MSc
London U King's C S of Med & Dentistry PhD☆/MPhil☆
London U London Hosp Med C PhD☆/MPhil☆
Manchester U PhD/MSc
Newcastle U PhD/MD/MPhil
Nottingham U PhD/MPhil
Oxford U DPhil☆/MSc☆
Sheffield U PhD/MMedSci
Southampton U PhD/MPhil
Wales U C of Med PhD☆/MSc☆

Pharmaceutical sciences
Aston U PhD/MPhil

Pnarmacology
London U UC PhD☆/MPhil☆
Manchester U PhD/MSc/dip

Pharmacology & clinical pharmacology
Dundee U PhD/MSc
London U St George's Hosp Med S PhD☆/MPhil☆
Southampton U PhD/MPhil

Pharmacology & therapeutics
Leicester U PhD/MD/MPhil

Liverpool U PhD/MSc
Sheffield U PhD/MMedSci
Wales U C of Med PhD☆/MSc☆

Pharmacy
London U Royal Postgraduate Med S PhD☆/MPhil☆

Pharmacy & biomedical sciences
Portsmouth P PhD☆/MPhil☆

Pharmacy & pharmacology
Bath U PhD☆/MSc☆

Physical education & sports science
Loughborough U PhD☆/MPhil☆

Physiological flow studies
London U Imperial C PhD/MD

Preclinical science & education
Glasgow U PhD/MSc(MedSci)

Primary medical care
Southampton U PhD/MPhil

Psychiatry
Cambridge U PhD☆/MSc☆
Dundee U PhD/MSc
Edinburgh U PhD/MPhil
Leeds U PhD/MPhil
Leicester U PhD/MPhil
Liverpool U PhD
London U Imperial C PhD☆/ MPhil☆
London U Inst of Psychiatry PhD☆/MPhil☆
London U Charing Cross & Westminster Med S PhD/MPhil
London U London Hosp Med C PhD☆/MPhil☆
London U Royal Free Hosp S of Med PhD☆/MPhil☆
London U St George's Hosp Med S PhD☆/MPhil☆
London U United Med & Dent S, Guys's & St Thomas's PhD☆/ MPhil☆
PhD☆/MPhil☆
Manchester U PhD/MSc
Newcastle U MD/MPhil
Nottingham U PhD/MPhil
Oxford U DPhil☆/MSc☆
Sheffield U PhD/MMedSci
Southampton U PhD/MPhil

Psychological medicine
Glasgow U PhD/MSc(MedSci)
London U King's C S of Med & Dentistry PhD☆/MPhil☆
London U St Bartholomew's Hosp Med C PhD/MPhil
Wales U C of Med PhD☆/MSc☆

Psychology
Southampton U PhD/MPhil

Psychology as applied to medicine
London U United Med & Dent S, Guys's & St Thomas's PhD✩/ MPhil✩

Psychotherapy
London U Imperial C PhD✩/ MPhil✩

Public health
Glasgow U PhD

Radiation oncology
Liverpool U PhD/MSc

Radiodiagnosis
Bristol U PhD✩/MSc✩
Liverpool U PhD/MSc
Sheffield U PhD/MMedSci

Radiology
Cambridge U PhD✩/MSc✩
Glasgow U PhD/MPhil
London U Imperial C PhD✩/ MPhil✩
Newcastle U MD/MPhil
Oxford U DPhil✩/MSc✩

Radiotherapy
Leeds U PhD/MPhil
London U St Bartholomew's Hosp Med C PhD/MPhil
London U United Med & Dent S, Guys's & St Thomas's PhD✩/ MPhil✩
Newcastle U PhD/MPhil

Radiotherapy & oncology
Dundee U PhD/MSc
London U Imperial C PhD✩/ MPhil✩
Oxford U DPhil✩/MSc✩

Rehabilitation studies
Southampton U PhD/MPhil

Renal disease
Wales U C of Med PhD✩/MSc✩

Renal medicine
Southampton U PhD/MPhil

Respiratory medicine unit
Nottingham U PhD/MPhil

Respiratory physiology
Oxford U DPhil✩/MSc✩

Rheumatology
Birmingham U PhD/MSc
London U Charing Cross & Westminster Med S PhD/MPhil
London U London Hosp Med C PhD✩/MPhil✩
London U St Bartholomew's Hosp Med C PhD/MPhil
London U United Med & Dent S, Guys's & St Thomas's PhD✩/ MPhil✩
PhD✩/MPhil✩

Manchester U PhD/MSc
Oxford U DPhil✩/MSc✩

Rheumatology & rehabilitation
London U Imperial C PhD✩/ MPhil✩

Social medicine
Birmingham U PhD/MSc

Sociology & applied social studies
Birmingham P PhD/MPhil

Sociology applied to medicine
London U London Hosp Med C PhD✩/MPhil✩
London U St Bartholomew's Hosp Med C PhD/MPhil

Sociology as applied to medicine
London U United Med & Dent S, Guys's & St Thomas's PhD✩/ MPhil✩

Speech
Newcastle U PhD/MPhil

Speech pathology
Leicester P PhD/MPhil

Speech science
London U UC PhD✩/MPhil✩

Speech therapy
Manchester U PhD

Sports science
Birmingham U PhD/MSc

Steroid endocrinology
Leeds U MMedSc

Systems science
City U PhD/MPhil

Tenovus research
Southampton U PhD/MPhil

Therapeutics
Nottingham U PhD/MPhil

Therapeutics & clinical pharmacology
Aberdeen U PhD✩/MPhil✩
Birmingham U PhD/MSc
Edinburgh U PhD/MPhil

Therapeutics & pharmacology
Belfast Queen's U PhD

Thoracic medicine
London U King's C S of Med & Dentistry PhD/MPhil
London U United Med & Dent S, Guys's & St Thomas's PhD✩/ MPhil✩

Toxicology
Birmingham U PhD✩/MSc✩

Traumatic & orthopaedic surgery
Wales U C of Med PhD✩/MSc✩

Tropical hygiene
London U S of Hygiene & Tropical Med PhD/MPhil

Tropical medicine
Incorporated Liverpool S of Tropical Med PhD✩/MSc✩
Liverpool U PhD/MSc
Oxford U DPhil✩/MSc✩

Tropical paediatrics
Liverpool U PhD/MSc

Tuberculosis & chest diseases
Wales U C of Med PhD✩/MSc✩

Urology
London U Imperial C PhD✩/ MPhil✩
London U London Hosp Med C PhD✩/MPhil✩
London U St Bartholomew's Hosp Med C PhD/MPhil
London U United Med & Dent S, Guys's & St Thomas's PhD✩/ MPhil✩
Oxford U DPhil✩/MSc✩

Venerology
London U Imperial C PhD✩/ MPhil✩

Veterinary medicine
Edinburgh U PhD/MPhil

Virology
London U London Hosp Med C PhD✩/MPhil✩

Vision sciences
Aston U PhD/MPhil

Surgery

Higher degrees by instruction

Biomedical engineering science
Dundee U MSc

Oral surgery
London U King's C S of Med & Dentistry MSc△
Manchester U MSc

Surgery
Glasgow U MSc(MedSci)

Surgical sciences (with anaesthesia)
Sheffield U MMedSci

Veterinary surgery
Glasgow U MVSc

Higher degrees by research

Cardiac surgery
Glasgow U PhD/MSc(MedSci)

Cardiothoracic surgery
London U St Bartholomew's
Hosp Med C PhD/MPhil

Clinical surgery
Edinburgh U PhD/MPhil

Conservative dental surgery
London U United Med & Dent S,
Guys's & St Thomas's PhD☆/
MPhil☆

Dental surgery
Bristol U PhD/MSc
Leeds U PhD/MDSc/MSc

Neuro surgery
London U Imperial C PhD☆/
MPhil☆

Neurological surgery
London U St Bartholomew's
Hosp Med C PhD/MPhil

Neurosurgery
Glasgow U PhD/MSc(MedSci)
Oxford U DPhil☆/MSc☆

Oral & maxillo facial surgery
London U King's C S of Med &
Dentistry PhD☆/MPhil☆
London U United Med & Dent S,
Guys's & St Thomas's PhD☆/
MPhil☆
Wales U C of Med PhD☆/MScD☆

Oral medicine & oral surgery
Bristol U PhD☆/MSc☆

Oral surgery
Newcastle U PhD/MDSc/MPhil

Oral surgery medicine & pathology
Wales U C of Med PhD☆/MScD☆

Orthopaedic & accident surgery
Liverpool U PhD/MSc
Nottingham U PhD/MPhil

Orthopaedic & traumatic surgery
Dundee U PhD/MSc
Newcastle U MD/MPhil

Orthopaedic surgery
Belfast Queen's U PhD
Edinburgh U PhD/MPhil
Leeds U PhD/MPhil/ChM
Leicester U PhD/MPhil
London U Imperial C PhD☆/
MPhil☆

London U United Med & Dent S,
Guys's & St Thomas's PhD☆/
MPhil☆
Manchester U PhD/MSc
Southampton U PhD/MPhil

Orthopaedic surgery & traumatology
Oxford U DPhil☆/MSc☆

Otolaryngology
Dundee U PhD/MSc
PhD☆/MPhil☆
Oxford U DPhil☆/MSc☆

Otorhinolaryngology
Belfast Queen's U PhD
London U Imperial C PhD☆/
MPhil☆

Paediatric surgery
Liverpool U PhD
London U Imperial C PhD☆/
MPhil☆

Plastic surgery
London U St Bartholomew's
Hosp Med C PhD/MPhil
Oxford U DPhil☆/MSc☆

Surgery
Aberdeen U PhD☆/MPhil☆/MSc☆
Belfast Queen's U PhD
Birmingham U PhD/MSc
Bristol U PhD☆/MSc☆
Cambridge U PhD☆/MSc☆
Dundee U PhD/MSc
Edinburgh U PhD/MPhil
Glasgow U PhD/MSc(MedSci)
Leeds U PhD/MPhil/MSc
Leicester U PhD/MPhil
Liverpool U PhD/MSc
London U Imperial C PhD☆/
MPhil☆
London U Charing Cross &
Westminster Med S PhD/MPhil
London U King's C S of Med &
Dentistry PhD☆/MPhil☆
London U London Hosp Med C
PhD☆/MPhil☆
London U Royal Free Hosp S of
Med PhD☆/MPhil☆
London U Royal Postgraduate
Med S PhD☆/MPhil☆
London U St Bartholomew's
Hosp Med C PhD/MPhil
London U St George's Hosp
Med S PhD☆/MPhil☆
London U United Med & Dent S,
Guys's & St Thomas's PhD☆/
MPhil☆
Manchester U PhD/MSc
Newcastle U MD/MPhil
Nottingham U PhD/MPhil
Oxford U DPhil☆/MSc☆
Sheffield U PhD/MMedSci

London U United Med & Dent S,
Guys's & St Thomas's PhD☆/
MPhil☆
Manchester U PhD/MSc
Southampton U PhD/MPhil

Southampton U PhD/MPhil
Wales U C of Med PhD☆/MSc☆

Surgical neurology
Dundee U PhD/MSc
Edinburgh U PhD/MPhil

Surgical studies
PhD☆/MPhil☆

Thoracic medicine
London U United Med & Dent S,
Guys's & St Thomas's PhD☆/
MPhil☆

Thoracic surgery
London U Imperial C PhD☆/
MPhil☆
London U United Med & Dent S,
Guys's & St Thomas's PhD☆/
MPhil☆

Traumatic & orthopaedic surgery
Wales U C of Med PhD☆/MSc☆

Veterinary surgery
Bristol U PhD☆/MSc☆
Edinburgh U PhD/MPhil

Veterinary surgery & obstetrics
London U Royal Veterinary C
PhD☆/MPhil☆

Veterinary studies

Higher degrees by instruction

Animal health
Edinburgh U MSc/dip
London U Royal Veterinary C
MSc☆

Animal nutrition
Aberdeen SAg MSc/dip
Aberdeen U MSc☆/dip☆
Newcastle U MSc☆/dip☆

Animal production
Aberdeen SAg MSc☆
Aberdeen U MSc☆
Reading U MSc☆/dip☆

Applied parasitology
Incorporated Liverpool S of
Tropical Med MVSc☆

Aquatic veterinary studies
Stirling U MSc☆/dip☆

Pig production
Aberdeen U MSc☆

Tropical animal production & health
Edinburgh U MSc☆/dip☆
Edinburgh U SAg MSc☆/dip☆

Tropical veterinary medicine
Edinburgh U MSc☆/dip☆

Tropical veterinary science
Edinburgh U MSc☆/dip☆

Veterinary anaesthesia
London U Royal Veterinary C
dip☆

Veterinary medicine
Glasgow U MVM/MVSc/dip☆

Veterinary microbiology
Surrey U MSc☆/dip☆

Veterinary pathology
London U Royal Veterinary C
MSc☆

Veterinary radiology
London U Royal Veterinary C
dip☆

Veterinary surgery
Glasgow U MVSc

Higher degrees by research

Anatomy
London U Royal Veterinary C
PhD☆/MPhil☆

Animal health
Edinburgh U PhD/MPhil

Animal husbandry
Bristol U PhD☆/MSc☆
Edinburgh U PhD/MPhil
London U Royal Veterinary C
PhD☆/MPhil☆

Animal nutrition
Aberdeen SAg PhD☆/MSc☆
Aberdeen U PhD☆/MPhil☆/MSc☆
Edinburgh U PhD/MPhil

Animal physiology & nutrition
Leeds U PhD/MPhil/MSc

Animal production & health
Aberdeen SAg PhD☆/MSc☆
Aberdeen U PhD☆/MPhil☆/MSc☆
Edinburgh U PhD/MPhil

Biochemistry
London U Royal Veterinary C
PhD☆/MPhil☆

Clinical veterinary medicine
Cambridge U PhD☆/MSc☆

Farm animals
London U Royal Veterinary C
PhD☆/MPhil☆

Immunology
London U Royal Veterinary C
PhD☆/MPhil☆

Laboratory animal science
London U Royal Veterinary C
PhD☆/MPhil☆

Medicine
London U Royal Veterinary C
PhD☆/MPhil☆

Microbiology & parasitology
Edinburgh U PhD/MPhil
London U Royal Veterinary C
PhD☆/MPhil☆

Molecular & cellular biology
London U Royal Veterinary C
PhD☆/MPhil☆

Neuroscience
London U Royal Veterinary C
PhD☆/MPhil☆

Pathology
London U Royal Veterinary C
PhD☆/MPhil☆

Pharmacology
London U Royal Veterinary C
PhD☆/MPhil☆

Physiology
London U Royal Veterinary C
PhD☆/MPhil☆

Tropical animal health
Edinburgh U PhD/MPhil

Veterinary anatomy
Edinburgh U PhD/MPhil

Veterinary biochemistry
Liverpool U PhD/MVSc

Veterinary clinical science
Liverpool U PhD/MVSc

Veterinary medicine
Bristol U PhD☆/MSc☆
Edinburgh U PhD/MPhil
Glasgow U PhD/MSc/MVM
West of Scotland C PhD☆/MSc☆

Veterinary microbiology
Edinburgh U PhD/MPhil

Veterinary parasitology
Edinburgh U PhD/MPhil
Liverpool U PhD/MVSc

Veterinary pathology
Edinburgh U PhD/MPhil
Liverpool U PhD/MVSc

Veterinary pharmacology
Edinburgh U PhD/MPhil
Liverpool U PhD/MVSc

Veterinary physiology
Edinburgh U PhD/MPhil
Liverpool U PhD/MVSc

Veterinary preventive medicine
Liverpool U PhD/MVSc

Veterinary science
Belfast Queen's U PhD/MSc

Veterinary surgery
Bristol U PhD☆/MSc☆
Edinburgh U PhD/MPhil

Veterinary surgery & obstetrics
London U Royal Veterinary C
PhD☆/MPhil☆

Zoology

Higher degrees by instruction

Animal parasitology
Bangor, U of Wales MSc☆/dip☆

Apiculture
Cardiff U of Wales C dip☆

Applied entomology
Glasgow U MSc/dip
London U Imperial C MSc/dip

Applied entomology & crop protection
Newcastle U MSc☆/dip☆

Applied fish biology
South West P MSc☆/dip☆

Applied marine science
Swansea UC MSc☆/dip☆

Applied nematology
London U Imperial C MSc/dip

Applied parasitology
Liverpool U MVSc

Applied parasitology & entomology
Liverpool U MSc☆

Applied zoology
Reading U MPhil☆

Behavioural ecology
Manchester P MSc△/dip△   ☐

Biological anthropology
Durham U MSc☆

Biological electron microscopy
Aberystwyth, UC of Wales
MSc☆/dip☆

Conservation
London U UC MSc☆/dip☆

Development of pest management systems
Birmingham U MSc☆

Ecology
Aberdeen U MSc☆/dip☆   *Env*
Bangor, U of Wales MSc☆/dip☆
Durham U MSc☆/dip☆

Experimental parasitology
Glasgow U MAppSci/dip

Fisheries biology
Buckingham U MSc☆

Fisheries biology & management
Bangor, U of Wales MSc☆/dip☆

Marine & fisheries science
Aberdeen U MSc☆/dip☆   □

Shellfish biology, fisheries & culture
Bangor, U of Wales MSc/dip

Tropical coastal management
Newcastle U MSc☆/dip☆

Vertebrate palaeontology
London U UC MSc

World animal production
Bangor, U of Wales MSc☆/dip☆

Zoology
East Anglia U MSc☆/dip☆

Higher degrees by research

Agricultural zoology
Aberdeen SAg PhD☆/MSc☆
Belfast Queen's U PhD/MSc
Glasgow U PhD/MSc

Animal & plant sciences
Bristol P PhD△/MPhil△/dip△

Animal biology
Bangor, U of Wales PhD☆/ MPhil☆

Anthropology
Durham U PhD/MA/MPhil/MSc

Applied sciences
Wolverhampton P PhD/MPhil

Cell biology
London U UC PhD☆/MPhil☆

Comparative physiology
Oxford U DPhil☆/MSc☆

Conservation
London U UC PhD☆/MPhil☆

Ecology
Aberdeen U PhD☆/MPhil☆/MSc☆
London U UC PhD☆/MPhil☆

Entomology
Oxford U DPhil☆/MSc☆

Field ornithology
Oxford U DPhil☆/MSc☆

Marine biology
Aberdeen U PhD☆/MPhil☆/MSc☆

Microbiology
London U UC PhD☆/MPhil☆

Parasitology
Aberdeen U PhD☆/MPhil☆
Liverpool U PhD/MSc
Portsmouth P PhD☆/MPhil☆

Physiology
London U Wye C PhD☆/MPhil☆

Plant science
Aberdeen U PhD☆/MPhil☆/MSc☆

Vertebrate palaeontology
Oxford U DPhil☆/MSc☆

Zoology
Aberdeen U PhD☆/MPhil☆/MSc☆
Bristol U PhD☆/MSc☆
Cambridge U PhD☆/MSc☆
Durham U PhD/MSc
Edinburgh U PhD/MPhil
Glasgow U PhD/MSc
Keele U PhD/MSc
Leicester U PhD/MPhil
Liverpool U PhD/MSc
London U UC PhD☆/MPhil☆
Manchester U PhD/MSc
Newcastle U PhD/MSc
Nottingham U PhD/MPhil
Oxford U DPhil☆/MSc☆
St Andrews U PhD/MSc
West of Scotland C PhD☆/MSc☆

Zoology & comparative physiology
Birmingham U PhD/MSc

Zoology (pure & applied)
Reading U PhD/MPhil

Applied insect taxonomy

dip
1 year full time
12 places
Department of Pure & applied biology, University of Wales College of Cardiff, PO Box 915, Cardiff CF1 3TL
Tel: 0222 874804

A full time course designed to train students and established field workers in effective taxonomic and biological studies on insect pest species and biological control agents. A research project in which original problems are tackled under supervision is a major course component. PhD and MPhil courses are also available for suitably qualified students.
Entrance requirements Degree or equivalent or suitable practical experience.
Course director Professor M F Claridge.

Aquaculture

MSc/Diploma
1 year full time
25-30 places
Academic Administrator,
Institute of Aquaculture,
University of Stirling, Stirling,
Scotland FK9 4LA
Tel: 0786 73171

Students are trained to establish, manage and appraise aquaculture enterprises and development programmes. Candidates study biology, nutrition, disease and husbandry of cultured fish and invertebrates in temperate, marine, and tropical waters. Engineering, water supply chemistry, limnology, oceanography, fishery and resource management, investment appraisal and systems analysis are also offered. **Entrance requirements** Good honours degree in an appropriate biological science, or an equivalent qualification. **Grants** Various.
Course director Dr L G Ross.

Behavioural ecology

MSc/Postgraduate diploma
2-3 years part time
Dr C Goldspink, Department
of Biological Sciences,
Manchester Polytechnic,
John Dalton Building,
Chester Street, Manchester
M1 5GD
Tel: 061 228 6171 ext 2368

This course provides a coherent overview of the theory and practice of behavioural ecology. Behavioural ecology is a rapidly expanding area of biological enquiry which brings together ecology, behaviour and evolutionary theory. Units available on the course include biological data processsing, dispersion and dispersal, reproductive strategies, maintenance behaviour and communication. Specialist options are available in conservation and urban pest control. Emphasis is on practical work throughout. Opportunities for overseas field work are available.
Entrance requirements Honours degree in biology or equivalent.
Head of department Dr T Looker.

Bioscience & biotechnology

PhD
full time
MSc
full time
MPhil
full time
Course details and
application forms from:,
Professor D R Berry,
Department of Bioscience &
Biotechnology, University of
Strathclyde, Royal College
Building, 204 George Street,
Glasgow G1 1XW
Tel: 041 552 4400, please
quote ref DOG 91

Research facilities are provided for suitably qualified graduates who wish to register for a research degree such as Master of Philosophy (MPhil), or Doctor of Philosophy (PhD). There are postgraduate diploma courses in Food Comoposition and Processing and also Applied Microbiology. A new instructional MSc in Food Biotechnology accepted its first students in October 1989.
Entrance requirements An appropriate degree in the biosciences.
Chairman of department (1988-92) Professor D R Berry.

Biotechnology

PhD
3 years full time
10 places
MPhil
1 or 2 years full time
Miss L Criscuolo, Student
Admissions Officer,
Biotechnology Centre,
Cranfield Institute of
Technology, Cranfield,
Bedford.MK43 0AL
Tel: 0234 750111 ext 2562

The rapidly expanding range of research interests in the Biotechnology Centre includes: bioelectrochemistry and biosensor technology; biotransformations producing industrially valuable products; protein engineeering; biochemical engineering and genetic engineering of bacteria. Opportunities for studentships continually arise as new industrial research contracts are negotiated.
Entrance requirements Good honours degree (or equivalent) in relevant subject especially microbiology, biochemistry and biochemical engineering.
Grants Research Council awards, CASE studentships and industrially sponsored research assistantships or studentships.
Head of Centre Professor I J Higgins.

Biotechnology

MSc
1 year full time
20 places
PhD
3 years full time
Dr D J Leak, Centre for
Biotechnology, Imperial
College of Science,
Technology & Medicine,
London SW7 0RN
Tel: 071 589 5111 ext 7090,
telex 929484 (IMPCOL G),
fax: 071 225 8942

MSc course units are in applied enzymology, genetic engineering, applied microbial biochemistry, fermentation technology, aspects of biochemical engineering and a four month research project. The latter may include industrial placement in a biotechnology based company. Research interests are: genetic engineering of plants and microorganisms, protein engineering, industrial enzymes, biosensors, microbial physiology, biotransformations, nuclear magnetic resonance, ethanol fermentations.
Entrance requirements MSc - second class honours degree in a life science subject or chemistry. PhD - upper second in a life science subject or chemistry.
Director of Centre Professor B S Hartley FRS.

General & medical microbiology

MSc/diploma
1 year full time
Dr D G Smith, Darwin
Building, Department of
Biology, University College
London, Gower Street,
London WC1E 6BT
Tel: 071 387 7050 ext 2679

The course trains students for posts in industrial or medical microbiology and provides a basis for proceeding to a PhD. Courses on medical bacteriology and mycology, virology, genetic engineering, immunology, structure and behaviour. Three month research project. Medical part of course held at London School of Hygiene and Tropical Medicine.
Entrance requirements Good honours degree in any biological field.
Head of department Professor G R Stewart.

Health services studies

MA
1 year full time
2 years part time
15 places
Dr T Rathwell, Course
Director, Nuffield Institute for
Health Services Studies,
Department of Social policy,
University of Leeds, 71-75
Clarendon Road, Leeds LS2
9PL
Tel: 0532 459034

This is a scheme of advanced study for those already in health related careers or those contemplating such careers. Syllabus: social policy; health and disease; epidemiology; health management ; a special option subject; and, dissertation.
There is the opportunity to obtain the degree by research, although places are limited. Also enquiries are welcome from those interested in studying for the MPhil or PhD.
Entrance requirements Good honours degree or equivalent in one of the social and behavioural sciences or medicine, dentistry, nursing or other related fields.
Course director Dr T Rathwell.

Immunology

MSc
1 year full time
15 places
Assistant Registrar, Faculty
of Science, University of
Birmingham, Birmingham
B15 2TT
Tel: 021 414 6373

The course offers theoretical, practical and research training in biological and medical aspects of immunology. Special attention is paid to the important contributions of immunology to biotechnological developments such as the production and applications of monoclonal antibodies, the cloning of lymphocytes, the study of surface markers on cell populations and aspects of molecular biology in relation to the working of the immune system and development of new vaccines.
Entrance requirements A good degree in biological, medical or veterinary sciences. Competence in English is also required. Closing date 30 April.
Grants MRC studentships.
Course tutor Dr D Catty.

Marine & fisheries science

MSc
1 year full time
15 places
dip
1 year full time
15 places
Head of Department,
Department of Zoology,
University of Aberdeen,
Tillydrone Avenue, Aberdeen
AB9 2TN
Tel: 0224 272859

The scientific approach to the exploitation and management of the marine environment and its living resources. A special feature is the input from scientists of the Department of Agriculture & Fisheries, Scotland and opportunity for practical research training. Topics include environmental quality and pollution; resource ecology; fish population dynamics, exploitation and management; resource economics, law and administration; resource utilization, gear technology, aquaculture.
Entrance requirements Normally good degree in biological subject or equivalent qualification.
Head of department Professor P A Racey.

Molecular genetics

MSc
1 year full time
16 places
Higher Degrees Office,
University of Leicester,
University Road, Leicester
LE1 7RH
Tel: 0533 522298

The course provides a link for graduates preparing for employment in biotechnology or basic research. Direct practical training in the techniques of microbial molecular genetics and recombinant DNA technology accompanies formal instruction and tutorial work leading to the development of a supervised research project.
Entrance requirements An honours degree in Biological Sciences or a related subject.
Grants SERC and MRC advanced course studentships.
Senior Lecturer Dr C F Roberts.

Toxicology

PhD
3 years full time
MSc
1 year full time
2 years part time
dip course (without
research project)
9 months full time
individual modules 5 weeks
full time
Dr J K Chipman, Department
of Biochemistry, University
of Birmingham, PO Box 363,
Birmingham B15 2TT
Tel: 021 414 5422

Toxicology is an expanding field with good career prospects. The MSc and diploma courses cover all major aspects of toxicology and comprise five modules and a research project.
1. Metabolism and excretion of xenobiotics
2. Pharmacological and clinical aspects of toxicology
3. Mechanisms and significance of toxicity and carcinogenesis.
4. Recognition and detection of acute and chronic toxicity
5. Environmental and occupational toxicology and specific target organ toxicity.
Teaching is by members of various university departments, hospitals, industrial and government research institutes.
Entrance requirements Good honours degree.
Grants MRC, European Science Foundation.
Course tutor Dr J K Chipman.

Toxicology

MSc
1 year full time
15 places
2 years part time
Dr R S Jones, Department of
Biochemistry, University of
Surrey, Guildford , Surrey
GU2 5XH
Tel: 0483 571281

The course introduces graduates of appropriate disciplines to the many facets of toxicology, with emphasis being placed on the molecular mechanisms of chemically induced injury and the assessment of toxicological hazard in industry and natural environments. It is taught in leading industrial and government research laboratories.
Entrance requirements A good honours degree in a subject with a strong biochemical content, including medicine and veterinary medicine. Appropriate professional qualifications will be recognised, though non-graduates holding such qualifications may be required to sit entrance examinations.
Grants (For home students only) MRC and SERC advanced course studentships and industrial scholarships are normally available.
Lecturer Dr R S Jones.

THE UNIVERSITY OF HULL

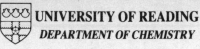

School of Chemistry

Research Degrees The School sustains active research in all major branches of the subject. Most notable is work on liquid crystals, in which the School is pre-eminent. Other Organic interests include synthesis in heterocyclic and medicinal chemistry, and structures of microbial polysaccharides. Areas of Inorganic research include magnetochemistry, bio-inorganic chemistry, superconductivity, homogeneous catalysis and inorganic liquid crystals. Major research in Physical chemistry covers catalysis, combustion and laser chemistry, colloid and surface chemistry. Analytical projects involve development of novel, selective assays using, for example, immobilised enzymes, flow-injection, and luminescence techniques. Opportunities for research to MSc or PhD level arise in all these areas.

MSc in Analytical Science This 1-year (full-time) course provides theoretical knowledge and practical experience of modern analytical methods. Applications of microcomputers, and a substantial research project, are part of the large practical component.

Further information and literature from:

**Secretary to the Dean
School of Chemistry, GS2
University of Hull, HU6 7RX
Telephone Hull (0482) 465461**

UNIVERSITY OF READING
DEPARTMENT OF CHEMISTRY

**Research opportunities: PhD 3 years full time
MPhil 2 years full time**

The main areas of research are inorganic materials including those for solid state devices; co-ordination chemistry; catalysis; chelating polymers; metal ion separations; metal ion-food stuff component interactions; molecular modelling. Organic synthesis with particular reference to medicinal chemistry, polymers, photochemical methods and the use of high pressures. Fermentation. Structural studies; X-ray crystallography; spectroscopy. Physical chemistry, especially gas-phase kinetics and spectroscopy. Emulsions; liquid crystals; electrochemistry. Theoretical calculations. Detailed booklet available.

The Department is well equipped with the necessary instrumentation and computer facilities.

For further details contact:

**Head of Department,
Department of Chemistry,
University of Reading,
Whiteknights, PO Box 224,
Reading,
Berks. RG6 2AD
Tel: 0734 318447**

UNIVERSITY OF NEWCASTLE UPON TYNE

Department of Chemistry

RESEARCH STUDENTSHIPS

Studentships are available for research in the following areas leading to the degree of Ph.D.
- Bioinorganic Mechanisms
- Biosensors and Analytical Chemistry
- Computational Chemistry and Molecular Graphics
- Electrochemistry and Surface Studies
- Medicinal Chemistry and Molecular Toxicology
- New Materials and Organometallics
- Structural Chemistry
- Synthesis of Biologically Active Molecules
- Carbon Science

Applications for the above are invited from candidates possessing or expecting to obtain a good honours degree in chemistry (at least 2,1 standard) for SERC studentships. For some projects other qualifications may be acceptable (e.g. B.Sc. in Biochemistry). In addition, SERC and other studentships are available for the 1 year M.Sc. Course in Biosensors.

Enquiries should be made to:
Professor A.K. Covington
Director of Postgraduate Studies
Department of Chemistry
The University of Newcastle upon Tyne
Newcastle upon Tyne
NE1 7RU.
Tel: 091-222 6785

How about branching out? Turn back to discover the alternatives available in the **Environmental Studies** section.

Chemical sciences

The graduate who wishes to take up further study or research in the chemical sciences will find a wide range of topics available, ranging from pure chemical research to materials technology, and from food science to pharmaceutical products. Typical areas of study include the synthesis and spectroscopic study of novel compounds or materials, the use of analytical techniques, and the development of new methods, such as using computer graphics in new product development.

If the graduate has a good degree and is successful in obtaining a studentship (see below), there are several directions in which the postgraduate course may develop. Doctorates (PhD or DPhil) are usually obtained after three years of original research (which is expected to contribute something new to scientific knowledge in general), while Master's degrees (MPhil or MSc) require less originality and independence in research, and often include lectures, seminars (usually compulsory) and more supervision than Doctorate research degrees. The Master's degree is usually of two years' duration. Many institutions initially register all their postgraduate students for Master's degrees, converting some to Doctorates once the necessary standard has been reached (generally after the completion of an interim report and oral exam).

Last year's proposed changes to the structure of Britain's university education system - the division of some departments into either research-only or teaching-only establishments - seem to have been postponed for the present. Consequently, the opportunities for research are still available at the majority of chemistry departments.

Changes have occurred, however, in the allocation of grants, especially those from Co-operative Awards in the Sciences of the Environment (CASE). The overall number of grants available from the awarding councils has been reduced, and instead of all CASE awards being allocated to individual members of staff on the basis of their research proposals, 60 per cent are now to be given to the heads of departments to allocate. This is likely to change again next year, when the proportion directed to individual researchers will be around 20 per cent.

This obviously affects the student's choices, as it is more likely that, at interview, discussions will be held with several members of staff on a variety of research topics before the head of department makes a decision on the allocation of grant to student.

Employment prospects
Figures published recently show that in the last few years, more graduates in chemistry go on to further research or study than in most other subject areas, and only a relatively small number of BSc chemistry graduates move straight into employment directly related to chemistry.

2 POSTGRADUATE OPPORTUNITIES

The possession of a postgraduate degree is seen by many employers as an indication that a candidate is able to organise his or her working timetable logically and efficiently, as well as possessing the ability to work independently where necessary and develop new ideas. These are qualities that a postgraduate course should bring out in a student, apart from giving the graduate some experience and possibly expertise in research techniques which may be of use in an industrial environment.

Course funding

Briefly, the majority of home graduates who are offered places as postgraduate research students will obtain their funding from one of the various research councils detailed below. Applications for these grants are made by the institution at which the research will take place. Especially in the case of the Science and Engineering Research Council (SERC) and the Natural Environmental Research Council (NERC), a quota system operates for ordinary studentships whereby the number of awards is fixed and they are then allocated by nomination of the heads of the departments in question.

- The SERC and the NERC both offer CASE awards. These involve the collaboration of an industrial firm and co-supervision by an industrial and an academic supervisor. The industrial partner will often supplement the normal SERC/NERC grant to the student, as well as offering the opportunity to work at the research establishment.
- The SERC also offers instant awards. These are tailored to the needs of graduates returning to research after a period in employment. As the name implies, they enable the institution involved to inform the candidate of the available finances at an early date.
- Research assistantships are offered by the research councils - SERC, NERC, the Agriculture and Food Research Council (AFRC) and the Medical Research Council (MRC). These are often available to graduates with less than an upper second class degree. Students are actually employed by the institution in a research post, whilst having the opportunity to pursue a postgraduate degree.

Jeanette Eldridge

This listing contains **taught courses** (under the heading 'Higher degrees by instruction') and **research opportunities** (under the heading 'Higher degrees by research'). All study exceeds two terms or six months and is offered on both a full-time and part-time basis unless otherwise indicated. Post-experience and in-service courses are only included when advertised.

☐ This symbol indicates that the **taught course(s)** or **research opportunities** are advertised at the end of this listing.

Biol   An italic abbreviation indicates that an advertisement has been placed at the end of another chapter.

☆   This symbol indicates full-time study only.

△   This symbol indicates part-time study only.

For quick reference to advertisements, please use the 'Advertiser's course entry index'. For further information regarding the listing, please refer to page 53.

General

Higher degrees by instruction

Analytical chemistry
Lancaster U MSc/dip

Chemical research
London U Imperial C MSc☆/dip☆
London U King's C MSc☆

Clinical pharmacy
Belfast Queen's U dip△

Colour chemistry
Leeds U MSc☆

Computer visualisation & animation
Dorset Inst dip☆

Corrosion science & engineering
Manchester UMIST MSc☆/
   dip☆   *Eng*

History & philosophy of science
Leeds U dip

Independent study
East London P MA/MSc/dip

Instrumentation & analytical science
Manchester UMIST MSc☆

Laboratory sciences
Nottingham P IMLS△

Law & science: intellectual property
London U Queen Mary & Westfield C MSc

New polymer synthesis
Lancaster U MSc☆

Science & science education
Glasgow U MSc

Science, technology & international affairs
Lancaster U MA☆

Higher degrees by research

Applied science
Middlesex P PhD/MPhil

Chemical engineering
Nottingham U PhD/MPhil   □

Chemical pathology
London U King's C S of Med & Dentistry PhD☆/MPhil☆

Chemistry
Lancaster U PhD/MPhil
London U UC PhD☆/MPhil☆

History of science & technology
Open U PhD/MPhil/BPhil

Independent study
East London P PhD/MPhil

Instrumentation & analytical science
Manchester UMIST PhD/MSc

Main group element chemistry
Sussex U DPhil/MPhil

Molecular dynamics & gas phase kinetics
Sussex U MPhil△

Science
Canterbury Christ Church C PhD/MPhil
Cardiff IHE PhD/MPhil/dip△
Humberside CHE PhD/MPhil
Worcester CHE PhD/MPhil

Science & technology
Thames Valley C MPhil

Science studies
Bath U PhD☆/MPhil☆

Science, mathematics & computing
Cheltenham & Gloucester CHE PhD/MPhil

Chemistry

Higher degrees by instruction

Advanced analytical chemistry
Bristol U MSc☆

Advanced chemical technology
Manchester UMIST MSc☆   □

Advanced studies in chemistry
London U King's C dip☆

Aerosol science & technology
Essex U MSc☆

Analytical chemistry
Aberdeen U MSc☆/dip☆
Belfast Queen's U MSc/dip
Hull U dip☆
Kingston P MSc△
Lancashire P MSc☆
Lancaster U MSc/dip
North East Wales IHE MPhil△/
   MSc△/dip☆
Salford U MSc   □

Analytical chemistry & instrumentation
Loughborough U MSc   □

Analytical science
Humberside CHE MSc/cert☆/dip

Applications of radiochemistry & analytical chemistry in inorganic & surface chemistry
Glasgow U MSc

Bioanalytical chemistry
Dundee U dip☆

Biochemistry & chemistry applied to medicine
London U London Hosp Med C MSc

Biocolloid chemistry
East Anglia U MSc☆

Biosensors
Newcastle U MSc☆

Chemical analysis
Thames P MSc△/dip△

Chemical education
East Anglia U MSc☆

Chemical physics
East Anglia U MSc☆
Sussex U MSc☆

Chemical research
London U Birkbeck C MSc
London U Imperial C MSc☆/dip☆
London U Queen Mary & Westfield C MSc☆
London U Royal Holloway & Bedford New C MSc☆

Chemical spectroscopy
East Anglia U MSc☆

Chemistry
Dundee U dip☆
East Anglia U dip☆
Fife CT RSC△
Glasgow U MAppSci☆/ MAppSci△/MSc/MSc
Hull U MSc☆
Kent U MSc☆/dip☆
Kingston P RSC
Lancaster U dip☆
London U Royal Holloway & Bedford New C dip☆
Napier P RSC
Salford U dip☆
Sandwell CFHE RSC II△
Southampton U MSc☆
Teesside P RSC☆

Chemistry & biological chemistry
Essex U dip☆

Chemistry & chemical education
Glasgow U MSc(SciEduc)

Colour chemistry
Leeds U MSc☆

Coordination chemistry
East Anglia U MSc☆

Crystallography
London U Birkbeck C MSc

Dyeing & finishing
Leeds U MSc☆

Environmental chemistry
Edinburgh U dip☆

Food science
Leeds U MSc☆/dip☆ ☐

Forensic science
London U King's C MSc☆
Strathclyde U MSc☆/dip☆

Geochemistry
Leeds U MSc

Instrumental chemical analysis
Wolverhampton P MSc△/dip△

Instrumentation & analytical science
Manchester UMIST dip☆

Marine pollution chemistry
Liverpool U dip☆

Mechanical properties of solids
Newcastle U MSc☆

Medicinal chemistry
Loughborough U MSc☆ ☐
Sussex U MSc☆

Modern chemical laboratory practice
Bangor, U of Wales MSc☆/dip☆

Molecular electronics
Cranfield IT MSc☆ _Eng_

Neurochemistry
London U Inst of Ophthalmology MSc☆
London U Inst of Psychiatry MSc☆

New polymer synthesis
Lancaster U MSc☆

Organic petrology & organic geochemistry
Newcastle U MSc☆

Organometallic chemistry
Sussex U MSc☆

Petrochemical & hydrocarbon chemistry
Manchester UMIST MSc☆ ☐

Physical chemistry
East Anglia U MSc☆

Physical organic chemistry
East Anglia U MSc☆

Pure & applied chemistry
Belfast Queen's U dip☆

Radiochemistry, radiation chemistry & nuclear technology
Salford U MSc

Science education
London U King's C MA/MEd△/ dip☆

Sedimentology & its applications
Reading U MSc☆

Silicate & solid state chemistry
Aberdeen U MSc☆

Spectroscopic & physical methods of chemical analysis
East Anglia U MSc☆

Strategies in organic synthesis
Manchester P MSc△/dip△

Surface chemistry & colloids
Bristol U MSc☆ ☐

Surface science & catalysis
Liverpool U MSc☆

Surface science & technology
Loughborough U MSc

Synthesis & synthetic matters
Thames P MSc☆

Synthetic organic chemistry
East Anglia U MSc☆

Higher degrees by research

Agricultural chemistry
Aberdeen U PhD☆/MPhil☆/MSc☆
Edinburgh U PhD/MPhil
Glasgow U PhD/MSc
West of Scotland C PhD☆/MSc☆

Applied chemical sciences
Napier P PhD/MPhil

Applied chemistry
Cardiff U of Wales C PhD☆/ MPhil☆
Coventry P PhD/MPhil

Applied chemistry & life sciences
North London P PhD/MPhil

Applied sciences
Kingston P PhD/MPhil
Staffordshire P PhD/MPhil
Wolverhampton P PhD/MPhil

Biochemistry & chemistry
London U Royal Free Hosp S of Med PhD☆/MPhil☆

Carbon research
Newcastle U MD/MPhil

Chemical & biochemical engineering
London U UC PhD☆/MPhil☆

Chemical & life sciences
Newcastle P PhD☆/MPhil☆

Chemical & physical sciences
Huddersfield P PhD/MPhil

Chemical crystallography
Oxford U DPhil☆/MSc☆

Chemical endocrinology
London U St Bartholomew's
Hosp Med C PhD/MPhil

Chemical engineering & applied chemistry
Aston U PhD/MPhil   Eng

Chemical pathology
Aberdeen U PhD☆/MPhil☆/MSc☆
London U Imperial C PhD☆/
MPhil☆
London U UC PhD☆/MPhil☆
London U Charing Cross &
Westminster Med S PhD/MPhil
London U Royal Postgraduate
Med S PhD☆/MPhil☆
London U St Bartholomew's
Hosp Med C PhD/MPhil
London U St George's Hosp
Med S PhD☆/MPhil☆
London U United Med & Dent S,
Guys's & St Thomas's PhD☆/
MPhil☆

Chemical pathology & human metabolism
London U Royal Free Hosp S of
Med PhD☆/MPhil☆
Southampton U PhD/MPhil

Chemical pathology & immunology
Leeds U PhD/MPhil/MSc

Chemical physics
Glasgow U PhD/MSc

Chemical physics & spectroscopy
Sussex U DPhil/MPhil

Chemical research
London U Royal Holloway &
Bedford New C MSc

Chemical sciences
East Anglia U PhD/MPhil
Hatfield P PhD/MPhil

Chemistry
Aberdeen U PhD☆/MPhil☆/MSc☆
Aberystwyth, UC of Wales
PhD☆/MPhil☆
Aston U PhD/MPhil
Bangor, U of Wales PhD☆/
MPhil☆
Belfast Queen's U PhD/MSc
Birmingham U PhD☆/MSc☆   □
Brighton P PhD/MPhil
Bristol P PhD△/MPhil△/dip△

Bristol U PhD☆/MSc☆
Brunel U PhD/MPhil   □
Cambridge U PhD☆/MSc☆
Cardiff U of Wales C PhD☆/
MPhil☆
City of London P PhD☆/MPhil☆
City U PhD/MPhil
Dundee U PhD/MSc
Durham U PhD/MSc
Edinburgh U PhD/MPhil
Exeter U PhD/MPhil
Glasgow U PhD/MSc
Heriot-Watt U PhD/MPhil   □
Hull U PhD/MSc
Keele U PhD/MSc
Kent U PhD/MPhil/MSc
Kingston P PhD/MPhil
Lancashire P PhD/MPhil
Lancaster U PhD/MPhil
Leeds U PhD/MPhil/MSc
Leicester P PhD/MPhil
Leicester U PhD/MPhil
Liverpool U PhD/MSc
London U Birkbeck C PhD/MPhil
London U Imperial C PhD/MPhil/
dip
London U King's C PhD☆/
MPhil☆/MSc☆
London U Queen Mary &
Westfield C PhD☆/MPhil☆
London U Royal Holloway &
Bedford New C PhD/MPhil
London U UC PhD☆/MPhil☆
Loughborough U PhD☆/MPhil☆
Luton CHE PhD☆/MPhil☆
Manchester P PhD/MPhil
Manchester U PhD/MSc
Manchester UMIST PhD/MSc
Mid Kent CHFE PhD/MPhil
North East Wales IHE PhD☆/
MSc☆
Nottingham U PhD/MPhil
Open U PhD/MPhil/BPhil
Paisley CT PhD/MPhil
Portsmouth P PhD☆/MPhil☆
Reading U PhD/MPhil
Robert Gordon's IT PhD/MPhil
St Andrews U PhD/MSc
Sheffield City P PhD/MPhil
Sheffield U PhD/MPhil
South West P PhD/MPhil
Southampton U PhD/MPhil   □
Staffordshire P PhD/MSc
Stirling U PhD/MSc
Sunderland P PhD/MPhil
Surrey U PhD/MPhil
Swansea UC PhD/MSc
Teesside P PhD☆/MPhil☆
Thames P PhD/MPhil
Ulster U DPhil/MPhil
Warwick U PhD☆/MSc☆

York U DPhil/MPhil/MSc

Chemistry & applied chemistry
Salford U PhD/MSc

Chemistry & biochemistry
Liverpool P PhD/MPhil

Chemistry & biological chemistry
Essex U PhD/MPhil/MSc

Chemistry & chemical technology
Bradford U PhD/MPhil

Chemistry (physical, organic, inorganic)
Bath U PhD☆/MSc☆

Clinical biochemistry
Manchester U PhD/MSc

Clinical chemistry
Birmingham U PhD/MSc
Edinburgh U PhD/MPhil
London U United Med & Dent S,
Guys's & St Thomas's PhD☆/
MPhil☆

Colour chemistry
Leeds U MSc

Colour chemistry & dyeing
Leeds U PhD/MPhil/MSc

Computers & fluids
Salford U PhD☆/MSc☆

Crystallography
London U Birkbeck C PhD/MPhil

Electrochemistry research
Newcastle U PhD/MPhil

Food & agricultural chemistry
Belfast Queen's U PhD/MSc

Food science
Leeds U PhD/MPhil/MSc   □

Immunochemistry
Southampton U PhD/MPhil

Inorganic & structural chemistry
Leeds U PhD/MPhil/MSc

Inorganic chemistry
Bristol U PhD☆/MSc☆
Newcastle U PhD/MPhil
Oxford U DPhil☆/MSc☆

Insect chemistry & physiology
Sussex U DPhil/MPhil

Irreversible processes in solids
Open U PhD/MPhil/BPhil

Main group element chemistry
Sussex U DPhil/MPhil

Materials science & condensed matter research
Keele U PhD/MSc

Metallurgy & engineering materials
Newcastle U PhD/MPhil

Metallurgy & materials science
Nottingham U PhD/MPhil   *Eng*
Sheffield U PhD/MPhil

Molecular dynamics & gas phase kinetics
Sussex U DPhil/MPhil☆

Organic chemistry
Bristol U PhD☆/MSc☆
Leeds U PhD/MPhil
Newcastle U PhD/MPhil
Oxford U DPhil☆/MSc☆

Organic synthesis
Sussex U DPhil/MPhil

Organometallic chemistry
Sussex U DPhil/MPhil

Paper science
Manchester UMIST PhD/MSc

Pharmaceutical chemistry
London U S of Pharmacy PhD☆/ MPhil☆

Pharmaceutical technology
Bradford U PhD/MPhil

Pharmacy & pharmacology
Bath U PhD☆/MSc☆

Photographic sciences
Central London P PhD☆/MPhil☆

Physical chemistry
Bristol U PhD☆/MSc☆
Leeds U PhD/MPhil
Newcastle U PhD/MSc
Oxford U DPhil☆/MSc☆

Physical oceanography
Bangor, U of Wales PhD☆/ MPhil☆

Physical organic & inorganic chemistry
Sussex U DPhil/MPhil

Physical sciences & scientific computing
South Bank P PhD/MPhil

Physiology
London U Royal Veterinary C PhD☆/MPhil☆

Propulsion, power & automotive engineering (gas turbine, wind turbine, automobile)
Cranfield IT PhD☆/MPhil☆

Pure & applied chemistry
Belfast Queen's U PhD☆/MSc☆
Strathclyde U PhD☆/MPhil☆/ MSc☆

Radiation & biophysical chemistry
Newcastle U PhD/MSc

Radiation chemistry
Leeds U PhD/MPhil

Radiation chemistry research
Leeds U PhD/MPhil   □

Science
Bristol P PhD/MPhil
Wales P PhD/MPhil

Structural & surface chemistry
Sussex U DPhil/MPhil

Textile science
Scottish C of Textiles PhD/MPhil

Theoretical chemistry
Bristol U PhD☆/MSc☆
Oxford U DPhil☆/MSc☆
Sussex U DPhil☆/MPhil☆

Thin film & surface research
Salford U PhD/MPhil/MSc

Transition metal chemistry
Sussex U DPhil/MPhil

Food science, dietetics

Higher degrees by instruction

Agricultural science
Belfast Queen's U dip☆

Animal nutrition
Aberdeen U MSc☆/dip☆

Brewing & distilling
Heriot-Watt U MSc☆/dip☆

Brewing science
Birmingham U MSc☆

Clinical pharmacy
Belfast Queen's U dip△

Dietetics
Leeds P dip☆
London U King's C dip☆
Queen's C Glasgow dip☆   □

Food & agricultural biotechnology
Reading U MSc☆

Food & management science
London U King's C MSc☆

Food analysis & composition
South Bank P MSc△

Food biotechnology
Strathclyde U MSc☆

Food composition & processing
Strathclyde U dip☆

Food policy & commodity trade
Swansea UC MSc(Econ)☆

Food resources related to community development
London U King's C dip☆

Food science
Belfast Queen's U dip☆
Leeds U MSc☆/dip☆   □
North East Wales IHE MSc
Reading U MSc☆

Food technology
Reading U MSc☆

Food technology in developing countries
London U King's C MSc☆

Human nutrition
Aberdeen U MSc☆/dip☆
London U S of Hygiene & Tropical Med MSc☆/dip☆

Meat science
Bristol U MSc☆
Nottingham U MSc☆

Nutrition
Glasgow U MSc(MedSci)
London U King's C MSc☆/dip☆

Nutritional biochemistry
Nottingham U MSc☆

Post harvest technology
Humberside CHE dip☆

Higher degrees by research

Animal nutriton
Belfast Queen's U PhD/MSc

Applied biochemistry & food science
Nottingham U PhD/MPhil

Applied biology & food science
South Bank P PhD/MPhil

Applied science
Leeds P PhD/MPhil/dip

Baking
South Bank P PhD/MPhil

Biochemistry
Southampton U PhD/MPhil

Bioscience & biotechnology
Strathclyde U PhD☆/MPhil☆/ MSc☆   *Biol*

Brewing & biological sciences
Heriot-Watt U PhD☆/MPhil☆

Catering
Middlesex P PhD/MPhil

Catering & home economics
Anglia HEC PhD☆/MPhil☆

Dairy technology
West of Scotland C PhD☆/MSc☆

Food & accommodation studies
North London P PhD/MPhil

Food & agricultural chemistry
Belfast Queen's U PhD/MSc

Food & tourism management
Sheffield City P PhD/MPhil

Food chemistry & biochemistry
Belfast Queen's U PhD/MSc

Food manufacture & distribution
Manchester P PhD/MPhil

Food marketing
Newcastle U PhD☆/MPhil☆

Food nutritional sciences
London U King's C PhD☆/MPhil☆

Food science
Leeds U PhD/MPhil/MSc   □
Reading U PhD/MPhil
Strathclyde U PhD☆/MPhil☆

Food science & agricultural microbiology
Belfast Queen's U PhD/MSc

Food science & dietetics
Queen's C Glasgow PhD/MPhil
Silsoe C PhD/MPhil

Food studies
Humberside CHE PhD/MPhil

Food technology
Reading U PhD/MPhil
Silsoe C PhD☆/MPhil☆

Home economics
Liverpool P PhD/MPhil
Manchester P PhD/MPhil
Robert Gordon's IT PhD/MPhil
Worcester CHE PhD/MPhil

Home economics & consumer studies
South Bank P PhD/MPhil

Home economics & institutional management
Cardiff U of Wales C PhD☆/ MPhil☆

Hotel, catering & food studies
Oxford P PhD/MPhil

Human nutrition
London U S of Hygiene & Tropical Med PhD/MPhil
Ulster U DPhil/MPhil

Malting & brewing
Birmingham U PhD/MSc

Meat science
Bristol U MSc☆

Nutrition
Glasgow U PhD/MSc(MedSci)
Southampton U PhD/MPhil

Nutritional science
Queen's C Glasgow PhD/MPhil
Robert Gordon's IT PhD/MPhil

Pharmacy, pharmacology

Higher degrees by instruction

Biochemical pharmacology
Southampton U MSc☆

Biopharmacy
London U King's C MSc

Clinical pharmacology
Aberdeen U MSc☆/dip☆
Glasgow U MSc(MedSci)
London U St Bartholomew's Hosp Med C dip☆

Clinical pharmacy
Belfast Queen's U dip△
Bradford U MPharm
London U S of Pharmacy MSc☆
Newcastle U dip☆
Strathclyde U MSc

Clinical pharmacy practice
Nottingham U dip△

Medicinal chemistry
Loughborough U MSc☆   □

Neuropharmacology
Bristol U MSc☆

Pharmaceutical analysis
Strathclyde U MSc☆/dip☆

Pharmaceutical analysis & quality control
London U King's C MSc

Pharmaceutical engineering
Teesside P BEng☆

Pharmaceutical sciences
Cardiff U of Wales C MSc☆
London U King's C cert☆
Sunderland P MSc△

Pharmaceutical technology
London U King's C MSc

Pharmacological biochemistry
Hatfield P MSc△

Pharmacology
Bradford U MSc☆
Cambridge U MPhil☆
East London P MSc△/dip△
London U King's C MSc☆
Manchester U MSc/dip☆

Strathclyde U MSc/dip☆

Quality assurance
Sunderland P dip△

Toxicology
Birmingham U MSc/dip☆   *Biol*
Surrey U MSc   *Biol*

Higher degrees by research

Analytical pharmacology
London U King's C S of Med & Dentistry PhD☆/MPhil☆

Biological sciences
Salford U PhD/MSc

Chemical & physical sciences
Huddersfield P PhD/MPhil

Chemistry
London U UC PhD☆/MPhil☆

Clinical pharmacology
London U Royal Postgraduate Med S PhD☆/MPhil☆
London U St Bartholomew's Hosp Med C PhD/MPhil
London U United Med & Dent S, Guys's & St Thomas's PhD☆/ MPhil☆
Oxford U DPhil☆/MSc☆

Clinical pharmacology & therapeutics
London U Imperial C PhD☆/ MPhil☆
London U Charing Cross & Westminster Med S PhD/MPhil

General pharmaceutics
London U S of Pharmacy PhD☆/ MPhil☆

Materia medica & therapeutics
Manchester U PhD/MSc

Pharmaceutical chemistry
London U S of Pharmacy PhD☆/ MPhil☆

Pharmaceutical engineering science
London U S of Pharmacy PhD☆/ MPhil☆

Pharmaceutical sciences
Aston U PhD/MPhil
Nottingham U PhD/MPhil
Sunderland P PhD/MPhil

Pharmaceutical technology
Bradford U PhD/MPhil

Pharmacognosy
London U S of Pharmacy PhD☆/ MPhil☆

Pharmacological sciences
Newcastle U PhD/MD/MSc

Pharmacology
Aberdeen U PhD☆/MPhil☆/MSc☆
Birmingham U PhD/MSc
Bradford U PhD/MPhil
Bristol U PhD☆/MSc☆
Cambridge U PhD☆
Edinburgh U PhD/MPhil
Glasgow U PhD/MSc
Leeds U PhD/MPhil/MSc
London U Imperial C PhD☆/
  MPhil☆
London U Inst of Psychiatry
  PhD☆/MPhil☆
London U King's C PhD☆/MPhil☆
London U Royal Veterinary C
  PhD☆/MPhil☆
London U S of Pharmacy PhD☆/
  MPhil☆
London U UC PhD☆/MPhil☆
London U Charing Cross &
  Westminster Med S PhD/MPhil
London U Royal Free Hosp S of
  Med PhD☆/MPhil☆
London U St Bartholomew's
  Hosp Med C PhD/MPhil
London U United Med & Dent S,
  Guys's & St Thomas's PhD☆/
  MPhil☆
PhD☆/MPhil☆
Manchester U PhD/MSc/dip
Oxford U DPhil☆/MSc☆

**Pharmacology & clinical
pharmacology**
Dundee U PhD/MSc
London U St George's Hosp
  Med S PhD☆/MPhil☆
Southampton U PhD/MPhil

Pharmacology & therapeutics
Leicester U PhD/MD/MPhil
Liverpool U PhD/MSc
London U London Hosp Med C
  PhD☆/MPhil☆
Sheffield U PhD/MMedSci
Wales U C of Med PhD☆/MSc☆

Pharmacy
Belfast Queen's U PhD/MSc
Bradford U PhD/MPhil
Brighton P PhD/MPhil
Cardiff U of Wales C PhD☆/
  MPhil☆
Leicester P PhD/MPhil
Liverpool P PhD/MPhil
London U King's C PhD☆/MPhil☆
London U Royal Postgraduate
  Med S PhD☆/MPhil☆
Manchester U PhD/MSc
Robert Gordon's IT PhD/MPhil

Strathclyde U PhD☆/MPhil☆/
  MSc☆

**Pharmacy & biomedical
sciences**
Portsmouth P PhD☆/MPhil☆

Pharmacy & pharmacology
Bath U PhD☆/MSc☆

Physiology
PhD☆/MPhil☆

Physiology & pharmacology
Nottingham U PhD/MPhil
St Andrews U PhD/MSc
Southampton U PhD/MPhil
Strathclyde U PhD☆/MPhil☆/
  MSc☆

Science
Bristol P PhD/MPhil

**Therapeutics & clinical
pharmacology**
Aberdeen U PhD☆/MPhil☆
Birmingham U PhD/MSc
Edinburgh U PhD/MPhil

Therapeutics & pharmacology
Belfast Queen's U PhD

Toxicology
Birmingham U PhD☆/MSc☆

Veterinary pharmacology
Edinburgh U PhD/MPhil
Liverpool U PhD/MVSc

Polymer science and technology

Higher degrees by instruction

Advanced materials technology
Surrey U MSc/dip

Applied polymer science
Manchester P MSc☆
Manchester U MSc☆/dip☆

Biochemical engineering
Swansea UC MSc☆

Chemical engineering
Swansea UC MSc☆/dip☆

Clinical pharmacy
Belfast Queen's U dip△

Clothing technology
Leeds U dip☆

Colour chemistry
Leeds U MSc☆

Materials engineering
Loughborough U MSc   *Eng*

Membrane technology
Glasgow U MSc☆/dip☆   *Phy*

New polymer synthesis
Lancaster U MSc☆

Plastics & rubber technology
North London P ALSPT/PRI

Plastics technology
Ulster U dip△

Polymer engineering
Cranfield IT MSc☆   □
Manchester P dip△
Manchester UMIST MSc☆/dip☆
Ulster U MSc△/dip△

Polymer science & engineering
Ulster U MSc☆

Polymer science & technology
Manchester UMIST MSc☆/dip☆
North London P MSc

Polymer technology
Loughborough U MSc/dip△   □

Surface chemistry & colloids
Bristol U MSc☆   □

Synthesis & synthetic methods
Nottingham P MSc

Textile industries
Leeds U dip☆

Textile science & engineering
Leeds U MSc☆

Textile technology
Manchester UMIST MSc/dip

Higher degrees by research

Applied chemical sciences
Napier P PhD/MPhil

Applied chemistry
Cardiff U of Wales C PhD☆/
  MPhil☆

**Applied chemistry & life
sciences**
North London P PhD/MPhil

Ceramics, glasses & polymers
Sheffield U PhD/MPhil

Chemical & physical sciences
Huddersfield P PhD/MPhil

Chemical engineering
Loughborough U PhD☆/MPhil☆

Chemistry
Birmingham U PhD☆/MSc☆   □
Exeter U PhD/MPhil

Heriot-Watt U PhD/MPhil □
Lancaster U PhD/MPhil
Liverpool U PhD/MSc
Southampton U PhD/MPhil☆ □

Fibre science
Leeds U PhD/MPhil/MSc

Materials science
Bath U PhD☆/MPhil☆   Eng

Metallurgy & materials science
Liverpool U PhD/MSc(Eng)

Molecular dynamics & gas phase kinetics
Sussex U DPhil/MPhil

Polymer chemistry
Lancaster U PhD/MPhil   □

Polymer chemistry & technology
Cardiff U of Wales C PhD☆/
MPhil☆

Polymer engineering
Cranfield IT PhD☆/MPhil☆/MSc☆

Polymer science
Sussex U DPhil/MPhil

Polymer science & technology
Manchester UMIST PhD/MSc

Polymer technology
Loughborough U PhD☆/MPhil☆
North London P PhD/MPhil

Textile industries
Leeds U PhD/MPhil/MSc(Eng)

Transition metal chemistry
Sussex U DPhil/MPhil

Advanced chemical technology

MSc
1 year full time
20 places
Dr B L Booth, Postgraduate Admissions Tutor, Department of Chemistry, UMIST - The University of Manchester Institute of Science and Technology, PO Box 88, Manchester M60 1QD
Tel: 061 236 3311

This course, designed for students seeking a career in chemical manufacture, contains lectures on chemical processing, industrial safety, thermodynamics, industrial analysis, catalysis, computation, and chemical engineering. Formal practical work and pilot plant projects are carried out during the first two terms and a full time research project during May to September.
Entrance requirements Honours degree or equivalent.
Reader Dr B L Booth.

Analytical chemistry

MSc (Modular)
1 year full time
2-3 years part time
Dr P J Baugh, Department of Chemistry & Applied Chemistry, University of Salford, The Crescent, Salford M5 4WT
Tel: 061 745 5000

The MSc programme is assessed by examination, practical work and research project. The modules available include atomic/molecular spectroscopy, separation science and chromatography, electrochemistry and classical methods of analysis. Under this programme it may also be possible to select options in petroleum analysis, thermal methods and radio chemistry. A course approved for exemption from part A of MChem A, part time and full time.
Entrance requirements A degree or equivalent qualification in a science subject or a preparatory course requirement.
Chairman of department Professor E Wyn-Jones.

Analytical chemistry & instrumentation

MSc
1 year full time
20 places
Dr T E Edmonds, Chemistry Department, Loughborough University of Technology, Loughborough, Leicestershire LE11 3TU
Tel: 0509 222576

Reliable information about the chemical composition of materials underpins successful manufacturing processes, medical diagnoses, environmental monitoring, consumer protection and, even, interplanetary exploration. Modern analytical chemistry combines reaction chemistry, quantitative physico-chemical phenomena, statistics, computing and information technology into a powerful set of methods for solving analytical problems. The course covers all these topics as well as automation and applications. Two terms of formal course work precede a supervised research project.
Entrance requirements Honours degree in chemistry or related topic.

Chemical engineering

PhD/MPhil
full time
and part time
MSc in Process and project
engineering
1 year full time
The Postgraduate
Admissions Tutor,
Department of Chemical
Engineering, University of
Nottingham, University Park,
Nottingham NG7 2RD
Tel: 0602 484848

Chemical engineers or industrially aware chemistry, maths, physics, engineering or bio-science graduates are invited to apply for research in: biochemical engineering, computer aids (plant layout, batch processing, expert systems), coal processing (liquefaction, catalyst deactivation), environment (acid gas removal, air classified waste recycling), fluids/particles (gas/liquid or solids flow, prilling, electrostatic precipitation), patents, process control (integrated use of measurements, pH, batch systems), process development (economic trade off in design, crystals by ammonia addition), separation processes (distillation design and efficiency, solids elutriation, low energy ethanol recovery). The MSc course covers modern process/project engineering (including computer aids) through lectures and project work.

Entrance requirements PhD/MPhil: good honours degree in a listed discipline. MSc: good honours degree normally in chemical engineering. Satisfactory scores in either the TOEFL or British Council ELTS language tests required where English has not been the medium of previous education.

Grants SERC and others possible for research.

Chemistry

PhD
3 years full time
5 years part time
MSc
min 1 year full time
Dr W B Jennings,
Postgraduate Tutor, School
of Chemistry, University of
Birmingham, Edgbaston,
Birmingham B15 2TT
Tel: 021 414 4360

Research in the following areas of chemistry: gas phase laser photochemistry, reaction dynamics and high resolution spectroscopy; synthesis and characterisation of polymers; co-ordination chemistry and non-linear optical properties; molecular recognition; solid state inorganic chemistry and superconductivity; chemistry of nucleosides, nucleotides and anti-viral agents; organofluorine chemistry; carbohydrate and protein chemistry.

Entrance requirements Honours degree in chemistry or equivalent.

Grants SERC, CASE, EEC, Industrial.

Head of School Professor I W M Smith.

Chemistry

PhD
2 or 3 years full time
4 years part time
MSc
1 year full time
2 years part time
Dr P N Preston, Department
of Chemistry, Heriot-Watt
University, Riccarton,
Edinburgh EH14 4AS

Topics can be selected in the following areas: *Polymer chemistry* including synthesis and physiochemical studies of new materials for use in liquid crystals, resin composites and polymer electrolytes. *Chemical synthesis* . A variety of projects in organic, inorganic and organometallic chemistry including new routes to biologically-active compounds, novel metal-containing catalysts and polymer bound coordination complexes. *Reaction dynamics* with special regard to laser-induced fluorescence, spectroscopy, and ion-molecule reactions. *Solid state chemistry* Preparation of novel intercalation compounds for advanced battery sources; chemistry and physics of laser depostion of amorphous silicon and diamond. *Coal chemistry* directed towards the mechanism of coal liquification.

Chemistry

PhD
3 years full time
4 years part time
MPhil
1 year full time
Dr J M Mellor, Department of Chemsitry, University of Southampton, The University, Southampton SO9 5NH
Tel: 0703 595000

Research in all branches of chemistry including analytical chemistry, bioorganic and bioinorganic chemistry, computer modelling, coordination and organometallic chemistry, electrochemistry, kinetics, organic synthesis, photochemistry, polymers including biopolymers, properties of liquid crystals, research into catalysts, semiconductor chemistry, solid state and surface chemistry , spectroscopy including magnetic resonance and lasers, and structural chemistry.
Entrance requirements Honours degree in chemistry or equivalent.
Grants SERC, NERC, CASE, industrial.
Head of department Professor G R Luckhurst.

Dietetics

dip
2 years full time
Mr J Bance, Recruitment & Publicity Officer, The Queen's College, Glasgow, 1 Park Drive, Glasgow G3 6LP
Tel: 041 334 8141

This course deals with the science of how both ill and healthy people eat and entrants should have scientific interests and aptitudes together with an interest in medicine. Entrants should also have an interest in food, menu planning, food preparation, cooking and meal budgeting for different groups and be interested in people as individuals. Most UK dieticians are employed in the National Health Service. However a number, particularly with postgraduate research experience, teach in universities and colleges or are employed as advisers in the development of food products. Opportunities exist with the Medical Research Council, government departments and private industry. The course consists of core studies in nutrition and diet therapy together with physiology and biochemistry with support studies in behavioural studies, management, food science and catering. The course includes 6 weeks catering placement and 31 weeks practical dietetic placement.
Entrance requirements The course is open to UK and overseas entrants who, essentially, will have a science degree which includes a substantial study of biochemistry and physiology. A competent command of the English language is essential.
Grants Students are eligible to apply for student allowances from the appropriate Local Authorities.
Head of School Mr A Gardner.

Food science

PhD
3 years full time
12 places
MPhil
2 years full time
12 places
MSc
1 year full time
Head of Department, Procter Department of Food Science, University of Leeds, Leeds LS2 9JT
Tel: 0532 334005

Research is concerned with the application of basic sciences to problems in food science and food biotechnology. Specific areas include both fundamental and applied chemical, biochemical and physical studies on protein, carbohydrates and fats, food enzymes, food additives, food analysis, food engineering, colloidal structure and rheology.
Entrance requirements First or upper second class honours degree in biochemistry, biological science, chemistry, chemical physics, chemical engineering, maths, physics or related science.
Grants AFRC Studentships, MAFF Studentships, Industrial Support.
Head of department Professor David S Robinson.

Food science

MSc
1 year full time
18 places
dip
1 year full time
Head of Department, Procter
Department of Food
Science, University of Leeds,
Leeds LS2 9JT
Tel: 0532 334005

This course provides a route whereby graduates in related disciplines: chemistry, biochemistry, other biological sciences or chemical engineering, may be trained as food scientists. The course includes lectures, tutorials, laboratory studies and individual research projects, sometimes in collaboration with industry.
Entrance requirements First or good second class honours degree.
Grants AFRC studentships.
Head of department Professor David S Robinson.

Medicinal chemistry and drug metabolism

MSc
1 year full time
16 places
Dr W G Salt, Chemistry
Department, Loughborough
University of Technology,
Loughborough,
Leicestershire LE11 3TU
Tel: 0509 222582

Medicinal chemistry may now be considered a discipline in its own right and concerns itself with the understanding of the chemical and biological mechanisms by which both natural and synthetic drug action can be explained. It includes aspects of the synthesis, computer aided design, formulation, manufacture and marketing of drugs and involves collaborative studies of chemistry, biochemistry, pharmacology, pharmaceutics, pharmacokinetics and microbiology. Pharmaceutical companies participate in teaching. Following six months of formal course work, each student undertakes a supervised research project.
Entrance requirements Degree in chemistry or related subjects.
Head of department Professor J N Miller.

Petrochemicals & hydrocarbon chemistry

MSc
1 year full time
20 places
Dr B L Booth, Postgraduate
Admissions Tutor,
Department of Chemistry,
UMIST - The University of
Manchester Institute of
Science and Technology, PO
Box 88, Manchester M60
1QD
Tel: 061 236 3311

This course involves lectures in large scale chemical processing, analytical methods, safety, catalysis, thermodynamics, oil refining, economic factors, and the mechanisms of important industrial reactions; formal practical work is carried out in the first two terms and a full time research project during May to September.
Entrance requirements Honours degree or equivalent.
Reader Dr B L Booth.

Polymer engineering

PhD 3 years
MSc
1 year full time
15 places
Dr J P Chubb, School of
Industrial Science, Cranfield
Institute of Technology,
Cranfield, Bedford MK43
0AL
Tel: 0234 750111

The MSc course is designed for engineers and scientists who wish to enter industry. An industrially relevant research project is a major part of the course and is supplemented by a lecture programme covering the structure and properties of polymers, and a management module. Visiting specialists from industry and a high level of contract research maintain industrial relevance.
Entrance requirements Good honours degree or equivalent.
Grants SERC advanced course studentships, bursaries.
Professor of Polymer Science Professor C B Bucknall.

Polymer science

PhD
3-4 years full time
MPhil
1-2 years full time
MSc
1 year full time
Dr D J Hourston, Director,
The Polymer Centre,
Lancaster University,
Lancaster LA1 4YA
Tel: 0524 65201 ext 3357
Fax: 0524 844037

This acknowledged centre of excellence in polymer science can offer PhD and MPhil projects in many areas of the subject eg reactive polymers, polymer modification, polymer blends and networks, polymer latices, polymers for optical and electronic uses, polymer membranes, copolymerisation, polymer photophysics and photochemistry, spectroscopy of polymers and oligomer synthesis. A one year MSc course in Polymer Science: Synthesis and Technology includes training in all aspects of polymer science and an industrially-based project.
Entrance requirements Good honours degree or equivalent.
Grants SERC quota, CASE and Advanced Course plus industrial support normally available.

Polymer technology

MSc
1 year full time
3 years part time
24 places
diploma
2 years part time
Admissions Tutor, Institute
of Polymer Technology and
Materials Engineering,
Loughborough University of
Technology, Loughborough,
Leicestershire LE11 3TU
Tel: 0509 223330

The course is designed to be an integrated approach to the science and technology of plastics and elastomers, and aims to provide training for the polymer materials and processing industries. Teaching is by lectures, tutorials and practical work. Three major options are available in the areas of polymer materials, polymer process engineering, and polymer surfaces and interfaces. An important part of the course is a major project in collaboration with industry, with opportunities to probably carry out work in France, Belgium or the USA (along with enhancement to any grant).
Entrance requirements Degree or equivalent in science, technology or engineering.
Grants SERC advanced course studentships available.
Head of department Dr D Gabe.

Radiation chemistry

PhD
3 years full time
part time
MPhil
2 years full time
part time
The Director, Cookridge
Radiation Research Centre,
University of Leeds,
Cookridge Hospital, Leeds
LS16 6QB
Tel: 0532 672511

Research is into the processes that occur when chemical systems are irradiated with ionising radiation, with emphasis on the nature and reactivity of the intermediates which are formed on irradiation. Radiation chemical methods provide a convenient means of studying the reactions of a wide range of radicals which are involved in many areas of chemistry. We are currently employing these techniques in studies of Acid Rain formation and chemistry relevant to nuclear reactor technology.
Entrance requirements Good honours degree or other equivalent in chemistry, chemical physics or physics.
Grants SERC studentships, industrially supported studentships, university scholarships.
Head of department Dr G A Salmon.

2 POSTGRADUATE OPPORTUNITIES

Science of advanced materials

MSc/dip
1 year full time
2 years part time
Dr C R Theocharis,
Department of Chemistry,
Brunel University, Uxbridge,
Middlesex UB8 3AT
Tel: 0895 74000

The course aims to provide specialist training in the synthesis, purification, identification and characterisation of modern bio-materials and solid state compounds, and in the determination of their molecular properties. It is suitable for graduates with honours degrees in chemistry, physics or materials science. One of the unique characteristics of this course is its modular format. All students take core modules in computing and methods of synthesis, purification, theoretical aspects and characterisation of advanced materials. They can then choose to take 3 optional modules from 6 offered. The option modules include: molecular materials with electronic properties; spectroscopy; diffraction techniques; advanced analytical techniques; catalyst; biological chemistry. Emphasis is placed on both theory and practice.
Entrance requirements First or second class honours degree in Chemistry, Physics or Materials Science.
Course directors Dr C C Perry or Dr C R Theocharis.

Surface chemistry & colloids

MSc
1 year full time
15 places
Dr S D Lubetkin, School of
Chemistry, University of
Bristol, Bristol BS8 1TS
Tel: 0272 303672 or
Secretary 303030 ext 4713

The course is intended to provide a broad background in surfaces, colloids and polymer science as a preparation for research in industry or academia. Teaching is initially by lectures and practicals and is then followed by a five month research project.
Entrance requirements Degree or equivalent in science, technology or pharmacy.
Grants SERC advanced course studentships, plus industrial studentships.
Head of department Professor R H Ottewill OBE FRS.

Mathematics

Postgraduate studies in mathematics are exciting: the ready availability of computational power and information processing provide a stimulating environment for both further study and careers. It is therefore very difficult to decide to take up a postgraduate study in mathematics. Before committing yourself to such a course of action you need to weigh up carefully your career objectives. There is a wide variety of opportunities for graduate mathematicians. Currently, employment in a wide range of jobs is relatively easy and is not necessarily enhanced by a further qualification. Competition for postgraduate grants is intense and you need to have a 2i or a first class degree to have a realistic chance of success.

However, the interest in postgraduates has generated an increasing level of industrial bursaries and it is worth investigating such possibilities either directly with companies or at your chosen institution.

Choosing a course

There are three different aims which you need to consider. Do you want a higher degree by research? You will need to have a strong desire to make a contribution to some specialised area of mathematics if you do. This will build on specialisations you have chosen in your first degree and in which you have already shown a particular flair. It is usually advisable to consult your lecturers in that area. By following up their suggestions you will be able to identify departments which you should contact. It is best to visit the institutions and discuss your interests with staff who may be willing to supervise such work. They will be interested in excellence.

Do you want to further your knowledge of an aspect of maths which you found fascinating in your first degree? In this case you should look for one of the MSc taught courses. If you look through the list included on the next few pages you can identify some likely courses. All departments will send you details of what is on offer and it is useful to discuss this with staff who lecture on your present degree course. If there are vacancies then you will find the course organisers will interview you, and you will have the opportunity to see if what is on offer will satisfy your thirst for more knowledge.

Finally you may want to broaden your expertise to give you a wider perspective. More than half the courses listed provide this opportunity. Although they expect competence in mathematics they enlarge the repertoire by specialising in subjects like statistics, computing, and operational research, or by focussing on specific applications, such as economics, physics, engineering, medicine or sociology.

The motivation for this choice is often vocational and you should therefore ask the departments concerned for details of the job placements of previous years' students.

IMPERIAL COLLEGE

MATHEMATICS DEPARTMENT

Postgraduate Studies 1991-92

ONE-YEAR COURSES
MSc

* Pure Mathematics
* Applied Mathematics
  & Numerical Analysis
* Computational Fluid Dynamics
  & Structural Mechanics

POSTGRADUATE
QUALIFYING YEAR

* Associate Diploma
  in Mathematics

RESEARCH DEGREES
MPhil, leading to PhD

* Pure Mathematics
* Statistics
* Applied Mathematics
* Numerical Analysis
* Mathematical Physics

ENQUIRIES & APPLICATIONS
Tutor to Graduate Students
Mathematics Department
Imperial College
London SW7 2BZ
England

UNIVERSITY OF SOUTHAMPTON
Faculty of Mathematical Studies

The following postgraduate opportunities are available in the Faculty.

CERTIFICATE COURSE IN STATISTICS The main purpose of this course is to prepare the students for further studies. The duration of the course is 9 months.

MSc/DIPLOMA COURSES The duration of an MSc course is 12 months. Courses available are:

(1) **Applied Mathematics and Theoretical Physics** Requires a background in quantum mechanics and special relativity.

(2) **Statistics with Applications in Medicine** Requires a knowledge of probability theory and statistical methods, or good mathematics honours.

(3) **Operational Research** Requires a good knowledge of mathematical methods.

M Phil/PhD DEGREES. The activities of the Faculty include: Applied and Industrial Mathematics, Mathematics Education, Operational Research, Pure Mathematics and Statistics. Research, leading to the award of MPhil and PhD degrees, may be undertaken in any of these areas. Illustrative examples are Fluid Mechanics, Solid Mechanics, Theory of Liquids, Group Theoretical Methods in Physics, Relativity, Antenna Design, Numerical Analysis, Optimisation, Linear and Integer Programming, Scheduling, OR in Health, Production Planning, Group Theory, Combinatorics, Dynamical Systems, Geometry, Topology, Experimental Design, Survey Sampling.

FURTHER INFORMATION (INCLUDING OPPORTUNITIES FOR PART TIME STUDY) FROM:

The Administrative Secretary, Faculty of Mathematical Studies, The University, Southampton, England SO9 5NH.

All departments have this information as they are required to provide it to the Science and Engineering Research Council (SERC) when seeking approval for student grants.

Career prospects

The career prospects for mathematicians are very good, providing you are prepared to use your skills in applied areas. However, most careers now involve using a computer. Jobs which involve only mathematics are very hard to find, except in education. Many mathematicians find opportunities in the rapidly expanding field of computing, and recent developments in software engineering, and knowledge-based systems have increased the demand for skills in pure mathematics. The more traditional applied fields in science and engineering continue to want applied mathematicians, though they increasingly involve extensive use of very powerful computing facilities. These are often research facilities in areas such as atomic physics, aeronautics and industrial control and automation.

The business field is increasingly interested in using advanced mathematical and statistical skills in areas frequently covered by operational research and management science. Often students with these areas of specialism take additional qualifications in accounting and enter the field of finance.

Career openings

There are career opportunities in the field of statistics, but again, the main thrust is in applied areas such as business, medicine and agriculture. These openings are very satisfying but involve an enthusiasm for another discipline, as well as willingness to.

work with other specialists in a research team.

In all these career fields considerable emphasis is placed on the ability of graduates to communicate. It is not enough to be numerate - you must be able to present your findings in oral or written form, in terms easily understood by management.

The great shortage of people with information technology (IT) skills has led to the provision of a range of MSc programmes designed to convert graduates from a wide range of disciplines into the IT profession. Maths graduates are especially welcome and the growing use of mathematical techniques in software engineering makes such opportunities a viable alternative to careers in applied mathematics. As with other courses, you should make a careful choice so that you apply for courses which will suit your needs.

Education

It may be that you wish to follow a career in education. For a job as a lecturer you will certainly need a higher degree but you need to carefully consider what work experience would also be relevant.

It is often a good idea to have some work experience before pursuing a higher degree, especially if a job opportunity in a relevant area is available. In secondary education you will be especially welcome as there is a desperate shortage of qualified mathematics teachers. You would be well advised to do a PGCE which involves teaching practice. There are now special bursaries available which enhance the normal grant to encourage you to follow this route. The experience of working in a school classroom is very valuable as some graduates find the teaching role rather more difficult than they expect. A realisation of the

different stresses involved may alter your career plan.

Donald Conway

This listing contains **taught courses** (under the heading 'Higher degrees by instruction') and **research opportunities** (under the heading 'Higher degrees by research'). All study exceeds two terms or six months and is offered on both a full-time and part-time basis unless otherwise indicated. Post-experience and in-service courses are only included when advertised.

☐ This symbol indicates that the **taught course(s)** or **research opportunities** are advertised at the end of this listing.

Biol An italic abbreviation indicates that an advertisement has been placed at the end of another chapter.

☆ This symbol indicates full-time study only.

△ This symbol indicates part-time study only.

For quick reference to advertisements, please use the 'Advertiser's course entry index'. For further information regarding the listing, please refer to page 53.

General

Higher degrees by instruction

Actuarial science
City U dip☆

Advanced methods in computer science
London U Queen Mary & Westfield C MSc☆

Analysis & partial differential equations
Sussex U MSc☆

Applied mathematics
Essex U MSc☆/dip☆

Exeter U MSc☆

Engineering mathematics
Newcastle U MSc☆/cert☆

Engineering surveying & geodesy
Nottingham U MSc☆

Geophysics
Durham U MSc☆

History & philosophy of science & mathematics
London U King's C MSc

Independent study
East London P MA/MSc/dip

Industrial mathematics
Strathclyde U MSc☆/dip☆

Mathematical sciences
Durham U MSc☆

Mathematical statistics
Exeter U MSc☆

Mathematics
Bangor, U of Wales MSc☆/dip☆
Hull U dip☆ ☐
London U Imperial C dip☆

Numerical analysis
Brunel U MSc ☐

Order & chaos
London U Imperial C MSc/dip

Pure mathematics
Bangor, U of Wales MSc☆/dip☆
Exeter U MSc☆/dip☆
Hull U dip ☐
Leeds U MSc

Quantum fields & fundamental forces
London U Imperial C MSc/ dip *Phy*

Higher degrees by research

Applied mathematics
East Anglia U PhD/MPhil
Exeter U PhD☆

Chemical engineering
Nottingham U PhD/MPhil   *Chem*

Computational fluid dynamics
London U Imperial C PhD/MPhil/
dip

Control systems
Manchester UMIST PhD/MSc

Independent study
East London P PhD/MPhil

Mathematical sciences
Exeter U PhD/MPhil
London U Queen Mary &
Westfield C PhD☆/MPhil☆

Mathematics
Dundee U PhD△/MSc
Heriot-Watt U PhD☆/MPhil☆
Hull U PhD   □
Keele U PhD/MSc
London U UC PhD☆/MPhil☆

Neural networks
Manchester UMIST PhD/MSc

Parallel distributed processing
Manchester UMIST PhD/MSc

Pure & applied mathematics
Exeter U PhD☆/MPhil☆

Pure mathematics
East Anglia U PhD/MPhil

Science, mathematics & computing
Cheltenham & Gloucester CHE
PhD/MPhil

Mathematics

Higher degrees by instruction

Actuarial science
City U dip☆

Advanced study in mathematics
Cambridge U cert☆

Applied mathematics
Aberystwyth, UC of Wales
MSc☆/dip☆

Bangor, U of Wales MSc☆/dip☆
Essex U MSc☆/dip☆
Exeter U MSc☆
London U Royal Holloway &
Bedford New C MSc
Reading U MSc☆
St Andrews U MSc

Applied mathematics & fluid mechanics
Manchester U MSc☆

Applied mathematics & theoretical physics
Southampton U MSc/dip

Applied stochastic science
London U UC MSc

Astrophysics
London U Queen Mary &
Westfield C MSc/dip

Control & information technology
Manchester UMIST MSc☆/
dip☆   *Eng*

Econometrics & mathematical economics
London U LSE MSc

Economic statistics & national accounts
East Anglia U dip☆

Elementary particle theory
Durham U MSc

Engineering mathematics
Newcastle U MSc☆/cert☆

Industrial mathematics
Glasgow C MSc☆/dip☆
Strathclyde U MSc☆/dip☆

Mathematical biology
Dundee U MSc☆

Mathematical computation
London U Queen Mary &
Westfield C MSc

Mathematical education
Edinburgh U MSc/dip
Roehampton I dip☆

Mathematical education & mathematics
Leeds U MSc△

Mathematical logic & the foundations of computer science
Manchester U MSc☆

Mathematical logic & the theory of computation
Bristol U MSc☆

Mathematical modelling
Royal Military C of Science
MSc△

Mathematical modelling & computer simulation
Coventry P MSc△/dip△
Sunderland P MSc△

Mathematical modelling & numerical analysis
Oxford U MSc☆

Mathematical modelling of material behaviour
Strathclyde U MSc☆/dip☆

Mathematical physics
London U Imperial C MSc/dip

Mathematical sciences
Aberdeen U dip☆
Durham U MSc☆
Salford U MSc△

Mathematical statistics
Exeter U MSc☆
Manchester U MSc☆/dip☆

Mathematical studies
Liverpool U MSc☆/dip☆
Ulster U cert△

Mathematical techniques & their applications
Newcastle U MSc

Mathematical, statistical & computing education
London U Inst of Education MSc

Mathematics
Aberdeen U MSc☆/dip☆
Bangor, U of Wales MSc☆/dip☆
Dundee U dip☆
Essex U cert☆
Glasgow U dip
Heriot-Watt U cert☆
Hull U dip☆   □
Lancaster U MSc☆/dip☆
Leicester P dip☆
London U Imperial C dip☆
London U King's C MSc/dip☆
London U LSE MSc
Nottingham U MSc/dip
Open U MSc△
St Andrews U dip☆
Sussex U MSc☆
Warwick U MSc
York U MSc☆

Mathematics applied to physical science
Heriot-Watt U MSc☆

Mathematics education
London U King's C MA/MEd△
Southampton U cert☆

Mathematics of modern control systems
Loughborough U MSc☆

Mathematics of non-linear models
Edinburgh U MSc/dip
Heriot-Watt U MSc☆

Mathematics, statistics & computing
Teesside P dip☆

Modelling in applied mathematics
East Anglia U MSc☆

Non-linear mathematics
Bath U MSc/dip

Numerical analysis
Brunel U MSc ☐

Numerical analysis & programming
Dundee U MSc

Numerical solution of differential equations
Reading U MSc/dip

Optimisation & computing
Loughborough U MSc

Pure & applied mathematics
London U Queen Mary & Westfield C MSc☆

Pure mathematics
Aberystwyth, UC of Wales MSc☆/dip☆
Bangor, U of Wales MSc☆/dip☆
Exeter U MSc☆/dip☆
Hull U dip ☐
Leeds U MSc
Liverpool U MSc☆
London U Royal Holloway & Bedford New C MSc
Manchester U MSc☆/dip☆
Manchester UMIST MSc☆
Sheffield U MSc

Science, technology & mathematics education
East Anglia U MSc☆

Software techniques for computer aided engineering
Cranfield IT MSc   *Comp*

Higher degrees by research

Actuarial mathematics & statistics
Heriot-Watt U PhD☆/MPhil☆

Applicable mathematics
Aston U PhD
Central London P PhD☆/MPhil☆

Applied & computational mathematics
Sheffield U PhD/MPhil

Applied computing & mathematics
Cranfield IT PhD☆/MPhil☆/MSc☆

Applied mathematical studies
Leeds U PhD/MPhil

Applied mathematics
Aberystwyth, UC of Wales PhD☆/MPhil☆
Aston U PhD/MPhil
Bangor, U of Wales PhD☆/MPhil☆
Exeter U PhD☆
Hull U PhD
London U Imperial C PhD/MPhil/dip
Newcastle U PhD/MPhil
St Andrews U PhD/MSc
Salford U PhD☆/MSc☆
Warwick U PhD

Applied mathematics & mathematical physics
Open U PhD/MPhil/BPhil

Applied mathematics & theoretical astronomy
Cardiff U of Wales C PhD☆/MPhil☆

Applied mathematics & theoretical physics
Belfast Queen's U PhD△/MSc△☐
Cambridge U PhD☆/MSc☆
Liverpool U PhD/MSc

Applied sciences
Staffordshire P PhD/MPhil

Astronomy
London U Queen Mary & Westfield C PhD☆/MPhil☆

Biomathematics
Oxford U DPhil☆/MSc☆

Computer studies & mathematics
Bristol P PhD△/MPhil△/dip△
Huddersfield P PhD/MPhil

Computing & mathematics
Royal Naval Engineering C PhD☆/MSc☆

Computing mathematics
Cardiff U of Wales C PhD☆/MPhil☆

Engineering mathematics
Belfast Queen's U PhD/MSc
Bristol U PhD☆/MSc☆
Newcastle U PhD/MPhil

History & philosophy of mathematics
Open U PhD/MPhil/BPhil

Information systems
East Anglia U PhD☆/MPhil☆/MSc☆

Mathematical compilation
London U Queen Mary & Westfield C PhD☆/MPhil☆

Mathematical education
Nottingham U PhD/MPhil

Mathematical sciences
Aberdeen U PhD☆/MPhil☆/MSc☆
Bradford U PhD/MPhil
Durham U PhD/MSc
Exeter U PhD/MPhil
London U Queen Mary & Westfield C PhD☆/MPhil☆
Loughborough U PhD☆/MPhil☆
Sheffield City P PhD/MPhil

Mathematical sciences & computer studies
Robert Gordon's IT PhD/MPhil

Mathematical sciences & computing
South Bank P PhD/MPhil

Mathematical statistics & operational research
Cardiff U of Wales C PhD☆/MPhil☆

Mathematics
Aston U PhD/MPhil
Bath U PhD☆/MPhil☆/MSc☆
Birmingham U PhD/MSc
Brighton P PhD/MPhil
Bristol U PhD☆/MSc☆
Buckingham U DPhil/MPhil
Cardiff U of Wales C PhD☆/MPhil☆
City U PhD/MPhil
Coventry P PhD/MPhil
East Anglia U PhD☆/MPhil☆
East London P PhD/MPhil
Edinburgh U PhD/MPhil
Essex U PhD/MPhil/MSc
Glasgow U PhD/MSc
Hatfield P PhD/MPhil
Heriot-Watt U PhD☆/MPhil☆
Hull U PhD ☐
Keele U PhD/MSc
Kent U PhD/MPhil/MSc
Kingston P PhD/MPhil
Lancaster U PhD/MPhil
Leicester U PhD/MPhil
Liverpool P PhD/MPhil
London U Birkbeck C PhD/MPhil
Goldsmiths' C London U PhD/MPhil
London U Imperial C PhD/MPhil/dip
London U King's C PhD/MPhil
London U LSE PhD/MPhil

London U Royal Holloway &
  Bedford New C PhD/MPhil
London U UC PhD☆/MPhil☆
Manchester U PhD/MSc
Manchester UMIST PhD/MSc
Middlesex P PhD/MPhil
Napier P PhD/MPhil
Nottingham U PhD/MPhil
Oxford U DPhil☆/MSc☆
Reading U PhD/MPhil
Southampton U PhD/MPhil
Staffordshire P PhD/MPhil
Stirling U PhD/MPhil
Strathclyde U PhD☆/MPhil☆
Sunderland P PhD/MPhil
Surrey U PhD/MPhil
Sussex U DPhil☆/MPhil☆
Swansea UC PhD/MPhil
Ulster U DPhil/MPhil
Warwick U PhD
Worcester CHE PhD/MPhil
York U DPhil/MPhil

**Mathematics & computer
science**
Salford U PhD/MSc
Wales P PhD/MPhil

**Mathematics & computer
studies**
Dundee IT PhD/MPhil

Mathematics & computing
Canterbury Christ Church C
  PhD/MPhil

Mathematics & statistics
Brunel U PhD/MPhil
City of London P PhD☆/MPhil☆
Lancashire P PhD/MPhil
Newcastle P PhD☆/MPhil☆
Paisley CT PhD/MPhil
Portsmouth P PhD☆/MPhil☆
South West P PhD/MPhil
Teesside P PhD☆/MPhil☆

**Mathematics, statistics &
computing**
Leicester P PhD/MPhil
North London P PhD/MPhil
Oxford P PhD/MPhil
Thames P PhD/MPhil

**Mathematics, statistics &
operational research**
Nottingham P PhD☆/MPhil☆

**Numerical analysis, applied
mathematics, & control theory**
Cardiff U of Wales C PhD☆/
  MPhil☆

**Propulsion, power & automotive
engineering (gas turbine, wind
turbine, automobile)**
Cranfield IT PhD☆/MPhil☆

Pure & applied mathematics
Exeter U PhD☆/MPhil☆
Sussex U DPhil/MPhil

Pure mathematics
Aberystwyth, UC of Wales
  PhD☆/MPhil☆
Bangor, U of Wales PhD☆/MSc☆
Belfast Queen's U PhD/MSc
Cardiff U of Wales C PhD☆/
  MPhil☆
East Anglia U PhD/MPhil
Hull U PhD/MSc
Kent U PhD/MPhil/MSc
Leeds U PhD/MPhil   ☐
Liverpool U PhD/MSc
London U Imperial C PhD/MPhil/
  dip
Newcastle U PhD/MPhil
Open U PhD/MPhil/BPhil
St Andrews U PhD/MSc
Sheffield U PhD/MPhil

**Pure mathematics &
mathematical statistics**
Cambridge U PhD☆/MSc☆

**Social & environmental
education**
Thames P PhD/MPhil

Numerical theory and method

Higher degrees by instruction

Applied mathematics
Essex U MSc☆/dip☆

**Computational fluid dynamics &
structural mechanics**
London U Imperial C MSc/
  dip   *Eng*

**Computational modelling &
finite elements in engineering
mechanics**
Swansea UC MSc☆/cert☆

Computing & statistics
Cardiff U of Wales C MSc☆/dip☆

Mathematical computation
London U Queen Mary &
  Westfield C MSc

**Mathematical modelling &
numerical analysis**
Oxford U MSc☆

**Mathematical techniques of
statistics & operational research**
London U Birkbeck C MSc△

Mathematics
Bangor, U of Wales MSc☆/dip☆
Dundee U dip☆
London U Imperial C dip☆
Sussex U MSc☆

**Mathematics of modern control
systems**
Loughborough U MSc☆

**Mathematics of non-linear
models**
Edinburgh U MSc/dip
Heriot-Watt U MSc☆

Numerical analysis
Brunel U MSc   ☐

Numerical analysis & computing
Manchester U MSc☆/dip☆

**Numerical analysis &
programming**
Dundee U MSc

**Numerical methods & software
systems**
Royal Military C of Science
  MSc△

**Numerical methods in
photogrammetry & surveying**
London U UC MSc☆/dip☆

**Numerical solution of
differential equations**
Reading U MSc/dip

Optimisation & computing
Loughborough U MSc

Pure mathematics
Bangor, U of Wales MSc☆/dip☆

**Quantitative development in
economics**
Warwick U MA/dip

Higher degrees by research

Applied mathematics
Bangor, U of Wales PhD☆/
  MPhil☆
Exeter U PhD☆
Salford U PhD☆/MSc☆

Mathematical sciences
Bradford U PhD/MPhil
Durham U PhD/MSc
Exeter U PhD/MPhil

Mathematical sciences & computing
South Bank P PhD/MPhil

Mathematics
Dundee U MSc
East London P PhD/MPhil
Heriot-Watt U PhD☆/MPhil☆
London U Imperial C PhD/MPhil/dip
Sussex U DPhil☆/MPhil☆

Mathematics & computer science
Salford U PhD/MSc

Mathematics & physics
Manchester P PhD/MPhil ☐

Nonlinear studies
Leeds U PhD/MPhil

Numerical analysis
Bath U MSc☆
Oxford U DPhil☆/MSc☆

Numerical analysis, applied mathematics, & control theory
Cardiff U of Wales C PhD☆/MPhil☆

Numerical optimisation
Hatfield P PhD△/MPhil△

Pure & applied mathematics
Exeter U PhD☆/MPhil☆

Pure mathematics
Bangor, U of Wales PhD☆/MSc☆

Statistics

Higher degrees by instruction

Actuarial science
City U dip☆

Applied mathematics
Bangor, U of Wales MSc☆/dip☆

Applied statistics
Oxford U MSc☆/dip☆

Applied statistics & computing
Bangor, U of Wales dip☆

Applied statistics & operational research
London U Birkbeck C MSc△

Applied statistics with applications in medicine
Southampton U MSc☆/dip

Applied stochastic science
London U UC MSc

Biometry
Reading U MSc

Computational statistics
Bath U MSc/dip

Computing & social statistics
Kent U MA

Computing & statistics
Cardiff U of Wales C MSc☆/dip☆

Demography
London U LSE MSc

Econometrics & social statistics
Kent U MA
Manchester U dip☆

Economic statistics & national accounts
East Anglia U dip☆

Educational statistics & child development
London U Inst of Education MA/MSc

Educational statistics & educational administration
London U Inst of Education MA

Educational statistics & psychology of education
London U Inst of Education MA/MSc

Epidemiology & medical statistics
London U S of Hygiene & Tropical Med dip△

Industrial programming technology
Sheffield U MSc☆

Mathematical sciences
Aberdeen U dip☆

Mathematical statistics
Cambridge U dip☆
Exeter U MSc☆
Manchester U MSc☆/dip☆

Mathematical, statistical & computing education
London U Inst of Education MSc

Mathematics
Bangor, U of Wales MSc☆/dip☆
Hull U dip☆ ☐
London U Imperial C dip☆
Sussex U MSc☆

Mathematics, statistics & computing
Teesside P dip☆

Medical demography
London U S of Hygiene & Tropical Med MSc/dip

Medical statistics
London U S of Hygiene & Tropical Med MSc

Newcastle U MSc☆

Medical statistics & information technology
Leicester P MSc☆/dip☆
Leicester U MSc☆/dip☆

Mining geostatistics
Leeds U MSc

Operational research
Lancaster U MSc☆/dip☆ *Bus*

Population studies
Exeter U MA☆

Pure mathematics
Hull U dip ☐

Quantitative development in economics
Warwick U MA/dip

Social research
Surrey U MSc/dip

Social statistics
Kent U MA
Manchester U MA(Econ)☆/dip☆
Southampton U MSc☆/dip ☐

Sociology & statistics
London U LSE MSc

Statistical & computational modelling
Liverpool U MSc

Statistical analysis & stochastic systems
Manchester UMIST MSc☆

Statistical applications in business & government
Central London P MSc△

Statistics
Aberystwyth, UC of Wales MSc☆/dip☆
Brunel U MSc/dip
Dundee U dip☆
Glasgow U MSc/dip
Hull U dip☆
Kent U MSc☆/dip☆
Lancashire P dip☆
Leeds U MSc☆
London U LSE MSc/dip
London U UC dip
Manchester U MSc☆/dip☆
St Andrews U dip☆
Salford U MSc
Sheffield U MSc☆/dip☆
Swansea UC dip☆
Warwick U MSc☆/dip☆

Statistics & operational research
Essex U MSc☆/dip☆
Loughborough U MSc

Statistics & operational research techniques
City U MSc△

Statistics (conversion)
Southampton U cert☆

Statistics with applications in medicine
Southampton U MSc☆

Higher degrees by research

Actuarial mathematics & statistics
Heriot-Watt U PhD☆/MPhil☆

Agriculture
London U Wye C PhD☆/MPhil☆

Applied mathematics
Bangor, U of Wales PhD☆/MPhil☆

Applied mathematics & theoretical physics
Belfast Queen's U PhD☆/MSc☆ □

Applied statistics
Central London P PhD☆/MPhil☆
Reading U PhD/MPhil

Applied statistics & operational research
Sheffield City P PhD/MPhil

Biometrics
London U Inst of Psychiatry PhD☆/MPhil☆

Community medicine & medical statistics
Southampton U PhD/MPhil

Computer science & statistics
London U Queen Mary & Westfield C PhD☆/MPhil☆

Econometrics & social statistics
Kent U PhD/MPhil

Economic statistics
Leeds U PhD/MA/MPhil

Mathematical sciences
Bradford U PhD/MPhil
Durham U PhD/MSc

Mathematical sciences & computing
South Bank P PhD/MPhil

Mathematical statistics & operational research
Cardiff U of Wales C PhD☆/MPhil☆

Mathematics
East London P PhD/MPhil
Hull U PhD □
Keele U PhD/MSc
London U Imperial C PhD/MPhil/dip
Sussex U DPhil☆/MPhil☆

Mathematics & computer science
Salford U PhD/MSc

Mathematics & statistics
Brunel U PhD/MPhil
City of London P PhD☆/MPhil☆
Lancashire P PhD/MPhil
Newcastle P PhD☆/MPhil☆
Paisley CT PhD/MPhil
Portsmouth P PhD☆/MPhil☆
South West P PhD/MPhil
Teesside P PhD☆/MPhil☆

Mathematics, statistics & computing
Leicester P PhD/MPhil
North London P PhD/MPhil
Oxford P PhD/MPhil
Thames P PhD/MPhil

Mathematics, statistics & operational research
Nottingham P PhD☆/MPhil☆

Medical computing & statistics
Edinburgh U PhD/MPhil

Medical demography
London U S of Hygiene & Tropical Med PhD/MPhil

Medical statistics
London U S of Hygiene & Tropical Med PhD/MPhil
Newcastle U MD/MPhil

Operational research & operations management
Lancaster U PhD/MPhil/MSc Bus

Population studies
Exeter U PhD/MPhil

Population studies/demography
London U LSE PhD/MPhil

Probability & statistics
Sheffield U PhD/MPhil

Pure & applied mathematics
Sussex U DPhil/MPhil

Pure mathematics
Bangor, U of Wales PhD☆/MSc☆

Pure mathematics & mathematical statistics
Cambridge U PhD☆/MSc☆

Social statistics
City U PhD/MPhil
Manchester U PhD/MA(Econ)
Southampton U PhD/MPhil

Statistical science
London U UC PhD☆/MPhil☆

Statistics
Aberdeen U PhD☆/MPhil☆/MSc☆
Aberystwyth, UC of Wales PhD☆/MPhil☆
Bath U PhD☆/MPhil☆
Birmingham U PhD/MSc
Brighton P PhD/MPhil
Buckingham U DPhil/MPhil
Edinburgh U PhD/MPhil
Glasgow U PhD/MSc
Hatfield P PhD/MPhil
Hull U PhD/MSc
Leeds U PhD/MPhil/MSc
Liverpool P PhD/MPhil
London U Birkbeck C PhD/MPhil
Goldsmiths' C London U PhD/MPhil
London U LSE PhD/MPhil
London U United Med & Dent S, Guys's & St Thomas's PhD☆/MPhil☆
Middlesex P PhD/MPhil
Newcastle U PhD/MPhil
Open U PhD/MPhil/BPhil
Oxford U DPhil☆/MSc☆
St Andrews U PhD/MSc
Salford U PhD☆/MSc☆
Swansea UC PhD/MPhil
Warwick U PhD☆/MPhil☆

Statistics & computational mathematics
Liverpool U PhD/MPhil

Statistics & operational research
Belfast Queen's U PhD/MSc
Coventry P PhD/MPhil

Statitics
Cardiff U of Wales C PhD☆/MPhil☆

Mathematics

PhD
3 years full time
MSc
1 year full time
dip
1 year full time
Professor N J Cutland,
Graduate Studies Chairman,
School of Mathematics,
University of Hull, Hull HU6
7RX
Tel: 0482 465025

Supervision for MSc/PhD is available in the current research areas of the school: *Pure Mathematics* stochastic analysis, nonstandard analysis and its applications, functional analysis (especially operator algebras), general topology, lattice theory; *Applied Mathematics* general relativity, quantum theory, thermodynamics, spectral theory of differential equations, group representations, industrial applied mathematics, fluid dynanics, heat transfer, ice accretion kinetics; *Statistics* foundations of inference, probability and stochastic processes on algebraic structures, applied probability.

A one year Postgraduate diploma in mathematics or statistics is available for prospective MSc/PhD students who need additional background for entry to these courses.
Entrance requirements Good honours degree in mathematics or statistics.
Graduate studies chairman Professor N J Cutland.

Mathematics & physics

PhD
MPhil
Department of Mathematics
and Physics, Manchester
Polytechnic, Chester Street,
Manchester M1 5GD
Tel: 061 228 6171

Full- and part-time opportunities for research are available in the Department of Mathematics and Physics. The main fields are: medium access control protocols for local area networks; computational fluid dynamics and hazard safety assessment; mathematical modelling of diffusion and stress; operational research; computational magnetism; multivariate time series analysis; instrumentation and flow measurement; material science; image analysis; magnetic properties of materials; moisture measurements.
Entrance requirements Honours degree in an appropriate discipline.
Grants SERC awards, research assistantships, industrially sponsored awards may be available.
Reader Dr D M Cavson.

Numerical analysis

MSc
1 year full time
2 years part time
Dr N Papamichael,
Department of Mathematics
and Statistics, Brunel
University, Uxbridge,
Middlesex UB8 3PH
Tel: 0895 74000 ext 2282

Topics covered include: functional analysis, approximation theory, linear algebra, spline functions, numerical solution of ordinary and partial differential equations of physics and engineering, including finite element methods. Machine problems on the University's computers form an integral part of the course.

The full-time course starts in October and lasts for one year. For the part-time course attendance is required on one day each week for two years. The course is designed for students qualified in fields such as mathematics, engineering or physics.
Entrance requirements Good honours degree or equivalent.
Grants SERC.
Head of department Professor J R Whiteman.

Pure mathematics

PhD
3 years full time
MPhil
2 years full time
MSc
1-2 years full time
Head of Department,
Department of Pure
Mathematics, University of
Leeds, Leeds LS2 9JT
Tel: 0532 335143

The main areas of research (leading to PhD or MPhil) are ring theory; group theory; functional analysis; differential topology; mathematical logic and theoretical computer science. The MSc course aims at an appreciation of current work in one or two of algebra, analysis or mathematical logic. Assessment is by written examinations and dissertation.
Entrance requirements First or good second class honours degree, including substantial pure mathematics.
Grants SERC studentships.
Head of department Professor H G Dales.

Social statistics

MSc
1 or 2 years full time
Postgraduate Admissions
Officer, Department of Social
Statistics, University of
Southampton, Southampton
SO9 5NH
Tel: 0703 595000

This course provides training for a career as a professional statistician in fields such as social research, market research, health administration and local or central government. The one-year course consists of (a) courses on statistical design, analysis and computing and on applications in areas such as demography and medicine, (b) a three month supervised dissertation by research. The two-year course includes, in addition, courses on mathematical methods and on statistical theory and methods.
Entrance requirements *One-year course* - good honours degree including major components of statistics.
Two-year course - honours degree including some mathematics and statistics, or certain non graduate qualifications providing degree level mathematical and statistical training. and post A-level mathematics.
Grants ESRC grants are available.
Head of department Professor D Holt.

Theoretical physics & applied mathematics

PhD
3 years full time
MSc
1 year full time
Dr D G Thompson,
Department of Applied
Mathematics and Theoretical
Physics, The Queen's
University of Belfast, Belfast
BT7 1NN
Tel: 0232 245133

Research projects leading to PhD are offered in the following areas; atomic and molecular structure and properties, electron and photon collisions with atoms, ions and molecules, heavy particle collisions including charge exchange, recombination in gases, applications in upper atmosphere physics and astrophysics; computational physics; theoretical quantum optics; statistics; operational research; numerical analysis. MSc degrees in Atomic and Molecular Processes, and Computational Science, may be obtained by examination after one year.
Entrance requirements First or upper second class honours degree.
Grants Grants available for suitably qualified candidates from the Northern Ireland Department of Education, the SERC and the University.
Head of department Professor B L Moiseiwitsch.

Physics and allied subjects

What are the options? When is further training a useful next step for a physicist? Can one delay entering postgraduate study? How do physicists finance their studies? These are the questions addressed in this chapter.

When each group of new physics graduates completes their studies, around 27 per cent stay within higher education on a full-time basis to commence further study for a postgraduate degree or diploma. Another four per cent usually elect to study for a graduate course in teacher training and a further three per cent begin other forms of postgraduate training. This all adds up to a sizeable number of about 720 graduates in physics, about one in every three, who go on to further study of some kind.

Options after graduation

First there is the choice between staying on immediately after your first degree to take a postgraduate course, studying for a degree on a part-time basis, or returning to further serious study after a period of employment. There are quite a few MSc courses which can be studied on a part-time basis (such as the MSc in applied cryogenics at Southampton University or that in nuclear and particle physics at Birkbeck College), but you must be living in a convenient location, close to the institution offering the course, to make this feasible.

Postgraduate study might allow you to indulge your curiosity and fascination for a subject, such as astronomy or nuclear particle physics, which was a part of your undergraduate course but is unlikely to present many opportunities for a long-term career. The dearth of career opportunites in these fields often makes it necessary to utilise the skills you gained through your studies, rather than the knowledge, in your future career. Postgraduate study might help you to change your career course into another field such as electronics or computing, in which there are numerous employment opportunities. There are also quite a few openings in areas such as materials physics, optics, laser technology, and medical physics (where a postgraduate qualification might help). Advanced courses to Master's or diploma level offer the chance to study a subject in depth through lectures, projects and private study, culminating in an exam. If a thesis results, that will be examined too. Alternatively these studies can give you experience in research, which will be important if you wish to pursue a research career.

Research degrees

Degrees by research involve the study of a project for three or more years for a PhD and a shorter time for an MPhil or MSc. Physics departments in universities and polytechnics offer opportunities for research in many branches of physics to those with a good honours degree.

Around 80 per cent of the finance for physicists' postgraduate study comes from the Science and Engineering Research Council (SERC). Each year it awards studentships for research and advanced courses of study. A few of these are earmarked for the study of nuclear physics, astronomy and planetary science. Many, for which physicists can apply, are assigned to other subjects in the sciences.

Opportunities in IT and engineering

Many physicists, these days, are attracted to careers in computing, management services and information technology (IT). It is possible to begin a career as a trainee in these fields straight after a first degree, but those who feel that they will be better prepared for a career in this area if they have studied some facet of it in depth first, can apply for one of over 900 studentships in IT. This covers MSc courses in computer science, micro-electronics, artificial intelligence and related subjects. Some of these courses are specifically designed to allow graduates to convert their skills and increase their knowledge in the area of IT. Others are available for those interested in research in this area. The physics of electronic materials and devices, optical fibres and laser technology and its applications are particularly important in IT.

It is quite common for physicists to obtain funding for postgraduate study in one of the areas of engineering, particularly materials science and electronics, and especially if they were taken as final-year options in an undergraduate course. The SERC Engineering Board awards numerous studentships each year for the study of the various aspects of engineering, many of which are open to physicists.

Teaching incentives

Such is the demand for teachers of physics in secondary schools, and so low was the application rate from physicists to take the one-year Postgraduate Certificate in Education (PGCE), that the Department of Education and Science is offering bursaries of £1350 to £2000 (which can be claimed in addition to local authority grants) for physicists to train as teachers.

Neil Harris

This listing contains **taught courses** (under the heading 'Higher degrees by instruction') and **research opportunities** (under the heading 'Higher degrees by research'). All study exceeds two terms or six months and is offered on both a full-time and part-time basis unless otherwise indicated. Post-experience and in-service courses are only included when advertised.

☐   This symbol indicates that the **taught course(s)** or **research opportunities** are advertised at the end of this listing.

Biol   An italic abbreviation indicates that an advertisement has been placed at the end of another chapter.

☆   This symbol indicates full-time study only.

△   This symbol indicates part-time study only.

For quick reference to advertisements, please use the 'Advertiser's course entry index'. For further information regarding the listing, please refer to page 53.

General

Higher degrees by instruction

Applied language studies
Salford U MA☆

Applied mathematics & theoretical physics
Southampton U MSc/dip

Engineering mathematics
Newcastle U MSc☆/cert☆

History & philosophy of science
Leeds U dip

History & philosophy of science & mathematics
London U King's C MSc

Independent study
East London P MA/MSc/dip

Information technology systems
Strathclyde U MSc☆/dip☆

Instrumentation & analytical science
Manchester UMIST MSc☆

Law & science: intellectual property
London U Queen Mary & Westfield C MSc

Materials research
London U Imperial C MSc☆/dip☆

Mathematical techniques & their applications
Newcastle U MSc

Nuclear & elementary particle physics
London U Royal Holloway & Bedford New C MSc

Physics & electronics
Lancaster U dip☆

Process integration
Manchester UMIST MSc☆

Pure & applied physics
Belfast Queen's U dip☆

Quantum fields & fundamental forces
London U Imperial C MSc/dip ☐

Science & science education
Glasgow U MSc

Science, technology & international affairs
Lancaster U MA☆

Higher degrees by research

Applied mathematics & theoretical physics
Liverpool U PhD/MSc

Applied physics
Hull U PhD/MSc

Applied science
Middlesex P PhD/MPhil

Applied, experimental & theoretical physics
London U Royal Holloway & Bedford New C PhD/MSc ☐

Astronomy
London U UC PhD☆/MPhil☆

Cultural studies
Cheltenham & Gloucester CHE PhD/MPhil

Electrical & electronic engineering & applied physics
Aston U PhD☆

Electronic & electrical engineering
London U UC PhD☆/MPhil☆

Experimental & theoretical physics
Nottingham U PhD/MPhil ☐

Geophysics & planetary physics
London U UC PhD☆/MPhil☆

History & philosophy of science
London U King's C PhD☆/MPhil☆

Image processing
London U UC PhD☆/MPhil☆

Independent study
East London P PhD/MPhil

Instrumentation & analytical science
Manchester UMIST PhD/MSc

Medical physics
London U UC PhD☆/MPhil☆

Mineral physics
London U UC PhD☆/MPhil☆

Physics
Aberdeen U PhD☆/MPhil☆/MSc☆
Lancaster U PhD/MPhil   □
London U Royal Holloway &
  Bedford New C PhD/MPhil
London U UC PhD☆/MPhil☆
Manchester U PhD/MSc/dip

Rock mechanics
London U UC PhD☆/MPhil☆

Science
Canterbury Christ Church C
  PhD/MPhil
Cardiff IHE PhD/MPhil/dip△
Humberside CHE PhD/MPhil

Science & technology
Thames Valley C MPhil

Science studies
Bath U PhD☆/MPhil☆

**Science, mathematics &
computing**
Cheltenham & Gloucester CHE
  PhD/MPhil

**Theoretical & computational
physics**
Belfast Queen's U PhD☆

**Theoretical & experimental
physics**
London U Imperial C PhD/MPhil/
  dip   □

Astronomy, space physics

Higher degrees by instruction

Astronomical technology
Edinburgh U MSc☆/dip☆

Astronomy
Sussex U MSc☆   □

Astronomy & astronautics
Hatfield P MSc△

Astrophysics
London U Queen Mary &
  Westfield C MSc/dip

**Experimental & theoretical
physics**
Manchester U MSc☆/dip☆   □

Geophysics & planetary physics
Newcastle U MSc☆/dip☆

**Mathematical astronomy &
computation**
London U Queen Mary &
  Westfield C MSc

**Optoelectronics & optical
information processing**
Belfast Queen's U MSc/dip

Physics
Sussex U MSc☆   □

Radio astronomy
Manchester U MSc☆/dip☆

Remote sensing
London U Imperial C MSc☆
London U UC MSc☆

Satellite communications
London U UC MSc☆

Space science
London U UC MSc☆

Spacecraft technology
London U UC MSc☆

Higher degrees by research

Aeronautics & astronautics
Southampton U PhD/MPhil

**Applied mathematics &
theoretical astronomy**
Cardiff U of Wales C PhD☆/
  MPhil☆

Applied physics
Sheffield City P PhD/MPhil

Astronomy
Cambridge U PhD☆/MSc☆
Glasgow U PhD/MSc
Hatfield P PhD/MPhil
Leicester U PhD/MPhil
London U Queen Mary &
  Westfield C PhD☆/MPhil☆
London U UC PhD☆/MPhil☆
Manchester U PhD/MSc
Sussex U DPhil/MPhil

Astronomy & astrophysics
Edinburgh U PhD/MPhil
St Andrews U PhD/MSc

Astronomy & space physics
Sheffield U PhD☆/MPhil☆

Astrophysics
Belfast Queen's U PhD/MSc
Cardiff U of Wales C PhD☆/
  MPhil☆
London U UC PhD☆/MPhil☆
Oxford U DPhil☆/MSc☆

Atmospheric physics
Belfast Queen's U PhD/MSc

London U UC PhD☆/MPhil☆

**Atmospheric, oceanic &
planetary physics**
Oxford U DPhil☆/MSc☆

**Experimental & theoretical
physics**
Manchester U PhD/MSc   □
Sussex U DPhil/MPhil☆

Geophysics & planetary physics
Newcastle U PhD/MPhil

Lunar & planetary sciences
London U UC PhD☆/MPhil☆

**Opto-electronics & optical
information processing**
Kent U PhD☆/MPhil☆

Physics
Keele U PhD☆/MSc☆
Kent U PhD/MPhil/MSc
London U Queen Mary &
  Westfield C PhD☆/MPhil☆   □
London U UC PhD☆/MPhil☆
Manchester U PhD/MSc/dip

Physics & astronomy
Lancashire P PhD/MPhil

Pure & applied physics
Belfast Queen's U PhD/MSc   □

Radio astronomy
Manchester U PhD/MSc

Remote sensing
London U UC PhD☆/MPhil☆

Space research
Birmingham U PhD/MSc
London U UC PhD☆/MPhil☆

**Theoretical & experimental
physics**
London U Imperial C PhD/MPhil/
  dip   □

Theoretical astronomy
Cardiff U of Wales C PhD☆/
  MPhil☆

Theoretical physics
London U UC PhD☆/MPhil☆

Atomic, nuclear physics

Higher degrees by instruction

Atomic & molecular processes
Belfast Queen's U MSc☆

Experimental & theoretical physics
Manchester U MSc☆/dip☆   □

Materials science (synchrotron radiation & neutron scattering applied to materials)
Keele U MSc

Nuclear & elementary particle physics
London U Royal Holloway & Bedford New C MSc

Nuclear & particle physics
London U Birkbeck C MSc△

Nuclear magnetic spectroscopy
Sheffield U MSc

Nuclear physics
London U Birkbeck C Dip△

Physics
Sussex U MSc☆   □

Physics & technology of nuclear reactors
Birmingham U MSc   □

Quantum fields & fundamental forces
London U Imperial C MSc/dip   □

Radiochemistry, radiation chemistry & nuclear technology
Salford U MSc

Higher degrees by research

Applied mathematics & theoretical physics
Belfast Queen's U PhD☆/
   MSc   *Math*
Liverpool U PhD/MSc

Applied physics
Hull U PhD/MSc
Sheffield City P PhD/MPhil

Applied, experimental & theoretical physics
London U Royal Holloway & Bedford New C PhD/MSc   □

Astrophysics
London U UC PhD☆/MPhil☆
Oxford U DPhil☆/MSc☆

Atomic & molecular physics
Belfast Queen's U PhD/MSc
Newcastle U PhD/MPhil

Atomic physics
London U UC PhD☆/MPhil☆

Atomic physics & laser physics
Oxford U DPhil☆/MSc☆

Experimental & theoretical physics
Manchester U PhD/MSc   □
Sussex U DPhil/MPhil

Nuclear medicine
London U King's C S of Med & Dentistry PhD☆/MPhil☆

Nuclear physics
Oxford U DPhil☆/MSc☆

Particle physics
London U UC PhD☆/MPhil☆

Physics
Lancaster U PhD/MPhil   □
Liverpool U PhD/MSc
London U Queen Mary & Westfield C PhD☆/MPhil☆   □
London U Royal Holloway & Bedford New C PhD/MPhil
London U UC PhD☆/MPhil☆
Manchester U PhD/MSc/dip
Stirling U PhD/MSc
Swansea UC PhD/MPhil
Ulster U DPhil/MPhil

Pure & applied physics
Belfast Queen's U PhD/MSc   □
Surrey U PhD/MPhil

Reactor research
London U Imperial C PhD/MPhil

Theoretical & experimental physics
London U Imperial C PhD/MPhil/
   dip   □

Theoretical physics
London U UC PhD☆/MPhil☆

Medical, radiation physics

Higher degrees by instruction

Applied radiation physics
Birmingham U MSc☆   □

Bioengineering
Strathclyde U MSc/dip

Biomedical engineering
Surrey U MSc☆/dip☆   *Eng*

Dental radiology
London U King's C S of Med & Dentistry MSc☆

Information technology (medical physics)
Aberdeen U MSc☆   *Comp*

Medical physics
Aberdeen U MSc☆/dip   □
Leeds U MSc
Surrey U MSc☆/dip☆

Medical radiodiagnosis
Edinburgh U dip△

Nuclear medicine
London U London Hosp Med C MSc
London U Royal Free Hosp S of Med MSc
London U Royal Postgraduate Med S MSc
London U United Med & Dent S, Guys's & St Thomas's MSc

Physics & technology of nuclear reactors
Birmingham U MSc   □

Radiation & environmental protection
Surrey U MSc/dip

Radiation biology
London U UC MSc
London U St Bartholomew's Hosp Med C MSc

Radiation physics
London U UC MSc

Radiochemistry, radiation chemistry & nuclear technology
Salford U MSc

Radiodiagnosis
Liverpool U dip☆

Higher degrees by research

Bioengineering
Strathclyde U PhD/MPhil/
   MSc   *Eng*

Biomedical engineering
Surrey U PhD/MPhil   *Eng*

Dental radiology
London U King's C S of Med & Dentistry PhD☆/MPhil☆
London U United Med & Dent S, Guys's & St Thomas's PhD☆/
   MPhil☆

Diagnostic radiology
Dundee U PhD/MSc
London U Royal Postgraduate Med S PhD☆/MPhil☆

London U St Bartholomew's
Hosp Med C PhD/MPhil
London U St George's Hosp
Med S PhD☆/MPhil☆
London U United Med & Dent S,
Guys's & St Thomas's PhD☆/
MPhil☆
Manchester U PhD/MSc
Wales U C of Med PhD☆/MSc☆

Electron microscopy
London U S of Hygiene &
Tropical Med PhD/MPhil

Experimental & theoretical physics
Sussex U MPhil△

Materials analysis & molecular medicine
City U PhD/MPhil

Measurement & instrumentation in medicine
City U PhD/MPhil

Medical biophysics
Manchester U PhD/MSc ☐

Medical electronics & physics
London U St Bartholomew's
Hosp Med C PhD/MPhil

Medical engineering & physics
London U King's C S of Med &
Dentistry PhD☆/MPhil☆

Medical physics
Leeds U PhD/MPhil/MSc
London U UC PhD☆/MPhil☆
London U Royal Free Hosp S of
Med PhD☆/MPhil☆
London U Royal Postgraduate
Med S PhD☆/MPhil☆
Newcastle U MD/MPhil

Medical physics & clinical engineering
Sheffield U PhD/MMedSci

Medical physics & engineering
Southampton U PhD/MPhil

Medical physics & medical engineering
Edinburgh U PhD/MPhil

Medical radiology
Edinburgh U PhD/MPhil

Nuclear medicine
London U St Bartholomew's
Hosp Med C PhD/MPhil
London U United Med & Dent S,
Guys's & St Thomas's PhD☆/
MPhil☆

Physics
Bath U PhD/MPhil ☐
Swansea UC PhD/MPhil
Ulster U DPhil/MPhil

Pure & applied physics
Surrey U PhD/MPhil

Radiation & biophysical chemistry
Newcastle U PhD/MSc

Radio astronomy
Manchester U PhD/MSc

Radiodiagnosis
Bristol U PhD☆/MSc☆
Liverpool U PhD/MSc
Sheffield U PhD/MMedSci

Radiology
Cambridge U PhD☆/MSc☆
London U Imperial C PhD☆/
MPhil☆
Newcastle U MD/MPhil
Oxford U DPhil☆/MSc☆

Radiotherapy
London U St Bartholomew's
Hosp Med C PhD/MPhil
London U United Med & Dent S,
Guys's & St Thomas's PhD☆/
MPhil☆
Newcastle U PhD/MPhil

Radiotherapy & oncology
London U Imperial C PhD☆/
MPhil☆
Oxford U DPhil☆/MSc☆

Physical science

Higher degrees by instruction

Acoustics vibration & noise control
Heriot-Watt U MSc△/dip△

Advanced materials technology
Surrey U MSc/dip

Applied & modern optics
Reading U MSc

Applied optics
London U Imperial C dip☆ ☐

Applied radiation physics
Birmingham U MSc☆ ☐

Chemical physics
Sussex U MSc☆

Laser engineering & pulsed power technology
St Andrews U MSc☆

Marine geotechnics
Bangor, U of Wales MSc☆/dip☆

Mathematics applied to physical science
Heriot-Watt U MSc☆

Mechanical properties of solids
Newcastle U MSc☆

Metrology & quality assurance
Cranfield IT MSc☆

Molecular science of materials
Thames P MSc

Non destructive testing of materials
Brunel U MSc☆

Nuclear & elementary particle physics
London U Royal Holloway &
Bedford New C MSc

Optoelectronic & laser devices
St Andrews U MSc/dip☆ ☐

Optoelectronics & optical information processing
Belfast Queen's U MSc△/dip

Photography
Glasgow SA dip☆

Physical measurement techniques & instrumentation
Manchester P MSc△

Physical oceanography
Bangor, U of Wales MSc☆/dip☆

Physics & technology of amorphous solids
Dundee U MSc☆

Plastics & rubber technology
North London P ALSPT/PRI

Pulsed power technology
St Andrews U MSc/dip☆

Sedimentology & its applications
Reading U MSc☆

Semiconductor devices
Lancaster U MSc☆

Solid state physics
Sheffield U MSc☆/dip

Sound & vibration studies
Southampton U MSc☆/cert☆/
dip☆

Surface science & catalysis
Liverpool U MSc☆

Higher degrees by research

Applied acoustics
Salford U PhD/MSc

Applied physics
Hull U PhD/MSc

Applied sciences
Wolverhampton P PhD/MPhil

Chemical & physical sciences
Huddersfield P PhD/MPhil

Chemical physics
Glasgow U PhD/MSc

Chemical physics & spectroscopy
Sussex U DPhil/MPhil

Experimental & theoretical physics
Nottingham U PhD/MPhil ☐
Sussex U DPhil/MPhil

Fluid physics
Belfast Queen's U PhD☆/MSc☆

Laser & photon physics
Belfast Queen's U PhD☆/MSc☆

Logic & scientific method
Sussex U DPhil/MPhil

Materials science
Bath U PhD☆/MPhil☆ *Eng*

Metallurgy & engineering materials
Newcastle U PhD/MPhil

Metallurgy & materials science
Nottingham U PhD/MPhil *Eng*

Optical & nano-electronics
Glasgow U PhD☆ *Eng*

Optoelectronics
Newcastle P PhD☆/MSc☆

Optometry
Cardiff U of Wales C PhD☆/MPhil☆

Physical chemistry
Leeds U PhD/MPhil
Newcastle U PhD/MSc
Oxford U DPhil☆/MSc☆

Physical electronics
Oxford U DPhil☆/MSc☆

Physical metallurgy
Liverpool U PhD/MSc(Eng)

Physical science
Coventry P PhD/MPhil

Physical sciences
Brighton P PhD/MPhil
East London P PhD/MPhil
Nottingham P PhD☆/MPhil☆

Physical sciences & scientific computing
South Bank P PhD/MPhil

Physics
Aberdeen U PhD☆/MPhil☆/MSc☆
Bristol U PhD☆/MSc☆

London U Queen Mary & Westfield C PhD☆/MPhil☆ ☐
London U Royal Holloway & Bedford New C PhD/MPhil
Sheffield U PhD/MPhil ☐

Plasma physics & ionisation phenomena
Oxford U DPhil☆/MSc☆

Pure & applied physics
Surrey U PhD/MPhil

Radiation chemistry
Leeds U PhD/MPhil

Radiation chemistry research
Leeds U PhD/MPhil *Chem*

Science
Wales P PhD/MPhil

Sound & vibration research
Southampton U PhD/MPhil

Thin film & surface research
Salford U PhD/MPhil/MSc

Physics

Higher degrees by instruction

Acoustics
Salford U MSc△

Acoustics vibration & noise control
Heriot-Watt U MSc△/dip△

Analytical physics
Swansea UC MSc/dip

Applied & modern optics
Reading U MSc

Applied mathematics
Bangor, U of Wales MSc☆/dip☆

Applied optics
London U Imperial C MSc☆ ☐
Salford U MSc☆

Applied radiation physics
Birmingham U MSc☆ ☐

Astronomy
Sussex U MSc☆ ☐

Atomic & molecular processes
Belfast Queen's U MSc☆

Biophysics & engineering
London U Inst of Ophthalmology MSc☆

Chemical physics
East Anglia U MSc☆
Sussex U MSc☆

Classical & quantum gravity
London U King's C dip☆

Computational physics
Salford U MSc△

Crystallography
London U Birkbeck C MSc

Electrical & electromagnetic engineering
Cardiff U of Wales C MSc/dip *Eng*

Elementary particle physics
London U Birkbeck C dip△

Elementary particle theory
Durham U MSc

Experimental & theoretical physics
Manchester U MSc☆/dip☆ ☐

Industrial physics
Aberdeen U dip☆

Information technology (medical physics)
Aberdeen U MSc☆ *Comp*

Instrument design
Aberdeen U MSc☆

Laser engineering & pulsed power technology
Strathclyde U MSc☆

Mathematical physics
London U Imperial C MSc/dip

Mathematics
London U King's C MSc/dip☆

Medical physics
Aberdeen U MSc☆/dip ☐

Microwave solid state physics
Portsmouth P MSc/dip

Molecular electronics
Cranfield IT MSc☆ *Eng*

Nuclear & elementary particle physics
London U Royal Holloway & Bedford New C MSc

Nuclear reactor science & engineering
London U Queen Mary & Westfield C MSc/dip

Optoelectronic & laser devices
Heriot-Watt U MSc
St Andrews U MSc/dip☆ ☐

Optoelectronic devices & systems
Glasgow U MSc/dip

Optoelectronics
Newcastle P MSc☆/dip☆ *Eng*

Optoelectronics & optical information processing
Belfast Queen's U MSc/dip

Order & chaos
London U Imperial C MSc/dip

Physics
Aberdeen U MSc☆
Cambridge U MPhil☆/cert☆
Dundee U dip
Edinburgh U dip☆
Essex U MSc☆/dip☆
Sussex U MSc☆ □

Physics & electronics
Lancaster U dip☆

Physics & technology of amorphous materials
Edinburgh U MSc☆

Physics & technology of amorphous solids
Dundee U MSc☆

Physics education
Sheffield U dip☆

Physics of advanced electronic materials
Bristol U MSc☆ □

Physics of energy resources
Salford U MSc△

Physics of materials
Reading U MSc

Physics of semiconductor materials
Bristol U MSc☆

Pure & applied physics
Belfast Queen's U dip☆

Science education
London U King's C MA/MEd△/
dip☆

Semiconductor devices
Lancaster U MSc☆

Semiconductor science & technology
London U Imperial C MSc/dip □

Solid state physics
Sheffield U MSc☆/dip

Solid state physics & devices
London U Birkbeck C MA△

Space science
London U UC MSc☆

Surface science & technology
Loughborough U MSc

Technology & society
Salford U MSc△

Theoretical physics
Aberdeen U dip☆
Essex U MSc☆

Higher degrees by research

Acoustics
Cardiff U of Wales C PhD☆/
MPhil☆

Applied acoustics
Salford U PhD/MSc

Applied mathematics & mathematical physics
Open U PhD/MPhil/BPhil

Applied mathematics & theoretical physics
Belfast Queen's U PhD△ *Math*
Cambridge U PhD☆/MSc☆
Liverpool U PhD/MSc

Applied physics
Coventry P PhD/MPhil
Hull U PhD/MSc
North London P PhD/MPhil
Sheffield City P PhD/MPhil

Applied physics & electronics
Durham U PhD/MSc

Applied physics & physical electronics
Portsmouth P PhD☆/MPhil☆

Applied sciences
Kingston P PhD/MPhil
Staffordshire P PhD/MPhil

Applied, experimental & theoretical physics
London U Royal Holloway &
Bedford New C PhD/MSc □

Astronomy
London U UC PhD☆/MPhil☆

Atomic & molecular physics
Belfast Queen's U PhD/MSc

Atomic physics & laser physics
Oxford U DPhil☆/MSc☆

Chemical physics & spectroscopy
Sussex U DPhil/MPhil

Clinical physics
Glasgow U PhD/MSc

Crystallography
London U Birkbeck C PhD/MPhil

Electrical & electronic engineering & applied physics
Aston U PhD/MPhil

Engineering & applied physics
North London P PhD/MPhil

Engineering & technology
Wolverhampton P PhD☆/MPhil☆

Environmental physics
Nottingham U PhD☆/MPhil☆

Experimental & theoretical physics
Manchester U PhD/MSc □
Nottingham U PhD/MPhil □
Sussex U DPhil/MPhil

Experimental, theoretical & applied physics
Essex U PhD/MPhil/MSc □
Strathclyde U PhD☆/MPhil☆/
MSc☆

Industrial physics
Cranfield IT PhD☆/MPhil☆/MSc☆

Irreversible processes in solids
Open U PhD/MPhil/BPhil

Materials science & physics
Thames P PhD/MPhil

Mathematics
East Anglia U PhD☆/MPhil☆

Mathematics & physics
Manchester P PhD/MPhil *Math*

Measurement & instrumentation
City U PhD/MPhil

Metallurgy & materials science
Sheffield U PhD/MPhil

Optical & nano-electronics
Glasgow U PhD☆ *Eng*

Optoelectronics
Newcastle P PhD☆/MSc☆

Opto-electronics & optical information processing
Kent U PhD☆/MPhil☆

Photographic sciences
Central London P PhD☆/MPhil☆

Physical oceanography
Bangor, U of Wales PhD☆/
MPhil☆

Physical sciences
Hatfield P PhD/MPhil

Physics
Aberdeen U PhD☆/MPhil☆/MSc☆
Aberystwyth, UC of Wales
PhD☆/MPhil☆
Aston U PhD/MPhil
Bangor, U of Wales PhD☆/
MPhil☆
Bath U PhD/MPhil □
Belfast Queen's U PhD/MSc
Birmingham U PhD/MSc
Bristol U PhD☆/MSc☆
Brunel U PhD/MPhil
Cambridge U PhD☆/MSc☆
Cardiff U of Wales C PhD☆/
MPhil☆
City of London P PhD☆/MPhil☆
City U PhD/MPhil

Dundee IT PhD/MPhil
Dundee U PhD/MSc
Durham U PhD/MSc
East Anglia U PhD/MPhil
Edinburgh U PhD/MPhil
Exeter U PhD/MPhil
Glasgow U PhD/MSc
Heriot-Watt U PhD☆/MPhil☆
Keele U PhD☆/MSc☆
Kent U PhD/MPhil/MSc
Kingston P PhD/MPhil
Lancaster U FhD/MPhil ☐
Leeds U PhD/MPhil/MSc
Leicester P PhD/MPhil
Leicester U PhD/MPhil
Liverpool P PhD/MPhil
Liverpool U PhD/MSc
London U Birkbeck C PhD/MPhil
London U King's C PhD☆/MPhil☆
London U Queen Mary &
  Westfield C PhD☆/MPhil☆ ☐
London U Royal Holloway &
  Bedford New C PhD/MPhil
London U UC PhD☆/MPhil☆
London U United Med & Dent S,
  Guys's & St Thomas's PhD☆/
  MPhil☆
Loughborough U PhD/MPhil ☐

Luton CHE PhD☆/MPhil☆
Manchester U PhD/MSc/dip
Mid Kent CHFE PhD/MPhil
Napier P PhD/MPhil
Newcastle P PhD☆/MPhil☆
Nottingham U PhD☆/MPhil☆
Open U PhD/MPhil/BPhil
Paisley CT PhD/MPhil
Reading U PhD/MPhil
Robert Gordon's IT PhD/MPhil
St Andrews U PhD/MSc
Sheffield U PhD/MPhil ☐
Southampton U PhD/MPhil
Staffordshire P PhD/MPhil
Stirling U PhD/MSc
Strathclyde U PhD☆/MPhil☆
Sunderland P PhD/MPhil
Swansea UC PhD/MPhil
Ulster U DPhil/MPhil
Warwick U PhD☆/MPhil☆/MSc☆
York U DPhil/MPhil

Physics & astronomy
Lancashire P PhD/MPhil

Propulsion, power & automotive engineering (gas turbine, wind turbine, automobile)
Cranfield IT PhD☆/MPhil☆

Pure & applied physics
Belfast Queen's U PhD/MSc ☐
Manchester UMIST PhD/MSc
Salford U PhD/MSc ☐
Surrey U PhD/MPhil

Solid state physics
Cardiff U of Wales C PhD☆/
  MPhil☆

Solid state physics & cryogenics
Oxford U DPhil☆/MSc☆

Theoretical & computational physics
Belfast Queen's U PhD☆

Theoretical & experimental physics
London U Imperial C PhD/MPhil/
  dip ☐

Theoretical physics
London U UC PhD☆/MPhil☆
Newcastle U PhD/MSc
Oxford U DPhil☆/MSc☆
St Andrews U PhD/MSc

Applied optics

MSc
1 year full time
25 places
dip
1 year full time
Dr R W Smith, Blackett Laboratory, Department of Physics, Imperial College of Science, Technology & Medicine, London SW7 2AZ
Tel: 081 589 5111 ext 8846

Lectures These cover most aspects of applied optics currently including geometrical optics, aberration theory, diffraction, image formation, lens design, thin film optics, optical testing, interferometry, lasers, non-linear optics, detection, holography, optical image processing, physiological optics, electron optics, integrated optics and optical communications. *Laboratory* A wide range of experimental work in aplied optics and computational work on lens design including use of optical design computer software. All students undertake a practical optical system design project. *Project* The three month summer project can be done in the university or in industry.
Entrance requirements First or second class honour degree in physics, mathematics or electrical engineering.
Grants SERC, EITB validated, TOPS.
Head of department Professor T W B Kibble FRS.

Applied radiation physics

MSc
1 year full time
Dr S A Durrani, Course Supervisor, School of Physics and Space Research, University of Birmingham, Birmingham B15 2TT
Tel: 021 414 4564 (direct line) Fax: 021 414 6709

The course provides training, through lectures, practical laboratories and Summer Projects, in the theory and applications of radiations and radioisotopes. Careers aimed at include: Radiological Protection, Medical and Hospital Physics, Radiation-based Environmental Studies, Geological and Archaeological Applications, etc.
Entrance requirements A good honours degree in Physics, Chemistry, or a related science. Course brochure gives other details.
Grants SERC Advanced Course studentships.
Head of School Professor D C Colley.

Applied, experimental & theoretical physics

PhD
3 years full time
MSc
1 year full time
2 years part time
Head of the Department,
Department of Physics,
Royal Holloway & Bedford
New College, University of
London, Egham, Surrey
TW20 0EX
Tel: 0784 434455 Fax: 0784
472794

The department is housed in new and modernised buildings in the University of London's country campus. Research in high energy physics at CERN, γ-ray spectroscopy, solid state spectroscopy, low temperatures, 2 dimensional systems, positrons, X-ray topography, electron-atom collisions, atomic theory, plasma physics, machine vision, acoustic signal processing, millimetric communications, superstring theory.

MSc courses in Physics Research and in Nuclear & Elementary Particle Physics.

Entrance requirements Good honours degree in physics or related degree.

Grants SERC quota and CASE awards.

Head of department Professor E R Dobbs.

Astronomy

MSc
1 year full time
The Astronomy Centre,
University of Sussex,
Division of Physics and
Astronomy, University of
Sussex, Falmer, Sussex BN1
9QH

Course content, compulsory: introduction to astronomy, structure of stars, structure of galaxies, high energy astrophysics and cosmology; *options:* three from five given each year, recent options include: accretion disks, cosmical electrodynamics, inflationary cosmology, interacting binary stars, cataclysmic variables, elementary particle physics, astrophysics and cosmology, interstellar medium, physics of pulsars, star formation, stellar evolution, stellar stability; written exam papers, project report (SERC).

Entrance requirements Degree in physics, astronomy or mathematics.

Contact Professor J D Barrow.

Experimental & theoretical & applied physics

PhD
3 years full time
5 years part time
MPhil
2 years full time
3 years part time
MSc
1 year full time
2 years part time
MSc Physics of Laser
Communications
1 year full time
2 years part time
The Chairman, Physics
Department, University of
Essex, Wivenhoe Park,
Colchester, Essex CO4 3SQ
Tel: 444 206 872851
Telex: 98440 (UNILIBG)

Research supervision for PhD and MSc by dissertation is available for both theoretical and experimental physics. The department has research groups in the following fields: laser applications and nonlinear optics, semiconductors and low-dimensional structures, ferroelectric-, electrochromic- and nonlinear optic- device materials, Langmuir-Blodgett organic films, electron microscopy, theoretical quantum optics, theoretical solid state physics. There is also an MSc taught course in Physics of Laser Communications which includes two intensive workshop courses and a project.

Entrance requirements First or upper second class degree in physics or appropriate equivalent - lower second or equivalent acceptable for MSc.

Grants Must be available from country of origin.

Head of department Prof D J Barber.

Experimental & theoretical physics

PhD 3 years
MPhil 2 years
Diploma of Imperial College (DIC) 1 year
The Registrar, Imperial College of Science, Technology & Medicine, London SW7 2AZ
Tel: 071 589 5111

Large and well equipped research groups exist in the following areas: astrophysics, biophysics, high energy physics, applied optics, laser optics and spectroscopy, plasma physics, solid state and semiconductor physics, space and atmospheric physics, elementary particle and quantum field theory.
Entrance requirements Good honours degree.
Grants SERC, MRC, and NERC, (including CASE), some university studentships.
Head of department Professor T W B Kibble FRS.

Experimental & theoretical physics

MSc
1-2 years full time
PhD further 2 years
25 places
Professor A Donnachie, Department of Physics, Schuster Laboratory, University of Manchester, Schuster Laboratory, Oxford Road, Manchester M13 9PL
Tel: 061 275 4200

The department offers facilities for research within the University in both pure and applied physics. Experimental and theoretical research is in progress in the fields of atomic and molecular physics, nuclear physics, high energy physics, low temperature physics, optics, polymer physics, astronomy, radioastronomy, theoretical physics, solid state physics, laser physics, x-ray crystal optics.
Entrance requirements Good honours degree (or equivalent) in physics.
Grants A few studentships available. Strong competition.
Head of department Professor A Donnachie.

Experimental & theoretical physics

PhD
3 years full time
Dr P J King, Department of Physics, University of Nottingham, University Park, Nottingham NG7 2RD
Tel: 0602 484848

PhD projects are available in semiconductor physics, semiconductor devices and 2D structures, high temperature superconductivity, low temperature physics, phonon spectroscopy, quantum fluids, magnetism, electron and acoustic magnetic resonance, nuclear magnetic resonance and medical imaging, optical spectroscopy, cosmic ray physics. The theory of solids and liquids, magnetic and thermal properties, phonon and photon interactions, semiconductors, high temperature superconductivity.
Entrance requirements Good honours degree.
Grants SERC, demonstratorships and university studentships.
Head of department Professor C A Bates.

Medical biophysics

MSc
1 or 2 years full time
PhD further 2 years
Dr D W L Hukins, Department of Medical Biophysics, University of Manchester, Stopford Building, Manchester M13 9PT
Tel: 061 275 5140

Postgraduate research training is offered in the application of physics, computer science and engineering to biology and medicine. Major areas of research are: computer vision and image analysis, connective tissues and biomaterials, radioisotopes and ultrasound.
Entrance requirements Good honours degree (or equivalent professional qualification) in a science or engineering subject.
Grants Research studentships and assistantships are usually available for well qualified applicants.
Head of department Professor C J Taylor.

Medical Imaging

MSc
1 year full time
Admissions Secretary,
Department of Biomedical
Physics & Bioengineering,
University of Aberdeen,
Foresterhill, Aberdeen AB9
2ZD
Tel: 0224 681818 ext 53192

This course provides instruction in a wide range of imaging techniques used in medicine, including radionuclide imaging, positron emission tomography, X-ray, nuclear magnetic resonance and ultrasound imaging and ophthalmology. Lectures will cover the physical principles of the techniques and the medical information produced, as well as supporting topics such as image processing, the measurement of image quality, electronics and anatomy. For further details contact the Admissions Secretary.
Head of department Professor J R Mallard.

Medical physics

PhD
3 years full time
MSc
1 year full time
Admissions Secretary,
Department of Biomedical
Physics & Bioengineering,
University of Aberdeen,
Foresterhill, Aberdeen AB9
2ZD
Tel: 0224 681818 ext 53192

The course content includes fundamental theory and applications of physics to medicine. Ionising and non-ionising radiations, imaging with NMR, isotopes, ultrasound, computers and medical information. Biological effects of radiation and ultrasound, radiation protection and health physics, circuitry theory and design, biomedical electronics and engineering, Fourier analysis, statistics and mathematical models. Hyperthermia. The department also offers MSc and PhD degrees by research. For further details contact the Admissions Secretary.
Grants Studentships available from the MRC.
Head of department Professor J R Mallard.

Membrane technology

MSc
1 year full time
20 places
dip
1 year full time
Dr W T Hanbury, Course
Tutor, Department of
Mechanical Engineering,
University of Glasgow,
James Watt Building,
Glasgow G12 8QQ
Tel: 041 339 8855 ext 4723

This course is run in conjunction with the Glasgow Membrane Group. It consists of three terms of lectures in the science behind the technology of membrane processes together with three months' project work. The syllabus includes:-basic thermodynamics, fluid mechanics and polymer chemistry, together with the course subjects of:-membrane mechanisms, membrane preparation, membrane manufacturing techniques, and the technology of the following membrane processes:-reverse osmosis, ultrafiltraton, electrodialysis, membrane distillation, pervaporation, dialysis and gas separations.
Entrance requirements BSc or equivalent in engineering or science.
Course leader Dr W T Hanbury.

Optoelectronic & laser devices

MSc/dip
1 year full time
2-3 years part time
PhD
Dr I M Firth, Department of
Physics & Astronomy,
University of St Andrews, St
Andrews, Fife KY16 9SS
Tel: 0334 76161
Fax: 0334 74487

The Department is internationally recognised for its contributions in semiconductor nonlinear optics, colour centre lasers, ultra high speed laser pulses and optoelectronics. PhD research places are offered in these areas.

MSc students undertake courses in modern optics, laser physics, semiconductor and optoelectronic devices, optical communications, etc. Time is spent at both St Andrews and Heriot-Watt University, with whom the course is shared. The course is tailored to the needs of the expanding optoelectronics industry; research projects are conducted at industrial companies. St Andrews University, which was founded in 1410 and lies on the east coast of Scotland, has a tradition of innovative research and teaching. The cultural, sporting and scenic advantages of this historical University are highly recommended.
Course director Dr I M Firth.

Physics

PhD/MPhil
full time
and part time
Director of Postgraduate
Studies, School of Physics,
University of Bath, Claverton
Down, Bath BA2 7AY
Tel: 0225 826826

Solid-state physics: non-linear acoustic properties, high P and T, phase transitions, superconductivity; metallic glasses; magnetic materials and sensors. Semiconductor physics: mm-wave technology; quantum well devices. Theory of electronic structure: metals, semiconductors, transition-metal compounds; interatomic forces, surfaces and overlayers: many-body theory of magnetism and superconductivity; convergent beam electron diffraction studies, including heterojunctions and superlattices. Underwater acoustics/ marine geophysics: sea-bed profiling; back-scattering from specific targets, including Schlieren studies; propagation of finite-amplitude acoustic waves in fluids, parametric sources. Medical applications of ultrasound.
Entrance requirements Good honours degree or equivalent in physics or a related science.
Grants A number of SERC and university or industry sponsored studentships are normally available.
Head of school Professor H O Berktay.

Physics

PhD 3 years
MPhil 1 year
MSc 1 year
Dr P M Lee, Department of
Physics, Lancaster
University, Lancaster LA1
4YB

Research fields include high energy nuclear physics, ultra low temperature physics, surface physics, physical electronics, millimetre wave electronics and various aspects of theoretical physics. There is an MSc course in Semiconductor Devices aimed at training graduates for both industrial and academic work in electronic devices.
Entrance requirements PhD: first or upper second class honours degree in physics. MPhil and MSc: first or second class honours degree in physics (or engineering for MSc).
Grants SERC.
Head of department Dr P M Lee.
Enquiries: quote reference Phys/DOG91.

Physics

PhD
full time
MPhil
full time
Department of Physics,
Queen Mary & Westfield
College, University of
London, Mile End Road,
London E1 4NS
Tel: 071 975 5077

Particle Physics: Experimental Particle Physics at accelerators, instrumentation development. *Theoretical Physics*: String Theory, Statistical Mechanics, Condensed Matter Physics, Field Theory. *Astrophysics*: Star formation, millimeter and submm wave line/continuum astronomy, IRAS analysis, detector development. *Polymer Physics and Molecular Electronics*: Electrically conductive and optically non-linear organic compounds, polaron formation and transport, electronic transport in organic low-dimensional structures. *Science and Technology of Measurement*: Quasioptical techniques for mm/submm applications, measurement techniques. *Medical Radiation Physics*: Perturbed angular correlation spectroscopy, positron annihalation and use of positronium.
Grants SERC, CASE, some university support.
Head of Department Dr J A Edgington.

Physics

MPhil/PhD
full time
part time
MSc
full time
part time
Department of Physics,
Loughborough University of
Technology, Loughborough,
Leicestershire LE11 3TU
Tel: 0509 223301

Research opportunities leading to MPhil and PhD degrees are available in a number of areas, including SOLID STATE PHYSICS, SURFACE PHYSICS, OPTOELECTRONICS, HOLOGRAPHY, THIN FILMS and the MECHANICAL PROPERTIES of MATTER. The taught course leading to an MSc in SURFACE SCIENCE AND TECHNOLOGY is an interdisciplinary course with components provided by staff from various Science and Engineering Departments, emphasizing the relation between the technology and science of surfaces. Graduates in Physics, Chemistry, Materials Science and Electronic Engineering are eligible to apply for this course.

Entrance requirements For research students: First or upper second class honours degree in physics or related science.

Grants For research students there are a number of SERC university and industry related grants available. The Training Agency offer studentships for the MSc course.

Head of department Professor K R A Ziebeck.

Physics

PhD/MPhil research
3 years full time
or part time
MSc and Diploma
Taught courses 1 year
Administrative Secretary,
Department of Physics,
University of Sheffield,
Sheffield S3 7RH
Tel: 0742 768555 ext 4278

Current research activities include: THEORETICAL CONDENSED MATTER - Theory of simple and polymeric liquids, high temperature superconductors, heavy fermion compounds, critical phenomena, complex magnetic systems, theory of magnetisation processes. SOLID STATE PHYSICS - Metallic alloy glasses, amorphous metals, high temperature superconductors, fluoride glasses, amorphous semiconductors, disordered biological systems, intrinsic magnetic properties, surface magnetism, defects in ferromagnetic materials. HIGH ENERGY PARTICLE PHYSICS - Electron-positron annihilation, Electro-weak interaction, LEP project at CERN, ALEPH collaboration. SPACE PHYSICS - Cometary Physics, meteorology of the upper atmosphere, theory of meteor trains, plasma and radio waves in the magnetosphere.

Entrance requirements First or second class (upper division) honours degree in physics or astronomy for PhD, MPhil.

Grants SERC and other studentships.

Postgraduate Admissions Tutor Dr N Cowlan.

Physics

DPhil
3 years full time
MSc
1 year full time
The Chairman of Physics or
Prof. P D Townsend, Physics
Division, University of
Sussex, Falmer , Brighton,
Sussex BN1 9QH

Experimental DPhil projects are available in a wide range of topics, including accelerator-based solid state physics, electron microscopy, studies of surface and crystal growth, liquid and solid helium, neutron physics, nuclear spectroscopy, semiconductor devices, solar energy, space and plasma physics, super conductivity, macroscopic quantum systems, non-innvasive sensors, opto-electronics.

Theoretical DPhil projects are available in particle, nuclear and condensed state physics.

The one-year MSc degree involves a mixture of course work and a research project.

Entrance requirements A good honours degree in physics.

Grants SERC and some other awards.

MATHEMATICS/SCIENCES 2

Physics & technology of nuclear reactors

MSc
full time
Dr D R Weaver, School of Physics and Space Research, University of Birmingham, Birmingham B15 2TT
Tel: 021 414 4564

The aim of this course is to provide the necessary background, both in breadth and in depth, for anyone wishing to enter the nuclear industry. Subjects include: reactor systems; reactor physics; kinetics and control; materials; health physics; nuclear detectors and dosimetry.
Entrance requirements Usually a good honours degree in physics or related subjects, or appropriate industrial experience with recognised professional qualification.
Grants Nuclear Electric PLC, BNFL sponsored studentships, SERC.
Head of School Professor G C Morrison.

Physics of advanced electronic materials

MSc
1 year full time
12 places
Dr J A Wilson, Department of Physics, University of Bristol, Tyndall Avenue, Bristol BS8 1TL
Tel: 0272 303030 ext 3643

The course provides a career oriented training in the more materials oriented aspects of current semi-conductor research and development. The course incorporates approximately 200 lectures, some given in one week intensive modular form (open to industrial participants). In the coming year modules will include scanning and transmission electron microscopy, surface science, plasma processing, and high temperature superconductivity. The final five months are devoted to the thesis project, usually undertaken in conjunction with an industrial partner.
Entrance requirements Honours degree in Physics or closely related subject.
Grants Most places funded by SERC or industrial sponsors.
Course direction Professor J W Steeds/Dr J A Wilson.

Pure & applied physics

PhD
3 years full time
MSc
1 year full time
Dr C H B Mee, Department of Pure and Applied Physics, The Queen's University of Belfast, Belfast BT7 1NN
Tel: 0232 245133

Research projects leading to MSc and PhD are available in the following areas: astrophysics and planetary science, atomic and molecular physics, laser interactions and opto-electronics, condensed matter physics. There are one year MSc and Graduate Diploma Courses in opto-electronics and optical information processing, and a Graduate Diploma course in Pure and Applied Physics.
Entrance requirements For PhD research: first or upper second class honours degree. For MSc by research or coursework: lower second class honours degree.
Grants Grants available for qualified candidates from the Northern Ireland Department of Education, SERC and the university.
Head of department Professor H B Gilbody.

Pure & applied physics

PhD
3 years full time
5 years part time
MSc
full time
and part time
Professor B Yates, Department of Pure and Applied Physics, University of Salford, The Crescent, Salford M5 4WT
Tel: 061 745 5713

Research fields include applied optics and surface waves, applied magnetic materials, separation science, neutron scattering and metal physics, electron microscopy, thermophysical properties of composites and computational physics. MSc courses on applied optics, computational physics, energy resources, science and technology, and management of technological change.
Entrance requirements Good honours degree in physics.
Grants SERC.
Head of department Professor B Yates.

459

2 POSTGRADUATE OPPORTUNITIES

Quantum fields & fundamental forces

MSc
1 year full time
2 years part time
Dr R J Rivers, Blackett
Laboratory, Imperial College
of Science, Technology &
Medicine, London SW7 2BZ
Tel: 071 589 5111

The Imperial College Theoretical Physics Group is internationally recognised for its contribution to our understanding of the unification of fundamental forces, the early universe, quantum gravity, string theory and many aspects of quantum field theory.

The taught MSc course aims to give students an awareness of, and facility in, this most exciting boundary of modern mathematical physics.

Lectures are given on all the above and on relevant mathematics. students are assessed by two separate sets of examinations and a project.

Accomodation in College halls of residence within walking distance of the department is guaranteed for single overseas students, on request.

Entrance requirements Good honours degree in mathematics or physics.

Grants No SERC funds available.

Head of group Professor T W B Kibble.

Semiconductor science & technology

MSc
1 year full time
2 years part time
30 places
dip
Professor R A Stradling,
Department of Physics,
Imperial College of Science,
Technology & Medicine,
London SW7 2BZ

The course provides an interdisciplinary career training for industries dependent on semiconductors and their applications following a first degree in physics, materials science or electrical engineering.

The course is structured to provide core courses, a choice of options, classes, practical courses and a four month project. The lecturers are drawn from three departments at Imperial College, industry and other London colleges.

Part-time registration for two years is possible.

Entrance requirements Degree in physics, materials science, electrical engineering or physical science with appropriate mathematical background.

3

POSTGRADUATE INSTITUTIONS

This section gives full details of all institutions offering postgraduate study to the would-be student. Use it to find out more about the places which seem to offer the most attractive prospects in terms of a postgraduate career.

Guide to institutions

The following pages provide information on all institutions which appear within the course listing. 'Postgraduate institutions' is therefore a comprehensive list of all institutions offering postgraduate courses and/or research facilities. Where possible, the following information has been provided for each institution.

Estimated students 1990-91. *Estimates of the total number of students and of the total number of postgraduates are provided. The institutions have provided this information over 12 months in advance of the real figures being known. The figures should be taken as an indication of the size of the institution concerned, the size of the postgraduate intake, and the proportionate emphasis on postgraduate study. Full-time and part-time breakdowns are provided where known.*

Graduate study areas. *The information provided under this heading is intended to give the reader an indication of the general subject groups elsewhere in the book in which the institution may appear. It is not intended to be used as a comprehensive source of information. The information is provided in the form of abbreviations, each of which refers to a particular part of the book, as follows:*

Arts   General arts
Lang   Languages and literature
Bus   Business administration and management
Educ   Education
Soc   Social sciences
Comp   Computer studies
Eng   Engineering and technology
Env   Environmental studies

3 POSTGRADUATE INSTITUTIONS

Biol   Biological studies
Chem Chemical sciences
Math Mathematics
Phy   Physics and allied subjects

Further details on the formulation of the course listing and the contents of each section can be found in the 'Guide to subjects and courses' on page 53.

Closing date. *The closing date for applications tends to vary according to demand and resources. It is advisable to check with the institution to ensure that the closing date has not changed. As always, the best rule of thumb is 'the sooner, the better'.*

Enquiries. *Information on particular courses and prospectuses can be obtained by writing to these addresses. Applications will normally be sent to the same addresses, with the following exceptions:*

- Postgraduate Certificate of Education (PGCE) courses: *information and application forms for all PGCE courses in England and Wales from the Graduate Teacher Training Registry (GTTR), 3 Crawford Place, London W1H 2BN*
- Art and design courses: *information and application forms for all art and design courses in the Art and Design Admissions Registry (ADAR) scheme from ADAR, Imperial Chambers, 24 Widemarsh Street, Hereford HR4 9EP*
- Ordination: *candidates for ordination should initially consult their church or religious centre for advice and information. Applications should not be made directly to theological colleges*

Abbreviations. *All institutions appear, within the main course listings, in an abbreviated form. For example, the University of Bogus would, if such a university existed, appear as Bogus U. The abbreviation used for each institution is listed under this heading.*

Extended entries that appear within the 'Postgraduate institutions' are advertisements paid for by institutions wishing to offer you more details about their postgraduate facilities.

Aberdeen College of Commerce

Estimated students 1991-92 Total students 9200: full time 1500, part time 7700. Postgraduate full time 50.
Graduate study areas Lang, Bus, Comp.
Closing date July 1991.
Enquiries To the Registrar, Aberdeen College of Commerce, Holburn Street, Rutherieston Centre, Aberdeen AB9 2YT - telephone 0224 572811.
Abbreviation Aberdeen CC.

Aberdeen School of Agriculture

(The Department of Agriculture at the University of Aberdeen in association with the North of Scotland College of Agriculture)
Estimated students 1991-92 Total students 390: full time 380, part time 10.
Postgraduate students 105: full time 85, part time 20.
Graduate study areas Bus, Eng, Env, Biol, Chem.
Closing date Mid August.
Enquiries To Professor A S Jones, Aberdeen School of Agriculture, 581 King Street, Aberdeen AB9 1UD - telephone 0224 480291.
Abbreviation Aberdeen SAg.

University of Aberdeen

Estimated students 1991-92 Total students 6350: full time 5700, part time 650.
Postgraduate students 920: full time 670, part time 250.
Graduate study areas Arts, Lang, Bus, Educ, Soc, Comp, Eng, Env, Biol, Chem, Math, Phy.
Closing date None, but candidates are encouraged to apply as early as possible.
Enquiries To the Postgraduate Office, University of Aberdeen, Regent Walk, Aberdeen AB9 1FX - telephone 0224 273506.
Abbreviation Aberdeen U.

University College of Wales, Aberystwyth

(Now incorporating the College of Librarianship)
Estimated students 1991-92 Total students 4150: full time 3850, part time 300.
Postgraduate students 850: full time 650, part time 200.
Graduate study areas Arts, Lang, Bus, Educ, Soc, Comp, Env, Biol, Chem, Math, Phy.
Closing date Early September (for entry in October to taught courses). No closing date for research schemes.
Enquiries To the Registrar & Secretary, University College of Wales, Aberystwyth, Old College, King Street, Aberystwyth, Dyfed SY23 2AX - telephone 0970 622020.
Abbreviation Aberystwyth, UC of Wales.

Abingdon College

Estimated students 1991-92 Total students 4500. Postgraduate students 20.
Graduate study areas Bus.
Closing date Applications accepted until 4 September.
Enquiries To Jenny Stacey, Abingdon College, Northcourt Road, Abingdon, Oxfordshire OX14 1NN - telephone 0235 555585.
Abbreviation Abingdon C.

Air Service Training Limited

Estimated students 1991-92 Total full time 300. Postgraduate full time 50.
Graduate study areas Eng.
Enquiries To the Principal, Air Service Training Limited, Perth Aerodrome, Scone, Perth, Scotland PH2 6NP - telephone 0738 52311.
Abbreviation Air Service Training Ltd.

Allen Hall

Estimated students 1991-92 Total students 57. Postgraduate students 6.

Graduate study areas Arts.
Closing date End of March.
Enquiries To the Vocations Director, Allen Hall, 28 Beaufort Street, Chelsea, London SW3 5AA - telephone 071 351 6975.
Abbreviation Allen Hall.

Anglia Higher Education College

(Formerly Cambridgeshire College of Arts & Technology and Essex Institute of Higher Education)
Estimated students 1991-92 Total students 20000: full time 10000, part time 10000. Postgraduate students 250: full time 200, part time 50.
Graduate study areas Arts, Bus, Educ, Soc, Eng, Biol, Chem.
Enquiries To Admissions, Anglia Higher Education College, Essex Campus, Victoria Road South, Chelmsford, Essex CM1 1LL - telephone 0245 493131.
Abbreviation Anglia HEC.

Architectural Association School of Architecture

Estimated students 1991-92 Total students 300. Postgraduate students 45.
Graduate study areas Arts, Eng, Env.
Closing date 17 March for overseas students..
Enquiries To Louise Jackson, Co-ordinator of the Graduate School, Architectural Association School of Architecture, 34-36 Bedford Square, London WC1B 3ES - telephone 071 636 0974.
Abbreviation Architectural Association S of Architecture.

Armagh College of Further Education

Estimated students 1991-92 Total full time 1000. Postgraduate full time 20.
Graduate study areas Bus.

Closing date Before 30 June.
Enquiries To Mr T G Gordon, Head of the Department of Business Studies, Armagh College of Further Education, Lonsdale Street, Armagh BT61 7HN - telephone 0861 522205.
Abbreviation Armagh CFE.

Aston University

Estimated students 1991-92 Total students 4000. Postgraduate students 700.
Graduate study areas Lang, Bus, Comp, Eng, Biol, Chem, Math, Phy.
Enquiries To the Postgraduate Admissions Tutor, relevant department, Aston University, Aston Triangle, Birmingham B4 7ET - telephone 021 359 3611.
Abbreviation Aston U.

Bala-Bangor College

Please refer to The College of Welsh Independence.

Bangor Normal College

Estimated students 1991-92 Total students 650: full time 500, part time 150. Postgraduate full time 39.
Graduate study areas Educ.
Closing date 1 May.
Enquiries To Mrs Pat Parry, Admissions Officer, Bangor Normal College/Y Coleg Normal, Bangor, Gwynedd LL57 2PX - telephone 0248 370171.
Abbreviation Bangor Normal C.

University of Wales, Bangor

Estimated students 1991-92 Total students 3500: full time 3100, part time 400. Postgraduate students 890: full time 590, part time 300.
Graduate study areas Arts, Lang, Educ, Soc, Comp, Eng, Env, Biol, Chem, Math.
Closing date 31 August.

Enquiries To the Academic Registrar, University of Wales, Bangor, Gwynedd LL57 2DG - telephone 0248 351151.
Abbreviation Bangor, U of Wales.

Bath College of Higher Education

(incorporating Bath Academy of Art)
Estimated students 1991-92 Total students 1915: full time 1690, part time 225. Postgraduate students 114: full time 99, part time 15.
Graduate study areas Educ.
Closing date No special date, but early application strongly recommended.
Enquiries To the Registrar, Bath College of Higher Education, Newton Park, Newton St Lowe, Bath BA2 9BN - telephone 0225 873701 Fax: 0225 874123.
Abbreviation Bath CHE.

University of Bath

Estimated students 1991-92 Total full time 4100. Postgraduate students 1150: full time 550, part time 600.
Graduate study areas Arts, Lang, Bus, Educ, Soc, Comp, Eng, Biol, Chem, Math, Phy.
Closing date No official closing date.
Enquiries To the Secretary & Registrar, University of Bath, Claverton Down, Bath BA2 7AY - telephone 0225 826826.
Abbreviation Bath U.

Bedford College of Higher Education

Estimated students 1991-92 Total students 1200: full time 1100, part time 100. Postgraduate students 120: full time 80, part time 40.
Graduate study areas Arts, Lang, Educ, Soc, Env.
Closing date Accept applications until places are filled.

Enquiries To the Assistant Academic Registrar, Bedford College of Higher Education, 37 Lansdowne Road, Bedford MK40 2BZ - telephone 0234 51966.
Abbreviation Bedford CHE.

The College of Business Studies, Belfast

Estimated students 1991-92 Total students 6000: full time 1000, part time 5000. Postgraduate full time 70.
Graduate study areas Lang, Bus.
Closing date 31 May 1990 but late applications considered.
Enquiries To the Head of Secretarial Studies, The College of Business Studies, Belfast, Brunswick Street, Belfast BT2 7GX - telephone 0232 245891.
Abbreviation Belfast C of Bus Studies.

The Queen's University of Belfast

Estimated students 1991-92 Total students 9650. Postgraduate students 2087.
Graduate study areas Arts, Lang, Educ, Soc, Comp, Eng, Env, Biol, Chem, Math, Phy.
Closing date Varies from course to course. Overseas students advised to apply before June/July to ensure accommodation..
Enquiries To the Admissions Officer, The Queen's University of Belfast, Belfast BT7 1NN - telephone 0232 245133.
Abbreviation Belfast Queen's U.

Bell College of Technology

Estimated students 1991-92 Total students 3500: full time 1400, part time 2100. Postgraduate students 160: full time 60, part time 100.
Graduate study areas Lang, Bus, Soc, Comp, Eng, Biol, Chem, Math, Phy.
Closing date 31 August.

Enquiries To the Registrar, Bell College of Technology, Almada Street, Hamilton, Strathclyde ML3 0JB - telephone 0698 283100.
Abbreviation Bell CT.

Birmingham Polytechnic

Estimated students 1991-92 Total students 12800: full time 5800, part time 7000. Postgraduate students 550: full time 130, part time 420.
Graduate study areas Arts, Lang, Bus, Educ, Soc, Comp, Eng, Env, Biol.
Closing date Students should apply as soon as possible.
Enquiries To Taught courses - Faculty Admissions Officer. Research - Miss Kate Jenns, Academic Registry, Birmingham Polytechnic, Feeney Building, Birmingham B42 2SU - telephone 021 331 5000.
Abbreviation Birmingham P.

University of Birmingham

Estimated students 1991-92 Total students 11000: full time 9900, part time 1100. Postgraduate students 2400: full time 1700, part time 700.
Graduate study areas Arts, Lang, Bus, Educ, Soc, Comp, Eng, Env, Biol, Chem, Math, Phy.
Closing date No set closing date. Early application is advised.
Enquiries To the Assistant Registrar of the appropriate faculty, University of Birmingham, Edgbaston, Birmingham B15 2TT - telephone 021 414 3344.
Abbreviation Birmingham U.

Bishop Grosseteste College

Estimated students 1991-92 Total students 466. Postgraduate students 55.
Graduate study areas Educ.
Closing date No closing date.

Enquiries To Mr Douglas Pearman, Course Tutor (Postgraduate), Bishop Grosseteste College, Newport, Lincoln LN1 3DY - telephone 0522 527347.
Abbreviation Bishop Grosseteste C.

Blackburn College

Estimated students 1991-92 Total students 12000: full time 4000, part time 8000. Postgraduate students 450: full time 150, part time 300.
Graduate study areas Bus, Educ, Comp.
Closing date Early September.
Enquiries To Audrey Thorpe, Divisional Director, Faculty of Business & Management, Blackburn College, Feilden Street, Blackburn BB2 1LH - telephone 0254 55144.
Abbreviation Blackburn C.

Blackpool & The Fylde College

Estimated students 1991-92 Total students 1350: full time 250, part time 1100. Postgraduate full time 25.
Graduate study areas Bus.
Closing date September.
Enquiries To Miss Barbara Newton, Department of Information & Office Technology, Blackpool & The Fylde College, Ashfield Road, Bispham, Blackpool, Lancashire FY2 0HB - telephone 0253 52352.
Abbreviation Blackpool & The Fylde C.

Bolton Institute of Higher Education

Estimated students 1991-92 Total students 4700: full time 2200, part time 2500. Postgraduate students 250: full time 20, part time 230.
Graduate study areas Arts, Lang, Bus, Educ, Soc, Eng, Biol.
Enquiries To Denise Simm, Marketing and Promotions, Bolton Institute of Higher Education, Deane Road, Bolton, Lancashire BL3 5AB - telephone 0204 28851.
Abbreviation Bolton IHE.

Bradford & Ilkley Community College

Estimated students 1991-92 Total students 3250. Postgraduate students 117.
Graduate study areas Lang, Bus, Educ, Soc, Env, Math.
Enquiries To the Admissions Officer, Bradford & Ilkley Community College, Great Horton Road, Bradford, West Yorkshire BD7 1AY - telephone 0274 753026.
Abbreviation Bradford & Ilkley Community C.

University of Bradford

Estimated students 1991-92 Total students 5413: full time 4786, part time 627. Postgraduate students 1246: full time 729, part time 517.
Graduate study areas Lang, Bus, Soc, Comp, Eng, Env, Biol, Chem, Math.
Closing date Applications should be submitted as early as possible before the desired date of entry. Taught courses generally start in October each year; research students may register throughout the year.
Enquiries To the Registrar & Secretary, University of Bradford, Bradford, West Yorkshire BD7 1DP - telephone 0274 733466.
Abbreviation Bradford U.

Bretton Hall

Estimated students 1991-92 Total full time 1150. Postgraduate students 192: full time 160, part time 32.
Graduate study areas Arts, Educ.
Closing date When full.
Enquiries To the Admissions Secretary, Bretton Hall, Wakefield WF4 4LG - telephone 0924 830261.
Abbreviation Bretton Hall.

Brighton College of Technology

Estimated students 1991-92 Total students 16300: full time 1300, part time 15000. Postgraduate students 32: full time 12, part time 20.
Graduate study areas Bus.
Enquiries To the Academic Registrar, Brighton College of Technology, Pelham Street, Brighton, East Sussex BN1 4FA - telephone 0273 667788.
Abbreviation Brighton CT.

Brighton Polytechnic

Estimated students 1991-92 Total students 9500: full time 7000, part time 2500. Postgraduate students 860: full time 500, part time 360.
Graduate study areas Arts, Lang, Bus, Educ, Soc, Comp, Eng, Env, Biol, Chem, Math, Phy.
Closing date No definite date, but early application recommended.
Enquiries To the Registrar, Brighton Polytechnic, Mithras House, Lewes Road, Brighton BN2 4AT - telephone 0273 600900.
Abbreviation Brighton P.

Bristol Baptist College

Estimated students 1991-92 Total students 35. Postgraduate students 3.
Graduate study areas Arts.
Closing date None.
Enquiries To the Principal, Bristol Baptist College, Woodland Road, Bristol BS8 1UN - telephone 0272 260248.
Abbreviation Bristol Baptist C.

Bristol Polytechnic

Estimated students 1991-92 Total students 10046: full time 4924, part time 5122. Postgraduate students 111: full time 58, part time 53.
Graduate study areas Arts, Lang, Bus, Educ, Soc, Comp, Eng, Env, Biol, Chem, Math, Phy.

Enquiries To the Postgraduate Admissions Office, Bristol Polytechnic, Coldharbour Lane, Frenchay, Bristol BS16 1QY - telephone 0272 656261 ext 2231; Fax 0272 583758.
Abbreviation Bristol P.

Postgraduate qualifications

Full time Education PGCE (CNAA); Law CPE; Law Society's Final Course; Information technology MSc/PG dip; Parallel computer systems MSc/PG dip; GRSC I & II.
Diplomas: European Business Administration; Broadcast Journalism; Housing Studies (with Bristol University); Management Studies; Advanced manufacturing systems engineering; Careers guidance (LGTB); Health education (CNAA); Marketing (CNAA); Personnel management (CNAA).
Part time Applied immunology MSc/PG dip (CNAA); Business administration MBA (CNAA); GRSC I & II; Education MEd (CNAA); Historical studies MA (CNAA); Instrumental analysis MSc/PG dip (CNAA); Town planning BTP (CNAA).
Diplomas: Housing studies; Management studies (CNAA); Marketing (CNAA).
Other PG/post experience/professional/in-service courses offered both full and part time.

University of Bristol

Estimated students 1991-92 Total students 8165: full time 7575, part time 590. Postgraduate students 1500: full time 1000, part time 500.
Graduate study areas Arts, Lang, Educ, Soc, Comp, Eng, Biol, Chem, Math, Phy.
Enquiries To the Registrar, University of Bristol, Senate House, Tyndall Avenue, Bristol BS8 1TH - telephone 0272 303030.
Abbreviation Bristol U.

Bromley College of Technology

Estimated students 1991-92 Total students 3900: full time 400, part time 3500. Postgraduate students 20.

Graduate study areas Lang, Bus.
Closing date June (but willing to accept after this date).
Enquiries To Mrs M Macdonald (Department of Secretarial, Languages & Communication Studies), Course Tutor, Bromley College of Technology, Rookery Lane, Bromley, Kent BR2 8HE - telephone 081 462 6331.
Abbreviation Bromley CT.

Brooklands Technical College

Graduate study areas Bus, Educ.
Enquiries To the Vice Principal, Brooklands Technical College, Heath Road, Weybridge, Surrey KT13 8TT - telephone 0932 853300.
Abbreviation Brooklands TC.

Brunel University

Estimated students 1991-92 Total full time 3880. Postgraduate full time 1120.
Graduate study areas Bus, Educ, Soc, Comp, Eng, Env, Biol, Chem, Math, Phy.
Enquiries To the Academic Secretary, Brunel University, Uxbridge, Middlesex UB8 3PH - telephone 0895 74000 Fax: 0895 32806.
Abbreviation Brunel U.

University of Buckingham

Estimated students 1991-92 Total students 770. Postgraduate students 37: full time 30, part time 7.
Graduate study areas Arts, Lang, Bus, Soc, Comp, Biol.
Closing date No closing date.
Enquiries To the Admissions Officer, University of Buckingham, Hunter Street, Buckingham MK18 1EG - telephone 0280 814080.
Abbreviation Buckingham U.

Buckinghamshire College of Higher Education

Estimated students 1991-92 Total students 6500: full time 2500, part time 4000. Postgraduate students 130: full time 100, part time 30.
Graduate study areas Bus, Eng.
Closing date Depends on course - home students. 31 May overseas students.
Enquiries To Mr Alan Davis, Academic Registrar, Buckinghamshire College of Higher Education, Queen Alexandra Road, High Wycombe, Buckinghamshire HP11 2JZ - telephone 0494 22141.
Abbreviation Buckinghamshire CHE.

Bulmershe College of Higher Education

Please refer to University of Reading.

Byam Shaw School of Art

Estimated students 1991-92 Total students 160. Postgraduate students 8.
Graduate study areas Arts.
Enquiries To Jenni Sharp, Byam Shaw School of Art, 2 Elthorne Road, London N19 4AD - telephone 071 281 4111.
Abbreviation Byam Shaw SA.

Camborne School of Mines

Estimated students 1991-92 Total full time 240. Postgraduate students 50: full time 47, part time 3.
Graduate study areas Eng, Env.
Closing date 1 July although late applications considered.

Enquiries To the Registrar, Camborne School of Mines, Pool, Redruth, Cornwall TR15 3SE - telephone 0209 714866.
Abbreviation Camborne S of Mines.

University of Cambridge

Estimated students 1991-92 Total students 14200. Postgraduate students 4200.
Graduate study areas Arts, Lang, Educ, Soc, Comp, Eng, Env, Biol, Chem, Math, Phy.
Closing date 31 March (but earlier in some subjects).
Enquiries To the Secretary, University of Cambridge, Board of Graduate Studies, 4 Mill Lane, Cambridge CB2 1RZ.
Abbreviation Cambridge U.

Cambridgeshire College of Arts & Technology

Please refer to Anglia Higher Education College.

Canterbury Christ Church College

Estimated students 1991-92 Total students 2000: full time 1500, part time 500. Postgraduate students 300: full time 250, part time 50.
Graduate study areas Arts, Lang, Bus, Educ, Soc, Comp, Env, Biol, Chem, Math, Phy.
Closing date Varies.
Enquiries To the Admissions Tutor, Canterbury Christ Church College, North Holmes Road, Canterbury, Kent CT1 1QU - telephone 0227 762444.
Abbreviation Canterbury Christ Church C.

Canterbury College

Estimated students 1991-92 Total students 1400. Postgraduate students 20.

Graduate study areas Bus.
Closing date 18 September.
Enquiries To Mr D C Le Breton, Head of Department of Business & Management, Canterbury College, New Dover Road, Canterbury, Kent CT1 3AJ - telephone 0227 66081.
Abbreviation Canterbury C.

Canterbury College of Art & Design

Please refer to Kent Institute of Art & Design at Canterbury.

Cardiff Institute of Higher Education

Estimated students 1991-92 Total students 5000. Postgraduate students 150.
Graduate study areas Arts, Bus, Educ, Env.
Closing date Early application recommended.
Enquiries To the Information Office, Cardiff Institute of Higher Education, Cyncoed Road, Cyncoed, Cardiff CF2 6XD - telephone 0222 551111.
Abbreviation Cardiff IHE.

University of Wales College of Cardiff

(Formerly University College, Cardiff and Cardiff UWIST)
Estimated students 1991-92 Total students 8500: full time 8000, part time 500. Postgraduate full time 1000.
Graduate study areas Arts, Lang, Bus, Educ, Soc, Comp, Eng, Env, Biol, Chem, Math, Phy.
Closing date No closing date.
Enquiries To the Assistant Registrar, Postgraduate Registry, University of Wales College of Cardiff, PO Box 68, Cardiff CF1 3XA - telephone 0222 874413.
Abbreviation Cardiff U of Wales C.

Cassio College

Estimated students 1991-92 Total students 7600. Postgraduate students 25.
Graduate study areas Bus.
Closing date Not applicable.
Enquiries To the Head of Business Studies Department, Cassio College, Langley Road, Watford WD1 3RH - telephone 0923 240311.
Abbreviation Cassio C.

Cauldon College of Further & Higher Education

Please refer to Stoke-on-Trent College.

Polytechnic of Central London

(Incorporating Harrow College of Higher Education)
Estimated students 1991-92 Total students 12000: full time 5000, part time 7000. Postgraduate students 1600.
Graduate study areas Arts, Lang, Bus, Soc, Comp, Eng, Env, Biol, Chem, Math, Phy.
Closing date No formal closing date. Applications accepted up to the beginning of the Autumn term.
Enquiries To L Neil, Central Admissions Unit. Research - K Pattison, Polytechnic of Central London, 309 Regent Street, London W1R 8AL - telephone 071 580 2020.
Abbreviation Central London P.

Central Manchester College of Technology

Estimated students 1991-92 Total students 15000: full time 2000, part time 13000. Postgraduate students 40.
Graduate study areas Bus.
Closing date No closing date.

Enquiries To Mr W J Davison, Head of the Faculty of Business Studies, Central Manchester College of Technology, City Centre Campus, Manchester M3 3ER - telephone 061 831 7791.
Abbreviation Manchester CT.

Central Saint Martins College of Art & Design

(Part of the London Institute. Formerly known as Central School of Art & Design and St Martin's School of Art)
Estimated students 1991-92 Total students 850: full time 150, part time 700. Postgraduate full time 120.
Graduate study areas Arts.
Closing date No formal closing date.
Enquiries To the Deputy Senior Administrative Officer, Central Saint Martins College of Art & Design, 107 Charing Cross Road, London WC2H 0DU - telephone 071 437 0611.
Abbreviation Central St Martins CAD .

Central School of Art & Design

Please refer to Central Saint Martins College of Art & Design.

Ceredigion College of Further Education

(The Ceredigion College of Further Education is an amalgamation of Aberystwyth College of Further Education, Cardigan College of Further Education and Felinfach College of Further Education)
Estimated students 1991-92 Total students 1330: full time 550, part time 780. Postgraduate students 40: full time 25, part time 15.
Graduate study areas Bus, Soc, Comp, Eng, Env, Biol, Math.
Closing date 2 September.

Enquiries To the Principal, Ceredigion College of Further Education, Llanbadarn Fawr, Aberystwyth, Dyfed SY23 3BP - telephone 0970 4511.
Abbreviation Ceredigion CFE.

Charlotte Mason College of Education

Estimated students 1991-92 Total students 600. Postgraduate students 45.
Graduate study areas Educ.
Closing date March.
Enquiries To the Registrar, Charlotte Mason College of Education, Ambleside, Cumbria LA22 9BB - telephone 05394 33066.
Abbreviation Charlotte Mason CE.

Chelsea College of Art & Design

(Part of the London Institute)
Estimated students 1991-92 Total students 1450: full time 750, part time 700. Postgraduate students 74: full time 39, part time 35.
Graduate study areas Arts.
Closing date January, but varies according to course.
Enquiries To the Registrar, Chelsea College of Art & Design, Manresa Road, London SW3 6LS - telephone 071 351 3844.
Abbreviation Chelsea CAD.

Cheltenham & Gloucester College of Higher Education

Estimated students 1991-92 Total students 9600: full time 2600, part time 7000.
Graduate study areas Bus, Educ, Comp, Env.
Enquiries To Registry, Cheltenham & Gloucester College of Higher Education, PO Box 220, The Park, Cheltenham, Gloucester GL50 2QF - telephone 0242 513836.
Abbreviation Cheltenham & Gloucester CHE.

Chester College of Higher Education

Estimated students 1991-92 Total students 1500. Postgraduate students 25.
Graduate study areas Educ.
Enquiries To the Registry, Chester College of Higher Education, Cheyney Road, Chester CH1 4BJ - telephone 0244 375444.
Abbreviation Chester CHE.

Chichester College of Technology

Estimated students 1991-92 Total students 6500. Postgraduate students 30.
Graduate study areas Bus.
Closing date 31 August.
Enquiries To D W Evans, Head of Department of Management & Business Studies, Chichester College of Technology, Westgate Fields, Chichester, West Sussex PO19 1SB - telephone 0243 786321.
Abbreviation Chichester CT.

Chichester Theological College

Estimated students 1991-92 Total students 45. Postgraduate students 20.
Graduate study areas Arts.
Closing date September.
Enquiries To the Reverend The Principal, Chichester Theological College, Chichester, West Sussex PO19 1SG - telephone 0243 783369.
Abbreviation Chichester Theol C.

Chippenham Technical College

Estimated students 1991-92 Total students 9250: full time 750, part time 8500. Postgraduate students 40: full time 20, part time 20.
Graduate study areas Arts, Bus.

Enquiries To the Director of Student Services, Chippenham Technical College, Cocklebury Road, Chippenham, Wiltshire SN15 3QD - telephone 0249 444501.
Abbreviation Chippenham TC.

City of London Polytechnic

Estimated students 1991-92 Total students 12752: full time 4256, part time 8496. Postgraduate students 369: full time 31, part time 338.
Graduate study areas Arts, Lang, Bus, Soc, Comp, Env, Biol, Math.
Enquiries To Taught Degrees: The Admissions Office , City of London Polytechnic, India House, 139 Minories, London EC3N 1NL. Research Degrees: the Secretary, Research Degrees Committee, City of London Polytechnic, 117-119 Houndsditch, London EC3 7BU - telephone 071 283 1030, fax 071 623 2858.
Abbreviation City of London P.

City of Westminster College

(Formerly Paddington College)
Graduate study areas Biol.
Enquiries To A J Medway, Head of Department, City of Westminster College, Paddington Green, London W2 1NB - telephone 071 723 8826.
Abbreviation City of Westminster C.

City University

Estimated students 1991-92 Total full time 2313. Postgraduate students 1980: full time 919, part time 1061.
Graduate study areas Arts, Bus, Educ, Soc, Comp, Eng, Env, Biol, Chem, Math, Phy.
Closing date Varies according to department.
Enquiries To the Academic Registrar, City University, Northampton Square, London EC1V 0HB - telephone 071 253 4399.
Abbreviation City U.

City University Business School

Estimated students 1991-92 Total students 1300. Postgraduate students 448: full time 240, part time 208.
Graduate study areas Bus.
Closing date 31 May 1991.
Enquiries To Mrs E Taylor, Admissions Officer, City University Business School, Frobisher Crescent, Barbican Centre, London EC2Y 8HB - telephone 071 920 0111 ext 2234/2292.
Abbreviation City U BS.

Clarendon College of Further Education

Estimated students 1991-92 Total students 10000. Postgraduate students 35.
Graduate study areas Bus.
Closing date September (early).
Enquiries To Peter Jordan, Head of Department of Business, Professional & Management Studies, Clarendon College of Further Education, Pelham Avenue, Nottingham NG5 1AL - telephone 0602 607201.
Abbreviation Clarendon CFE.

Colchester Institute

Estimated students 1991-92 Total students 6500. Postgraduate students 80.
Graduate study areas Bus, Eng.
Closing date June.
Enquiries To the Director, Colchester Institute, Sheepen Road, Colchester, Essex CO3 3LL - telephone 0206 761660.
Abbreviation Colchester Inst.

Cornwall College

Estimated students 1991-92 Total students 7000: full time 2000, part time 5000. Postgraduate part time 30.
Graduate study areas Bus.
Closing date No closing date.
Enquiries To Dr K Woodcock, Head of Faculty of Business & Information Technology, Cornwall College, Pool, Redruth, Cornwall TR15 3RD - telephone 0209 712911.
Abbreviation Cornwall C.

Coventry Polytechnic

Estimated students 1991-92 Total students 8323: full time 6557, part time 1766. Postgraduate students 550: full time 190, part time 360.
Graduate study areas Arts, Lang, Bus, Soc, Comp, Eng, Env, Biol, Chem, Math, Phy.
Closing date None.
Enquiries To the Academic Registrar, Coventry Polytechnic, Coventry, CV1 5FB - telephone 0203 631313; fax: 0203 258597; telex: 9312102228(CP G).
Abbreviation Coventry P.

Coventry Technical College

Estimated students 1991-92 Total students 9000. Postgraduate students 100.
Graduate study areas Bus.
Closing date August.
Enquiries To Mrs Lander, Coventry Technical College, Butts, Coventry CV1 3GD - telephone 0203 257221.
Abbreviation Coventry TC.

Craigie College of Education

Estimated students 1991-92 Total full time 400. Postgraduate full time 45.
Graduate study areas Educ.
Closing date 15 December each year.
Enquiries To Mrs P Lowrie, Vice Principal , Craigie College of Education, Ayr KA8 0SR - telephone 0292 260321.
Abbreviation Craigie CE.

Cranfield Institute of Technology

Estimated students 1991-92 Total full time 3000. Postgraduate full time 2300.
Graduate study areas Bus, Soc, Comp, Eng, Env, Biol, Chem, Math, Phy.
Closing date Variable.
Enquiries To the Registrar (Admissions), Cranfield Institute of Technology, Cranfield, Bedford MK43 0AL - telephone 0234 750111. For courses on the Silsoe campus: To the Student Recruitment Executive, Room 5, Cranfield Institute of Technology, Silsoe College, Silsoe, Bedford MK45 4DT - telephone 0525 60428. For courses on the RMCS, Shrivenham campus: To the Academic Registrar, Cranfield Institute of Technology, Royal Military College of Science, Shrivenham, Swindon, Wiltshire SN6 8LA - telephone 0793 782551.
Abbreviation Cranfield IT.

Cranfield School of Management

Estimated students 1991-92 Postgraduate students 350.
Graduate study areas Bus.
Enquiries To the Admissions Officer, Cranfield School of Management, Cranfield Institute of Technology, Cranfield , Bedford MK43 0AL - telephone 0234 751122.
Abbreviation Cranfield S of Management.

Cranfield School of Management, a university management school, is contained within Cranfield Institute of Technology, a largely postgraduate university with an international reputation in management and other areas.

MBA - an intensive 12 month programme covering the whole range of business management. Entry requirements normally include an honours degree or equivalent and three years business experience.

MSc Project management - an intensive 12 month programme run alongside the MBA.

Executive MBA - a two year part time programme with the content and syllabus closely modelled on the full time MBA.

MPhil/PhD programme - research studies can be undertaken on a full time or part time basis. Entry requirements include a good degree or equivalent qualification and a research interest in any aspect of management. A number of bursaries are available.

Cranmer Hall/St John's College

Estimated students 1991-92 Total students 75. Postgraduate students 30.
Graduate study areas Arts.
Enquiries To the Principal, Cranmer Hall/St John's College, 3 South Bailey, Durham DH1 3RJ - telephone 091 374 3579.
Abbreviation Cranmer Hall/St John's C.

Crawley College of Technology

Estimated students 1991-92 Total students 6950: full time 950, part time 6000. Postgraduate students 30: full time 25, part time 5.
Graduate study areas Bus.
Closing date None.
Enquiries To the Registrar, Crawley College of Technology, College Road, Crawley, West Sussex RH10 1NR - telephone 0293 612686.
Abbreviation Crawley CT.

Crewe & Alsager College of Higher Education

Estimated students 1991-92 Total students 2600: full time 2200, part time 400. Postgraduate students 147: full time 147, part time 0.
Graduate study areas Educ.
Closing date No set date - we recruit until course is full.
Enquiries To the Registry (Admissions), Crewe & Alsager College of Higher Education, Crewe, Cheshire CW1 1DU - telephone 0270 589995.
Abbreviation Crewe & Alsager CHE.

Croydon College

Estimated students 1991-92 Total students 10500: full time 2500, part time 8000.
Graduate study areas Bus, Educ, Soc, Eng.
Closing date September (late applications may be considered).
Enquiries To the College Information Centre, Croydon College, Fairfield, Croydon CR9 1DX - telephone 081 686 5700.
Abbreviation Croydon C.

Derbyshire College of Higher Education

Estimated students 1991-92 Total students 5500: full time 2000, part time 3500. Postgraduate students 300: full time 100, part time 200.
Graduate study areas Arts, Bus, Educ, Soc, Eng, Biol, Chem.
Closing date As late as is consistent with available places.
Enquiries To the Registry Officer, Derbyshire College of Higher Education, Kedleston Road, Derby DE3 1GB - telephone 0332 47181.
Abbreviation Derbyshire CHE.

Doncaster College

Estimated students 1991-92 Total students 12000: full time 2000, part time 10000. Postgraduate students 100.
Graduate study areas Bus.
Closing date Applications accepted at any time.
Enquiries To the Chief Administrative Officer, Doncaster College, Waterdale, Doncaster DN1 3EX - telephone 0302 322122.
Abbreviation Doncaster C.

Dorset Institute

(Dorset Institute will become Bournemouth Polytechnic this year)
Estimated students 1991-92 Total students 6700: full time 4600, part time 2100. Postgraduate students 690: full time 150, part time 540.
Graduate study areas Arts, Lang, Bus, Soc, Comp, Eng, Env, Biol, Chem.
Enquiries To Academic Secretary, Bournemouth Polytechnic, Talbot Campus, Fern Barrow, Dorset BH12 5BB - telephone 0202 524111.
Abbreviation Dorset Inst.

Drama Studio London

Estimated students 1991-92 Total full time 56. Postgraduate full time 56.
Graduate study areas Arts.
Closing date July.
Enquiries To Lesley Cockburn, Drama Studio London, Grange Court, 1 Grange Road, Ealing, London W5 5QN - telephone 081 579 3897.
Abbreviation Drama Studio.

Duncan of Jordanstone College of Art

Estimated students 1991-92 Total full time 1060. Postgraduate full time 40.
Graduate study areas Arts, Env.
Closing date 31 March.

Enquiries To Irene Donaldson, Assistant Registrar, Duncan of Jordanstone College of Art, 13 Perth Road, Dundee DD1 4HT - telephone 0382 23261.
Abbreviation Duncan of Jordanstone CA.

Dundee College of Further Education

Estimated students 1991-92 Total students 9000: full time 3000, part time 6000. Postgraduate students 200: full time 140, part time 60.
Graduate study areas Bus.
Closing date June.
Enquiries To the Chief Administrative Officer, Dundee College of Further Education, Old Glamis Road, Dundee DD3 8LE - telephone 0382 819021 or 0382 29151.
Abbreviation Dundee CFE.

Dundee Institute of Technology

Estimated students 1991-92 Total students 3550: full time 2850, part time 700. Postgraduate students 140: full time 100, part time 40.
Graduate study areas Bus, Comp, Eng, Biol, Chem, Math, Phy.
Closing date 31 May.
Enquiries To the Registrar, Dundee Institute of Technology, Bell Street, Dundee DD1 1HG - telephone 0382 27225.
Abbreviation Dundee IT.

University of Dundee

Estimated students 1991-92 Total full time 4500. Postgraduate full time 500.
Graduate study areas Arts, Lang, Bus, Educ, Soc, Comp, Eng, Env, Biol, Chem, Math, Phy.
Closing date No specific closing date, but early application advised especially for overseas applicants.
Enquiries To the Postgraduate Office, University of Dundee, Dundee DD1 4HN - telephone 0382 23181.
Abbreviation Dundee U.

University of Durham

Estimated students 1991-92 Total students 5685: full time 5400, part time 285. Postgraduate students 1035: full time 750, part time 285.
Graduate study areas Arts, Lang, Bus, Educ, Soc, Comp, Eng, Env, Biol, Chem, Math, Phy.
Closing date None.
Enquiries To the Postgraduate Admissions Office, University of Durham, 30 Old Elvet, Durham DH1 3HN - telephone 091 374 2865.
Abbreviation Durham U.

Ealing College London

Estimated students 1991-92 Total students 8663: full time 3584, part time 5079. Postgraduate students 787: full time 207, part time 580.
Graduate study areas Arts, Lang, Bus, Soc, Comp.
Closing date None.
Enquiries To the Admissions Unit (Ref B 31), Ealing College London, St Mary's Road, London W5 5RF - telephone 081 579 5000.
Abbreviation Ealing C London.

University of East Anglia

Estimated students 1991-92 Total students 4515: full time 4300, part time 215. Postgraduate students 1250: full time 860, part time 390.
Graduate study areas Arts, Lang, Bus, Educ, Soc, Comp, Eng, Env, Biol, Chem, Math, Phy.
Enquiries To the Admissions Officer of relevant School of Study, University of East Anglia, Norwich NR4 7TJ - telephone 0603 56161.
Abbreviation East Anglia U.

Polytechnic of East London

Estimated students 1991-92 Total students 8900: full time 5600, part time 3300. Postgraduate students 1280: full time 110, part time 1170.
Graduate study areas Arts, Lang, Bus, Educ, Soc, Comp, Eng, Env, Biol, Chem, Math, Phy.
Enquiries To the Assistant Registrar (Barking), Polytechnic of East London, Longbridge Road, Dagenham, Essex RM8 2AS - telephone 081 590 7722.
Abbreviation East London P.

Edge Hill College of Higher Education

Estimated students 1991-92 Total students 1650. Postgraduate students 180.
Graduate study areas Arts, Educ, Soc.
Enquiries To the Admissions Officer, Edge Hill College of Higher Education, Ormskirk, Lancashire L39 4QP - telephone 0695 575171.
Abbreviation Edge Hill CHE.

Founded in 1885 in Liverpool, the College was transferred in 1933 to the outskirts of Ormskirk, a market town in the centre of a rich agricultural area 13 miles from Liverpool, nine from Southport, to which towns it is linked by a frequent train or bus service. The M6 motorway can be reached in a few minutes.

The teaching accommodation includes an excellent modern library, an extensive resource centre, a theatre, a television studio, science laboratories, a language laboratory, specialist rooms or studios for all subjects, gymnasia and swimming bath. The attractive grounds, nearly 50 acres in extent, offer pleasant gardens, an athletics track, pitches for rugby, soccer, hockey and cricket, and tennis courts.

Academic information

Postgraduate certificate in education. For teachers in primary and secondary schools and in further education. Secondary/FE courses are available in English, Social studies/economics. The course is examined by continuous assessment procedures.

During the course postgraduate students spend 12 weeks on supervised teaching practice and two weeks on school attachment. Many curriculum courses are school based.
MA Reading studies (full and part time)
MA Crime deviance & social policy (part time)
MA History (part time)
MA Writing studies (part time).

Edgehill Theological College/Edgehill Christian Education Centre

Estimated students 1991-92 Total students 105: full time 30, part time 75. Postgraduate full time 1.
Graduate study areas Arts.
Closing date 30 June.
Enquiries To the Principal, Edgehill Theological College/Edgehill Christian Education Centre, Lennoxvale, Belfast BT9 5BY - telephone 0232 665870.
Abbreviation Edgehill Theol C.

Edinburgh College of Art

Estimated students 1991-92 Total full time 980. Postgraduate full time 80.
Graduate study areas Arts, Env.
Closing date 1 June.
Enquiries To the Registration Office, Edinburgh College of Art, Lauriston Place, Edinburgh EH3 9DF - telephone 031 229 9311.
Abbreviation Edinburgh CA.

Edinburgh Theological College

Estimated students 1991-92 Total students 25. Postgraduate students 25.
Graduate study areas Arts.
Closing date End of June.

Enquiries To the Principal, Edinburgh Theological College, Rosebery Crescent, Edinburgh EH12 5JT - telephone 031 337 3838.
Abbreviation Edinburgh Theol C.

University of Edinburgh

Estimated students 1991-92 Total students 11380: full time 10420, part time 960. Postgraduate students 2430: full time 1620, part time 810.
Graduate study areas Arts, Lang, Bus, Educ, Soc, Comp, Eng, Env, Biol, Chem, Math, Phy.
Closing date 31 March.
Enquiries To the Secretary to the University, University of Edinburgh, Old College, South Bridge, Edinburgh EH8 9YL - telephone 031 667 1011.
Abbreviation Edinburgh U.

Edinburgh University School of Agriculture

Estimated students 1991-92 Total full time 455. Postgraduate full time 87.
Graduate study areas Soc, Eng, Env, Biol, Chem.
Closing date 31 March normally, although later applications may be considered.
Enquiries To the Agriculture Department Office, Edinburgh University School of Agriculture, The King's Buildings, Edinburgh EH9 3JG - telephone 031 667 1041.
Abbreviation Edinburgh U SAg.

Erith College of Technology

Estimated students 1991-92 Postgraduate students 9.
Graduate study areas Bus.
Enquiries To the Academic Officer, Admissions, Erith College of Technology, Tower Road, Belvedere, Kent DA17 6JA - telephone 0322 442331.
Abbreviation Erith CT.

Essex Institute of Higher Education

Please refer to Anglia Higher Education College.

University of Essex

Estimated students 1991-92 Total students 3600. Postgraduate students 700.
Graduate study areas Arts, Lang, Bus, Soc, Comp, Eng, Env, Biol, Chem, Math, Phy.
Closing date Preferably one month before term begins.
Enquiries To the Admissions Officer, University of Essex, Wivenhoe Park, Colchester, Essex CO4 3SQ - telephone 0206 873666.
Abbreviation Essex U.

European School of Management (EAP)

Estimated students 1991-92 Total full time 500. Postgraduate full time 380.
Graduate study areas Bus.
Closing date 30 March.
Enquiries To David Penwarden, Tutor for Admissions, European School of Management (EAP), 12 Merton Street, Oxford OX1 4JH - telephone 0865 724545.
Abbreviation European S of Management .

Exeter College

Estimated students 1991-92 Total students 2200. Postgraduate students 40.
Graduate study areas Bus.
Closing date 7 September.
Enquiries To the Head of School of Business Administration, Exeter College, Hele Road, Exeter, Devon EX4 4JS - telephone 0392 77977.
Abbreviation Exeter C.

Exeter College of Art & Design

Please refer to Polytechnic South West.

University of Exeter

Estimated students 1991-92 Total students 8000: full time 6000, part time 2000. Postgraduate students 1150: full time 1000, part time 150.
Graduate study areas Arts, Lang, Bus, Educ, Soc, Comp, Eng, Env, Biol, Chem, Math, Phy.
Enquiries To the Registrar & Secretary, University of Exeter, Northcote House, The Queen's Drive, Exeter EX4 4QJ - telephone 0392 263263.
Abbreviation Exeter U.

Falkirk College of Technology

Graduate study areas Bus, Comp.
Enquiries To Mr G S Carlow, Student Adviser, Falkirk College of Technology, Grangemouth Road, Falkirk FK2 9AD - telephone 0324 24981.
Abbreviation Falkirk CT.

Falmouth School of Art & Design

Estimated students 1991-92 Total students 950. Postgraduate full time 24.
Graduate study areas Arts.
Closing date March.
Enquiries To A S Schorah, Academic Registrar, Falmouth School of Art & Design, Falmouth, Cornwall TR11 4RA - telephone 0326 211077.
Abbreviation Falmouth SAD.

Farnborough College of Technology

Estimated students 1991-92 Total students 7850: full time 1150, part time 6700. Postgraduate students 115: full time 55, part time 60.
Graduate study areas Bus, Educ, Comp, Env.
Closing date September.
Enquiries To the Central Admissions Office, Farnborough College of Technology, Boundary Road, Farnborough, Hampshire GU14 6SB - telephone 0252 515511.
Abbreviation Farnborough CT.

Fife College of Technology

(Formerly Kirkaldy College of Technology)
Estimated students 1991-92 Total students 6000: full time 2000, part time 4000. Postgraduate students 110: full time 50, part time 60.
Graduate study areas Bus, Comp, Eng, Chem.
Closing date Not applicable.
Enquiries To Ann Justice, Marketing Coordinater, Fife College of Technology, St Brycedale Ave, Kirkaldy, Fife KY1 1EX - telephone 0592 268591.
Abbreviation Fife CT.

Filton College

(Formerly Filton Technical College)
Estimated students 1991-92 Total students 5400. Postgraduate students 50.
Graduate study areas Bus.
Closing date July.
Enquiries To John Parnham, Head of Business & Management Studies Department, Filton College, Filton Avenue, Filton, Bristol BS12 7AT - telephone 0272 694217.
Abbreviation Filton C.

French Institute

Please refer to Institut Francais du Royaume-Uni.

Gateshead College

(Formerly Gateshead Technical College)
Estimated students 1991-92 Total students 9820: full time 820, part time 9000. Postgraduate full time 24.
Graduate study areas Arts.
Enquiries To Dr R D Harley, Principal, Gateshead College, Durham Road, Gateshead NE9 5BN - telephone 091 477 0524.
Abbreviation Gateshead C.

Glasgow College

Estimated students 1991-92 Total students 3800. Postgraduate students 440.
Graduate study areas Bus, Soc, Comp, Eng, Biol, Chem, Math, Phy.
Closing date Overseas students are advised to apply by 31 January, but there is no formal closing date.
Enquiries To the Admissions Officer, Glasgow College, Cowcaddens Road, Glasgow G4 0BA - telephone 041 331 3000.
Abbreviation Glasgow C.

Glasgow College of Building & Printing

Estimated students 1991-92 Total full time 1200. Postgraduate full time 16.
Graduate study areas Eng.
Closing date 28 February.
Enquiries To the Academic Registrar, Glasgow College of Building & Printing, 60 North Hanover Street, Glasgow G1 2BP - telephone 041 332 9969.
Abbreviation Glasgow C of Building & Printing.

Glasgow Northern College of Nursing

Graduate study areas Soc, Biol, Chem, Phy.
Enquiries To Mrs S M Liddle, Assistant Director of Nurse Education, Glasgow Northern College of Nursing, 300 Balgrayhill Road, Glasgow G21 3UR - telephone 041 557 3443.
Abbreviation Glasgow Northern C of Nursing.

Glasgow School of Art

Estimated students 1991-92 Total students 900. Postgraduate students 30: full time 25, part time 5.
Graduate study areas Arts, Env.
Closing date September, but early application may be given preference.
Enquiries To A G Vogt, Glasgow School of Art, 177 Renfrew Street, Glasgow G3 6RQ - telephone 041 332 9797.
Abbreviation Glasgow SA.

University of Glasgow

Estimated students 1991-92 Total students 13300: full time 11900, part time 1400. Postgraduate students 2400: full time 1400, part time 1000.
Graduate study areas Arts, Lang, Bus, Educ, Soc, Comp, Eng, Env, Biol, Chem, Math, Phy.
Closing date End of June.
Enquiries To the Registrar, University of Glasgow, Glasgow G12 8QQ - telephone 041 339 8855.
Abbreviation Glasgow U.

Gloucestershire College of Arts & Technology

Please refer to Cheltenham & Gloucester College of Higher Education.

Guildford College of Technology

Estimated students 1991-92 Total full time 20. Postgraduate students 15.
Graduate study areas Bus.
Closing date 9 September.
Enquiries To Mrs J Douglas, Course Director, Guildford College of Technology, Stoke Road, Guildford, Surrey GU1 6PZ - telephone 0483 31251.
Abbreviation Guildford CT.

Guildhall School of Music & Drama

Estimated students 1991-92 Total students 680. Postgraduate students 180.
Graduate study areas Arts.
Closing date 31 January.
Enquiries To the Registrar, Guildhall School of Music & Drama, Barbican, London EC2Y 8DT - telephone 071 628 2571.
Abbreviation Guildhall S of Mus & Drama.

Gwent College of Higher Education

Estimated students 1991-92 Postgraduate students 220: full time 80, part time 140.
Graduate study areas Arts, Bus, Educ.
Enquiries To the Registrar of the relevant faculty: Faculty of Education & Combined Studies, Gwent College of Higher Education, College Crescent, Caerleon, Newport, Gwent NP6 1XJ - telephone 0633 421292; Faculty of Management & Professional Studies, Gwent College of Higher Education, Allt-yr-yn Avenue, Newport, Gwent NP9 5XA - telephone 0633 251525; Faculty of Art & Design, Gwent College of Higher Education, Clarence Place, Newport, Gwent NP9 0UW - telephone 0633 259984
Abbreviation Gwent CHE.

Hammersmith & West London College

Estimated students 1991-92 Total students 10000: full time 2500, part time 7500. Postgraduate part time 250.
Graduate study areas Bus, Eng, Env.
Closing date September.
Enquiries To Hammersmith & West London College, Gliddon Road, Barons Court, London W14 9BL - telephone 081 741 1688 or 081 743 3321.
Abbreviation HWLC.

Harlow Tertiary College

(Formerly Harlow College)
Estimated students 1991-92 Total students 6500. Postgraduate students 40.
Graduate study areas Bus.
Closing date 18 September.
Enquiries To Dr J Kew, Head of the Division of Business Studies, Harlow Tertiary College, The High, Harlow, Essex CM20 1LT - telephone 0279 441288.
Abbreviation Harlow TC.

Harper Adams Agricultural College

Estimated students 1991-92 Total students 800. Postgraduate students 30.
Graduate study areas Env, Biol.
Enquiries To the Academic Registrar, Harper Adams Agricultural College, Newport, Shropshire TF10 8NB - telephone 0952 820280.
Abbreviation Harper Adams AgC.

Harrow College of Higher Education

(Harrow College of Higher Education has now merged with the Polytechnic of Central London)
Estimated students 1991-92 Total students 1000. Postgraduate students 60.

Graduate study areas Arts, Bus.
Enquiries To the Faculty of Art & Design or Faculty of Business & Management, Harrow College of Higher Education, Watford Road, Northwick Park, Harrow, Middlesex HA1 3TP - telephone 081 864 5422.
Abbreviation Harrow CHE.

Hatfield Polytechnic

Estimated students 1991-92 Total students 7000: full time 4900, part time 2100. Postgraduate students 750: full time 500, part time 250.
Graduate study areas Arts, Lang, Bus, Educ, Soc, Comp, Eng, Env, Biol, Chem, Math, Phy.
Closing date September.
Enquiries To the Admissions Office, Hatfield Polytechnic, College Lane, Hatfield, Hertfordshire AL10 9AB - telephone 0707 279000.
Abbreviation Hatfield P.

Hendon College

Estimated students 1991-92 Total students 8200: full time 1200, part time 7000. Postgraduate full time 20.
Graduate study areas Bus.
Closing date None.
Enquiries To the Admissions Unit, Hendon College, Corner Mead, Grahame Park, Colindale, London NW9 5RA - telephone 081 200 8300.
Abbreviation Hendon C.

Heriot-Watt University

Estimated students 1991-92 Total students 5100: full time 4600, part time 500. Postgraduate students 1000: full time 625, part time 375.
Graduate study areas Lang, Bus, Soc, Comp, Eng, Env, Biol, Chem, Math, Phy.
Closing date 1 September.
Enquiries To Postgraduate Office, Heriot-Watt University, Riccarton, Edinburgh EH14 4AS - telephone 031 449 5111.
Abbreviation Heriot-Watt U.

Hertfordshire College of Art & Design

Estimated students 1991-92 Total students 1120: full time 260, part time 860. Postgraduate students 140: full time 50, part time 90.
Graduate study areas Arts, Educ, Soc.
Closing date None.
Enquiries To the Divisional Office, Hertfordshire College of Art & Design, 7 Hatfield Road, St Albans, Hertfordshire AL1 3RS - telephone 0727 45544.
Abbreviation Hertfordshire CAD.

Homerton College

Estimated students 1991-92 Total students 720. Postgraduate students 160.
Graduate study areas Educ.
Enquiries To the Admissions Secretary, Homerton College, Cambridge CB2 2PH - telephone 0223 411141.
Abbreviation Homerton C.

Huddersfield Polytechnic

Estimated students 1991-92 Total students 7700: full time 5100, part time 2600. Postgraduate students 400: full time 75, part time 325.
Graduate study areas Arts, Bus, Educ, Soc, Comp, Eng, Env, Chem, Math.
Closing date 31 July for taught courses; no closing date for research applicants.
Enquiries To the Relevant department for taught courses. To the Dean of Research for research degrees, Huddersfield Polytechnic, Queensgate, Huddersfield HD1 3DH - telephone 0484 422288.
Abbreviation Huddersfield P.

University of Hull

Estimated students 1991-92 Total students 6600. Postgraduate students 1350.
Graduate study areas Arts, Lang, Bus, Educ, Soc, Comp, Eng, Env, Biol, Chem, Math, Phy.
Closing date None.
Enquiries To the Postgraduate Office, University of Hull, Hull HU6 7RX - telephone 0482 46311.
Abbreviation Hull U.

Hull is a pleasant east coast city 300 km north of London, boasting the longest single span suspension bridge in the world. It is well served by motorways and by ferry services to Holland and Belgium and is within easy reach of the historic cities of York and Lincoln, the Yorkshire Moors and the East coast.
The University itself stands on an attractive campus to the north east of the city. The University has a large amount of accommodation for its students and reserves sufficient places to meet the needs of most postgraduate students from overseas. The region is well known for the warmth and friendliness of its people and this is one factor which accounts for the popularity of the University.

Academic information

All departments admit students to read for masters and doctorate degrees by research. Taught courses leading to examination for masters degrees are available in many departments including Accounting, Adult Education, Chemistry, Computer Science, Drama, Economics. Education, English, European and Modern Dutch studies, French, History, Italian, Law, Management Systems and Sciences, Mathematics, Music, Nursing Studies, Philosophy, Politics, Psychology, Social Policy and Professional Studies, Sociology, South-East Asian Studies and Theology.
Full details of all courses may be found in the Postgraduate Prospectus which is available free from the Postgraduate Office.

Humberside College of Higher Education

Estimated students 1991-92 Total students 6500: full time 2500, part time 4000. Postgraduate students 200.
Graduate study areas Arts, Bus, Soc, Env, Biol, Chem.
Enquiries To the Admissions, Humberside College of Higher Education, Cottingham Road, Hull HU6 7RT - telephone 0482 440550.
Abbreviation Humberside CHE.

Institut Francais du Royaume-Uni

Estimated students 1991-92 Total students 120. Postgraduate students 50.
Graduate study areas Lang, Bus.
Closing date 8 September.
Enquiries To Mrs L Towers, Institut Francais du Royaume-Uni, 14 Cromwell Place, London SW7 2JR - telephone 071 589 6211/5812701.
Abbreviation Institut Francais du Royaume-Uni.

Irish Baptist College

Graduate study areas Arts.
Enquiries To Irish Baptist College, 67 Sandown Road, Belfast BT5 6GU - telephone 0232 471908.
Abbreviation Irish Baptist C.

Jews' College

Estimated students 1991-92 Total students 120: full time 40, part time 80. Postgraduate students 60: full time 20, part time 40.
Graduate study areas Arts, Lang, Educ.
Closing date 30 September.

Enquiries To the Registrar, Jews' College, Albert Road, Hendon, London NW4 2SJ - telephone 081 203 6427.
Abbreviation Jews' C.

Jordanhill College of Education

Estimated students 1991-92 Total students 1900. Postgraduate students 450.
Graduate study areas Educ, Soc.
Closing date 15 December.
Enquiries To the Registrar, Jordanhill College of Education, Southbrae Drive, Jordanhill, Glasgow G13 1PP - telephone 041 950 3246.
Abbreviation Jordanhill CE.

University of Keele

Estimated students 1991-92 Total full time 3600. Postgraduate students 1000: full time 450, part time 550.
Graduate study areas Arts, Lang, Bus, Educ, Soc, Comp, Eng, Env, Biol, Chem, Math, Phy.
Enquiries To the Director of Academic Affairs, University of Keele, Keele, Staffordshire ST5 5BG - telephone 0782 621111.
Abbreviation Keele U.

Kent College for the Careers Service

Estimated students 1991-92 Total students 60. Postgraduate students 60.
Graduate study areas Soc.
Enquiries To the Principal, Kent College for the Careers Service, College Road, Hextable, Swanley, Kent BR8 7RN - telephone 0322 64407.
Abbreviation Kent C for the Careers Service.

Kent Institute of Art & Design

Estimated students 1991-92 Total students 1813: full time 1700, part time 113.
Postgraduate students 68: full time 61, part time 7.
Graduate study areas Arts, Env.
Enquiries To Jane Seaman, Marketing Officer, Kent Institute of Art & Design, Oakwood Park, Maidstone, Kent ME16 8AG - telephone 0622 757286.
Abbreviation Kent IAD.

University of Kent at Canterbury

Estimated students 1991-92 Total students 4850: full time 4350, part time 500.
Postgraduate students 700: full time 500, part time 200.
Graduate study areas Arts, Lang, Bus, Soc, Comp, Eng, Env, Biol, Chem, Math, Phy.
Closing date No closing date.
Enquiries To the Graduate Office, the Registry, University of Kent at Canterbury, Canterbury, Kent CT2 7NZ - telephone 0227 764000.
Abbreviation Kent U.

Kidderminster College

Estimated students 1991-92 Total students 400.
Graduate study areas Arts.
Closing date Early application advisable.
Enquiries To the Head of the Department of Carpet Studies, Art & Design, Kidderminster College, Hoo Road, Kidderminster, Worcestershire DY10 1LX - telephone 0562 820811.
Abbreviation Kidderminster C.

Kilburn College

(Formerly Kilburn Polytechnic)
Estimated students 1991-92 Total students 6200: full time 1200, part time 5000.
Postgraduate full time 40.
Graduate study areas Bus.

Closing date 31 August for September 1990 start, 31 January for February 1991 start.
Enquiries To the Head of Department, Business & Professional Studies, Kilburn College, Priory Park Road, London NW6 7UJ - telephone 071 328 8241.
Abbreviation Kilburn C.

King Alfreds College

Estimated students 1991-92 Total students 2000: full time 1400, part time 600. Postgraduate students 50.
Graduate study areas Educ.
Closing date No set date, but it is advisable to submit applications early.
Enquiries To King Alfreds College, Sparkford Road, Winchester, Hampshire SO22 4NR - telephone 0962 841515.
Abbreviation King Alfreds C.

Kingston Polytechnic

Estimated students 1991-92 Total students 8450: full time 6387, part time 2063. Postgraduate students 1168: full time 335, part time 833.
Graduate study areas Arts, Bus, Educ, Soc, Comp, Eng, Env, Chem.
Closing date No official closing date.
Enquiries To the Admissions Office, Kingston Polytechnic, Penrhyn Road, Kingston upon Thames, Surrey KT1 2EE - telephone 081 549 1366.
Abbreviation Kingston P.

La Sainte Union College of Higher Education

Estimated students 1991-92 Total students 900. Postgraduate students 60.
Graduate study areas Educ, Comp.
Enquiries To the Tutor for Admissions, La Sainte Union College of Higher Education, The Avenue, Southampton SO9 5HB - telephone 0703 228761.
Abbreviation La Sainte Union CHE.

Laban Centre for Movement & Dance

Estimated students 1991-92 Total students 280. Postgraduate students 120.
Graduate study areas Arts.
Closing date Mid June.
Enquiries To the Registrar, Laban Centre for Movement & Dance, Laurie Grove, New Cross, London SE14 6NW - telephone 081 692 4070.
Abbreviation Laban Centre for Movement & Dance.

Lancashire Polytechnic

(Formerly known as Preston Polytechnic)
Estimated students 1991-92 Total students 9500: full time 5500, part time 4000. Postgraduate students 580: full time 240, part time 340.
Graduate study areas Arts, Lang, Bus, Soc, Comp, Eng, Env, Biol, Chem, Math, Phy.
Closing date No closing date.
Enquiries To the Educational Liaison Officer, Lancashire Polytechnic, Preston PR1 2TQ - telephone 0772 201201.
Abbreviation Lancashire P.

Lancaster University

Estimated students 1991-92 Total students 6500: full time 5500, part time 1000. Postgraduate students 2400: full time 1500, part time 900.
Graduate study areas Arts, Lang, Bus, Educ, Soc, Comp, Eng, Env, Biol, Chem, Math, Phy.
Closing date 1 April or earlier.
Enquiries To Miss S Arkwright, Graduate Studies Office, Lancaster University, Lancaster LA1 4YW - telephone 0524 65201.
Abbreviation Lancaster U.

The College of Law

Estimated students 1991-92 Total students 3800.
Graduate study areas Arts.

Enquiries To the Registrar, The College of Law, Braboeuf Manor, St Catherines, Portsmouth Road, Guildford GU3 1HA - telephone 0483 576711.
Abbreviation Law C.

Leeds Polytechnic

Estimated students 1991-92 Total students 11450: full time 6350, part time 5100.
Postgraduate students 1000: full time 650, part time 350.
Graduate study areas Arts, Bus, Educ, Soc, Comp, Eng, Env, Biol, Chem.
Closing date No formal closing date.
Enquiries To the Admissions Officer, Leeds Polytechnic, Calverley Street, Leeds LS1 3HE - telephone 0532 832600.
Abbreviation Leeds P.

University of Leeds

Estimated students 1991-92 Total students 12540: full time 11410, part time 1130.
Postgraduate students 3090: full time 2040, part time 1050.
Graduate study areas Arts, Lang, Bus, Educ, Soc, Comp, Eng, Env, Biol, Chem, Math, Phy.
Enquiries To the Postgraduate Office (Admissions), University of Leeds, Leeds LS2 9JT - telephone 0532 334005.
Abbreviation Leeds U.

Leicester Polytechnic

Estimated students 1991-92 Total students 11150: full time 8650, part time 2500.
Postgraduate students 601: full time 267, part time 334.
Graduate study areas Bus, Educ, Soc, Comp, Eng, Env, Biol, Chem, Math, Phy.
Enquiries To the Assistant Registrar (Admissions), Leicester Polytechnic, PO Box 143, Leicester LE1 9BH - telephone 0533 551551.
Abbreviation Leicester P.

University of Leicester

Estimated students 1991-92 Total students 5630: full time 5140, part time 490.
Postgraduate students 1550: full time 1120, part time 430.
Graduate study areas Arts, Lang, Bus, Educ, Soc, Comp, Eng, Env, Biol, Chem, Math, Phy.
Enquiries To the Higher Degrees Office, University of Leicester, University Road, Leicester LE1 7RH - telephone 0533 522298.
Abbreviation Leicester U.

Leo Baeck College

Estimated students 1991-92 Total students 27: full time 15, part time 12.
Graduate study areas Arts.
Closing date 31 December.
Enquiries To the Registrar, Leo Baeck College, 80 East End Road, London N3 2SY - telephone 081 349 4525.
Abbreviation Leo Baeck C.

Lewisham College

(Formerly South East London College)
Estimated students 1991-92 Total full time 140. Postgraduate full time 40.
Graduate study areas Bus.
Closing date 15 September.
Enquiries To Mrs M D Drew, Lewisham College, Tressillian Building, Lewisham Way, Lewisham, London SE4 1UT - telephone 081 692 0353.
Abbreviation Lewisham C.

College of Librarianship

Please refer to University College of Wales, Aberystwyth.

Lincoln Theological College

Estimated students 1991-92 Total students 70. Postgraduate students 40.

Graduate study areas Arts.
Enquiries To the Principal, Lincoln
Theological College, Drury Lane, Lincoln
LN1 3BP - telephone 0522 538885.
Abbreviation Lincoln Theol C.

Liverpool Institute of Higher Education

Estimated students 1991-92 Total students
1900. Postgraduate students 166.
Graduate study areas Educ.
Closing date None - but places are strictly
limited so early application is advisable.
Enquiries To the Postgraduate Secretary,
Liverpool Institute of Higher Education, PO
Box 6, Liverpool L16 9JD - telephone 051
722 2361.
Abbreviation Liverpool IHE.

The Liverpool Polytechnic

Estimated students 1991-92 Total students
13500: full time 9000, part time 4500.
Postgraduate students 600: full time 300,
part time 300.
Graduate study areas Arts, Lang, Bus,
Educ, Soc, Comp, Eng, Env, Biol, Chem,
Math, Phy.
Closing date 31 August each year.
Enquiries To Access Services, The
Liverpool Polytechnic, Rooney House, 70
Mount Pleasant, Liverpool L3 5UX -
telephone 051 207 3581.
Abbreviation Liverpool P.

The Incorporated Liverpool School of Tropical Medicine

Estimated students 1991-92 Postgraduate
students 450: full time 430, part time 20.
Graduate study areas Biol.

Enquiries To the Dean, The Incorporated
Liverpool School of Tropical Medicine,
Pembroke Place, Liverpool L3 5QA -
telephone 051 708 9393.
Abbreviation Incorporated Liverpool S of
Tropical Med.

University of Liverpool

Estimated students 1991-92 Total students
8785: full time 7790, part time 995.
Postgraduate students 1950: full time 1230,
part time 720.
Graduate study areas Arts, Lang, Bus,
Educ, Soc, Comp, Eng, Env, Biol, Chem,
Math, Phy.
Enquiries To the Registrar, University of
Liverpool, PO Box 147, Liverpool L69 3BX -
telephone 051 794 2000.
Abbreviation Liverpool U.

Llandrillo Technical College

Estimated students 1991-92 Total students
1500. Postgraduate students 20.
Graduate study areas Bus.
Closing date August prior to September of
commencement.
Enquiries To the Principal, Llandrillo
Technical College, Llandrillo Road, Rhos on
Sea, Colwyn Bay, Clwyd LL28 4HZ -
telephone 0492 46666.
Abbreviation Llandrillo TC.

London Bible College

Estimated students 1991-92 Total students
220. Postgraduate students 20.
Graduate study areas Arts.
Closing date UK students: 30 June;
overseas students: 31 March.
Enquiries To the Academic Registrar,
London Bible College, Green Lane,
Northwood, Middlesex HA6 2UW -
telephone 09274 26061.
Abbreviation London Bible C.

London College of Furniture

Estimated students 1991-92 Total students 1774: full time 654, part time 1120. Postgraduate full time 28.
Graduate study areas Arts, Eng.
Closing date Varies.
Enquiries To the Senior Administration Officer, London College of Furniture, 41-71 Commercial Road, London E1 1LA - telephone 071 247 1953.
Abbreviation London C of Furniture.

London College of Printing

(Part of the London Institute)
Estimated students 1991-92 Total full time 1200. Postgraduate full time 75.
Graduate study areas Arts.
Enquiries To the Senior Admissions Tutor, London College of Printing, Elephant & Castle, London SE1 6SB - telephone 071 735 8484.
Abbreviation London C of Printing.

London Contemporary Dance School

Estimated students 1991-92 Total students 150. Postgraduate students 16.
Graduate study areas Arts.
Closing date June.
Enquiries To the Audition Secretary, London Contemporary Dance School, The Place, 17 Dukes Road, London WC1H 9AB - telephone 071 387 0152.
Abbreviation London Contemporary Dance S.

London International Film School

Estimated students 1991-92 Total students 140. Postgraduate students 100.

Graduate study areas Arts.
Closing date January, April, September (3 intakes per year).
Enquiries To the Administrator, London International Film School, 24 Shelton Street, London WC2H 9HP - telephone 071 836 9642.
Abbreviation London International Film S.

London School of Translation Studies

Estimated students 1991-92 Postgraduate full time 30.
Graduate study areas Lang.
Enquiries To the Principal, London School of Translation Studies, University of London Union, Malet Street, London WC1E 7HY - telephone 071 580 6740.
Abbreviation London S of Translation Studies.

UNIVERSITY OF LONDON

The **University of London** is made up of the following colleges, institutes and schools

Birkbeck College

Estimated students 1991-92 Total students 3835: full time 395, part time 3440. Postgraduate students 1790: full time 325, part time 1465.
Graduate study areas Arts, Lang, Soc, Comp, Env, Biol, Chem, Math, Phy.
Closing date Varies according to subject.
Enquiries To the Registrar, Birkbeck College, Malet Street, London WC1E 7HX - telephone 071 631 6561.
Abbreviation London U Birkbeck C.

Courtauld Institute of Art

Estimated students 1991-92 Total students 330: full time 200, part time 130.
Postgraduate students 240: full time 110, part time 130.
Graduate study areas Arts.
Closing date 16 January.
Enquiries To the Registrar, Courtauld Institute of Art, Somerset House, Strand, London WC2R 2LS - telephone 071 872 0220.
Abbreviation London U Courtauld Inst of Art.

Goldsmiths' College

Estimated students 1991-92 Total students 3573: full time 2641, part time 932.
Postgraduate students 1442: full time 514, part time 928.
Graduate study areas Arts, Lang, Educ, Soc, Comp, Math.
Enquiries To the Higher Degrees Assistant, Goldsmiths' College, New Cross, London SE14 6NW - telephone 081 692 7171.
Abbreviation Goldsmiths' C London U.

Heythrop College

Estimated students 1991-92 Total full time 200. Postgraduate students 90: full time 60, part time 30.
Graduate study areas Arts.
Closing date 1 May.
Enquiries To the Assistant Registrar, Heythrop College, 11-13 Cavendish Square, London W1M 0AN - telephone 071 580 6941.
Abbreviation London U Heythrop C.

Imperial College of Science, Technology & Medicine

(incorporating St Mary's Hospital Medical School)
Estimated students 1991-92 Total students 6100. Postgraduate students 1900.
Graduate study areas Bus, Soc, Comp, Eng, Env, Biol, Chem, Math, Phy.
Closing date 1 April, although late applications will be considered.
Enquiries To the Senior Assistant Registrar (Admissions), Imperial College of Science, Technology & Medicine, London SW7 0RN - telephone 071 589 5111 ext 3245/6, telex 929484 (IMPCOL G), fax 071 584 7596.
Medical research: The Secretary, St Mary's Hospital Medical School, Norfolk Place, Paddington, London W2 1PG - telephone 071 723 1252, fax 071 724 7349
Abbreviation London U Imperial C.

The Imperial College of Science, Technology and Medicine, located in the South Kensington and Paddington districts of London adjacent to the Royal Parks, was established by Royal Charter 'to give the highest specialised instruction, and to provide the fullest equipment for the most advanced training and research in various branches of science, especially in its application to industry'. It is a School of the federal University of London.

Imperial College is itself a federation of four constituent colleges: the Royal College of Science, the Royal School of Mines and the City and Guilds College have been linked since 1907 and between them embrace the work of the College in the broad fields of the physical sciences, the life sciences, the earth sciences, mining, metallurgy and allied subjects, the main branches of engineering, including computing, and applied social studies. A fourth constituent college was established in August 1988 by the merger with St Mary's Hospital Medical School.

Academic information

Postgraduate courses A wide range of advanced courses in science and technology is offered. They are primarily full time and of one year's duration. All postgraduate taught courses are recognised for the award of the Diploma of the Imperial College (DIC) or the MSc degree of the University of London or both.

Research Original research leading to the degree of MPhil/PhD or DIC is undertaken in all the major disciplines taught at the College, and there is extensive activity in many interdisciplinary areas.

Facilities and amenities

There are extensive computing and library facilities; the national Science Museum Library is located on the campus.

Over two thousand students live in College residences and most overseas students enjoy residential accommodation for their first year of study.

Further information

Booklets giving details of the postgraduate courses and research opportunities are available for each department, individually or as a set; they can be obtained free of charge from the Senior Assistant Registrar (Admissions). Copies are also widely available in libraries and British Council offices.

Application forms are obtained from the Senior Assistant Registrar (Admissions) or the Secretary of the Medical School at the addresses given.

Imperial College of Science, Technology & Medicine - The Management School

Estimated students 1991-92 Postgraduate students 180: full time 130, part time 50.
Graduate study areas Bus.
Closing date 1 July full time programme, 1 October part time programme.
Enquiries To Miss K Randall, Imperial College of Science, Technology & Medicine - The Management School, 53 Prince's Gate, London SW7 2PG - telephone 071 589 5111.
Abbreviation London U Imperial C.

Institute of Commonwealth Studies

Estimated students 1991-92 Postgraduate students 21: full time 11, part time 10.
Graduate study areas Arts, Soc.
Closing date 15 June.
Enquiries To the Administrative Secretary, Institute of Commonwealth Studies, 28 Russell Square, London WC1B 5DS - telephone 071 580 5876.
Abbreviation London U Inst of Commonwealth Studies.

Institute of Education

Estimated students 1991-92 Postgraduate students 2500.
Graduate study areas Arts, Educ, Soc.
Enquiries To the Academic Registrar, Institute of Education, 20 Bedford Way, London WC1H 0AL - telephone 071 636 1500.
Abbreviation London U Inst of Education.

Institute of Historical Research/Institute of US Studies

Graduate study areas Arts.
Closing date Normally 1 June.
Enquiries To the Administrative Officer,
Institute of Historical Research/Institute of
US Studies, 31 Tavistock Square, London
WC1H 9EZ -telephone 071 387 5534.
Abbreviation London U Inst of Historical
Research/US Studies.

Institute of Latin American Studies

Graduate study areas Arts, Lang, Soc, Env.
Closing date 31 May.
Enquiries To Institute of Latin American
Studies, 31 Tavistock Square, London WC1H
9HA - telephone 071 387 5671.
Abbreviation London U Inst of Latin
American Studies.

Institute of Neurology

Estimated students 1991-92 Total students
165: full time 15, part time 150.
Postgraduate students 165: full time 15, part
time 150.
Graduate study areas Biol, Chem.
Enquiries To the Assistant Secretary for
Students, Institute of Neurology, The
National Hospital, Queen Square, London
WC1N 3BG -telephone 071 837 3611.
Abbreviation London U Inst of Neurology.

Institute of Ophthalmology

Estimated students 1991-92 Total students
40. Postgraduate students 40.
Graduate study areas Biol.
Enquiries To the Dean, Institute of
Ophthalmology, 17-25 Cayton Street,
London EC1V 9AT - telephone 071 387
9621.
Abbreviation London U Inst of
Ophthalmology.

Institute of Psychiatry

Estimated students 1991-92 Total students
380. Postgraduate students 380.

Graduate study areas Soc, Biol, Chem,
Math.
Enquiries To the Registry, Institute of
Psychiatry, De Crespigny Park, Denmark
Hill, London SE5 8AF - telephone 071 703
5411.
Abbreviation London U Inst of Psychiatry.

King's College, London

Estimated students 1991-92 Total students
6140: full time 5290, part time 850.
Postgraduate students 2013: full time 1181,
part time 832.
Graduate study areas Arts, Lang, Bus,
Educ, Comp, Eng, Env, Biol, Chem, Math,
Phy.
Closing date August/September: contact
specific departments.
Enquiries To the Postgraduate Office,
King's College, London, Strand, London
WC2R 2LS - telephone 071 836 5454.
Abbreviation London U King's C.

London Business School

Estimated students 1991-92 Total students
540: full time 360, part time 180.
Postgraduate students 450.
Graduate study areas Bus.
Closing date Full time 1st March; part time
30th September.
Enquiries To Nandee Sugarman or Joan
Forsyth, The Information Officer, London
Business School, Sussex Place, Regents
Park, London NW1 4SA - telephone 071 262
5050.
Abbreviation London U London BS.

The London School of Economics & Political Science

Estimated students 1991-92 Total students
4400. Postgraduate students 1900: full time
1400, part time 500.
Graduate study areas Arts, Lang, Bus, Soc,
Comp, Env, Math.

Enquiries To the Graduate Admissions Office, The London School of Economics & Political Science, Houghton Street, London WC2A 2AE - telephone 071 955 7159/60; Fax 071 831 1684; Telex 24655 L8ELON G.
Abbreviation London U LSE.

Queen Mary & Westfield College

Estimated students 1991-92 Total students 4381: full time 4171, part time 210. Postgraduate students 919: full time 665, part time 254.
Graduate study areas Arts, Lang, Bus, Soc, Comp, Eng, Env, Biol, Chem, Math, Phy.
Closing date As early as possible in academic year prior to that of entry.
Enquiries To the Registry, Queen Mary & Westfield College, Mile End Road, London E1 4NS - telephone 071 975 5555.
Abbreviation London U Queen Mary & Westfield C.

Royal Holloway & Bedford New College

Estimated students 1991-92 Total students 2800. Postgraduate students 400: full time 300, part time 100.
Graduate study areas Arts, Lang, Soc, Comp, Env, Biol, Math, Phy.
Closing date Preferably by Easter.
Enquiries To Ruth White, Assistant Registrar, Royal Holloway & Bedford New College, Egham Hill, Egham, Surrey TW20 0EX - telephone 0784 434455 ext 3351.
Abbreviation London U Royal Holloway & Bedford New C.

Royal Veterinary College

Estimated students 1991-92 Total students 420. Postgraduate students 70.
Graduate study areas Biol.
Closing date None.

Enquiries To the Registrar, Royal Veterinary College, Royal College Street, London NW1 0TU - telephone 071 387 2898.
Abbreviation London U Royal Veterinary C.

London School of Hygiene & Tropical Medicine

Estimated students 1991-92 Total full time 500. Postgraduate full time 500.
Graduate study areas Soc, Biol, Chem, Math.
Closing date Normally 31 March for taught courses. No closing date for research training.
Enquiries To the Admissions Officer, London School of Hygiene & Tropical Medicine, Keppel Street, London WC1E 7HT - telephone 071 636 8636.
Abbreviation London U S of Hygiene & Tropical Med.

School of Oriental & African Studies

Estimated students 1991-92 Total students 1300: full time 1000, part time 300. Postgraduate students 500: full time 300, part time 200.
Graduate study areas Arts, Lang, Soc.
Closing date None.
Enquiries To the Registrar, School of Oriental & African Studies, Thornhaugh Street, Russell Square, London WC1H 0XG - telephone 071 637 2388.
Abbreviation London U SOAS.

The School of Pharmacy

Estimated students 1991-92 Total students 450. Postgraduate students 100.
Graduate study areas Eng, Biol, Chem.
Closing date Applications considered throughout the year.

Enquiries To the Registrar, The School of Pharmacy, 29-39 Brunswick Square, London WC1 1AX - telephone 071 837 7651.
Abbreviation London U S of Pharmacy.

School of Slavonic & East European Studies

Estimated students 1991-92 Total students 405: full time 375, part time 30.
Postgraduate students 60: full time 30, part time 30.
Graduate study areas Arts, Lang, Soc.
Closing date 1 April.
Enquiries To the Registrar, School of Slavonic & East European Studies, Senate House, Malet Street, London WC1E 7HU - telephone 071 637 4934.
Abbreviation London U SSEES.

University College London

(Incorporating the Institute of Archaeology)
Estimated students 1991-92 Total students 8500. Postgraduate students 2350.
Graduate study areas Arts, Lang, Bus, Soc, Comp, Eng, Env, Biol, Chem, Math, Phy.
Closing date Varies.
Enquiries To the Registrar, University College London, Gower Street, London WC1E 6BT - telephone 071 387 7050 ext 2679.
Abbreviation London U UC.

Founded in 1826, University College London is the oldest and largest of the various Colleges and Institutes that make up the University of London.

At present almost one-third of the total number of students are of graduate status, most of them reading for higher degrees of the University of London.

Academic information

Postgraduate courses and research All departments of the College, in the Faculties of Arts, Engineering, Laws, Mathematical and Physical Studies, Environmental

Studies, Life Sciences (Biological and Medical) and Clinical Sciences, admit students for training in research leading to MPhil and PhD degrees and most also provide advanced courses of instruction leading to diplomas or Masters degrees.

Diplomas and Certificates

In addition to the above Masters courses the College offers a range of courses leading to postgraduate Certificates and Diplomas (awarded by the University of London or by UCL).

For details of such courses, further information about specific courses and application forms please write to the address given.

Warburg Institute

Estimated students 1991-92 Postgraduate students 40.
Graduate study areas Arts.
Closing date 30 April.
Enquiries To the Secretary & Registrar, Warburg Institute, Woburn Square, London WC1H 0AB - telephone 071 580 9663.
Abbreviation London U Warburg Inst.

Wye College

Estimated students 1991-92 Total students 640: full time 625, part time 15.
Postgraduate students 260: full time 245, part time 15.
Graduate study areas Bus, Soc, Eng, Env, Biol, Chem.
Closing date No specific closing date but it is advisable to apply as early as possible during the academic year prior to the proposed year of entry.
Enquiries To the Registrar, Wye College, Wye, Ashford, Kent TN25 5AH - telephone 0233 812401 Fax: 0233 813320 Telex: 94017832 WYEC G.
Abbreviation London U Wye C.

UNIVERSITY OF LONDON MEDICAL SCHOOLS

Charing Cross & Westminster Medical School

Estimated students 1991-92 Total students 955: full time 875, part time 80.
Postgraduate students 110: full time 30, part time 80.
Graduate study areas Biol.
Enquiries To the Registrar, Charing Cross & Westminster Medical School, The Reynolds Building, St Dunstans Road, London W6 8RP - telephone 081 846 7234.
Abbreviation London U Charing Cross & Westminster Med S.

Guy's Hospital Medical School

Please refer to United Medical & Dental Schools of St Guy's & St Thomas's.

King's College School of Medicine & Dentistry

Estimated students 1991-92 Total students 915: full time 825, part time 90.
Postgraduate students 143: full time 53, part time 90.
Graduate study areas Biol.
Closing date Varies.
Enquiries To the Administrative Assistant, King's College School of Medicine & Dentistry, Bessemer Road, London SE5 9JP - telephone 071 274 6222.
Abbreviation London U King's C S of Med & Dentistry.

London Hospital Medical College

Estimated students 1991-92 Total full time 1140. Postgraduate students 100.
Graduate study areas Biol.

Enquiries To Dr Brian Colvin, Medical Sub-Dean, London Hospital Medical College, Turner Street, London E1 2AD - telephone 071 377 7637.
Abbreviation London U London Hosp Med C.

Royal Free Hospital School of Medicine

Estimated students 1991-92 Total students 615: full time 550, part time 65.
Postgraduate students 105: full time 40, part time 65.
Graduate study areas Soc, Biol, Chem.
Enquiries To the Registrar, Royal Free Hospital School of Medicine, Rowland Hill Street, London NW3 2PF - telephone 071 794 0500.
Abbreviation London U Royal Free Hosp S of Med.

Royal Postgraduate Medical School

Estimated students 1991-92 Postgraduate students 750.
Graduate study areas Biol, Chem, Phy.
Closing date No uniform closing date for applications.
Enquiries To the School Registry, Royal Postgraduate Medical School, Hammersmith Hospital, Ducane Road, London W12 0NN - telephone 081 740 3118.
Abbreviation London U Royal Postgraduate Med S.

The Medical College of St Bartholomew's Hospital

Estimated students 1991-92 Total students 500: full time 420, part time 80.
Postgraduate students 140: full time 60, part time 80.
Graduate study areas Comp, Eng, Biol, Chem, Phy.
Closing date No closing date for research courses - candidates accepted throughout the year.

Enquiries To the Academic Registrar (Higher Degrees), The Medical College of St Bartholomew's Hospital, West Smithfield, London EC1A 7BE - telephone 071 982 6000.
Abbreviation London U St Bartholomew's Hosp Med C.

St George's Hospital Medical School

Estimated students 1991-92 Total full time 790. Postgraduate full time 140.
Graduate study areas Biol, Chem.
Closing date None. Postgraduate research studies may begin at any time during the year.
Enquiries To the Head of relevant department, St George's Hospital Medical School, Cranmer Terrace, London SW17 0RE - telephone 081 672 9944.
Abbreviation London U St George's Hosp Med S.

St Thomas's Hospital Medical School

Please refer to United Medical & Dental Schools of Guy's & St Thomas's.

United Medical & Dental Schools of Guy's & St Thomas's Hospitals

Estimated students 1991-92 Total full time 1500. Postgraduate students 410: full time 80, part time 330.
Graduate study areas Biol, Chem, Phy.
Enquiries To Kathryn M Wood, Registry, United Medical & Dental Schools of Guy's & St Thomas's Hospitals, Guy's Campus, Guy's Hospital, London Bridge, London SE1 9RT - telephone 071 928 9292.
Abbreviation London U United Med & Dent S, Guys's & St Thomas's.

University College & Middlesex School of Medicine (incorporating the Institute of Laryngology & Otology, the Institute of Orthopaedics & the Institute of Urology

Please refer to University College, London.

Loughborough College

Estimated students 1991-92 Total students 4500. Postgraduate students 15.
Graduate study areas Lang, Bus.
Enquiries To Loughborough College, Radmoor, Loughborough LE11 3BT - telephone 0509 215831.
Abbreviation Loughborough C.

Loughborough University of Technology

Estimated students 1991-92 Total full time 5900. Postgraduate full time 1000.
Graduate study areas Arts, Lang, Bus, Educ, Soc, Comp, Eng, Env, Biol, Chem, Math, Phy.

Closing date Applications accepted at any time.
Enquiries To the Higher Awards Office, Loughborough University of Technology, Loughborough, Leicestershire LE11 3TU - telephone 0509 263171.
Abbreviation Loughborough U.

Loughborough University of Technology is at the forefront of a new generation of British universities. Since receiving University status in 1966 it has become a leader in technological research and innovation. It has established strong and growing industrial links whilst maintaining a strong tradition of teaching and research directed towards the needs of the community as a whole. Staff and postgraduate students collaborate closely with industry and commerce on a number of research topics.

It has a self-contained spacious campus one mile from the market town of Loughborough, close to the cities of Nottingham, Leicester and Derby and well served by road, rail and air links to London. The campus has excellent facilities for both social and academic pursuits. Campus accommodation (single-room, self- and full-catering) is available for postgraduates.

Research leading to MPhil and PhD degrees can be carried out in all departments. A wide variety of courses is offered leading to Master's degrees and diplomas, including some bridging courses

Loughry College of Agriculture & Food Technology

Estimated students 1991-92 Total students 270. Postgraduate students 15.
Graduate study areas Env.
Closing date 1 September.
Enquiries To Dr R Stevenson, Principal, Loughry College of Agriculture & Food Technology, Cookstown, County Tyrone, Northern Ireland BT80 9AA - telephone 0648 762491.
Abbreviation Loughry CAg & Food Technology.

Luton College of Higher Education

Estimated students 1991-92 Total students 8700. Postgraduate students 45.
Graduate study areas Bus, Educ, Soc, Env, Biol, Chem.
Closing date Variable.
Enquiries To Information Officer, Luton College of Higher Education, Park Square, Luton, Bedfordshire LU1 3JU - telephone 0582 34111.
Abbreviation Luton CHE.

Manchester Business School

Estimated students 1991-92 Postgraduate students 420: full time 300, part time 120.
Graduate study areas Bus.
Closing date 30 June.
Enquiries To the Admissions Secretary, Manchester Business School, Booth Street West, Manchester M15 6PB - telephone 061 275 6311.
Abbreviation Manchester BS.

Manchester Polytechnic

Estimated students 1991-92 Total students 19000. Postgraduate students 1000.
Graduate study areas Arts, Lang, Bus, Educ, Soc, Comp, Eng, Env, Biol, Chem, Math, Phy.
Closing date Details are available from individual departments. For postgraduate courses in art & design application must first be made to the Art & Design Admissions Registry by 31 January.
Enquiries To the Academic Registrar, Manchester Polytechnic, All Saints Building, All Saints, Manchester M15 6BH - telephone 061 228 6171.
Abbreviation Manchester P.

University of Manchester

Estimated students 1991-92 Total students 12000. Postgraduate students 3300: full time 2000, part time 1300.
Graduate study areas Arts, Lang, Bus, Educ, Soc, Comp, Eng, Env, Biol, Chem, Math, Phy.
Enquiries To the Registrar, University of Manchester, Oxford Road, Manchester M13 9PL - telephone 061 275 2000.
Abbreviation Manchester U.

Manchester is the largest unitary university in the country and offers excellent facilities for postgraduate work. It is situated in a city which is an important commercial, cultural and communications centre with its own international airport.

Academic information

There are opportunities for postgraduate work in all the faculties of the University which include Arts, Economic & Social Studies, Education, Law, Medicine, Science and Theology. A wide variety of courses is offered leading to the award of diplomas, masters and PhD degrees.

Finance and grants

The University offers a limited number of awards for research and advanced study.

Facilities and amenities

The University has excellent laboratory and computer facilities, a library of international standing with a wealth of holdings that few can match and its own art gallery and museum. A thriving postgraduate society offers excellent social and recreational facilities.

UMIST - The University of Manchester Institute of Science and Technology

Estimated students 1991-92 Total students 4500. Postgraduate full time 1100.
Graduate study areas Lang, Bus, Soc, Comp, Eng, Env, Biol, Chem, Math, Phy.
Closing date As early as possible.
Enquiries To the Registrar, UMIST - The University of Manchester Institute of Science and Technology, PO Box 88, Manchester M60 1QD - telephone 061 236 3311.
Abbreviation Manchester UMIST.

Mansfield College

Estimated students 1991-92 Total students 160. Postgraduate students 35.
Graduate study areas Arts, Eng, Math, Phy.
Closing date No formal closing date, but application before 1 May advised.
Enquiries To the Tutor for Admissions, Mansfield College, Mansfield Road, Oxford OX1 3TF - telephone 0865 270999.
Abbreviation Mansfield C.

Matthew Boulton College

Estimated students 1991-92 Total students 1000. Postgraduate full time 20.
Graduate study areas Bus, Comp.
Closing date 1 September each year.
Enquiries To the Head of Department of Business & Humanities, Matthew Boulton College, Sherlock Street, Birmingham B5 7DB - telephone 021 446 4545.
Abbreviation Matthew Boulton C.

Memorial College

Please refer to The College of Welsh Independence.

Mid Kent College of Higher & Further Education

Estimated students 1991-92 Total students 11000: full time 3000, part time 8000. Postgraduate students 70: full time 20, part time 50.
Graduate study areas Bus, Educ, Soc, Chem.
Closing date 1 September.
Enquiries To Mr D A Letchford, Admissions Officer, Mid Kent College of Higher & Further Education, Maidstone Road, Chatham, Kent ME5 9UQ - telephone 0634 830633.
Abbreviation Mid Kent CHFE.

Middlesex Polytechnic

Estimated students 1991-92 Total students 7850: full time 7000, part time 850. Postgraduate students 1375: full time 1000, part time 375.
Graduate study areas Arts, Lang, Bus, Educ, Soc, Comp, Eng, Env, Math, Phy.
Closing date No pre-determined closing date; courses close when they are full.
Enquiries To the Admissions Enquiries, Middlesex Polytechnic, Bounds Green Road, London N11 2NQ - telephone 081 368 1299.
Abbreviation Middlesex P.

Millbrook College (Bankfield Site)

Estimated students 1991-92 Postgraduate full time 25.
Graduate study areas Bus.
Closing date End of June, though late applicants may be considered.

Enquiries To the Head of the Faculty of Business Studies, Millbrook College (Bankfield Site), Bankfield Road, Liverpool L13 0BQ -telephone 051 259 1124.
Abbreviation Millbrook C.

Moray House College of Education (incorporating the Scottish Centre for Physical Education, Movement & Leisure Studies)

Estimated students 1991-92 Total students 2620: full time 2003, part time 617. Postgraduate full time 575.
Graduate study areas Educ, Soc, Env.
Closing date 15 December for teacher training and community education, 1 February for recreation/leisure.
Enquiries To the Registrar, Moray House College of Education (incorporating the Scottish Centre for Physical Education, Movement & Leisure Studies), Holyrood Road, Edinburgh EH8 8AQ - telephone 031 556 8455.
Abbreviation Moray House CE.

Napier Polytechnic of Edinburgh

Estimated students 1991-92 Total students 8600. Postgraduate students 300.
Graduate study areas Lang, Bus, Comp, Eng, Env, Biol, Chem, Math, Phy.
Closing date As soon as possible in year prior to session start.
Enquiries To the Information Office, Napier Polytechnic of Edinburgh, Freepost, Edinburgh EH14 0PA - telephone 031 444 2266 ext. 4330.
Abbreviation Napier P.

Nene College, Northampton

Estimated students 1991-92 Total students 8000: full time 3000, part time 5000.
Postgraduate full time 50.
Graduate study areas Educ.
Closing date May.
Enquiries To Mr M Bell, PGCE Course Leader, Nene College, Northampton, Moulton Park, Northampton NN2 7AL - telephone 0604 715000.
Abbreviation Nene C.

New College Durham

Estimated students 1991-92 Total students 12500: full time 1500, part time 11000.
Postgraduate full time 10.
Graduate study areas Bus.
Enquiries To the Admissions Officer, New College Durham, Framwellgate Moor Centre, Durham DH1 5ES - telephone 091 386 2421.
Abbreviation New C.

Newcastle upon Tyne Polytechnic

Estimated students 1991-92 Total students 12500. Postgraduate students 800.
Graduate study areas Arts, Lang, Bus, Educ, Soc, Comp, Eng, Env, Chem, Math, Phy.
Closing date No set date, but preferably before end of December for education & before end of March for others.
Enquiries To the Registry, Newcastle upon Tyne Polytechnic, Ellison Building, Ellison Place, Newcastle upon Tyne NE1 8ST - telephone 091 232 6002.
Abbreviation Newcastle P.

The Polytechnic offers a range of taught postgraduate courses, both full and part time. They include MA and MSc degree courses and a wide range of recognised professional qualifications in management, the professions (including law), education and librarianship.

Academic information

Part time courses include: MSc in Analytical chemistry, MSc Materials engineering, MSc Advanced experimental physics, MA and postgraduate diploma in History of ideas, advanced diploma in Industrial management, diploma in Management studies (general or public administration), MA Fine art, MA and postgraduate diploma in French area studies and postgraduate diploma in MEd Educational development, MA and postgraduate diploma in Urban studies.

A wide range of short courses is offered annually, many of them designed for graduates who need to update or expand their qualifications.

The Polytechnic also offers opportunities for individual research programmes in a wide range of disciplines by full or part time study, leading to the award of a research degree.

Further information

Details about courses currently offered and initial enquiries regarding research should be addressed to the Registrar.

University of Newcastle upon Tyne

Estimated students 1991-92 Total students 9470: full time 8700, part time 770.
Postgraduate students 1950: full time 1290, part time 660.
Graduate study areas Arts, Lang, Bus, Educ, Soc, Comp, Eng, Env, Biol, Chem, Math, Phy.
Closing date No closing date, but applications by 31 July preferred.
Enquiries To the Admissions Officer, University of Newcastle upon Tyne, 6 Kensington Terrace, Newcastle upon Tyne NE1 7RU - telephone 091 222 6000.
Abbreviation Newcastle U.

Newman & Westhill Colleges

Estimated students 1991-92 Total students 1000. Postgraduate students 33.
Graduate study areas Educ.
Closing date None.

Enquiries To Ms C Wilkinson, Newman College, Newman & Westhill Colleges, Birmingham B32 3NT - telephone 021 476 1181/Mrs V Haines, Westhill College, Birmingham B29 6LL - telephone 021 472 7245
Abbreviation Newman & Westhill C.

North Cheshire & Warrington College of Further & Higher Education, Warrington

Estimated students 1991-92 Total students 12300: full time 1300, part time 11000.
Postgraduate students 300: full time 30, part time 270.
Graduate study areas Bus, Educ.
Closing date End of August (overseas students by end of second week in August).
Enquiries To the Head of School of Integrated Office Studies (Secretarial courses), Head of In-Service Education (Inset courses), North Cheshire & Warrington College of Further & Higher Education, Warrington, Winwick Road, Warrington, Cheshire WA2 8QA - telephone 0925 814343.
Abbreviation North Cheshire C.

North East Surrey College of Technology

Estimated students 1991-92 Total students 10000: full time 1900, part time 8100.
Postgraduate students 50: full time 20, part time 30.
Graduate study areas Bus, Biol.
Closing date 31 August.
Enquiries To the Marketing Office, North East Surrey College of Technology, Reigate Road, Ewell, Epsom, Surrey KT17 3DS - telephone 081 394 1731.
Abbreviation North East Surrey CT.

North East Wales Institute of Higher Education

Estimated students 1991-92 Total students 13300: full time 4500, part time 8800.
Postgraduate students 151: full time 28, part time 123.
Graduate study areas Bus, Educ, Soc, Biol, Chem.
Enquiries To Bethan Lloyd Jones, North East Wales Institute of Higher Education, Kelserton Road, Connah's Quay, Deeside, Clwyd CH5 4BR -telephone 0244 831531.
Abbreviation North East Wales IHE.

North East Worcestershire College

Estimated students 1991-92 Total students 14000: full time 1500, part time 12500.
Postgraduate students 450: full time 50, part time 400.
Graduate study areas Bus, Eng.
Enquiries To the Admissions Secretary, North East Worcestershire College, School Drive, Bromsgrove, Worcestershire B60 1PQ - telephone 0527 79500.
Abbreviation North East Worcestershire C.

North Lincolnshire College

(Formerly known as Lincoln College of Technology)
Estimated students 1991-92 Total students 7160: full time 1760, part time 5400.
Postgraduate students 30.
Graduate study areas Bus.
Closing date No closing date.
Enquiries To the Dean of the Faculty of Business & Management Studies, North Lincolnshire College, Cathedral Street, Lincoln LN2 5HQ -telephone 0522 510530.
Abbreviation North Lincolnshire C.

Polytechnic of North London

Estimated students 1991-92 Total students 7382: full time 5160, part time 2222. Postgraduate students 1100: full time 400, part time 700.
Graduate study areas Arts, Lang, Bus, Educ, Soc, Comp, Eng, Env, Biol, Chem, Math, Phy.
Closing date September.
Enquiries To the Communications Office (courses), Polytechnic of North London, Holloway Road, London N7 8DB - telephone 071 607 2789 ext 2030/1 (24 hour answer service: 071 6075755).
Abbreviation North London P.

North Riding College

Estimated students 1991-92 Total full time 600. Postgraduate full time 75.
Graduate study areas Educ.
Enquiries To the Tutor for Admissions, North Riding College, Filey Road, Scarborough, North Yorkshire YO11 3AZ - telephone 0723 362392.
Abbreviation North Riding C.

North Wales Baptist College

Graduate study areas Arts.
Enquiries To the Principal, North Wales Baptist College, 8 Ffriddoedd Road, Bangor LL57 2EH - telephone 0248 362608.
Abbreviation North Wales Baptist C.

North West College of Technology

Estimated students 1991-92 Total students 5800: full time 1000, part time 4800.
Graduate study areas Bus.
Closing date 30 August.

Enquiries To Mr J K McCormack, College Liaison Officer, North West College of Technology, Strand Road, Londonderry BT48 7BY - telephone 0504 266711.
Abbreviation North West CT.

Northbrook College: Design + Technology

Estimated students 1991-92 Total students 16000: full time 2000, part time 14000. Postgraduate students 65: full time 20, part time 45.
Graduate study areas Bus.
Closing date Start of course.
Enquiries To the Information Centre, Northbrook College: Design + Technology, Broadwater Road, Worthing, West Sussex BN14 8HJ - telephone 0903 31445.
Abbreviation Northbrook CDT.

Northern Baptist College

Estimated students 1991-92 Total students 40.
Graduate study areas Arts.
Closing date No definite date, the earlier the better.
Enquiries To the Principal, Northern Baptist College, Luther King House, Brighton Grove, Rusholme, Manchester M14 5JP - telephone 061 224 2214.
Abbreviation Northern Baptist C.

Northern College (United Reformed & Congregational)

Estimated students 1991-92 Total full time 45. Postgraduate full time 8.
Graduate study areas Arts.
Closing date 1 September.
Enquiries To the Tutor for Admissions, Northern College (United Reformed & Congregational), Luther King House, Brighton Grove, Rusholme, Manchester M14 5JP - telephone 061 224 4381.
Abbreviation Northern C.

3 POSTGRADUATE INSTITUTIONS

Northern College of Education

(Formerly two colleges, Aberdeen College of Education and Dundee College of Education)
Estimated students 1991-92 Total full time 2000. Postgraduate full time 344.
Graduate study areas Educ, Soc.
Closing date 15 December advisedly.
Enquiries To the College Secretary, Northern College of Education, Hilton Place, Aberdeen AB9 1FA - telephone 0224 482341.
Abbreviation Northern CE.

Norwich City College

Estimated students 1991-92 Total students 11747: full time 2876, part time 8871. Postgraduate students 215: full time 115, part time 100.
Graduate study areas Bus, Educ, Soc.
Closing date None.
Enquiries To the Student Services Centre, Norwich City College, Ipswich Road, Norwich NR2 2LJ - telephone 0603 660011.
Abbreviation Norwich City C.

Nottingham Polytechnic

(Formerly Trent Polytechnic)
Estimated students 1991-92 Total students 12482: full time 8821, part time 3661. Postgraduate students 601: full time 186, part time 415.
Graduate study areas Arts, Lang, Bus, Educ, Soc, Comp, Eng, Env, Biol, Chem, Math, Phy.
Enquiries To the Academic Registrar, Nottingham Polytechnic, Burton Street, Nottingham NG1 4BU - telephone 0602 418418.
Abbreviation Nottingham P.

University of Nottingham

Estimated students 1991-92 Total students 7000. Postgraduate students 1400: full time 800, part time 600.
Graduate study areas Arts, Lang, Bus, Educ, Soc, Comp, Eng, Env, Biol, Chem, Math, Phy.
Closing date Applications accepted all year round.
Enquiries To the Registrar, University of Nottingham, University Park, Nottingham NG7 2RD - telephone 0602 484848.
Abbreviation Nottingham U.

Oak Hill College

Estimated students 1991-92 Total full time 105.
Graduate study areas Arts.
Enquiries To the Admissions Officer, Oak Hill College, Chase Side, Southgate, London N14 4PS - telephone 081 449 0467.
Abbreviation Oak Hill C.

The Open University

Estimated students 1991-92 Total students 100000: full time 140, part time 99860. Postgraduate students 5080: full time 140, part time 4940.
Graduate study areas Arts, Lang, Bus, Educ, Soc, Comp, Eng, Env, Biol, Chem, Math, Phy.
Closing date Various.
Enquiries To the Central Enquiry Service, The Open University, PO Box 71, Milton Keynes MK7 6AG - telephone 0908 653231.
Abbreviation Open U.

Oxford Air Training School

Estimated students 1991-92 Total students 350. Postgraduate students 30.
Graduate study areas Eng.

Enquiries To the Registrar, Oxford Air Training School, Oxford Airport, Kidlington, Oxford OX5 1RA - telephone 0865 841234.
Abbreviation Oxford Air Training S.

Oxford Polytechnic

Estimated students 1991-92 Total students 7600: full time 5900, part time 1700. Postgraduate students 700: full time 400, part time 300.
Graduate study areas Arts, Lang, Bus, Educ, Soc, Comp, Eng, Env, Biol, Chem, Math, Phy.
Closing date No closing date, but early application for taught courses advisable.
Enquiries To the Relevant department, Oxford Polytechnic, Headington, Oxford OX3 0BP - telephone 0865 741111.
Abbreviation Oxford P.

University of Oxford

Estimated students 1991-92 Total students 13300. Postgraduate students 3400.
Graduate study areas Arts, Lang, Bus, Educ, Soc, Comp, Eng, Env, Biol, Chem, Math, Phy.
Closing date 31st January (15th January for applicants for Brit. Acad/ESRC studentships).
Enquiries To the Graduate Admissions Office, University of Oxford, University Offices, Wellington Square, Oxford OX1 2JD - telephone 0865 270001.
Abbreviation Oxford U.

University of Oxford: Management Studies

Estimated students 1991-92 Postgraduate students 60.
Graduate study areas Bus.
Closing date 31 March.
Enquiries To the Academic Secretary (Postgraduate), Management & Industrial Relations Committee, University of Oxford: Management Studies, c/o Templeton College, Kennington, Oxford OX1 5NY - telephone 0865 735422.
Abbreviation Oxford U.

Academic information

The Oxford University MPhil in Management Studies is a two year postgraduate degree involving an examination and a thesis. There are smaller classes, less structured learning and far more opportunity for independent study and enquiry than in a typical Master of Business Administration (MBA) degree course.

The MSc in Management (industrial relations) focusses on the management of IR and provides the opportunity for a comparative analysis of IR in several different countries. This is a one year programme examined by three papers and a dissertation.

Traditionally the Oxford teaching method provides a close relationship between tutor and student. The programmes are especially well suited to those who are interested in studying aspects of the theory and practice of management in some depth. The programmes have been designed for those who wish to attend seminars and to think, rather than for those who wish to hear answers in a classroom.

Students should show high levels of achievement in their first degree.

Awards and grants

Some financial assistance is available for UK students.

Paddington College

Please refer to City of Westminster College.

Paisley College of Technology

Estimated students 1991-92 Total full time 3000. Postgraduate full time 250.
Graduate study areas Bus, Soc, Comp, Eng, Biol, Chem, Math, Phy.
Closing date Applications accepted for most subjects until course commencement.

Enquiries To Head of appropriate department, Paisley College of Technology, High Street, Paisley PA1 2BE - telephone 041 887 1241.
Abbreviation Paisley CT.

Parkside & Harrow College of Nursing & Midwifery

(Formerly St Mary's School of Nursing)
Estimated students 1991-92 Total full time 235. Postgraduate full time 20.
Graduate study areas Biol.
Closing date Applications accepted all year.
Enquiries To the Nursing Careers Adviser, Parkside & Harrow College of Nursing & Midwifery, St Mary's Hospital, Praed Street, London W2 1NY - telephone 071 725 1128.
Abbreviation Parkside & Harrow C of nursing & midwifery.

Parson Cross College

Estimated students 1991-92 Total students 5500.
Graduate study areas Bus.
Closing date Applications accepted until 15 September.
Enquiries To Mrs Linda Foster, Parson Cross College, Remington Road, Sheffield S5 9PB - telephone 0742 322841.
Abbreviation Parson Cross C.

Pitman Education & Training

(Colleges in Oxford, Cambridge, Leeds, Central London)
Estimated students 1991-92 Total students 6500: full time 4000, part time 2500. Postgraduate students 2900: full time 2500, part time 400.
Graduate study areas Bus, Comp.
Closing date Courses run all year round.

Enquiries To the Registrar, Pitman Education & Training, 154 Southampton Row, London WC1B 5AX - telephone 071 837 4481.
Abbreviation Pitman Education & Training.

Plymouth Polytechnic

Please refer to Polytechnic South West.

Portsmouth Polytechnic

Estimated students 1991-92 Total students 8183: full time 5545, part time 2638. Postgraduate students 572: full time 200, part time 372.
Graduate study areas Lang, Bus, Educ, Soc, Comp, Eng, Env, Biol, Chem, Math, Phy.
Closing date No specific deadline.
Enquiries To the Assistant Registrar (Admissions), Portsmouth Polytechnic, Ravelin House, Museum Road, Portsmouth PO1 2QQ - telephone 0705 827681.
Abbreviation Portsmouth P.

Queen Margaret College, Edinburgh

Estimated students 1991-92 Total students 1400. Postgraduate students 25.
Graduate study areas Bus.
Closing date Applications preferred by 15 December.
Enquiries To the Admissions, Queen Margaret College, Edinburgh, Clerwood Terrace, Edinburgh EH12 8TS - telephone 031 317 3585 or 031 317 3000 (switchboard).
Abbreviation Queen Margaret C.

Queen's College, Birmingham

Graduate study areas Arts.

Enquiries To Queen's College, Birmingham, Somerset Road, Birmingham B15 2QH - telephone 021 454 1527.
Abbreviation Queen's C Birmingham.

The Queen's College, Glasgow

Estimated students 1991-92 Total students 1600: full time 1300, part time 300. Postgraduate students 60.
Graduate study areas Bus, Soc, Chem.
Enquiries To the Registry, The Queen's College, Glasgow, 1 Park Drive, Glasgow G3 6LP - telephone 041 334 8141.
Abbreviation Queen's C Glasgow.

The College has three sites; Park is in the West End of the city; Southbrae is on the campus of Jordanhill College of Education, with access to their facilities; Gibson Hall is a residence between the two.

All sites have easy access to buses, Underground, shops and entertainment in the city of Glasgow.

The College offers higher diploma, CNAA degree and postgraduate study in a broad range of health studies (Human nutrition and dietetics, Physiotherapy, Orthoptics, Podiatric medicine, Occupational therapy, Radiography) and Management studies (Consumer and marketing/management studies, Hotel catering, Social work, Beauty therapy).

The College welcomes overseas students interested in postgraduate or undergraduate studies.

Reading College of Technology

Estimated students 1991-92 Total students 8000.
Graduate study areas Bus.
Closing date Applications accepted at any time.
Enquiries To Mrs Sheila Hicks, Tutor, Reading College of Technology, Green Road, Reading, Berkshire RG6 2BS - telephone 0734 583501.
Abbreviation Reading CT.

University of Reading

(incorporating Bulmershe College of Higher Education)
Estimated students 1991-92 Total students 8500: full time 7500, part time 1000. Postgraduate students 2750: full time 1750, part time 1000.
Graduate study areas Arts, Lang, Bus, Educ, Soc, Comp, Eng, Env, Biol, Chem, Math, Phy.
Closing date 1 August.
Enquiries To the Registrar, University of Reading, Whiteknights, Reading RG6 2AH - telephone 0734 875123.
Abbreviation Reading U.

Regent's Park College

Estimated students 1991-92 Total students 80. Postgraduate students 15.
Graduate study areas Arts.
Closing date Early June prior to year of entry.
Enquiries To the Admissions Tutor, Regent's Park College, Oxford OX1 2LB - telephone 0865 59887.
Abbreviation Regent's Park C.

College of Resurrection

Estimated students 1991-92 Total students 43. Postgraduate students 33.
Graduate study areas Arts.
Closing date 31 August.

Enquiries To the Registrar, College of Resurrection, Stocks Bank Road, Mirfield, West Yorkshire WF14 0BW - telephone 0924 490441.
Abbreviation Resurrection C.

Richmond College

Please refer to Stradbroke College.

Ridley Hall

Estimated students 1991-92 Total students 58: full time 54, part time 4. Postgraduate students 51: full time 49, part time 2.
Graduate study areas Arts, Bus.
Closing date September 1991.
Enquiries To the Principal, Ridley Hall, Sidgwick Avenue, Cambridge CB3 9HG - telephone 0223 353040.
Abbreviation Ridley Hall.

Ripon College

Estimated students 1991-92 Total full time 70. Postgraduate full time 55.
Graduate study areas Arts.
Closing date None.
Enquiries To the Principal, Ripon College, Cuddesdon, Oxford OX9 9EX - telephone 0867 74427.
Abbreviation Ripon C.

Robert Gordon's Institute of Technology

Estimated students 1991-92 Total students 3650. Postgraduate students 300.
Graduate study areas Bus, Soc, Comp, Eng, Env, Chem, Math, Phy.
Closing date Applications accepted for most courses up to date of commencement.
Enquiries To the Assistant Registrar (Student Administration), Robert Gordon's Institute of Technology, Schoolhill, Aberdeen, Scotland AB9 1FR - telephone 0224 633611.
Abbreviation Robert Gordon's IT.

Roehampton Institute

Estimated students 1991-92 Total students 4200: full time 3600, part time 600. Postgraduate students 500: full time 300, part time 200.
Graduate study areas Arts, Educ, Soc, Biol.
Closing date None.
Enquiries To the Registrar, Roehampton Institute, Senate House, Roehampton Lane, London SW15 5PU - telephone 081 878 8117.
Abbreviation Roehampton I.

Rolle College

Please refer to Polytechnic South West.

Royal Academy of Music

Estimated students 1991-92 Total full time 490. Postgraduate full time 150.
Graduate study areas Arts.
Closing date 2 October.
Enquiries To the Admissions Officer, Royal Academy of Music, Marylebone Road, London NW1 5HT - telephone 071 935 5461.
Abbreviation Royal Academy of Mus.

Royal Agricultural College

Estimated students 1991-92 Total full time 850. Postgraduate students 40.
Graduate study areas Bus, Env.
Closing date None.
Enquiries To the Admissions Secretary, Royal Agricultural College, Cirencester, Gloucestershire GL7 6JS - telephone 0285 652531.
Abbreviation Royal AgC.

Royal College of Art

Estimated students 1991-92 Total students 600. Postgraduate students 600.
Graduate study areas Arts, Bus, Eng, Env.
Closing date 28 February.

Enquiries To the Registrar, Royal College of Art, Kensington Gore, London SW7 2EU - telephone 071 584 5020.
Abbreviation Royal CA.

Royal College of Music

Estimated students 1991-92 Total full time 480. Postgraduate full time 150.
Graduate study areas Arts.
Closing date 1 October.
Enquiries To D J Harpham, Admissions Tutor, Royal College of Music, Prince Consort Road, London SW7 2BS - telephone 071 589 3643; fax 071 589 7740.
Abbreviation Royal C of Mus.

Royal Military College of Science (Cranfield)

Estimated students 1991-92 Total students 5000: full time 4995, part time 5.
Postgraduate students 150: full time 145, part time 5.
Graduate study areas Bus, Comp, Eng, Chem, Math, Phy.
Closing date 31 July.
Enquiries To the Academic Registrar, Royal Military College of Science (Cranfield), Shrivenham, Swindon, Wiltshire SN6 8LA - telephone 0793 785402 ext 213.
Abbreviation Royal Military C of Science.

Royal Naval Engineering College

Estimated students 1991-92 Total students 300. Postgraduate students 50.
Graduate study areas Eng.
Closing date October.
Enquiries To the Academic Registrar, Royal Naval Engineering College, Manadon, Plymouth, Devon PL5 3AQ - telephone 0752 553740 ext Manadon 81213.
Abbreviation Royal Naval Engineering C.

Royal Northern College of Music

Estimated students 1991-92 Total students 520. Postgraduate students 70.
Graduate study areas Arts.
Closing date October (wind instruments), December (others).
Enquiries To the Secretary for Admissions, Royal Northern College of Music, 124 Oxford Road, Manchester M13 9RD - telephone 061 273 6283.
Abbreviation Royal Northern C of Mus.

Royal Scottish Academy of Music & Drama

Estimated students 1991-92 Total students 470: full time 400, part time 70.
Postgraduate full time 30.
Graduate study areas Arts.
Closing date 31 January.
Enquiries To the Secretary, Royal Scottish Academy of Music & Drama, 100 Renfrew Street, Glasgow G2 3DB - telephone 041 332 4101.
Abbreviation Royal Scottish Academy Music & Drama.

St Andrew's College of Education

Estimated students 1991-92 Total students 1000. Postgraduate students 275.
Graduate study areas Educ.
Closing date 15 December.
Enquiries To the Admissions Secretary, St Andrew's College of Education, Bearsden, Glasgow G61 4QA - telephone 041 943 1424.
Abbreviation St Andrew's CE.

University of St Andrews

Estimated students 1991-92 Total students 3800. Postgraduate students 520.

Graduate study areas Arts, Lang, Bus, Soc, Comp, Env, Biol, Chem, Math, Phy.
Closing date 10th September for taught courses (no closing date for research degrees).
Enquiries To the Postgraduate Office, University of St Andrews, 79 North Street, St Andrews KY16 9AJ - telephone 0334 76161.
Abbreviation St Andrews U.

St David's University College

Estimated students 1991-92 Total students 900: full time 870, part time 30. Postgraduate students 65: full time 37, part time 28.
Graduate study areas Arts, Lang, Env.
Closing date Preferably 1 June, but late applications considered.
Enquiries To the Deputy Registrar, St David's University College, Lampeter, Dyfed SA48 7ED - telephone 0570 422351.
Abbreviation St David's UC.

St George's District School of Nursing

Estimated students 1991-92 Total students 750. Postgraduate students 60.
Graduate study areas Soc, Biol.
Closing date Any date.
Enquiries To the Director of Nursing Education, St George's District School of Nursing, 2nd Floor Grosvenor Wing, St George's Hospital, Blackshaw Road, London SW17 0QT - telephone 081 672 1255.
Abbreviation St George's District S of Nursing.

St Godric's College, London

Estimated students 1991-92 Total full time 400. Postgraduate full time 50.
Graduate study areas Lang, Bus.

Enquiries To the Head of Training, St Godric's College, London, 2 Arkwright Road, Hampstead, London NW3 6AD - telephone 071 435 9831.
Abbreviation St Godric's C, London.

St John's College

Estimated students 1991-92 Total full time 125. Postgraduate full time 60.
Graduate study areas Arts.
Closing date No formal closing date.
Enquiries To the Admissions Tutor, St John's College, Chilwell Lane, Bramcote , Nottingham NG9 3DS - telephone 0602 251114.
Abbreviation St John's C.

St John's is an independent Anglican Theological College, with a commitment to providing a wide range of courses in theology and pastoral studies. Full time courses for graduates: two year BTh vocational honours degree, two year Diploma in Theological Studies (DTS), and for theological graduates one year Diploma in Pastoral Studies (DPS). Part time courses are offered by 'extension', and thus available to students throughout the country. The Diploma in Religious Education (DipRE) is open to qualified teachers who wish to retrain to teach RE, and the Diploma in Pastoral Counselling (DipPC) is open to all graduates or others with similar standing or experience. All courses (except DPS) are validated either by Nottingham University or by CNAA and CNAA validated research degrees are also available.

College of St Mark & St John

Estimated students 1991-92 Total students 1550: full time 1200, part time 350. Postgraduate students 270: full time 150, part time 120.
Graduate study areas Educ, Soc, Eng, Math.

Enquiries To Mrs H Kearney, Admissions Officer, College of St Mark & St John, Derriford Road, Plymouth PL6 8BH - telephone 0752 777188 ext 218.
Abbreviation St Mark & St John C.

S Martin's College

Estimated students 1991-92 Total students 1300. Postgraduate students 220.
Graduate study areas Arts, Educ, Soc.
Enquiries To the Academic Registrar, S Martin's College, Lancaster LA1 3JD - telephone 0524 63446.
Abbreviation S Martin's C.

St Martin's School of Art

Please refer to Central Saint Martins College of Art & Design.

St Mary's College, Belfast

Estimated students 1991-92 Total students 770: full time 720, part time 50. Postgraduate full time 65.
Graduate study areas Educ.
Closing date 1 December.
Enquiries To the Registrar, St Mary's College, Belfast, BT12 6FE - telephone 0232 327678.
Abbreviation St Mary's C Belfast.

St Mary's College, Strawberry Hill

Estimated students 1991-92 Total full time 1350. Postgraduate full time 175.
Graduate study areas Arts, Educ.
Closing date No formal closing date.
Enquiries To the Registry, St Mary's College, Strawberry Hill, Twickenham, Middlesex TW1 4SX - telephone 081 892 0051.
Abbreviation St Mary's C Strawberry Hill.

St Mary's School of Nursing

Please refer to Parkside & Harrow College of Nursing & Midwifery.

St Michael's College

Estimated students 1991-92 Total students 65: full time 35, part time 30. Postgraduate students 15.
Graduate study areas Arts.
Enquiries To the Warden, St Michael's College, 54 Cardiff Road, LLandaff, Cardiff CF5 2YJ - telephone 0222 563379.
Abbreviation St Michael's C.

College of St Paul & St Mary

Please refer to Cheltenham & Gloucester College of Higher Education.

St Stephen's House

Graduate study areas Arts.
Enquiries To St Stephen's House, 16 Marston Street, Oxford OX4 1JX - telephone 0865 247874; fax 0865 794338.
Abbreviation St Stephen's House.

Salford College of Further Education

Estimated students 1991-92 Total students 3100: full time 1100, part time 2000. Postgraduate students 36.
Graduate study areas Lang, Bus.
Closing date Applications should be received before the commencement of the course.
Enquiries To the Course Admissions, Salford College of Further Education, Freepost, Salford M5 3GL - telephone 061 872 3466.
Abbreviation Salford CFE.

3 POSTGRADUATE INSTITUTIONS

University of Salford

Estimated students 1991-92 Total students 5075: full time 4200, part time 875. Postgraduate students 870: full time 630, part time 240.
Graduate study areas Lang, Bus, Soc, Comp, Eng, Env, Biol, Chem, Math, Phy.
Closing date No specific date but early application is advised.
Enquiries To the The Registrar, University of Salford, Salford M5 4WT - telephone 061 736 5843.
Abbreviation Salford U.

Salisbury College of Technology

Estimated students 1991-92 Total students 7000. Postgraduate students 30.
Graduate study areas Bus.
Closing date 28 February (but later applications always considered).
Enquiries To the Head of Faculty of Business, Management & Food, Salisbury College of Technology, Southampton Road, Salisbury SP1 2LW -telephone 0722 23711.
Abbreviation Salisbury CT.

Salisbury & Wells Theological College

Estimated students 1991-92 Total students 70.
Graduate study areas Arts.
Enquiries To Salisbury & Wells Theological College, 19 The Close, Salisbury SP1 2EE - telephone 0722 332235.
Abbreviation Salisbury & Wells Theol C.

Sandwell College of Further & Higher Education

Estimated students 1991-92 Total students 19000. Postgraduate students 1000.
Graduate study areas Bus, Chem.

Enquiries To the Registrar, Sandwell College of Further & Higher Education, Wednesbury campus, Woden Road South, Wednesbury, Sandwell WS10 0PE - telephone 021 556 6000; fax 021 556 6069.
Abbreviation Sandwell CFHE.

Scottish Baptist College

Estimated students 1991-92 Total students 17.
Graduate study areas Arts.
Enquiries To the Principal, Scottish Baptist College, 12 Aytoun Road, Pollokshields, Glasgow G41 5RT - telephone 041 424 0747.
Abbreviation Scottish Baptist C.

Confederation of Scottish Business Schools

(A trade association of providers of management education and training in Scotland)
Graduate study areas Bus.
Closing date Different for each member.
Enquiries To the Manager, Confederation of Scottish Business Schools, 23 Nelson Mandela Place, Glasgow G2 1EU.
Abbreviation Confederation of Scottish BS.

Scottish College of Textiles

(Subject to approval the Scottish College of Textiles will become the Faculty of Textiles of Heriot-Watt University.)
Estimated students 1991-92 Total students 650. Postgraduate students 55.
Graduate study areas Arts, Bus, Comp, Chem.
Enquiries To the Academic Registrar, Scottish College of Textiles, Netherdaler, Galashiels, Selkirkshire TD1 3HF - telephone 0896 3351.
Abbreviation Scottish C of Textiles.

Scottish Congregational College

Estimated students 1991-92 Total students 17. Postgraduate students 2.
Graduate study areas Arts.
Closing date 15 December.
Enquiries To the Honorary Secretary, Scottish Congregational College, Rosebery Crescent, Edinburgh EH12 5YN - telephone 031 337 9718.
Abbreviation Scottish Congregational C.

Seale-Hayne College

Please refer to Polytechnic South West.

Sheffield City Polytechnic

Estimated students 1991-92 Total students 14000: full time 9500, part time 4500. Postgraduate students 1125: full time 225, part time 900.
Graduate study areas Arts, Lang, Bus, Educ, Soc, Comp, Eng, Env, Biol, Chem, Math, Phy.
Closing date Applicants are advised to apply early in the academic year preceding that in which they intend to start their courses.
Enquiries To the Enquiries Office, Sheffield City Polytechnic, Pond Street, Sheffield S1 1WB - telephone 0742 720911.
Abbreviation Sheffield City P.

University of Sheffield

Estimated students 1991-92 Total students 7800. Postgraduate students 1000.
Graduate study areas Arts, Lang, Bus, Educ, Soc, Comp, Eng, Env, Biol, Chem, Math, Phy.

Enquiries To the Postgraduate Admissions Office, Academic Registrar's Department, University of Sheffield, Sheffield S10 2TN - telephone 0742 768555.
Abbreviation Sheffield U.

Shrewsbury College of Arts & Technology

Estimated students 1991-92 Total students 5800: full time 1300, part time 4500. Postgraduate students 24.
Graduate study areas Bus.
Enquiries To the Admissions Office, Shrewsbury College of Arts & Technology, London Road, Shrewsbury SY2 6PR - telephone 0743 231544.
Abbreviation Shrewsbury CAT.

Silsoe College (Cranfield)

Estimated students 1991-92 Total students 480. Postgraduate students 340.
Graduate study areas Bus, Comp, Eng, Env, Biol.
Closing date No specific closing date, but applications preferably made as early as possible in the academic year preceding that in which candidates wish to begin their studies.
Enquiries To the Student Recruitment Executive, Silsoe College (Cranfield), Silsoe, Bedford MK45 4DT - telephone 0525 60428.
Abbreviation Silsoe C.

Slough College of Higher Education

Please refer to Thames Valley College.

Solihull College of Technology

Estimated students 1991-92 Total students 6100: full time 2600, part time 3500. Postgraduate full time 15.
Graduate study areas Bus.

Closing date 31 August.
Enquiries To Mrs M M Bixby, Schools
Liaison Officer, Solihull College of
Technology, Blossomfield Road, Solihull,
West Midlands B91 1SB - telephone 021 711
2111.
Abbreviation Solihull CT.

Somerset College of Arts & Technology

Estimated students 1991-92 Total students
10500: full time 2000, part time 8500.
Postgraduate students 75: full time 25, part
time 50.
Graduate study areas Lang, Bus.
Closing date September.
Enquiries To J B Foster, Head of Business
Studies, Somerset College of Arts &
Technology, Wellington Road, Taunton,
Somerset TA1 5AX -telephone 0823 283403.
Abbreviation Somerset CAT.

South Bank Polytechnic

Estimated students 1991-92 Total students
9764: full time 5420, part time 4344.
Postgraduate students 2236: full time 542,
part time 1694.
Graduate study areas Lang, Bus, Educ,
Soc, Comp, Eng, Env, Biol, Math, Phy.
Closing date No official closing date.
Applicants advised to apply early.
Enquiries To The Central Registry, South
Bank Polytechnic, Borough Road, London
SE1 0AA - telephone 071 928 8989.
Abbreviation South Bank P.

Academic information

MSc Biotechnology (2 years part time),
Civil engineering, Construction
management, Design of integrated circuit
systems (2 years part time), Energy
resources management (2 years part time),
Environmental acoustics (2 years part
time), Environmental engineering (1 year
full time/2 years part time), Food analysis
& composition (2 to 3 years part time),
Information systems engineering (1 year
full/2 years part time), Mathematical

education (2 years part time), Property
development (project management)(6
terms part time), Public service
management (2 years part time), Scientific
computing, Scientific information
technology, Sociology (2 years part time),
Urban planning studies (2 years part time).
MA Applied European studies (2 years part-
time). *Access studies (2 years part time),
Finance & investment (3 terms part time),
Town planning (3 years part time).
Diplomas/Certificates: A wide range of
courses is available leading to Polytechnic
and CNAA awards and examinations of
professional bodies. Courses can be either
postgraduate or post-experience, full time
or part time.
Full time Applied social studies,
Architecture, Business linguists, Careers
guidance, Computer science, Environmental
engineering, European business certificate,
Health education, Health service
administration (for overseas students),
Health visiting, Intelligent management,
Product design for automated manufacture,
Professional studies in education
(computing), Computing and artificial
intelligence.
Part-time Accountancy, Architecture,
Building, Internal auditing, Languages,
Management, Marketing, Mathematical
education, Nursing, Taxation, Town
planning, Urban planning studies, Access
studies, Finance & investment, European
studies, Professional studies in education
(maths), Design of integrated circuit
systems, environmental acoustics.
Research Full time and part time research
leading to CNAA degrees of MPhil and PhD
is encouraged in all departments. Enquiries
should be sent to the relevant Head of
Department.

South East London College

Please refer to Lewisham College.

South Glamorgan School of Nursing

Estimated students 1991-92 Total students
800. Postgraduate students 10.

Graduate study areas Biol.
Closing date 31 March.
Enquiries To Mr C C Morgan (School of Nursing), Director of Nurse Education, South Glamorgan School of Nursing, Combined Training Institute, University Hospital of Wales, Heath Park, Cardiff CF4 4XW -telephone 0222 755944.
Abbreviation South Glamorgan S of Nursing.

South Lothian College of Nursing & Midwifery

Estimated students 1991-92 Total students 1120. Postgraduate students 10.
Graduate study areas Biol.
Enquiries To South Lothian College of Nursing & Midwifery, Royal Infirmary, 23 Chalmers Street, Edinburgh EH3 9EW - telephone 031 229 2477.
Abbreviation South Lothian C of Nursing & Midwifery.

South Wales Baptist College

Graduate study areas Arts.
Enquiries To South Wales Baptist College, 54 Richmond Road, Cardiff CF2 3UR - telephone 0222 496060.
Abbreviation South Wales Baptist C.

South West London College

Estimated students 1991-92 Total students 9500.
Graduate study areas Bus.
Enquiries To the Registrar, South West London College, Tooting Broadway, London SW17 0TQ - telephone 081 672 2441.
Abbreviation South West London C.

Plymouth: Polytechnic South West

(Formerly Plymouth Polytechnic, Exeter College of Art & Design, Rolle College and Seale-Hayne College)
Estimated students 1991-92 Total students 10900: full time 7600, part time 3300. Postgraduate students 425: full time 235, part time 190.
Graduate study areas Arts, Lang, Bus, Educ, Soc, Comp, Eng, Env, Biol, Chem, Math, Phy.
Closing date No specific closing date but it is advisable to apply well in advance of the start of the course.
Enquiries To the Polytechnic Registrar, Plymouth: Polytechnic South West, Drake Circus, Plymouth, Devon PL4 8AA - telephone 0752 232140.
Abbreviation South West P.

Southampton Institute of Higher Education

Estimated students 1991-92 Total students 13800: full time 1800, part time 12000. Postgraduate students 1350: full time 250, part time 1100.
Graduate study areas Arts, Lang, Bus, Educ, Soc, Comp, Eng, Env, Math.
Closing date Subject to places being available, up to the first day of the course.
Enquiries To the Academic Registrar, Southampton Institute of Higher Education, East Park Terrace, Southampton SO9 4WW - telephone 0703 229381.
Abbreviation Southampton IHE.

University of Southampton

Estimated students 1991-92 Total students 7780: full time 7000, part time 780. Postgraduate students 1865: full time 1120, part time 745.
Graduate study areas Arts, Lang, Bus, Educ, Soc, Comp, Eng, Env, Biol, Chem, Math, Phy.

Enquiries To the Postgraduate Admissions Office, University of Southampton, Highfield, Southampton SO9 5NH - telephone 0703 595000.
Abbreviation Southampton U.

University of Southern California

Graduate study areas Arts.
Closing date None.
Enquiries To The Director, University of Southern California, Regent's College, Inner Circle, Regent's Park, London NW1 4NS - telephone 071 486 9635.
Abbreviation Southern California U.

Spurgeon's College

Estimated students 1991-92 Total students 180: full time 100, part time 80.
Postgraduate part time 14.
Graduate study areas Arts.
Closing date 31 May but some late applications may be considered.
Enquiries To the Director of Research, Spurgeon's College, 189 South Norwood Hill, London SE25 6DJ - telephone 081 653 0850.
Abbreviation Spurgeon's C.

Staffordshire Polytechnic

Estimated students 1991-92 Total students 8100: full time 5800, part time 2300.
Postgraduate students 700: full time 300, part time 400.
Graduate study areas Arts, Lang, Bus, Educ, Soc, Comp, Eng, Env, Biol, Chem, Math, Phy.
Enquiries To the Academic Registrar, Staffordshire Polytechnic, College Road, Stoke on Trent ST4 2DE - telephone 0782 744531.
Abbreviation Staffordshire P.

University of Stirling

Estimated students 1991-92 Total students 3900: full time 3300, part time 600.
Postgraduate students 950: full time 650, part time 300.
Graduate study areas Arts, Lang, Bus, Educ, Soc, Comp, Env, Biol.
Closing date 1 July.
Enquiries To Paula M Elliot, Admissions Office, University of Stirling, Stirling, Scotland FK9 4LA - telephone 0786 73171.
Abbreviation Stirling U.

Stockport College of Further & Higher Education

Estimated students 1991-92 Total students 13800: full time 2300, part time 11500.
Graduate study areas Bus, Soc, Biol.
Closing date Not applicable. All courses commence first week of September..
Enquiries To A Pryer, Information Officer, Stockport College of Further & Higher Education, Wellington Road South, Stockport, Cheshire SK1 3UQ - telephone 061 474 3412.
Abbreviation Stockport C.

Stoke-on-Trent College

(Formerly called Cauldon College of Further & Higher Education)
Estimated students 1991-92 Total students 22000: full time 2000, part time 20000.
Postgraduate students 70: full time 40, part time 30.
Graduate study areas Bus, Educ, Eng.
Closing date 13 September, but late applications considered.
Enquiries To the Faculty of Professional Studies, Stoke-on-Trent College, Stoke Road, Shelton, Stoke on Trent ST4 2DG - telephone 0782 208208.
Abbreviation Stoke-on-Trent C.

Stradbroke College

(Formerly Richmond College)
Estimated students 1991-92 Total students
5953: full time 994, part time 4959.
Postgraduate full time 50.
Graduate study areas Arts, Lang, Bus.
Closing date No formal closing date.
Enquiries To the Principal, Stradbroke
College, Spinkhill Drive, Sheffield S13 8FD -
telephone 0742 392621.
Abbreviation Stradbroke C.

Stranmillis College

Estimated students 1991-92 Total full time
700. Postgraduate full time 70.
Graduate study areas Educ.
Closing date 1 February of year of entry.
Enquiries To the Senior Tutor
(Admissions), Stranmillis College, Belfast
BT9 5DY - telephone 0232 381271.
Abbreviation Stranmillis C.

University of Strathclyde

Estimated students 1991-92 Total students
8535: full time 7913, part time 622.
Postgraduate students 2618: full time 1606,
part time 1012.
Graduate study areas Arts, Lang, Bus, Soc,
Comp, Eng, Env, Biol, Chem, Math, Phy.
Closing date 31 March, but later
applications considered.
Enquiries To the Registry - General,
University of Strathclyde, Glasgow G1 1XQ -
telephone 041 552 4400.
Abbreviation Strathclyde U.

Suffolk College of Higher & Further Education

Estimated students 1991-92 Total students
27000. Postgraduate part time 250.
Graduate study areas Bus.

Enquiries To the Chief Administrative
Officer, Suffolk College of Higher & Further
Education, Rope Walk, Ipswich, Suffolk IP4
1LT - telephone 0473 255885.
Abbreviation Suffolk CHFE.

Sunderland Polytechnic

Estimated students 1991-92 Total students
7957: full time 5926, part time 2031.
Postgraduate students 755: full time 263,
part time 492.
Graduate study areas Arts, Lang, Bus,
Educ, Soc, Comp, Eng, Env, Biol, Chem,
Math, Phy.
Closing date Apply as early as possible.
Enquiries To the Admissions Officer,
Sunderland Polytechnic, Edinburgh
Building, Chester Road, Sunderland, Tyne &
Wear SR1 3SD - telephone 091 5152082.
Research: Research Section, Langham
Tower, Ryhope Road, Sunderland SR2 7EE
Abbreviation Sunderland P.

University of Surrey

Estimated students 1991-92 Total students
4785: full time 3955, part time 830.
Postgraduate students 1546: full time 716,
part time 830.
Graduate study areas Arts, Lang, Bus,
Educ, Soc, Comp, Eng, Env, Biol, Chem,
Math, Phy.
Closing date Varies for different courses.
Further details from departmental
postgraduate admissions tutors or from
postgraduate prospectus.
Enquiries To the Postgraduate Admissions
Officer, Registry, University of Surrey,
Guildford , Surrey GU2 5XH - telephone
0483 571281.
Abbreviation Surrey U.

University of Sussex

Estimated students 1991-92 Total students
5895: full time 5092, part time 803.
Postgraduate students 1831: full time 1058,
part time 773.
Graduate study areas Arts, Lang, Bus,
Educ, Soc, Comp, Eng, Env, Biol, Chem,
Math, Phy.

Closing date 1st May.
Enquiries To the Admissions Office, University of Sussex, Sussex House, Falmer, Brighton BN1 9RH - telephone 0273 678416.
Abbreviation Sussex U.

University College of Swansea

Estimated students 1991-92 Total students 4500. Postgraduate students 680.
Graduate study areas Arts, Lang, Bus, Educ, Soc, Comp, Eng, Env, Biol, Chem, Math, Phy.
Closing date No formal closing date.
Enquiries To the Academic Registrar, University College of Swansea, Singleton Park, Swansea, West Glamorgan SA2 8PP - telephone 0792 205678.
Abbreviation Swansea UC.

Teesside Polytechnic

Estimated students 1991-92 Total students 7500: full time 5000, part time 2500. Postgraduate students 900: full time 550, part time 350.
Graduate study areas Arts, Lang, Bus, Soc, Comp, Eng, Biol, Chem, Math.
Closing date For taught courses early application advised to increase chances of funding (limited number of studentships available).No funding available for overseas students.
Enquiries To the Student Administration (Postgraduate), Teesside Polytechnic, Borough Road, Middlesbrough, Cleveland TS1 3BA - telephone 0642 218121 ext 4213.
Abbreviation Teesside P.

Thames Polytechnic, London

Estimated students 1991-92 Total students 8400: full time 5400, part time 3000. Postgraduate students 580: full time 480, part time 100.
Graduate study areas Arts, Bus, Educ, Comp, Eng, Env, Biol, Chem, Math, Phy.

Enquiries To the Academic Registrar, Thames Polytechnic, London, Wellington Street, Woolwich, London SE18 6PF - telephone 081 316 8111.
Abbreviation Thames P.

Thames Valley College

(Formerly Slough College of Higher Education)
Estimated students 1991-92 Total students 11000: full time 1000, part time 10000. Postgraduate students 470: full time 19, part time 451.
Graduate study areas Bus.
Closing date 31 August (30 July for overseas students).
Enquiries To the Registrar, Thames Valley College, Wellington Street, Slough, Berkshire SL1 1YG - telephone 0753 34585.
Abbreviation Thames Valley C.

Trent Polytechnic

Please refer to Nottingham Polytechnic.

Trinity & All Saints' College

Estimated students 1991-92 Total students 1190. Postgraduate students 100.
Graduate study areas Educ.
Enquiries To the Deputy Registrar, Trinity & All Saints' College, Brownberrie Lane, Horsforth, Leeds LS18 5HD - telephone 0532 584341.
Abbreviation Trinity & All Saints' C.

Trinity College, Bristol

Estimated students 1991-92 Total full time 130. Postgraduate students 20: full time 5, part time 15.
Graduate study areas Arts.
Closing date 15 September.
Enquiries To the Admissions Tutor, Trinity College, Bristol, Stoke Hill, Bristol BS9 1JP - telephone 0272 682803.
Abbreviation Trinity C Bristol.

Trinity College, Carmarthen

Estimated students 1991-92 Total full time 800. Postgraduate full time 500.
Graduate study areas Educ.
Closing date No formal closing date.
Enquiries To the Registrar, Trinity College, Carmarthen, Dyfed SA31 3EP - telephone 0267 237971.
Abbreviation Trinity C Carmarthen.

Trinity College of Music

Estimated students 1991-92 Total students 460: full time 420, part time 40. Postgraduate full time 35.
Graduate study areas Arts.
Closing date 2 February.
Enquiries To the Registrar, Trinity College of Music, 11-13 Mandeville Place, London W1M 6AQ - telephone 071 935 5773.
Abbreviation Trinity C of Mus.

University of Ulster

Estimated students 1991-92 Total students 17133: full time 8296, part time 8837. Postgraduate students 2315: full time 503, part time 1812.
Graduate study areas Arts, Lang, Bus, Educ, Soc, Comp, Eng, Env, Biol, Chem, Math, Phy.
Closing date Varies for different courses.
Enquiries To the Admissions Office, University of Ulster, Coleraine, County Londonderry BT52 1SA - telephone 0265 44141.
Abbreviation Ulster U.

United Theological College, Aberystwyth

Estimated students 1991-92 Total students 45: full time 40, part time 5. Postgraduate students 7: full time 4, part time 3.
Graduate study areas Arts.
Closing date 1 September.

Enquiries To the Principal, United Theological College, Aberystwyth, King Street, Aberystwyth SY23 2LT - telephone 0970 624574.
Abbreviation United Theol C, Aberystwyth.

Polytechnic of Wales

Estimated students 1991-92 Total students 6000: full time 4000, part time 2000. Postgraduate students 150: full time 70, part time 80.
Graduate study areas Arts, Lang, Bus, Educ, Soc, Comp, Eng, Env, Biol, Chem, Math, Phy.
Closing date Applications considered at any time.
Enquiries To the Assistant Academic Registrar, Polytechnic of Wales, Llantwit Road, Treforest, Pontypridd, Mid Glamorgan CF37 1DL - telephone 0443 480480.
Abbreviation Wales P.

University of Wales College of Medicine

Estimated students 1991-92 Total students 1398: full time 1010, part time 388. Postgraduate students 482: full time 226, part time 256.
Graduate study areas Biol.
Enquiries To the Registrar & Secretary, University of Wales College of Medicine, Heath Park, Cardiff CF4 4XN - telephone 0222 755944; fax 0222 762208.
Abbreviation Wales U C of Med.

University of Warwick

Estimated students 1991-92 Total students 8276. Postgraduate students 1756: full time 1018, part time 738.
Graduate study areas Arts, Lang, Bus, Educ, Soc, Comp, Eng, Biol, Chem, Math, Phy.
Enquiries To the Academic Registrar, University of Warwick, Coventry CV4 7AL - telephone 0203 523523.
Abbreviation Warwick U.

Watford College

Estimated students 1991-92 Total students 7000: full time 1200, part time 5800. Postgraduate students 60.
Graduate study areas Bus, Eng.
Closing date 8 September.
Enquiries To Mr B Pepper, Vice Principal, Watford College, Hempstead Road, Watford, Hertfordshire WD1 3EZ - telephone 0923 57500.
Abbreviation Watford C.

Webber Douglas Academy of Dramatic Art

Estimated students 1991-92 Total full time 120. Postgraduate full time 14.
Graduate study areas Arts.
Closing date 1 April.
Enquiries To the Registrar, Webber Douglas Academy of Dramatic Art, 30 Clareville Street, London SW7 5AP - telephone 071 370 4154.
Abbreviation Webber Douglas Academy

Welsh Agricultural College

Estimated students 1991-92 Total full time 250.
Graduate study areas Env.
Enquiries To the Principal, Welsh Agricultural College, Llanbadarn Fawr, Aberystwyth SY23 3AL - telephone 0970 624471.
Abbreviation Welsh AgC.

Welsh College of Music & Drama

Estimated students 1991-92 Total students 325. Postgraduate students 40.
Graduate study areas Arts.
Closing date 1 May.
Enquiries To the Registrar, Welsh College of Music & Drama, Castle Grounds, Cathays Park, Cardiff CF1 3ER - telephone 0222 342854.
Abbreviation Welsh C of Mus & Drama.

The College of Welsh Independence

(Also known as Coleg Yr Annibynwyr Cymraeg. Formerly Bala-Bangor College and Memorial College)
Estimated students 1991-92 Total students 18. Postgraduate students 2.
Graduate study areas Arts.
Closing date September.
Enquiries To the Principal, The College of Welsh Independence, 38 Pier Street, Aberystwyth, Dyfed - telephone 0970 615154.
Abbreviation Welsh Independence C.

Wesley College

Graduate study areas Arts.
Enquiries To Wesley College, College Park Drive, Henbury Road, Bristol BS10 7QD - telephone 0272 591200.
Abbreviation Wesley C.

Wesley House

Estimated students 1991-92 Total full time 34. Postgraduate full time 30.
Graduate study areas Arts.
Enquiries To the Principal, Wesley House, Jesus Lane, Cambridge CB5 8BJ - telephone 0223 355081.
Abbreviation Wesley House.

Wessex Institute of Technology - Computational Mechanics Institute

Estimated students 1991-92 Postgraduate full time 20.

Enquiries To Dr W Blain, Director of Studies, Wessex Institute of Technology - Computational Mechanics Institute, Ashurst Lodge, Ashurst, Southampton S04 2AA - telephone 0421 293223.
Abbreviation Wessex IT.

West Cheshire College

Estimated students 1991-92 Total students 10100: full time 1100, part time 9000.
Postgraduate students 30.
Graduate study areas Bus.
Closing date 1 September.
Enquiries To Mrs M Ellwood, Course Tutor, West Cheshire College , Eaton Road, Handbridge, Chester CH4 7ER - telephone 0244 677677.
Abbreviation West Cheshire C.

West Glamorgan Institute of Higher Education

Estimated students 1991-92 Total students 5000: full time 2000, part time 3000.
Postgraduate students 60: full time 20, part time 40.
Graduate study areas Arts, Bus, Educ, Comp, Eng, Math.
Closing date Not specified. Overseas students 31 July.
Enquiries To the Principal, West Glamorgan Institute of Higher Education, Townhill Road, Swansea SA2 0UT - telephone 0792 203482.
Abbreviation West Glamorgan IHE.

West London Institute of Higher Education

Estimated students 1991-92 Total students 3700: full time 2100, part time 1600.
Postgraduate students 182: full time 152, part time 30.
Graduate study areas Arts, Educ, Soc, Env.
Closing date None - all applications considered.

Enquiries To the Academic Registry, West London Institute of Higher Education, Gordon House, 300 St Margaret's Road, Twickenham, Middlesex TW1 1PT - telephone 081 891 0121.
Abbreviation West London IHE.

West Midlands College of Higher Education

Please refer to Wolverhampton Polytechnic.

The West of Scotland College

Estimated students 1991-92 Total students 1600: full time 600, part time 1000.
Postgraduate full time 60.
Graduate study areas Bus, Eng, Env, Biol.
Enquiries To the Deputy Principal, The West of Scotland College, Auchincruive, Ayr KA6 5HW - telephone 0292 520331.
Abbreviation West of Scotland C.

West Sussex Institute of Higher Education

Estimated students 1991-92 Total students 1400. Postgraduate students 104.
Graduate study areas Educ.
Closing date When full.
Enquiries To the Admissions Office, West Sussex Institute of Higher Education, The Dome, Upper Bognor Road, Bognor Regis, West Sussex PO21 1HR - telephone 0243 865581 ext. 202.
Abbreviation West Sussex IHE.

Westcott House

Estimated students 1991-92 Total students 50. Postgraduate students 48.
Graduate study areas Arts.
Enquiries To Westcott House, Jesus Lane, Cambridge CB5 8BP - telephone 0223 350074.
Abbreviation Westcott House.

3 POSTGRADUATE INSTITUTIONS

Westminster College, Cambridge

Estimated students 1991-92 Total students 41. Postgraduate students 11.
Graduate study areas Arts.
Closing date 30 July for self financed students. 30 April for students seeking United Reformed Church grant.
Enquiries To the Principal, Westminster College, Cambridge CB3 0AA - telephone 0223 353997.
Abbreviation Westminster C Cambridge.

Westminster College, London

Estimated students 1991-92 Total students 8000. Postgraduate students 20.
Graduate study areas Bus.
Closing date No special date, will accept until course is full.
Enquiries To the Head of Courses, Management, Hotel & Catering Studies, Westminster College, London, Vincent Square, London SW1P 2PD - telephone 071 828 1222.
Abbreviation Westminster C London.

Westminster College, Oxford

Estimated students 1991-92 Total students 900. Postgraduate students 105.
Graduate study areas Arts, Educ.
Closing date Open until full.
Enquiries To the Registrar, Westminster College, Oxford OX2 9AT - telephone 0865 247644.
Abbreviation Westminster C Oxford.

Weymouth College

(Formerly known as South Dorset Technical College)
Estimated students 1991-92 Total students 1100. Postgraduate students 12.
Graduate study areas Lang, Bus.
Closing date 31 August.
Enquiries To the Head of Business Studies, Weymouth College, Cranford Avenue, Weymouth, Dorset DT4 7LQ - telephone 0305 761100.
Abbreviation Weymouth C.

Winchester School of Art

Estimated students 1991-92 Total students 460: full time 400, part time 60.
Postgraduate students 31: full time 6, part time 25.
Graduate study areas Arts.
Closing date April.
Enquiries To the Admissions Officer, Winchester School of Art, Park Avenue, Winchester, Hampshire SO23 8DL - telephone 0962 842500.
Abbreviation Winchester SA.

Wolverhampton Polytechnic

(incorporating West Midlands College of Higher Education)
Estimated students 1991-92 Total students 11062: full time 7249, part time 3813.
Postgraduate students 480: full time 180, part time 300.
Graduate study areas Arts, Lang, Bus, Educ, Soc, Comp, Eng, Env, Biol, Chem, Phy.
Closing date Before start of course. Early application advised.
Enquiries To the Academic Registrar (Attention of Admissions Unit), Wolverhampton Polytechnic, Quadrant Chambers, Lichfield Street, Wolverhampton - telephone 0902 313001.
Abbreviation Wolverhampton P.

Worcester College of Higher Education

Estimated students 1991-92 Total students 1650: full time 1250, part time 400.
Postgraduate students 250: full time 180, part time 70.
Graduate study areas Arts, Lang, Educ, Soc, Comp, Env, Biol, Chem, Math, Phy.

Closing date 31 July.
Enquiries To the Registry, Worcester College of Higher Education, Henwick Grove, Worcester WR2 6AJ - telephone 0905 748080.
Abbreviation Worcester CHE.

Worcester Technical College

Estimated students 1991-92 Postgraduate students 25.
Graduate study areas Bus.
Closing date September.
Enquiries To the Department of Business Studies, Worcester Technical College, Deansway, Worcester WR1 2JF - telephone 0905 723383.
Abbreviation Worcester TC.

York College of Arts & Technology

Estimated students 1991-92 Total full time 1750. Postgraduate full time 45.
Graduate study areas Bus.
Closing date August.
Enquiries To the Courses Director, School of Business Studies, York College of Arts & Technology, Dringhouses, York Y02 1UA - telephone 0904 704141.
Abbreviation York CAT.

York: College of Ripon & York St John

Estimated students 1991-92 Total students 2000: full time 1800, part time 200. Postgraduate students 95: full time 65, part time 30.
Graduate study areas Lang, Educ, Soc.
Closing date Determined by number of applications received.
Enquiries To York: College of Ripon & York St John (Registrar), Lord Mayor's Walk, York YO3 7EX - telephone 0904 656771.
Abbreviation York C of Ripon & York St John.

University of York

Estimated students 1991-92 Total students 4400: full time 4100, part time 300. Postgraduate students 1300: full time 1000, part time 300.
Graduate study areas Arts, Lang, Educ, Soc, Comp, Eng, Env, Biol, Chem, Math, Phy.
Closing date No fixed closing date.
Enquiries To the Graduate Office, University of York, Heslington, York Y01 5DD - telephone 0904 432142.
Abbreviation York U.

4

INDEXES

These indexes are your key to finding the specific information you require about courses, research opportunities and the institutions which have chosen to advertise their facilities in more detail.

Guide to indexes

The indexes provide an essential reference point to ALL advertisements that appear within the book and to particular subjects within the course listings. There are two indexes, each of which provides a different service to the reader.

Advertisers index *This index provides the reader with a quick reference to ALL advertisements. The index refers the reader to a particular course, department, faculty or unit, or to the institution as a whole, and includes the following types of advertisement:*
- *course advertisements, which appear within the course listings at the end of each subject group*
- *display advertisements, which appear throughout the book*
- *institution advertisements that appear within 'Postgraduate institutions'*

The advertisements are listed in alphabetical order by institution with display advertisements listed in italics.

General subject index *The course listing is divided into four general subject sections containing 12 major subject areas, each of which is broken down into relevant subject headings. The 'General subject index' provides the reader with a quick reference to particular subject headings of interest.*

Advertisers index

4 INDEXES

4 INDEXES

General subject index

NOTES

NOTES

NOTES

NOTES

NOTES

NOTES

NOTES